DATE DUE

COMMUNICATION SYSTEMS AND TECHNIQUES

INTER-UNIVERSITY ELECTRONICS SERIES

Books in Series

Vol. 1: *Jamieson et al.* Infrared Physics and Engineering, 1964
Vol. 2: *Bennett and Davey.* Data Transmission, 1965
Vol. 3: *Sutton.* Direct Energy Conversion, 1966
Vol. 4: *Schwartz, Bennett, and Stein.* Communications Systems and Techniques, 1966

COMMUNICATION SYSTEMS AND TECHNIQUES

MISCHA SCHWARTZ

Professor of Electrical Engineering
Polytechnic Institute of Brooklyn

WILLIAM R. BENNETT

Professor of Electrical Engineering
Columbia University

SEYMOUR STEIN

Associate Director, Applied Research Laboratory
Sylvania Electronic Systems

McGRAW-HILL BOOK COMPANY

New York   San Francisco   Toronto   London   Sydney

COMMUNICATION SYSTEMS AND TECHNIQUES

55754

1234567890MP721069876

INTER-UNIVERSITY ELECTRONICS SERIES

Series Purpose

The explosive rate at which knowledge in electronics has expanded in recent years has produced the need for unified state-of-the-art presentations that give authoritative pictures of individual fields of electronics.

The Inter-University Electronics Series is designed to meet this need by providing volumes that deal with particular areas of electronics where up-to-date reference material is either inadequate or is not conveniently organized. Each volume covers an individual area, or a series of related areas. Emphasis is upon providing timely and comprehensive coverage that stresses general principles, and integrates the newer developments into the over-all picture. Each volume is edited by an authority in the field and is written by several coauthors, who are active participants in research or in educational programs dealing with the subject matter involved.

The volumes are written with a viewpoint and at a level that makes them suitable for reference use by research and development engineers and scientists in industry and by workers in governmental and university laboratories. They are also suitable for use as textbooks in specialized courses at graduate levels. The complete series of volumes will provide a reference library that should serve a wide spectrum of electronics engineers and scientists.

The organization and planning of the Series is being carried out with the aid of a Steering Committee, which operates with the counsel of an Advisory Committee. The Steering Committee concerns itself with the scope of the individual volumes and aids in the selection of editors for the different volumes. Each editor is in turn responsible for selecting his coauthors and deciding upon the detailed scope and content of his particular volume. Over-all management of the Series is in the hands of the Consulting Editor.

Frederick Emmons Terman

PREFACE

In common with most other areas of modern-day technology, the field of communications has expanded explosively in the past two decades. Both theory and applications have developed at a tremendous rate, yet, too often, theoreticians and practitioners have been unaware of each other's activities. This gap between theory and practice has been bridged where possible in this book by emphasizing not only theory and basic principles but by describing applications to current technology as well. It is hoped, therefore, that the book will serve a twofold purpose: as a graduate text for students interested in obtaining a fundamental introduction to the communications field, and as a self-study volume or reference for experienced communications engineers desirous of expanding their basic theoretical knowledge as well as applying some of the significant developments in the field to their current problems.

It is apparent that in a field as vast as communications a single volume cannot possibly do justice to all important aspects of the subject. The book must of necessity be considered a "selected topics" volume, with the topics chosen representing the interests and background of the authors. Yet, within this selected topics structure, there is a definite order and logic of presentation.

Part I, covering Chapters 1 to 3, describes the fundamental aspects of communications in the presence of noise, directing its attention to the two major classes of signal representation—digital and continuous-wave (CW). It thus provides a self-contained introduction to statistical communication theory and lays the groundwork for the chapters that follow. In Chapter 1, various methods of signal and noise representation are introduced. Chapter 2 on digital systems utilizes a decision-theory viewpoint, and an attempt is made where possible to relate the theory to current practice. Chapter 3 on CW systems utilizes the classic methods of spectral analysis in a comparative S/N evaluation of AM and FM systems and attempts to unify several methods of handling FM noise problems. Modern FM systems, such as phase-locked loops and FM demodulators with feedback, are considered here.

In Part II, Chapters 4 to 6, CW and pulse-modulation systems are again considered but with somewhat different emphasis. The discussion here reviews the art of modulation as practiced in modern communication systems. Emphasis is placed on the structure of the signals transmitted, methods of generating and detecting the signals, the response of systems to the various types of signals transmitted, spectral analysis, and the various types of distortion typically encountered. Specifically, a discussion is given of the basic techniques of amplitude modulation and of the principal ways in which an initially amplitude-modulated wave can be modified for more effective use of bandwidth, power, and equipment. Angle- and pulse-modulation systems are analyzed and their performances in the presence of noise are demonstrated. The problems associated with the multiplexing of channels in both the frequency and time domain are treated. Chapter 6 concludes with an elucidation of the digital representation of analog signals as exemplified by pulse-code modulation and delta modulation.

The material of Part III, Chapters 7 through 11, covers digital communications theory and principles, with particular emphasis upon the applications to problems of transmission and reception over fading radio channels. In this material, the decision made was to concentrate upon the reasonably well-developed body of knowledge surrounding binary communications and to give substantially less attention to either M-ary or error-control coded channels, or so-called feedback communications systems. An understanding of binary techniques should make readily intelligible the communication-systems literature in these latter areas.

Within this choice of scope, the intent of the presentation in Part III has been to collect, in a consistent framework, a large body of information hitherto available only in journal articles. The emphasis is on interpretation of the basic models and associated results, so as to develop a consistent qualitative view of the principles involved. At the same time, an attempt has been made to provide sufficient depth in the mathematical analyses to provide a useful body of techniques and results for the reader interested in undertaking new analyses of related problems. Some of the material is new. In the large portion derived from the literature, an attempt has been made to reference the appropriate sources fully; apologies are offered beforehand for any unintentional errors of omission in such citations.

It is presumed that the reader has a good background in the theory of linear systems and random processes, equivalent to that given at the first-year graduate level in most universities today, as well as a basic understanding of communication systems as taught at the senior level in most schools.

The material of Part I has been used for several years in preliminary note form as the text for a one-semester graduate course in statistical communications theory at the Polytechnic Institute of Brooklyn. This course introducing a graduate communications sequence follows a required one-semester course in Probability and Random Processes. The material of Part II has served as a basis for a one-semester course in modulation theory at Columbia University.   Portions of Part III were utilized by Dr. Stein, while Visiting Professor at the Polytechnic, in teaching a selected topics course in the graduate communications sequence at the Institute.

Mischa Schwartz
William R. Bennett
Seymour Stein

CONTENTS

COMMUNICATION SYSTEMS AND TECHNIQUES

PART 1

Mischa Schwartz

CHAPTER 1

GENERAL TUTORIAL MATERIAL

1-1. Summary of Statistical Properties of Noise[1]

This section is to be considered of a review and summary nature, with the reader referred to the references cited below for detailed considerations and evaluation of techniques utilized.

We consider at this point Gaussian-type white noise only. Examples are thermal noise, shot noise in vacuum tubes, both thermal and shot noise generated in semiconductors (diodes, transistors), etc. In nonelectrical applications the "noise" would consist of random pressure fluctuations, thermal motion of ideal gas molecules (giving rise to the Maxwell-Boltzmann statistics), the random thermal motion of liquid molecules (Brownian motion), etc. All of these are characterized by the

---

[1] Books and articles of a tutorial nature that treat both the physical sources of noise and its statistical properties include:

D. A. Bell, "Electrical Noise," D. Van Nostrand Company, Inc., Princeton, N.J., 1960.

J. S. Bendat, "Principles and Applications of Random Noise Theory," John Wiley & Sons, Inc., New York, 1958.

W. R. Bennett, "Electrical Noise," McGraw-Hill Book Company, New York, 1960.

W. R. Bennett, Methods of Solving Noise Problems, *Proc. IRE*, vol. 44, pp. 609–638, May, 1956.

W. B. Davenport, Jr., and W. L. Root, "Introduction to Random Signals and Noise," McGraw-Hill Book Company, New York, 1958.

J. J. Freeman, "Principles of Noise," John Wiley & Sons, Inc., New York, 1958.

W. W. Harman, "Principles of the Statistical Theory of Communication," McGraw-Hill Book Company, New York, 1963.

J. L. Lawson and G. E. Uhlenbeck, "Threshold Signals," McGraw-Hill Book Company, New York, 1950.

A. Papoulis, "Probability, Random Variables, and Stochastic Processes," McGraw-Hill Book Company, 1965, esp. part II.

S. O. Rice, Mathematical Analysis of Random Noise, *Bell System Tech. J.*, vol. 23, pp. 282–333, July, 1944; vol. 24, pp. 96–157, January, 1945 (reprinted in N. Wax, "Selected Papers on Noise and Stochastic Processes," Dover Publications, Inc., New York, 1954).

M. Schwartz, "Information Transmission, Modulation, and Noise," chaps. 5–7, McGraw-Hill Book Company, 1959.

A. Van der Ziel, "Noise," Prentice-Hall, Inc., Englewood Cliffs, N.J., 1954.

chance or random motion of countless numbers of *independent* (or non-interacting) particles. The two distinguishing features of *large* numbers of *independent* particles give rise to the Gaussian statistics that characterize the behavior of systems comprising these particles.

By Gaussian noise we mean that the probability distribution of the instantaneous value $n(t)$ of a random voltage, current, pressure, velocity, or other random time function is given by

$$p(n) = \frac{e^{-n^2/2\sigma^2}}{\sqrt{2\pi\sigma^2}} \tag{1-1-1}$$

Here the average value is assumed to be zero. The one significant statistic is then the variance σ^2, equal in this case to the ensemble mean-squared value of n.

The term "white noise" implies that the spectral density of the noise, *when generated,* is constant for all frequencies. This is of course characteristic of thermal noise, where for example the mean-squared noise voltage generated by a resistor R at $T°$K is given by

$$\langle n^2 \rangle = 4kTR\,\Delta f \tag{1-1-2}$$

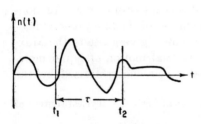

FIG. 1-1-1. Random-noise process.

with k the Boltzmann constant, and Δf any prescribed bandwidth. (The pointed brackets represent ensemble averaging.) For the shot noise generated by a temperature-limited vacuum diode, the mean-squared current is given by

$$\langle i^2 \rangle = 2eI_{dc}\,\Delta f \tag{1-1-3}$$

with I_{dc} the average (direct) current. $\langle i^2 \rangle$ represents the mean-squared fluctuation about I_{dc} due to random emission of electrons from the cathode.

In general, then, white noise has a mean-squared value given by

$$\langle n^2 \rangle = K\,\Delta f \tag{1-1-4}$$

K represents the (one-sided) spectral density of the noise. If $n(t)$ is a voltage, the units are volts^2/cps. We shall frequently use the units watts/cps. The implication then is that we have normalized to a 1-ohm resistor.

The spectral density of the random-noise process is defined precisely as the Fourier transform of the autocorrelation function of the noise. The autocorrelation function $R_n(t_1,t_2)$ is in turn defined as the ensemble average of the noise at two time instants t_1 and t_2[1] (Fig. 1-1-1)

$$R_n(t_1,t_2) \equiv \langle n(t_1)n(t_2) \rangle \tag{1-1-5}$$

[1] Papoulis, *op. cit.,* Chap. 10. Davenport and Root, *op. cit.,* Sec. 4-5.

For a stationary random process all statistics are independent of the time origin and

$$R_n(t_1,t_2) = R_n(t_1 - t_2) \tag{1-1-6}$$

A wide-sense stationary random process is one for which Eq. (1-1-6) holds although higher-order statistics may not necessarily be independent of the time origin. (The ensemble mean of the process must also be a constant, independent of time, in this case.)

Assuming a wide-sense stationary random process we then define the (two-sided) spectral density $G_n(f)$ to be

$$G_n(f) \equiv \int_{-\infty}^{\infty} R_n(\tau)e^{-j\omega t}\, d\tau \qquad \omega = 2\pi f \tag{1-1-7}$$

By virtue of Fourier transform pairs,

$$
\begin{aligned}
R_n(\tau) &= \int_{-\infty}^{\infty} G_n(f)e^{j\omega\tau}\, df \qquad \omega = 2\pi f \\
&= \int_{0}^{\infty} 2G_n(f)\cos \omega\tau\, df
\end{aligned} \tag{1-1-8}
$$

If $G_n(f) = K/2$ (constant over all frequencies), the noise is called *white noise*, as noted previously. Such noise is, strictly speaking, physically inadmissible, implying infinite power. But it is a good approximation in many problems of interest, where the spectral density may be assumed constant over the range of frequencies of interest. For white noise the autocorrelation function is an impulse:

$$R_n(\tau) = \frac{K}{2}\, \delta(\tau)$$

From the definition of the autocorrelation function, the ensemble mean-squared value of $n(t)$ is just

$$N \equiv \langle n^2(t) \rangle = R_n(t,t) \tag{1-1-9}$$

For a wide-sense stationary process

$$N = R_n(0) = \int_{-\infty}^{\infty} G_n(f)\, df \tag{1-1-10}$$

using Eq. (1-1-8).

Equation (1-1-10) indicates the significance of the spectral density concept: Integrating over all frequencies we get the total power of the random noise.

If noise of spectral density $G_n(f)$ is now passed through a linear filter with transfer function $H(\omega)$ the output noise may be shown to have spectral density $G_{n_o}(f)$ given by[1]

$$G_{n_o}(f) = |H(\omega)|^2 G_n(f) \tag{1-1-11}$$

[1] This is easily proved by finding the autocorrelation function of the noise at the output and then taking its Fourier transform. See, e.g., Papoulis, *op. cit.*, Sec. 10-3.

and total noise power

$$N_o = \int_{-\infty}^{\infty} G_{n_o}(f)\, df \qquad (1\text{-}1\text{-}12)$$

White noise passing through an arbitrary linear filter is shown in Fig. 1-1-2. Here the subscript o has been dropped for simplicity's sake.

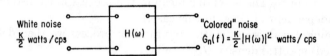

FIG. 1-1-2. Noise at the output of a linear device.

Examples

1. As an example, if the filter happens to be an idealized low-pass filter with

$$|H(\omega)| = A \qquad -2\pi B < \omega < 2\pi B$$

and zero elsewhere (Fig. 1-1-3a), white noise applied at the input emerges

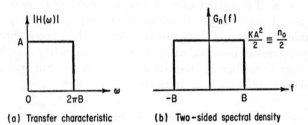

(a) Transfer characteristic   (b) Two-sided spectral density

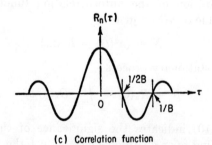

(c) Correlation function

FIG. 1-1-3. Ideal rectangular filter.

as band-limited white noise with $G_n(f) = A^2K/2 \equiv n_0/2$, $-B < f < B$, and $N = n_0B$ volts.   Then

$$R_n(\tau) = KA^2B \frac{\sin 2\pi B\tau}{2\pi B\tau} = N \frac{\sin 2\pi B\tau}{2\pi B\tau}$$

and for $\tau > 1/2B$, $R_n(\tau) \to 0$ (Fig. 1-1-3c).

The correlation thus approaches zero as the spacing between samples increases beyond the reciprocal of the bandwidth, as expected intuitively.

2. Assume the linear network is the RC network of Fig. 1-1-4a. Then

$$G_n(f) = \left| \frac{1/j\omega C}{R + 1/j\omega C} \right|^2 \frac{K}{2} = \frac{K/2}{1 + (\omega/\omega_o)^2} = \frac{K/2}{1 + (f/f_o)^2}$$

$$\omega_o \equiv \frac{1}{RC} \qquad f_o = 1/2\pi RC$$

Then $N = \int_{-\infty}^{\infty} G_n(f)\,df = K\omega_o/4$. Physically, we would expect the correlation "width" of noise at the output to be $= 1/\omega_o = RC$. Therefore,

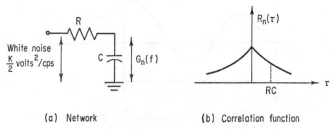

(a) Network   (b) Correlation function

FIG. 1-1-4. Noise at the output of an RC network.

for $\tau > RC$, the correlation $\rightarrow 0$ and the samples n_1 and n_2 become independent. Calculation of $R_n(\tau)$ gives

$$R_n(\tau) = \frac{K\omega_o}{4} e^{-\omega_o|\tau|} = N e^{-\omega_o|\tau|}$$

substantiating the expected behavior (Fig. 1-1-4b).

Since $N = R_n(0)$ represents the ensemble mean-squared value of the random noise process, Eq. (1-1-1) may be rewritten as

$$p(n) = \frac{e^{-n^2/2N}}{\sqrt{2\pi N}} \qquad (1\text{-}1\text{-}13)$$

Note that the statistics of the Gaussian random variable $n(t)$ at one instant of time depend solely on the mean-squared value N. (We are assuming zero mean value.) Since the band-limiting properties of a system come into effect when considering two values of the system output at two different instants of time, the joint statistics of the random variables $n_1 \equiv n(t_1)$ and $n_2 \equiv n(t_2) = n(t_1 + \tau)$ must depend on the spectral density $G_n(f)$ or on the correlation function $R_n(t_1, t_2) = R_n(\tau)$. (We are assuming a stationary random process.) For a Gaussian random process these statistics are given by the two-dimensional, or bivariate, Gaussian distribution obtained as follows.

Let $n(t) = n_1$ and $n(t + \tau) = n_2$ (see Fig. 1-1-5). Assume we have available an ensemble of identical noise sources and experimentally measure pairs of n_1 and n_2 from this ensemble. We then define the joint probability distribution

$$p(n_1, n_2) \, dn_1 \, d\bar{n}_2$$

as the probability of finding $n_1 \pm dn_1/2$, $n_2 \pm d\acute{n}_2/2$ simultaneously (jointly). This will depend on the separation τ and the spectral properties of the noise.

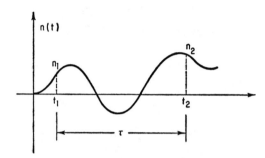

FIG. 1-1-5. Correlation of $n(t)$.

Various averages can be written:[1]

$$m_{10} = av \; n_1 = \langle n_1 \rangle = \int\int n_1 p_1(n_1, n_2) \, dn_1 \, dn_2$$
$$= 0 \qquad \text{here} \tag{1-1-14}$$
$$m_{01} = av \; n_2 = 0 \tag{1-1-15}$$
$$m_{11} = av \; n_1 n_2 = \langle n_1 n_2 \rangle = \int n_1 n_2 p(n_1, n_2) \, dn_1 \, dn_2 \tag{1-1-16}$$

Our assumption of a stationary Gaussian process gives us

$$m_{11} = R_n(\tau) \tag{1-1-17}$$

Also
$$m_{20} = \langle n_1{}^2 \rangle = \int\int n_1{}^2 p(n_1, n_2) \, dn_1 \, dn_2 \tag{1-1-18}$$
$$m_{02} = \langle n_2{}^2 \rangle$$

Then
$$\sigma_1{}^2 = m_{20} - m_{10}{}^2 = \sigma^2 = N \tag{1-1-19}$$
$$\sigma_2{}^2 = \sigma_1{}^2 = N$$

$R_n(\tau)$ and/or m_{11} are a measure of independence or correlation, for with n_1 and n_2 independent, $m_{11} = \langle n_1 n_2 \rangle = 0$ here. We can define a normalized correlation coefficient

$$\rho = \frac{m_{11} - m_{01} m_{10}}{\sigma_1 \sigma_2} \tag{1-1-20}$$

Then
$$-1 \leq \rho \leq 1 \tag{1-1-21}$$

Thus, with $n_1 = n_2$, $m_{11} = \sigma^2$, and $\rho = 1$.
    If $m_{11} = m_{01} m_{10}$ however, $\rho = 0$.

---

[1] The symbols $\langle \; \rangle$ are again used to denote ensemble averages.

The bivariate Gaussian distribution for the case $\langle n_1 \rangle = \langle n_2 \rangle = 0$ is given by

$$p(n_1,n_2) = \frac{1}{2\pi M} \exp\left[-\frac{1}{2(1-\rho^2)} \left(\frac{n_1{}^2}{\sigma_1{}^2} - \frac{2\rho n_1 n_2}{\sigma_1 \sigma_2} + \frac{n_2{}^2}{\sigma_2{}^2} \right) \right] \quad (1\text{-}1\text{-}22)$$

$$M \equiv \sigma_1{}^2 \sigma_2{}^2 (1 - \rho^2)$$

With $\rho = 0$, $p(n_1,n_2) = p(n_1)p(n_2)$, and the two Gaussian variables are independent. Two uncorrelated variables are thus necessarily independent if they have a Gaussian joint distribution.

The multivariate Gaussian distribution will be considered later when needed.

Why this emphasis on the correlation properties of noise? We shall have occasion later to utilize these in discussing the noise spectra at the output of AM and FM detectors. In addition, we shall frequently have occasion to deal with successive samples of noise spaced τ sec apart. The statistical properties of these samples will depend on whether they are independent or not. This depends on the correlation function and in turn on the spectral properties of the noise in the network.

1-2. Orthogonal Series Representations of Noise

Although the random function $n(t)$ strictly speaking can be represented only in terms of its probability density functions, it will be useful in much of the material that follows to utilize various functional representations for $n(t)$. One such representation is a Fourier-series expansion. Another representation is a more generalized expansion in terms of orthonormal functions. We shall consider these representations in this section. Hilbert transform representations will be considered in Secs. 1.6 and 1.7, as well as in Chap. 2. These various expansions will find applications in this chapter and in Chaps. 2 and 3.

We begin with the Fourier-series expansion and consider its properties:

Consider an interval T sec long. Over this interval $n(t)$, assumed to have zero average value, may be expanded in the complex Fourier series

$$n(t) = \frac{1}{T} \sum_{m=-\infty}^{\infty} c_m e^{j\omega_m t} \qquad \omega_m = 2\pi \frac{m}{T} \qquad (1\text{-}2\text{-}1)$$

$$c_m = \int_{-T/2}^{T/2} n(t) e^{-j\omega_m t} \, dt = |c_m| e^{j\theta_m} \qquad (1\text{-}2\text{-}2)$$

Since the noise is random, we would find the coefficients $|c_m|$ and θ_m to be random; each time we were to expand a strip T sec long we would find different values for $|c_m|$ and θ_m, and these would follow some statistical distribution if we repeated the calculation many times.

In particular, if $n(t)$ is assumed to be Gaussian, c_m must also be Gaussian since it is obtained, from Eq. (1-2-2), by linearly operating on $n(t)$. (It happens to be an example of a complex Gaussian process.) The mean-squared value of c_m in an ensemble sense can be shown to depend on the autocorrelation function (and hence spectral density) of $n(t)$, as might be expected. Thus, utilizing Eq. (1-2-2) we find that

$$
\begin{aligned}
\langle |c_m|^2 \rangle &= \int_{-T/2}^{T/2} \int_{-T/2}^{T/2} \langle n(s)n(t) \rangle e^{-j\omega_m(t-s)} \, dt \, ds \\
&= \int_{-T/2}^{T/2} \int_{-T/2}^{T/2} R_n(t-s) e^{-j\omega_m(t-s)} \, dt \, ds
\end{aligned}
\tag{1-2-3}
$$

with $R_n(t - s)$ the autocorrelation function of $n(t)$ defined in an ensemble sense. For a stationary process, as assumed here, $\langle n(s)n(t) \rangle$ depends only on the time difference $(t - s)$.

The correlation between Fourier coefficients c_l and c_m can also be found in a similar manner:

$$
\begin{aligned}
\langle c_l c_m{}^* \rangle &= \int_{-T/2}^{T/2} \int_{-T/2}^{T/2} R_n(t-s) e^{-j\omega_l t} e^{j\omega_m s} \, dt \, ds \\
&= \int_{-T/2}^{T/2} \left[\int_{-T/2-s}^{T/2-s} R_n(x) e^{-j\omega_l x} \, dx \right] e^{js(\omega_m - \omega_l)} \, ds
\end{aligned}
\tag{1-2-4}
$$

Now consider two special cases:

1. White noise, two-sided spectral density $n_0/2$

Then
$$
R_n(x) = \frac{n_0}{2} \, \delta(x)
$$

Evaluating Eq. (1-2-4) for this special case (recall that

$$
\int_a^b \delta(x) f(x) \, dx = f(0)
$$

if $a < 0 < b$) we get

$$
\begin{aligned}
\langle c_l c_m{}^* \rangle &= \frac{n_0 T}{2} \frac{\sin (\omega_m - \omega_l) T/2}{(\omega_m - \omega_l) T/2} \\
&= 0 \qquad m \neq l \\
&= \frac{n_0 T}{2} \qquad m = l
\end{aligned}
\tag{1-2-5}
$$

(Here use is made of the fact that $\omega_m = 2m\pi/T$.)

The Fourier coefficients in the case of white noise are thus *uncorrelated*, while

$$
\frac{1}{T} \langle |c_m|^2 \rangle = \frac{n_0}{2} = G_n(f_m)
\tag{1-2-6}
$$

is just the spectral density of the noise, evaluated at $f = f_m$. Note the intimate connection between the ensemble mean-squared value of the Fourier coefficients and the noise spectral density. This will be encountered again in similar form in the next special case.

2. $T \to \infty$ (i.e., infinite strip of noise), but noise not necessarily white. Then

$$\lim_{T \to \infty} \int_{-T/2-s}^{T/2-s} R_n(x)e^{-j\omega_l x}\, dx = G_n(f_l)$$

independent of s. Equation (1-2-4) then gives, in this limiting case,

$$\lim_{T \to \infty} \langle c_l c_m{}^* \rangle = G_n(f_l) \lim_{T \to \infty} T \frac{\sin (\omega_m - \omega_l)T/2}{(\omega_m - \omega_l)T/2}$$

Clearly then

$$\lim_{T \to \infty} \frac{1}{T} \langle c_l c_m{}^* \rangle = \begin{cases} G_n(f) & m = l \\ 0 & m \neq l \end{cases} \tag{1-2-7}$$

The Fourier coefficients are thus again uncorrelated in this special case where the Fourier-series interval becomes infinitely long. Note that the spectral density of the noise again appears proportional to the ensemble average of the square of the magnitude of the Fourier coefficient.

As a check, consider $\langle n^2(t) \rangle$. Using Eq. (1-2-1) this is given by

$$\langle n^2(t) \rangle = \frac{1}{T} \sum_m \sum_l \frac{1}{T} \langle c_m c_l{}^* \rangle e^{j\omega_m t} e^{-j\omega_l t} \tag{1-2-8}$$

In the limit as $T \to \infty$, we have, from Eq. (1-2-7), letting $\Delta f = \dfrac{1}{T}$,

$$\langle n^2 \rangle = \lim_{\Delta f \to 0} \sum_{l=-\infty}^{\infty} G_n(f_l)\, \Delta f = \int_{-\infty}^{\infty} G_n(f)\, df = N \tag{1-2-9}$$

in agreement with the considerations of the previous section.

Now consider the noise $n(t)$ passed through a linear network with transfer function $H(\omega)$. Superposition is valid because of the assumed linearity of the network. The output noise $n_o(t)$ then has a Fourier-series representation

$$n_o(t) = \frac{1}{T} \sum_{m=-\infty}^{\infty} c_m H(\omega_m)e^{j\omega_m t} \tag{1-2-10}$$

It is then easily shown that in the limit, as $T \to \infty$,

$$N_o = \langle n_o{}^2 \rangle = \lim_{\Delta f \to 0} \sum_{l=-\infty}^{\infty} |H(\omega_l)|^2 G_n(f_l)\, \Delta f$$

$$= \int_{-\infty}^{\infty} |H(\omega)|^2 G_n(f)\, df \tag{1-2-11}$$

We thus have, checking the relation stated in the previous section,

$$G_{n_o}(f) = |H(\omega)|^2 G_n(f) \tag{1-2-12}$$

The Fourier-series representation of noise in the limit of infinite period $(T \to \infty)$ thus contains within it the linear input-output relations discussed in the previous section.

Now consider a fixed interval T sec long and assume "colored" (non-white) Gaussian noise. Then the Fourier coefficients of a noise process $n(t)$ expanded over this interval will be statistically correlated. We shall show that an expansion of $n(t)$ into an orthogonal series other than the Fourier series with uncorrelated coefficients is still possible, however. One special case, corresponding to band-limited white noise, will be considered here. This material will be useful in Chap. 2, in which detection of binary signals defined over an interval T sec long will be considered. This expansion of $n(t)$ into an orthogonal series with uncorrelated coefficients is called the *Karhunen-Loève expansion*.[1]

Consider a set of functions $\phi_l(t)$ defined over the interval 0, T. ($l =$ 1,2, . . . ,∞). These are said to be orthogonal if

$$\int_0^T \phi_j \phi_l \, dt = 0 \qquad j \neq l$$

(For simplicity's sake, real functions are assumed here.) In particular, if $\int_0^T \phi_l{}^2 \, dt = 1$, they are said to be orthonormal. (This normalization is always possible. The Fourier series $\sqrt{2/T} \cos \omega_n t$, $\sqrt{2/T} \sin \omega_n t$ is one example.) The expansion of an arbitrary function into a series of such orthonormal functions is possible under conditions similar to those of the usual Fourier-series expansion (the so-called Dirichlet conditions). The series then represents the function in the usual mean-squared sense.

Assume now that we expand the noise function $n(t)$ into the following orthogonal series:

$$n(t) = \sum_{l=1}^{\infty} n_l \phi_l(t) \tag{1-2-13}$$

The coefficients n_l are readily found by multiplying left- and right-hand sides by $\phi_j(t)$ and integrating from 0 to T. With the functions assumed orthonormal this gives

$$n_l = \int_0^T n(t) \phi_l(t) \, dt \tag{1-2-14}$$

just as in the special case of the sine and cosine Fourier series. Note that if $n(t)$ is Gaussian, as assumed here, n_l is Gaussian also. The correlation between n_l and n_m, found by ensemble-averaging their product, is given by

$$\langle n_l n_m \rangle = \int_0^T \int_0^T \langle n(t) n(s) \rangle \phi_l(t) \phi_m(s) \, dt \, ds$$

$$= \int_0^T \int_0^T R_n(t - s) \phi_l(t) \phi_m(s) \, dt \, ds \tag{1-2-15}$$

again replacing the ensemble average $\langle n(t) n(s) \rangle$ by the autocorrelation function $R_n(t - s)$.

[1] Davenport and Root, *op. cit.*, pp. 96 et seq. C. W. Helstrom, "Statistical Theory of Signal Detection," pp. 96 et seq., Pergamon Press, New York, 1960. Papoulis, *op. cit.*, pp. 457 et seq.

The terms n_l and n_m will be uncorrelated if we can find a set of functions $\phi_l(t)$ such that $\langle n_l n_m \rangle = \sigma_l^2 \delta_{lm}$, with δ_{lm} the Kronecker delta

$$\delta_{lm} = \begin{cases} 1 & l = m \\ 0 & l \neq m \end{cases}$$

From Eq. (1-2-15) such a set is given by the solution of the integral equation

$$\int_0^T R_n(t - s)\phi_l(t) \, dt = \sigma_l^2 \phi_l(s) \tag{1-2-16}$$

For, introducing this solution into Eq. (1-2-15), we get $\langle n_l n_m \rangle = \sigma_l^2 \delta_{lm}$ as desired. This is the Karhunen-Loève expansion. The constant σ_l^2 is then the mean-squared value of n_l. Consider these special cases:

1. White noise; $R_n(x) = (n_0/2) \, \delta(x)$.

Then *any* orthonormal set $\phi_l(t)$ satisfies Eq. (1-2-16). We have already shown the Fourier series has this property for white noise. Note that $\sigma_l^2 = n_0/2$ for this case.

2. Band-limited white noise:

$$G_n(f) = \begin{cases} \dfrac{n_0}{2} & -B < f < B \\ 0 & \text{elsewhere} \end{cases} \tag{1-2-17}$$

Then
$$R_n(\tau) = n_0 B \frac{\sin 2\pi B\tau}{2\pi B\tau} \tag{1-2-18}$$

Noise samples $\tau = 1/2B$ sec apart are then uncorrelated. It may then be shown that the appropriate orthonormal set $\phi_l(t)$ for this case [i.e., those satisfying the integral equation (1-2-16)] consists of the so-called prolate spheroidal functions.[1] In the limit of large T (where $BT \gg 1$) these approach the $\sin x/x$ functions $\sqrt{2B} \, [\sin \pi(2Bt - l)]/[\pi(2Bt - l)]$ encountered in sampling theory (Sec. 2-6). For it may readily be shown that

$$\int_{-\infty}^{\infty} \frac{\sin \pi(2Bt - l)}{\pi(2Bt - l)} \frac{\sin \pi(2Bt - m)}{\pi(2Bt - m)} \, dt = \frac{1}{2B} \delta_{lm} \tag{1-2-19}$$

Since $R_n(\tau)$ is also of this $\sin x/x$ form, it is apparent that for large T [using the range $(-T/2, T/2)$ rather than $(0,T)$] the integral equation (1-2-16) is approximately satisfied by the $\sin x/x$ functions.

To this approximation the Fourier coefficients n_l are then given by $(1/\sqrt{2B})n(l/2B)$, with $n(l/2B)$ the value of $n(t)$ sampled at $t = l/2B$. The band-limited function $n(t)$ defined over the interval T sec long

---

[1] D. Slepian and H. O. Pollack, Prolate Spheroidal Wave Functions, Fourier Analysis and Uncertainty—I, *Bell System Tech. J.*, vol. 40, pp. 43–63, January, 1961. See also A. Papoulis, "The Fourier Integral and Its Applications," pp. 67–69, McGraw-Hill Book Company, New York, 1962; A. Papoulis, "Probability, Random Variables, and Stochastic Processes," p. 460, McGraw-Hill Book Company, New York, 1965.

$(BT \gg 1)$ is then approximately representable as

$$n(t) \doteq \sum_{l=1}^{2BT} n\left(\frac{l}{2B}\right) \frac{\sin \pi(2Bt - l)}{\pi(2Bt - l)} \tag{1-2-20}$$

Here too

$$\frac{\sigma_l^2}{2} = \frac{n_0}{2} = \langle n_l^2 \rangle \qquad \text{and} \qquad \left\langle n^2\left(\frac{l}{2B}\right) \right\rangle = n_0 B = N$$

These orthonormal representations of noise with uncorrelated Fourier coefficients will be utilized in Chap. 2 in considering the application of statistical decision theory to signal-detection problems.

Before concluding this section it is of interest to introduce still another form of the Fourier-series representation of noise. This is the model used by W. R. Bennett:[1]

$$n(t) = \sum_{l=1}^{\infty} \sqrt{4G_n(f_l)\,\Delta f}\, \cos\,(\omega_l t + \theta_l) \tag{1-2-21}$$

Here $\Delta f \equiv 1/T$, $\omega_l = (2\pi l)/T$, and θ_l is a uniformly distributed random variable. The different θ_l terms are assumed independent.

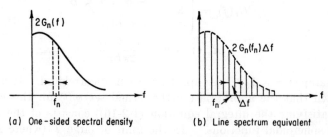

(a) One-sided spectral density   (b) Line spectrum equivalent

FIG. 1-2-1. Discrete representation of noise.

Although the Fourier amplitudes are not random in this model, the random distribution of the phase angles θ_l ensures that $n(t)$ is Gaussian-distributed. (Recall from the central limit theorem that the distribution of the sum of a large number of random variables approaches the Gaussian distribution under very broad conditions.)

This representation of $n(t)$ is equivalent to approximating the one-sided continuous spectral density $2G_n(f)$ by the line spectrum of Fig. 1-2-1.[2]

Note that the ensemble mean-squared value of $n(t)$, averaging over the θ_l's, is given by

$$\langle n^2(t) \rangle = \sum_{l=1}^{\infty} 2G_n(f_l)\,\Delta f \tag{1-2-22}$$

by virtue of the independence of the θ_l's.

[1] Bennett, "Methods of Solving Noise Problems."

[2] Schwartz, "Information Transmission, Modulation, and Noise."

In the limit, as $T \to \infty$, $\Delta f \to df$ and

$$\langle n^2 \rangle \to \int_0^\infty 2G_n(f) \, df = N \tag{1-2-23}$$

agreeing with the result of Eq. (1-1-12).

Consider now two values of $n(t)$ spaced τ sec apart in time. As noted previously, these are related by the autocorrelation function $R_n(\tau)$ and its Fourier transform $G_n(f)$. That this transform relation is contained within the Fourier model of Eq. (1-2-21) is easily shown:

$$R_n(\tau) \equiv \langle n(t)n(t + \tau) \rangle = \left\langle \sum_{l=1}^\infty \sum_{m=1}^\infty 4 \sqrt{G_n(f_l)G_n(f_m)} \, \Delta f \cos \right.$$

$$\left. (\omega_l t + \theta_l) \cos (\omega_m t + \omega_m \tau + \theta_m) \right\rangle$$

$$= \sum_{l=1}^\infty 2G_n(f_l) \cos \omega_l \tau \, \Delta f \tag{1-2-24}$$

after interchanging the order of summation and ensemble-averaging and noting that

$$\langle \cos (\omega_l t + \theta_l) \cos [\omega_m(t + \tau) + \theta_m] \rangle = \begin{cases} 0 & m \neq l \\ \dfrac{\cos \omega_l \tau}{2} & m = l \end{cases} \tag{1-2-25}$$

[Here, as in the manipulations leading to Eq. (1-2-22), we expand the product into sum and difference angle terms and average over θ_l.] Again taking the limit as $T \to \infty$, $\Delta f \to df$, we get

$$R_n(\tau) = \int_0^\infty 2G_n(f) \cos \omega\tau \, df \tag{1-2-26}$$

This particular model for the noise process will prove useful in our discussion of detection theory.

1-3. A Simple Application to Binary Transmission[1]

Assume we are interested in transmitting a binary coded message given by a sequence of on-off pulses, or of bipolarity pulses as shown in Fig. 1-3-1. These represent a particular sequence of 0s and 1s. (We shall consider binary transmission in great detail later in this book.)

Gaussian noise is added in the process of transmission and errors may very well be made at the receiver in determining the actual symbols transmitted. We wish to calculate the probability of error at any instant during which the signal-plus-noise combination is sampled.

In the case of the on-off pulse sequence the probability distributions of signal plus noise, and of noise alone in the absence of signal (the "off"

[1] Schwartz, *op. cit.*

case), are both Gaussian and are shown in Fig. 1-3-2a. The voltage $v(t)$ represents the sampled voltage at any instant of time. The probability distributions in the bipolarity case are shown in Fig. 1-3-2b.

If either symbol, 0 or 1, is equally likely to be transmitted, it would appear intuitively obvious to set a threshold level halfway between the expected signal amplitudes. This would be $A/2$ in the on-off case, 0 in the bipolarity case. A voltage appearing above this threshold would be most likely to be a 1; below the threshold it would be most likely to be a

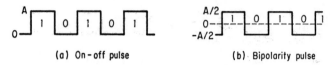

(a) On-off pulse   (b) Bipolarity pulse

FIG. 1-3-1. Binary pulse sequence.

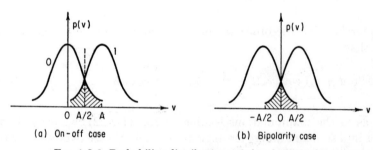

(a) On-off case   (b) Bipolarity case

FIG. 1-3-2. Probability distributions of signal plus noise.

0. We shall show in Chap. 2 that this intuitive approach agrees with that developed on the basis of more sophisticated statistical techniques.

Setting such a threshold gives rise to the possibility of errors, however. The chance of errors occurring is given by the area of any one of the curves in Fig. 1-3-2 overlapping into the region beyond the threshold reserved for the opposite symbol. Note from the symmetry of the curves that this area is the same in all four cases, as is shown in hatched lines in Fig. 1-3-2.

The probability of error (that a 1 will be mistaken for a 0 or vice versa) is given by

$$P_e = \int_{A/2}^{\infty} \frac{e^{-v^2/2N}}{\sqrt{2\pi N}}\, dv = \frac{1}{2}\left(1 - \operatorname{erf}\frac{\sqrt{\gamma}}{2}\right) = \frac{1}{2}\operatorname{erfc}\frac{\sqrt{\gamma}}{2} \quad (1\text{-}3\text{-}1)$$

where $\operatorname{erf} x \equiv (2/\sqrt{\pi}) \int_0^x e^{-y^2}\, dy$, $\operatorname{erfc} x \equiv 1 - \operatorname{erf} x$, and $\gamma \equiv A^2/2N$. The error function of x is tabulated in most books on statistics,[1] as is the

[1] See, e.g., H. Cramer, "Mathematical Methods of Statistics," Princeton University Press, Princeton, N.J., 1951; A. M. Mood and F. A. Graybill, "Introduction to the Theory of Statistics," 2d ed., McGraw-Hill Book Company, New York, 1963.

complementary error function erfc x.   This error probability of mistaking a binary 1 for a 0 or vice versa is shown plotted versus peak signal-to-noise ratio $A/\sqrt{N}$ in Fig. 1-3-3.   Note that for $A/\sqrt{N} < 8$ (18 db) the probability of error increases rapidly, approaching an error probability of 0.5 for $A = 0$.   (When the pulse heights are so small as to be practically zero, the decision made at the receiver will still be right half the time on the average.)

Above $A/\sqrt{N} = 8$ (approximately), the probability of error decreases very rapidly with small changes in signal.   For example, for $A/\sqrt{N} = 7.4$ P_e is 10^{-4}.   This means that on the average 1 digit in 10^4 transmitted will be judged incorrectly.   If 10^5 digits per second are being transmitted, this means a mistake every 0.1 sec, on the average, which may not be satisfactory.   However, if the signal is increased to $A/\sqrt{N} = 11.1$, a change of 3.5 db, P_e decreases to 10^{-8}.   For 10^5 digits per second this means a mistake every 1,000 sec or 16 min on the average, which is much more likely to be tolerable.

The existence of a narrow range of signal-to-noise ratios above which the error rate is tolerable and below which errors occur quite frequently is termed a *threshold effect*.   (This is not to be confused with the threshold *levels* of Fig. 1-3-2.)   Such threshold effects

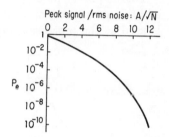

FIG. 1-3-3. Error probability in binary transmission.

occur in all wideband communication systems, as will be noted later in Chap. 3.[1]

Decreased Noise Effects by Repetition.   In some applications it may very well happen that the peak signal-to-noise ratios available are just not large enough to provide a tolerable probability of error.   This is frequently true in high-frequency communication, where propagation effects lead to signal fading (see Chap. 9).   It could also be the case where the peak signal powers available at the receiver are just not large enough to overcome the noise introduced.   (This is a problem in radio astronomy, for example, requiring the use of both low-noise receivers and radiometer circuits.   It is also a problem in many search radars in space communications because of the large distances involved.)

Is there any way in which we can still obtain a tolerable error probability?   Intuitively we may feel that we could do this by repeating the signal several times, at intervals *greater than the correlation time* of the noise, or at intervals greater than 1/system bandwidth.   The noise voltages sampled at the successive intervals are then effectively independent, while the signal voltages are essentially the same.   (This assumes that

[1] See also Schwartz, *op. cit.*, Chap. 6.

if signal fading is the problem, the fading rate is slow compared with the sampling intervals.)[1] We might thus expect that we could increase the chance of correctly detecting the signal. This is of course in keeping with the statistical concept that more reliable estimates can be made with several measurements or samples of a given quantity than with just one.

The catch, however, is that for this improvement, the signal itself must be assumed to be completely coherent over the total time involved for the signal repetition. If high-frequency transmission is involved, this leads to rather strict requirements on signal phase coherence among the successive processed signal samples and therefore requires a high degree of stability and "locking in" between receiver and transmitter oscillators.

This requirement of phase coherence is readily understood if simple addition or integration of the repeated signal-plus-noise voltage samples is used as the processing procedure. (We shall show in Chap. 2, using

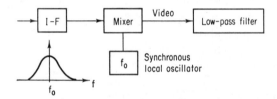

Fig. 1-3-4. Synchronous detection.

the concepts of statistical decision theory, that this corresponds to the optimum method of processing the repeated signal samples if additive Gaussian noise is assumed and minimum probabilities of error are required.) Direct summation of signals is difficult, so that normally we would consider frequency-translating the signal-plus-noise combinations down to video frequencies by injecting a *synchronous* local oscillator signal (Fig. 1-3-4).

In either case, whether addition of high-frequency signals or of the synchronously detected video signals is attempted, the signal components of the signal-plus-noise voltages will add *linearly*, providing they are phase-coherent. The noise component is assumed to vary randomly from sample to sample (or repetition interval to repetition interval), so that the noise samples add quadratically in a mean-squared sense.[2] The resultant voltage signal-to-noise ratio will then be expected to increase as $\sqrt{n}$, with n the number of samples added. We can demonstrate this quantitatively using the binary on-off case as an example as follows:

[1] Signal repetition in the presence of both rapid and slow fading is considered in M. Schwartz, Effect of Signal Fluctuation on Detection of Pulse Signals in Noise, *IRE Trans. Inform. Theory*, vol. IT-2, pp. 66–71, June, 1956.

[2] If phase coherence cannot be maintained, envelope detection becomes necessary and is commonly utilized in many systems. This is discussed in the next section.

Assume n repetitions of the binary signals. A "1" again will b by a received voltage of A volts. The signal plus added noise one sample again will have a Gaussian distribution, so that the di tion of the sum of n such samples itself will be Gaussian with the average value increased by a factor of n and the variance increased n times. The resultant distributions of the sum of the signal-plus-noise combinations in the two cases will be given by

$$p(v) = \frac{e^{-v^2/2nN}}{\sqrt{2\pi nN}} \tag{1-3-2}$$

if a "0" is transmitted n times in succession, and

$$p(v) = \frac{e^{-(v-nA)^2/2nN}}{\sqrt{2\pi nN}} \tag{1-3-3}$$

if the signal is a "1."

These are sketched in Fig. 1-3-5. An obvious threshold level to be used to distinguish between the 0 and the 1 would be $nA/2$. Note that

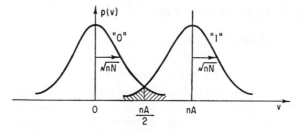

FIG. 1-3-5. Gaussian distribution of sum of n variables.

although the width of the curves goes up as $\sqrt{n}$, the average values increase directly with n. The probability of error, shown by the hatched area in either case, thus decreases with n if $A/\sqrt{N}$ is kept fixed.

The probability of error P_e is the same as that plotted in Fig. 1-3-3 and is given by Eq. (1-3-1), if A is replaced by nA and N by nN. The effective signal-to-noise ratio is thus $\sqrt{n}\,(A/\sqrt{N})$, and Fig. 1-3-3 can be used for the repeated signal case also.

Simple addition or integration of repetitions of a signal is not the only possible method of handling the n statistical samples of signal plus noise. A coincidence method, in which one or more of the received samples is asked to exceed a specified threshold level, could also be used. As noted previously, however, we shall show in Chap. 2 that simple addition in the case of additive Gaussian noise is normally an optimum procedure. In one example considered, the best possible coincidence procedure does fall short of the addition technique.[1]

[1] M. Schwartz, A Coincidence Procedure for Signal Detection, *IRE Trans. Inform. Theory*, vol. IT-2, December, 1956.

Repetition of transmitted information is common in many communications systems. An obvious example is the telephone, in which a key word is spelled out ("A as in Arthur, M as in Mary," etc.). In some telegraph applications, individual symbols are repeated twice. In most radar systems many successive pulses received from a particular target are added up to improve signal detectability. These are examples of *time repetition* of signals. (In information-theory terminology the repetition serves to increase the message redundancy. The chance of error is thus reduced at the expense of increased time or bandwidth needed for repetition.)

Space and/or frequency repetition of signals is also commonly used with various *diversity techniques* to overcome signal losses due to fading. Here the outputs of n receivers differing in location or in frequency are combined after weighting in any one of several different ways. Diversity techniques will be discussed in detail in Chap. 10. As will be shown there, the basic signal-noise properties are identical with those obtained for the addition of signals repeated in time.[1] Indeed, actual repetition of signals has been considered in fading systems, usually being termed *time diversity*.

Repetition of signals is thus a useful and simple technique for increasing the effective signal-to-noise ratio or for decreasing the probability of message-reception errors. It is desirable, however, only where the transmitter has limited peak power, or where lower-noise receivers cannot be used or are too expensive to use. (The same effective signal-to-noise ratio could of course be obtained by increasing A or decreasing $\sqrt{N}$ proportionately.) A given probability of signal detectability requires a specified amount of signal *energy*. The repetition technique merely serves to spread it out in time or to decrease the power in any signal interval.

1-4. Narrowband Noise and Envelope Detection[2]

Continuing with our study of the properties of noise, with particular application to communication systems, it is of great interest to discuss the noise at the output of a narrow-bandpass filter. This then represents the noise at the output of the i-f stages of most communications receivers. Because of the narrowband properties of this noise we shall be able to define both the envelope and phase of the noise in this section and discuss the statistical properties of each. An obvious application is envelope

---

[1] This statement is almost obvious but was overlooked for many years by radar engineers and the designers of diversity equipment, who independently repeated each other's analyses, obtaining similar curves and results.

[2] A more general and systematic approach to the statistics of narrowband noise will be developed in Secs. 1-6 and 1-7 using a Hilbert-transform formulation. The Fourier-series approach of this section is more intuitive and so is utilized first.

detection of signals. Later, in Chap. 3, we shall utilize the concepts of narrowband noise in comparing the signal-to-noise performance of idealized AM and FM receivers.

The study of narrowband noise, and envelope detection as an important application, is particularly appropriate at this point, for envelope detection used in conjunction with a binary transmission system obviates the requirement of signal phase coherence stressed in the previous sections.

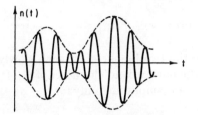

FIG. 1-4-1. Narrowband noise. FIG. 1-4-2. Narrowband bandpass filter.

Envelope detection is also more simply instrumented than the synchronous detection of Fig. 1-3-4, in which a video binary signal is recovered by heterodyning down to video frequencies by in-phase carrier injection. It will thus be of interest to compare binary error probabilities using envelope detection with the error curve of Fig. 1-3-3, obtained assuming signal coherence.

Consider then noise at the output of a narrowband linear device with center frequency f_0 cps and bandwidth $B \ll f_0$. The output noise $n(t)$ would be expected to "look" almost like a sine wave of frequency f_0 but with slowly varying and randomly modulated phase and amplitude (Fig. 1-4-1).

The linear device, which presumably represents the frequency characteristics of the i-f section of the receiver and includes any filtering done in the r-f, has a frequency transfer function $H(\omega)$ with an amplitude characteristic $|H(\omega)|$ as shown in Fig. 1-4-2.

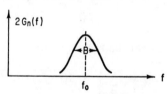

FIG. 1-4-3. One-sided noise spectral density at narrowband filter output.

The narrowband noise $n(t)$ can be expressed mathematically by rewriting Eq. (1-2-21) in a somewhat different form, due to S. O. Rice. Starting with Eq. (1-2-21),

$$n(t) = \sum_{l=1}^{\infty} \sqrt{4G_n(f_l)\,\Delta f}\,\cos\,(\omega_l t + \theta_l) \qquad (1\text{-}4\text{-}1)$$

Here the one-sided spectral density is

$$2G_n(f) = K|H(\omega)|^2 \qquad (1\text{-}4\text{-}2)$$

as previously, and has the typical form shown in Fig. 1-4-3.

Most of the Fourier coefficients of Eq. (1-4-1) will be zero or close to zero. The only ones differing substantially from zero will correspond to those values of f_l within a range B cps about f_0. To portray the narrowband character of $n(t)$ analytically, let $\omega_l = (\omega_l - \omega_0) + \omega_0$, and expand Eq. (1-4-1) in terms of the frequencies $(\omega_l - \omega_0)$ and ω_0. Then

$$n(t) = \left\{ \sum_{l=1}^{\infty} \sqrt{4G_n(f_l)\,\Delta f} \cos[(\omega_l - \omega_0)t + \theta_l] \right\} \cos \omega_0 t$$

$$- \left\{ \sum_{l=1}^{\infty} \sqrt{4G_n(f_l)\,\Delta f} \sin[(\omega_l - \omega_0)t + \theta_l] \right\} \sin \omega_0 t \qquad (1\text{-}4\text{-}3)$$

Now note that the quantities inside the two brackets are each slowly varying with respect to ω_0 because of the narrowband character of $G_n(f)$. (The frequencies $f_l - f_0$ will have significant amplitudes only for $f_l - f_0 < B \ll f_0$.) We then write

$$n(t) = x(t) \cos \omega_0 t - y(t) \sin \omega_0 t \qquad (1\text{-}4\text{-}4)$$

with
$$x(t) = \sum_{l=1}^{\infty} \sqrt{4G_n(f_l)}\,\Delta f \cos[(\omega_l - \omega_0)t + \theta_l] \qquad (1\text{-}4\text{-}5)$$

and
$$y(t) = \sum_{l=1}^{\infty} \sqrt{4G_n(f_l)}\,\Delta f \sin[(\omega_l - \omega_0)t + \theta_l] \qquad (1\text{-}4\text{-}6)$$

Both $x(t)$ and $y(t)$ are slowly varying random time functions. They are Gaussian-distributed random variables, as was $n(t)$ itself, by virtue of the central limit theorem. [Recall that the θ_l's are uniformly distributed random variables in the particular representation of noise of Eq. (1-4-1).]

The mean-squared values of x and y are each

$$\langle x^2 \rangle = \langle y^2 \rangle = N = \langle n^2 \rangle \qquad (1\text{-}4\text{-}7)$$

as can be seen by actually performing the ensemble average of x^2 or y^2:

$$\langle x^2 \rangle \equiv \left\langle \sum_m \sum_l \sqrt{4G_n(f_m)4G_n(f_l)}\,\Delta f \cos[(\omega_m - \omega_0)t + \theta_m] \right.$$
$$\left. \cos[(\omega_l - \omega_0)t + \theta_l] \right\rangle \qquad (1\text{-}4\text{-}8)$$

Interchanging the order of summation and ensemble averaging, all terms vanish except for the case $m = l$. The ensemble average in this case is $\frac{1}{2}$, so that

$$\langle x^2 \rangle = \sum_l 2G_n(f_l)\,\Delta f \qquad (1\text{-}4\text{-}9)$$

Taking the limit as $T \to \infty$, $\Delta f \to df$,

$$\langle x^2 \rangle = \int_0^{\infty} 2G_n(f)\,df = N \qquad (1\text{-}4\text{-}10)$$

$\langle y^2 \rangle$ is found similarly.

The two random variables x and y thus have probability distributions

$$p(x) = \frac{e^{-x^2/2N}}{\sqrt{2\pi N}} \tag{1-4-11}$$

$$p(y) = \frac{e^{-y^2/2N}}{\sqrt{2\pi N}} \tag{1-4-12}$$

It is readily shown that the Gaussian-distributed x and y variables are uncorrelated $[\langle x(t)y(t)\rangle = 0]$ and therefore independent. Thus, following the procedure used in evaluating $\langle x^2 \rangle$,

$$\langle x(t)y(t)\rangle = \Big\langle \sum_m \sum_l \sqrt{4G_n(f_m)4G_n(f_l)} \, \Delta f$$
$$\cos\left[(\omega_m - \omega_0)t + \theta_m\right] \sin\left[(\omega_l - \omega_0)t + \theta_l\right] \Big\rangle = 0 \tag{1-4-13}$$

since *all* terms vanish on ensemble averaging. It is important to note, however, that $x(t)$ and $y(t + \tau)$, $\tau > 0$, are in general correlated. This will be discussed in Sec. 1.7.

Because $x(t)$ and $y(t)$ are independent, their joint distribution is given by

$$p(x,y) \, dx \, dy = \frac{e^{-(x^2+y^2)/2N}}{2\pi N} \, dx \, dy \tag{1-4-14}$$

This is a very fortunate result for it enables us to find the probability distributions of the envelope and phase of the noise voltage $n(t)$ quite simply. Thus, rewrite $n(t)$ as follows:

$$n(t) = x(t) \cos \omega_0 t - y(t) \sin \omega_0 t$$
$$= r(t) \cos (\omega_0 + \theta) \tag{1-4-15}$$

with $r = \sqrt{x^2 + y^2}$, $\theta = \tan^{-1}(y/x)$.

To find the distributions of the envelope r and phase θ we simply transform from (x,y) to (r,θ) coordinates in two dimensions. Since there is a one-to-one correspondence between x, y and r, θ we can equate joint probabilities, getting

$$p(x,y) \, dx \, dy = p(r,\theta) \, dr \, d\theta \tag{1-4-16}$$

Using Eq. (1-4-14).

$$p(x,y) = \frac{e^{-(x^2+y^2)/2N}}{2\pi N} = \frac{e^{-r^2/2N}}{2\pi N}$$

Then, since $dx \, dy = r \, dr \, d\theta$,

$$p(r,\theta) \, dr \, d\theta = \frac{re^{-r^2/2N}}{2\pi N} \, dr \, d\theta \tag{1-4-17}$$

The distribution for r alone $p(r)$ is found by averaging $p(r,\theta)$ over all values of θ from 0 to 2π. Thus,

$$p(r) = \int_0^{2\pi} p(r,\theta) \, d\theta = \frac{re^{-r^2/2N}}{N} \tag{1-4-18}$$

This probability distribution of the envelope of narrowband noise is called the Rayleigh distribution and is shown in Fig. 1-4-4.[1]

That $p(r)$ is properly normalized is easily seen, since

$$\int_0^\infty p(r)\,dr = \int_0^\infty \frac{e^{-r^2/2N}}{N}\,dr = 1$$

(Note that r takes on positive values only.)

The distribution in phase is given by

$$p(\theta) = \frac{1}{2\pi} \qquad 0 < \theta < 2\pi \tag{1-4-19}$$

as can be readily shown by integrating $p(r,\theta)$ over all r. Since $p(r,\theta)$

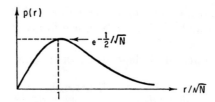

FIG. 1-4-4. Rayleigh distribution.

can be written as $p(r)p(\theta)$ in this case, r and θ are independent random variables, as were x and y.

Some of the properties of the Rayleigh distribution are of interest:

1. By differentiating $p(r)$ we find the peak to occur at $r = \sqrt{N}$. This is indicated in Fig. 1-4-4.

2. The median or 50 per cent cumulative distribution point is found by writing

$$0.5 = \int_r^\infty p(r)\,dr = e^{-r^2/2N}$$

Then $r = 1.185\sqrt{N}$ gives the median value.

3. The average value is

$$m_1 = \langle r \rangle = \sqrt{\frac{\pi}{2}}\sqrt{N} = 1.25\sqrt{N} \tag{1-4-20}$$

4. The second moment is

$$m_2 = 2N \tag{1-4-21}$$

5. The variance is

$$\sigma^2 \equiv m_2 - m_1{}^2 = N\left(2 - \frac{\pi}{2}\right) \tag{1-4-22}$$

An a-c coupled true rms meter would thus read $a\sqrt{N}\sqrt{2 - \frac{\pi}{2}}$ if con-

[1] See Schwartz, "Information Transmission, Modulation, and Noise," p. 453, for the distribution of the *square* of the envelope, useful if the actual envelope detector has some curvature in its characteristics.

nected to the output of a linear envelope detector, with output-input characteristic defined as $y = ar$. Similarly, a d-c meter would read, $a \sqrt{N} \sqrt{\dfrac{\pi}{2}}$. The ratio of the two readings would be 0.525, independent of the detector constant a. This is frequently of interest in checking the validity of the Rayleigh distribution in various applications and is also useful in measuring the linearity of an envelope detector.

The Rayleigh distribution represents the probability distribution of the envelope of *noise* alone at the output of a narrowband bandpass filter, such as an i-f strip. In high-frequency communications we normally have present also a sinusoidal signal at or near the frequency f_0. This could be a carrier in the case of AM or FM, one of the two transmitting states of an FSK binary transmission system, or the "on" state for on-off telegraph or binary transmission. The sinusoidal signal to be detected appears at the i-f output in the presence of noise. It is thus of interest to investigate the statistical properties of the *envelope* of the composite signal plus noise. We shall focus attention on this primarily because of the applications to follow. The probability distribution of the phase is found in a similar way, and is discussed in the references.[1]

Assuming an unmodulated carrier of amplitude A and at frequency f_0, the resultant signal-plus-noise voltage at the i-f output is

$$\begin{aligned}
v(t) &= n(t) + A \cos \omega_0 t \\
&= (x + A) \cos \omega_0 t - y \sin \omega_0 t \\
&= r \cos (\omega_0 t + \theta)
\end{aligned} \qquad (1\text{-}4\text{-}23)$$

(The phase of the signal term is purely arbitrary and does not affect the results obtained.)

In this case the envelope and phase are given by

$$r^2 = (x + A)^2 + y^2 = x'^2 + y^2$$

$$\theta = \tan^{-1} \frac{y}{x + A} = \tan^{-1} \frac{y}{x'}$$

As before

$$\begin{aligned}
p(r,\theta) \, dr \, d\theta &= p(x',y) \, dx' \, dy \\
&= \frac{e^{-[(x'-A)^2+y^2]/2N}}{2\pi N} \, dx' \, dy
\end{aligned} \qquad (1\text{-}4\text{-}24)$$

with the variable $x' = x + A$ Gaussian-distributed about an average value of A.

---

[1] See, e.g., Schwartz, *ibid.*, pp. 410–413. The distribution of the phase of narrowband noise plus an unmodulated carrier is of interest in some navigation systems and in digital transmission systems utilizing phase modulation and detection. Error curves for digital phase-modulation systems, obtained using the phase distribution, are given in C. R. Cahn, Combined Digital Phase and Amplitude Modulation Communication Systems, *IRE Trans. Commun. Systems*, vol. CS-8, pp. 150–155, September, 1960. A more direct approach to error rates for digital phase-modulation systems will be considered in Chap. 7.

Expanding the exponent and converting to r, θ coordinates,

$$p(r,\theta) = \frac{re^{-(r^2+A^2-2rA\cos\theta)/2N}}{2\pi N}\, dr\, d\theta \qquad (1\text{-}4\text{-}25)$$

The distribution of the envelope is again found by integrating over θ:

$$p(r) = \int_0^{2\pi} p(r,\theta)\, d\theta = \frac{r}{N} e^{-r^2/2N} e^{-A^2/2N} I_0\left(\frac{rA}{N}\right) \qquad (1\text{-}4\text{-}26)$$

where $I_0(z)$, the modified Bessel function of the first kind and zeroth order is given by

$$I_0(z) \equiv \frac{1}{2\pi} \int_0^{2\pi} e^{z\cos\theta}\, d\theta \qquad (1\text{-}4\text{-}27)$$

This distribution is discussed in some detail in most of the references cited in Sec. 1-1.[1]

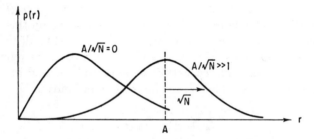

FIG. 1-4-5. Distribution of the envelope of signal plus noise.

For large peak signal-to-noise ratio $(A/\sqrt{N} \gg 1)$, the distribution peaks at about $r = A$ and can be shown to approach a Gaussian distribution in shape. This is indicated in Fig. 1-4-5.

1.5. Application to Binary Transmission

The probability distributions of the envelope of narrowband noise with or without a sinusoidal carrier again can be used to calculate the probability of error due to noise when transmitting binary information. Signal phase coherence is not necessary in this case, and the receiver requires only a simple envelope detector following the i-f strip. This contrasts with in-phase local carrier injection required to implement the binary system of Sec. 1-3.

Here we assume the 0 and 1 symbols to be carried by on-off bursts of r-f power. (Bipolarity binary transmission would require a phase detector instead of an envelope detector, and is discussed in Chaps. 3 and 7.) As previously we assume the 0s and 1s are equally likely to be transmitted.

[1] See, e.g., Rice, Schwartz, Davenport and Root.

It would again seem logical to pick some voltage level b at the envelope detector output to test for the presence of a 0 or a 1. If the voltage fell below b we would assume à 0 had been transmitted; if it appeared above, a 1 had been transmitted.

The particular choice of b to be used is not quite so obvious as in the Gaussian-noise case discussed in Sec. 1-3. The two distributions corresponding to a 0 transmitted and to a 1 transmitted are not the same anymore and the choice of $b = A/2$ made previously (Fig. 1-3-2) does not necessarily appear to be as intuitive in this case. Various choices could be made: pick b halfway between the peaks of the distribution, pick $b = A/2$, pick b such that the probability of error in either case is the same, etc. In Chap. 2, we shall show that choosing b at the intersection between the two curves in Fig. 1-5-1 corresponds to the minimum overall

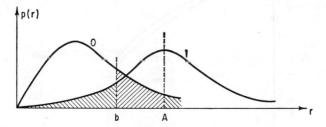

FIG. 1-5-1. Threshold level in binary transmission.

probability of error, for equal a priori probabilities of transmission. Actually, if $A/\sqrt{N} \gg 1$, all these choices give essentially the same results.

For simplicity's sake here we shall pick b at the point corresponding to equal error probabilities in the two cases. This corresponds to having the hatched areas in Fig. 1-5-1 equal.[1]

In this case we have

$$P_e = \int_b^\infty \frac{r}{N} e^{-r^2/2N} \, dr = \int_0^b e^{-A^2/2N} \frac{re^{-r^2/2N}}{N} I_0\left(\frac{rA}{N}\right) dr \quad (1\text{-}5\text{-}1)$$

Note that the particular value of $b/\sqrt{N}$ depends on the choice of P_e. With P_e specified, the left-hand integral gives $b/\sqrt{N}$. With both P_e and b given, the required value of peak signal-to-noise ratio $A/\sqrt{N}$ can be found from the right-hand integral.

The right-hand integral can be written in terms of the so-called Q

[1] The problem then becomes essentially the telegraph signal example discussed by W. R. Bennett in Methods of Solving Noise Problems, *Proc. IRE*, vol. 44, p. 609, May, 1956. A similar example involving envelope detection in radar, where the probabilities of error differ by large orders of magnitude, is discussed in Schwartz, "Information Transmission, Modulation, and Noise," pp. 403–410.

function, first tabulated in detail by Marcum[1-3] in connection with radar detection problems. The Q function is defined by

$$Q(a,b) \equiv \int_b^\infty x \exp\left(\frac{-a^2 - x^2}{2}\right) I_0(ax)\, dx \tag{1-5-2}$$

In terms of this definition the right-hand integral of Eq. (1-5-1) is given by

$$P_e = 1 - Q(\sqrt{2\gamma},\, b_0) \tag{1-5-3}$$

where $\gamma = A^2/2N$ is the average power signal-to-noise ratio introduced

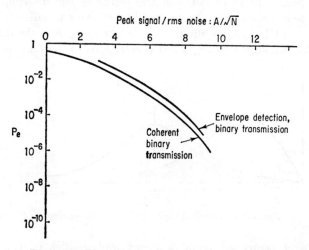

FIG. 1-5-2. Binary transmission error probabilities.

previously in Eq. (1-3-1) and $b_0 \equiv b/\sqrt{N}$ is the normalized voltage level for detection.

The Q function formulation will be used extensively in Chap. 8 in connection with generalized error analyses of digital systems, and various properties of the Q function will be considered there.

Detailed properties of the Q function are also listed in Appendix A.

The right-hand integral of Eq. (1-5-1) has also been evaluated as an infinite series by W. R. Bennett and S. O. Rice and appears as Fig. 7, Sec. 3-10 in Rice's classic paper, previously cited.

The solution to Eq. (1-5-1) provides the error curve of Fig. 1-5-2. Superimposed is the plot from Fig. 1-3-3 for the case of coherent binary

[1] J. I. Marcum, A Statistical Theory of Target Detection by Pulsed Radar, *IRE Trans. Inform. Theory*, vol. IT-6, pp. 59–267, April, 1960. This is a reprint of an earlier *Rand Corp. Memo* RM-753, July, 1948, and RM-754, December, 1947.

[2] J. I. Marcum, Tables of the Q-function, *Rand Corp. Memo* RM-399, January, 1950.

[3] D. E. Johansen, New Techniques for Machine Computation of the Q-functions, Truncated Normal Deviates, and Matrix Eigenvalues, Applied Research Laboratory, Sylvania Electronic Systems, AFCRL-556, July, 1961.

on-off transmission. Note that for a given peak signal-to-noise ratio the chance of error is somewhat smaller in the coherent-transmission case. Alternatively, for given P_e the envelope-detection procedure requires a somewhat larger $A/\sqrt{N}$. This is as might be expected since we are essentially throwing away useful information by ignoring the phase in the envelope-detection case.

We shall discuss the case of envelope detection further after introducing some of the elements of statistical decision theory in Chap. 2. In particular, the effect of adding successive samples of *detected* signal plus noise will be considered in Chap. 2 and compared with the discussion in Sec. 3 of this chapter.[1]

1-6. Hilbert-transform Representation of Signals

Much of the material of the previous sections, particularly that relating to the statistical properties of noise, can be obtained in a particularly succinct fashion by utilizing Hilbert-transform representations of signals and the concept of analytic signals derived from these. This has begun to be utilized a great deal in the literature of noise and communication theory, and certain aspects of the Hilbert-transform formulation will be useful in succeeding chapters. Again the references supply a more detailed treatment than is possible here.[2]

It is instructive to introduce the Hilbert-transform concept by means of an example. We consider specifically the problem of an analytic representation of a single-sideband (SSB) signal.

It is well known[3] that one possible method of generating an SSB signal is the one indicated in Fig. 1-6-1. Here an arbitrary modulating signal $x(t)$ is multiplied by the carrier term $\cos \omega_0 t$ in a balanced modulator and then subtracted from a signal obtained by passing $x(t)$ through a wideband $-90°$ phase shifter and multiplying the resultant $x(t)$ by $\sin \omega_0 t$. The resultant output signal $s(t)$ is in the proper SSB form. (The practical

---

[1] See also Schwartz, *op. cit.*, pp. 419–422.

[2] A tutorial paper summarizing some unpublished work at the Bell Telephone Laboratories and containing a detailed bibliography to the published literature is the one by F. F. Kuo and S. L. Freeney, Hilbert Transforms and Modulation Theory, *Proc. Nat. Electron. Conf.*, pp. 51–58, Chicago, October, 1962.

The concept of preenvelope and its application to Gaussian noise appears in the papers of R. Arens, Complex Processes for Envelopes of Normal Noise, *IRE Trans. Inform. Theory*, vol. IT-3, pp. 204–207, September, 1957 and J. Dugundji, Envelopes and Pre-Envelopes of Real Waveforms, *IRE Trans. Inform. Theory*, vol. IT-4, pp. 53–57, March, 1958.

Further applications of the Hilbert-transform representation of signals appear in E. Bedrosian, The Analytic Signal Representation of Modulated Waveforms, *Proc. IRE*, vol. 50, no. 10, pp. 2071–2076, October, 1962.

[3] See Sec. 4-4. Also, Schwartz, *op. cit.*, p. 106.

difficulty involved in the method of generating SSB signals is of course the design problem of synthesizing a wideband phase shifter with a constant phase shift of $-90°$ over the entire bandwidth of $x(t)$.)

That $s(t)$ is an SSB signal is simply shown. Call the output of the $90°$ phase shifter $\hat{x}(t)$, as indicated in Fig. 1-6-1. Then it is apparent that

$$s(t) = x(t) \cos \omega_0 t - \hat{x}(t) \sin \omega_0 t \qquad (1\text{-}6\text{-}1)$$

Alternatively, consider the complex signal

$$z(t) \equiv x(t) + j\hat{x}(t) \qquad (1\text{-}6\text{-}2)$$

Then we also have

$$s(t) = \text{Re} \, [z(t)e^{j\omega_0 t}] \qquad (1\text{-}6\text{-}3)$$

where Re [ ] stands for "the real part of."

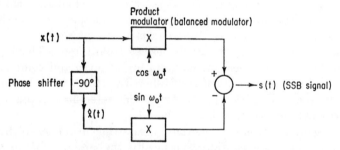

FIG. 1-6-1. Phase-shift method of generating SSB signal.

Equation (1-6-3) is one example of the complex representation of a signal that will be useful in later chapters. We shall now demonstrate quite readily that the spectrum of the complex signal $z(t)$ is given, to within a constant factor of 2, by the positive frequency spectrum of the modulating signal $x(t)$. (It has no negative frequency components.) Since multiplication by $e^{j\omega_0 t}$ corresponds to a frequency translation upwards, the resultant signal must have frequency components above the carrier frequency f_0 only. This will then prove the single-sideband nature of $s(t)$.

The Fourier transform of $z(t)$ is, from Eq. (1-6-2), given by

$$Z(\omega) = X(\omega) + j\hat{X}(\omega) \qquad (1\text{-}6\text{-}4)$$

where $\hat{X}(\omega)$ is the transform of $\hat{x}(t)$
But, by hypothesis,

$$\hat{X}(\omega) = \begin{cases} -jX(\omega) & \omega \geq 0 \\ +jX(\omega) & \omega < 0 \end{cases} \qquad (1\text{-}6\text{-}5)$$

(This represents the action of the phase shifter. Recall that the phase characteristic is always an *odd* function of frequency.)

Introducing Eq. (1-6-5) into (1-6-4) we get,

$$Z(\omega) = \begin{cases} 2X(\omega) & \omega \geq 0 \\ 0 & \omega < 0 \end{cases} \qquad (1\text{-}6\text{-}4a)$$

proving the stated relation (Fig. 1-6-2).

The 90° phase-shift operation of Fig. 1-6-1, as expressed by Eq. (1-6-5), corresponds identically to taking the Hilbert transform of $x(t)$. The function $\hat{x}(t)$ is then, by definition, the Hilbert transform of $x(t)$, and the phase shifter could also be called a Hilbert transformer. Eqs. (1-6-1) and (1-6-3) are the analytic representations of a SSB signal which are useful in studying the transmission of SSB signals. (One example will be given shortly; others in a later chapter.) The complex signal $z(t)$ is

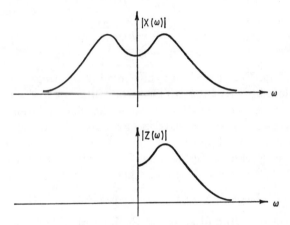

FIG. 1-6-2. Spectrum of analytic signal.

frequently called an *analytic signal* or, also commonly, the *preenvelope* of $x(t)$. (The reason for this designation will be made clear shortly.)

Using Eq. (1-6-5), the transform representation of the Hilbert-transform process, we can show that the Hilbert transform $\hat{x}(t)$ is related to $x(t)$ by the linear operation

$$\hat{x}(t) \equiv H[x(t)] = \frac{1}{\pi} \int_{-\infty}^{\infty} \frac{x(\tau)}{t - \tau} \, d\tau \qquad (1\text{-}6\text{-}6)$$

The symbol $H[\ ]$ stands for the "Hilbert transform of." The principal value of the integral is meant here to ensure convergence. The integral is thus defined as the limit of the sum of two integrals. It is apparent that $\hat{x}(t)$ represents the convolution of $x(t)$ with $1/t$.

The derivation of Eq. (1-6-6) proceeds by noting from Eq. (1-6-4a) or from Fig. 1-6-2, that

$$Z(\omega) = 2U(\omega)X(\omega) \qquad (1\text{-}6\text{-}7)$$

with $U(\omega)$ the unit-step function defined in the frequency domain. The inverse Fourier transform of U is then

$$g(t) = \int_{-\infty}^{\infty} U(\omega)e^{j\omega t}\, df$$

$$= \frac{1}{-2\pi jt} + \pi\delta(2\pi t) = \frac{-1}{2\pi jt} + \frac{1}{2}\delta(t) \qquad (1\text{-}6\text{-}8)$$

with $\delta(t)$ the unit-impulse function. [Recall that the Fourier transform of the more commonly encountered unit step in time is $1/j\omega + \pi\delta(\omega)$. Replacing ω by $-2\pi t$ gives Eq. (1-6-8).]

The Fourier-transform relation of Eq. (1-6-7) indicates that $z(t)$ is the convolution of $2g(t)$ and $x(t)$, so that

$$z(t) = 2\int_{-\infty}^{\infty} x(\tau)g(t-\tau)\, d\tau$$

$$= x(t) + \frac{j}{\pi}\int_{-\infty}^{\infty} \frac{x(\tau)\, d\tau}{(t-\tau)}$$

$$= x(t) + j\hat{x}(t) \qquad (1\text{-}6\text{-}9)$$

upon introducing Eq. (1-6-8) into the convolution integral.

As a simple example of the utility of the Hilbert-transform representation of SSB signals [Eq. (1-6-1)] consider the demodulation of the SSB $s(t)$ at a receiver. In-phase carrier injection or multiplication by an in-phase carrier (synchronous or homodyne detection) is normally required at the receiver. But assume the injected carrier is out of phase by θ radians. The detected signal is then

$$s(t)\cos(\omega_0 t + \theta) = \tfrac{1}{2}x(t)\cos\theta + \tfrac{1}{2}\hat{x}(t)\sin\theta$$

utilizing Eq. (1-6-1), and filtering out the high (double-carrier) frequency terms.

The first term represents the derived signal, the second term a distortion term due to lack of phase synchronism. If $\theta = 0$, $x(t)$ is reproduced as desired. If $\theta = \pi/2$, however, the distortion term is the only one appearing.

Properties of Hilbert Transforms. Most of the properties of Hilbert transforms tabulated below can be proved quite readily using the 90° frequency domain description of the transform process. These properties will be useful in the application of Hilbert transforms to signal-and-noise processes that follow.

1. If

$$x(t) = x(-t) \qquad \hat{x}(t) = -\hat{x}(-t) \qquad (1\text{-}6\text{-}10)$$

If the real function $x(t)$ is even in t, $\hat{x}(t)$ is odd in t. This can be proved from the integral representation for $\hat{x}(t)$ or by noting that with $x(t)$ even, $X(\omega)$ is even in f and real. Then $\hat{X}(\omega)$ is odd in f and imaginary, so that $\hat{x}(t)$ is odd.

2. If

$$x(t) = -x(-t) \qquad \hat{x}(t) = \hat{x}(-t) \qquad (1\text{-}6\text{-}11)$$

If $x(t)$ is odd, $\hat{x}(t)$ is even. Again this is proved by noting that $X(\omega)$ is imaginary and odd in f. Then $\hat{X}(\omega)$ is real and even in f, and $\hat{x}(t)$ is likewise even.

As examples, consider

a.
$$x(t) = \frac{1}{1 + t^2} \qquad X(\omega) = \pi e^{-|\omega|}$$

Then
$$\hat{x}(t) = \int_{-\infty}^{\infty} \hat{X}(\omega)e^{j\omega t} \, df$$

$$= \frac{1}{\pi} \int_{0}^{\infty} X(\omega) \sin \omega t \, d\omega \qquad (1\text{-}6\text{-}12)$$

if $X(\omega)$ is even.

For this example, then,

$$\hat{x}(t) = \int_{0}^{\infty} e^{-\omega} \sin \omega t \, d\omega = \frac{t}{1 + t^2}$$

an odd function of time. Both $x(t)$ and $\hat{x}(t)$ in this example are shown in Fig. 1-6-3a.

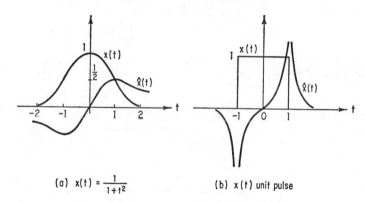

(a) $x(t) = \dfrac{1}{1+t^2}$ (b) x(t) unit pulse

FIG. 1-6-3. Examples of Hilbert transforms.

b. $x(t)$ the unit pulse of Fig. 1-6-3b.

Then
$$X(\omega) = 2\frac{\sin \omega}{\omega}$$

and
$$\hat{x}(t) = \frac{1}{\pi} \ln \frac{|t + 1|}{|t - 1|}$$

from Eq. (1-6-12). If $x(t)$ were the modulating intelligence in an SSB system, (a simple example would be a data-transmission system), $\hat{x}(t)$ would be the distortion term due to lack of phase synchronism, as indicated previously.

c. $x(t) = \cos \omega_0 t \qquad \hat{x}(t) = \sin \omega_0 t$
d. $x(t) = \sin \omega_0 t \qquad \hat{x}(t) = -\cos \omega_0 t$

Both of these examples are apparent from the $-\pi/2$ phase-shift definition of Hilbert transforms.

3.
$$H[\hat{x}(t)] = -x(t) \qquad (1\text{-}6\text{-}13)$$

The Hilbert transform of the Hilbert transform of $x(t)$ reproduces $-x(t)$. This is obvious, since this corresponds to a total phase shift of π radians for all frequency components of $x(t)$. As a trivial example, consider $x(t) = \cos \omega_0 t$ and note examples c and d above.

4.
$$\int_{-\infty}^{\infty} x^2(t) \, dt = \int_{-\infty}^{\infty} [\hat{x}(t)]^2 \, dt \qquad (1\text{-}6\text{-}14)$$

The energy in the signal $x(t)$ and its Hilbert transform $\hat{x}(t)$ are thus the same. This is again apparent from the frequency description of the Hilbert transform or by noting from Parseval's theorem that

$$\int_{-\infty}^{\infty} x^2(t)\, dt = \int_{-\infty}^{\infty} |X(\omega)|^2\, df$$

and
$$\int_{-\infty}^{\infty} [\hat{x}(t)]^2\, dt = \int_{-\infty}^{\infty} |\hat{X}(\omega)|^2\, df = \int_{-\infty}^{\infty} |X(\omega)|^2\, df$$

5. Orthogonality.
$$\int_{-\infty}^{\infty} x(t)\hat{x}(t)\, dt = 0 \qquad (1\text{-}6\text{-}15)$$

A function and its Hilbert transform are thus orthogonal to one another. This is also easily proven by invoking the Parseval theorem

$$\int_{-\infty}^{\infty} x(t)\hat{x}(t)\, dt = \int_{-\infty}^{\infty} \hat{X}(\omega)[X(\omega)]^*\, df$$
$$= j \int_{-\infty}^{0} |X(\omega)|^2\, df - j \int_{0}^{\infty} |X(\omega)|^2\, df = 0$$

(The asterisk * represents complex conjugate.)

6. Band-limited signals.

Consider a signal $v(t)$ given in the form

$$v(t) = x(t)\cos \omega_0 t - y(t)\sin \omega_0 t \qquad (1\text{-}6\text{-}16)$$

With x and y *slowly* varying, this is the narrowband-signal representation used in Sec. 1-4. At this point however, we only stipulate that x and y are each band-limited to $B \le f_0$ cps.

Then the Hilbert transform of $v(t)$ is

$$\hat{v}(t) = x\sin \omega_0 t + y\cos \omega_0 t \qquad (1\text{-}6\text{-}17)$$

The proof of this statement follows readily by rewriting $v(t)$ in the complex-signal form

$$v(t) = \text{Re}\,[(x + jy)e^{j\omega_0 t}]$$
$$= \text{Re}\,[ue^{j\omega_0 t}]$$
$$= \text{Re}\,[z(t)] \qquad (1\text{-}6\text{-}16a)[1]$$

with
$$z(t) \equiv u(t)e^{j\omega_0 t}$$

But note that $u(t)$ must also be band-limited to $B \le f_0$. Then $z(t)$ has a positive frequency spectrum only and must be an *analytic signal*, such that

$$z(t) = v(t) + j\hat{v}(t) \qquad (1\text{-}6\text{-}18)$$

We thus have
$$\hat{v}(t) = \text{Im}\,[z(t)] = x\sin \omega_0 t + y\sin \omega_0 t \qquad (1\text{-}6\text{-}17a)$$

as was to be proven. (Im stands for "imaginary part of".) As special cases we also have

$$H[x(t)\cos \omega_0 t] = x(t)\sin \omega_0 t \qquad (1\text{-}6\text{-}19)$$
$$H[x(t)\sin \omega_0 t] = -x(t)\cos \omega_0 t \qquad (1\text{-}6\text{-}20)$$

with $B \le f_0$.

7. Random variables: correlation functions and spectral densities.

If $x(t)$ is a stationary random variable with two-sided spectral density $G_x(f)$ and autocorrelation function $R_x(\tau)$, the following relations are easily obtained

a.
$$R_x(\tau) = R_{\hat{x}}(\tau) \qquad G_x(f) = G_{\hat{x}}(f) \qquad (1\text{-}6\text{-}21)$$

[1] Note that the complex function $x + jy$ is *not* an analytic signal. Multiplying by $e^{j\omega_0 t}$, with $B \le f_0$, *does* produce the analytic signal $z = v + j\hat{v}$.

The function and its Hilbert transforms thus have the same autocorrelation function and spectral densities (Fig. 1-6-4). This follows quite readily by noting that $\hat{x}(t)$ is obtained by passing $x(t)$ through the linear network providing 90° phase shift. Then, as in Secs. 1-1 and 1-2, $G_{\hat{x}}(f) = |H(\omega)|^2 G_x(f) = G_x(f)$ in this case.

b.
$$R_{x\hat{x}}(\tau) = \hat{R}_x(\tau) \tag{1-6-22}$$

The cross-correlation between $x(t)$ and $\hat{x}(t + \tau)$ is thus the Hilbert transform of the autocorrelation function of $x(t)$. Here the cross-correlation function is defined as

$$R_{x\hat{x}}(\tau) \equiv \langle x(t)\hat{x}(t + \tau) \rangle \tag{1-6-22a}$$

The proof follows quite readily by noting that $\hat{x}(t)$ can be written as

$$\hat{x}(t) = \int_{-\infty}^{\infty} h(\lambda) x(t - \lambda)\, d\lambda \tag{1-6-23}$$

with $h(t)$ the impulse response of the 90° phase shifter of Fig. 1-6-4. Inserting this convolution integral into Eq. (1-6-22a) and interchanging the order of integration and ensemble-averaging, we obtain

$$R_{x\hat{x}}(\tau) = \int_{-\infty}^{\infty} h(\lambda) R_x(\tau - \lambda)\, d\lambda = \hat{R}_x(\lambda) \tag{1-6-24}$$

by comparison with Eq. (1-6-23).

c.
$$R_{x\hat{x}}(0) = 0 \tag{1-6-25}$$

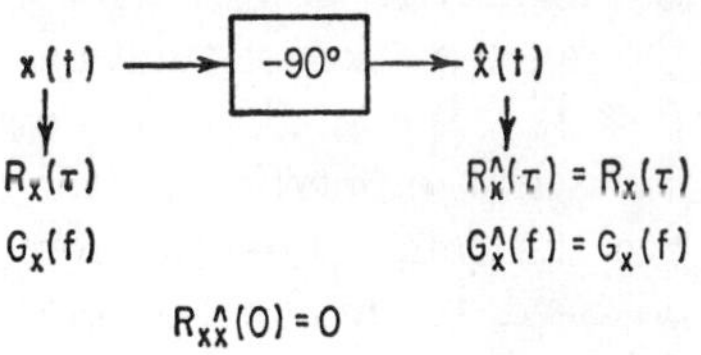

The random variable $x(t)$ and its Hilbert transform are thus uncorrelated at a given instant of time. This is apparent from the fact that since $R_x(\tau)$ is even in τ, $\hat{R}_x(\tau)$ must be odd, or $\hat{R}_x(0) = 0$. This fact will be particularly useful in rederiving the envelope statistics of noise, using the Hilbert-transform formulation.

Fig. 1-6-4. Hilbert-transform relations for a random process.

d.
$$R_z(\tau) \equiv \langle z^*(t)z(t + \tau) \rangle = 2[R_x(\tau) + j\hat{R}_x(\tau)] \tag{1-6-26}$$

$$G_z(f) = \begin{cases} 4G_x(f) & f > 0 \\ 0 & f < 0 \end{cases} \tag{1-6-27}$$

Here $R_z(\tau)$ represents the autocorrelation function of the analytic signal or preenvelope

$$z(t) = x(t) + j\hat{x}(t) \tag{1-6-28}$$

The proof of Eq. (1-6-26) follows directly from the definition of $R_z(\tau)$ as the ensemble average $\langle z^*(t)z(t + \tau) \rangle$. Inserting Eq. (1-6-28) in for $z(t)$, averaging term by term, and making use of Eqs. (1-6-21) and (1-6-22), Eq. (1-6-26) is obtained.

Note the interesting fact that with $z(t)$ the analytic signal of $x(t)$, $R_z(\tau)/2$ is the analytic signal of $R_x(\tau)$. Then the Fourier transform of $R_z(\tau)$, $G_z(f)$, must have a positive spectrum only, and in particular is given by Eq. (1-6-27).

1-7. Preenvelope and Envelope of Signals; Application to Noise

In Sec. 1-4 we utilized the Fourier-series representation of noise and the assumption that the noise bandwidth $B \ll f_0$, the carrier frequency, to obtain the statistics of the envelope of noise, and signal plus noise. The approach utilized there was a rather intuitive one. For the assumption of narrowband noise (bandwidth $B \ll f_0$) enabled us to state that the noise in-phase and quadrature terms $x(t)$ and $y(t)$ in the expression

$$n(t) = x(t) \cos \omega_0 t - y(t) \sin \omega_0 t \tag{1-7-1}$$

varied "slowly enough" with respect to the carrier that an envelope could be defined. In particular, we wrote

$$n(t) = r(t) \cos (\omega_0 t + \theta) \tag{1-7-2}$$

with $\quad\quad\quad r(t) \equiv \sqrt{x^2 + y^2} \quad\quad$ the envelope

and $\quad\quad\quad \theta \equiv \tan^{-1} \dfrac{y}{x} \quad\quad$ the phase

Note that Eq. (1-7-1) represents a special case of Eq. (1-6-16).

We shall now utilize the Hilbert-transform representation of signals to *define* the envelope of an arbitrary signal $v(t)$. As a special case the representation of Eqs. (1-7-1) and (1-7-2) will follow directly but with the much weaker stipulation, as in Eq. (1-6-16), that $B \leq f_0$ rather than $B \ll f_0$. We shall then show, in the case of Gaussian noise, that the statistical properties of the envelope of Gaussian noise discussed in Sec. 1.4 follow directly from Hilbert-transform properties and there is no need to invoke the Fourier-series representation of noise used in Sec. 1.4.

The envelope of an arbitrary function $v(t)$ is *defined* as the magnitude $|z(t)|$ of the (complex) analytic signal $z(t)$, discussed previously and formed by writing

$$z(t) = v(t) + j\hat{v}(t) \tag{1-7-3}$$

[see Eq. (1-6-2)].

$z(t)$ can also be written in the phasor form

$$z(t) = |z(t)| e^{j\theta_z} \tag{1-7-4}$$

with the envelope

$$|z| = \sqrt{v^2 + \hat{v}^2} \tag{1-7-5}$$

and phase

$$\theta = \tan^{-1} \frac{\hat{v}}{v} \tag{1-7-6}$$

As an example, let

$$v(t) = x(t) \cos \omega_0 t$$

with $x(t)$ band-limited to $B \leq f_0$. This is the usual representation of a double-sideband (DSB) signal. Then, from Eq. (1-6-19) in the previous section,

$$\hat{v}(t) = x(t) \sin \omega_0 t$$

and the envelope of $v(t)$ is

$$|z| = \sqrt{x^2} = |x|$$

as would be expected intuitively. (Note that $\theta_z = \omega_0 t$, also as would be expected.) The one extension beyond our intuitive notion of envelope in this case is the fact that it is not necessary to stipulate the narrowband condition $B \gg f_0$. The much weaker condition $B \leq f_0$ suffices.

The physical significance of the stipulation $B \leq f_0$ lies in the fact that both sidebands about f_0 appear wholly on the positive-frequency side of the frequency axis, while the sidebands about $-f_0$ lie wholly in the negative-frequency range. Thus there is no ambiguity due to the folding over of sidebands, as would be the case for $B > f_0$.

It is instructive to consider the example

$$v(t) = \cos \omega_m t \, \cos \omega_0 t$$

to further clarify this point. One might be tempted to jump to the hasty conclusion that the envelope of $v(t)$ is just $|\cos \omega_m t|$. Yet it is apparent that if $f_m > f_0$ the role of "modulating signal" and carrier are interchanged. The envelope is then more properly written

$$\begin{aligned} |\cos \omega_m t| &\quad \text{if} \quad f_m \leq f_0 \\ |\cos \omega_0 t| &\quad \text{if} \quad f_m > f_0 \end{aligned}$$

The reader should demonstrate for himself that the envelope defined by Eq. (1-7-5) does agree with the result of this example.

As another example, let

$$v(t) = x \cos \omega_0 t - y \sin \omega_0 t = Re\ [ue^{j\omega_0 t}] \qquad (1\text{-}7\text{-}7)$$

with $B \leq f_0$, as previously. It is then apparent, as indicated in Eq. (1-6-16a), that $z = ue^{j\omega_0 t}$ is the desired analytic signal or preenvelope of $v(t)$, and that $|z| = |u| = \sqrt{x^2 + y^2}$, in agreement with the result of Sec. 1.4 and Eq. 1-7-2. Note again, however, that the requirement on x and y is solely that $B \leq f_0$, rather than the "narrowband" condition $B \ll f_0$ specified previously.

The resolution of an arbitrary band-limited signal $v(t)$ into the "narrowband" form of Eq. (1-7-7) is readily accomplished using phasor notation. For, writing

$$z = ue^{j\omega_0 t} = v + j\hat{v}$$

with

$$u = x + jy$$

we have

$$u = ze^{-j\omega_0 t}$$

Equating real and imaginary parts we find

$$x(t) = v(t) \cos \omega_0 t + \hat{v}(t) \sin \omega_0 t \qquad (1\text{-}7\text{-}8)$$
$$y(t) = \hat{v} \cos \omega_0 t - v \sin \omega_0 t \qquad (1\text{-}7\text{-}9)$$

The choice of "carrier frequency" f_0 is perfectly arbitrary, subject only to the limitation that $B \leq f_0$, with B the bandwidth of $u(t)$ [or $x(t)$ and $y(t)$]. This again ensures that $z(t)$ is an analytic signal. For a signal $v(t)$ with a spectrum such as that shown in Fig. 1-7-1, the minimum choice of f_0 is $f_{max}/2$ with f_{max} the maximum frequency component in $v(t)$. In this case the bandwidth B is simply $f_0 = f_{max}/2$.

Another example of a band-limited signal is shown in Fig. 1-7-2. Here again the choice of f_0 is perfectly arbitrary, providing that $B \leq f_0$,

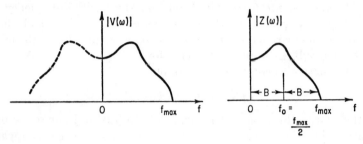

FIG. 1-7-1. Band-limited signal.   Minimum choice of carrier frequency.

with B given by the larger of the two bandwidths $f_2 - f_0$ and $f_0 - f_1$. [Note that B is the bandwidth of the analytic signal $z(t)$, *not* of the band-limited signal $v(t)$].

Application to Gaussian Noise.   We now proceed to apply some of the concepts of analytic signals and preenvelopes to a discussion of the statistical properties of the envelope of Gaussian noise. This duplicates the material of Sec. 1.4 to some extent, but avoids the Fourier-series representation of noise utilized there.

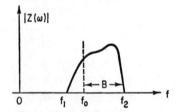

FIG. 1-7-2. Another example of band-limited signal.

Consider a Gaussian-noise wave $n(t)$ obtained by passing Gaussian white noise of two-sided spectral density $n_0/2$ through a linear filter with transfer function $H(\omega)$. Then, as noted in previous sections, the mean-squared noise at the filter output is

$$N = \langle n^2 \rangle = \int_{-\infty}^{\infty} \frac{n_0}{2} |H(\omega)|^2 \, df = \int_{-\infty}^{\infty} G_n(f) \, df \qquad (1\text{-}7\text{-}10)$$

with $G_n(f)$ the two-sided spectral density.   Assuming the noise has zero average value, we have

$$p(n) = \frac{1}{\sqrt{2\pi N}} e^{-n^2/2N} \qquad (1\text{-}7\text{-}11)$$

Assume now that this noise is applied at the input of an envelope detector.   What is the probability distribution at the output?   Proceeding formally we first find the preenvelope $z(t) = n(t) + j\hat{n}(t)$ of the process.   Then $|z|$ is the desired envelope and $p(|z|)$ the desired distribution.   This is readily found by recalling from Eq. (1-6-25) of the previous section that since $R_{n\hat{n}}(0) = 0$, $n(t)$ and $\hat{n}(t)$ are uncorrelated.   Since $n(t)$

is Gaussian and $\hat{n}(t)$ corresponds to a linear operation on $n(t)$, $\hat{n}(t)$ must be Gaussian also. In particular, it has the same spectral density and mean-squared value N as $n(t)$. Then

$$p(n,\hat{n}) = p(n)p(\hat{n}) = \frac{e^{-(n^2+\hat{n}^2)/2N}}{2\pi N}$$

$$= \frac{e^{-|z|^2/2N}}{2\pi N} \qquad (1\text{-}7\text{-}12)$$

Converting to polar coordinates, with

$$n \equiv |z| \cos \theta$$

and

$$\hat{n} \equiv |z| \sin \theta$$

and then integrating over the resultant uniformly distributed θ, just as in Sec. 1.4, we find

$$p(|z|) = \frac{|z|e^{-|z|^2/2N}}{N} \qquad (1\text{-}7\text{-}13)$$

This is of course just the Rayleigh distribution found previously. However, there was no need in this case to assume a "narrowband" process!

The distribution of the envelope for signal plus noise can similarly be found. Extension of these concepts to the joint distribution of m complex Gaussian variables is treated in the literature.[1]

Now assume the noise $n(t)$ is band-limited. It can then be written in the "narrowband" form

$$n(t) = \text{Re}[ue^{j\omega_0 t}] = x \cos \omega_0 t - y \sin \omega_0 t \qquad u \equiv x + jy \qquad (1\text{-}7\text{-}14)$$

with $x(t)$ and $y(t)$ obtained as in Eqs. (1-7-8) and (1-7-9). It is of interest to find the autocorrelation functions and spectral densities of $x(t)$ and $y(t)$. These will be used later in Chap. 3. Defining $R_x(\tau)$ as $\langle x(t)x(t+\tau)\rangle$, utilizing Eq. (1-7-8) with $n(t)$ written instead of $v(t)$, and performing the indicated ensemble average, we find

$$R_x(\tau) = R_n(\tau) \cos \omega_0\tau + \hat{R}_n(\tau) \sin \omega_0\tau \qquad (1\text{-}7\text{-}15)$$

and

$$R_y(\tau) = R_x(\tau) \qquad (1\text{-}7\text{-}16)$$

Taking the Fourier transform of $R_x(\tau)$ to find its two-sided spectral density $G_x(f)$ and making use of the fact that x is band-limited to $B \leq f_0$, we find

$$G_x(f) = \begin{cases} G_n(f + f_0) + G_n(f - f_0) & -f_0 < f < f_0 \\ 0 & \text{elsewhere} \end{cases} \qquad (1\text{-}7\text{-}17)$$

In the special case where $G_n(f)$ is symmetrical about frequency f_0 (the original white noise having been passed through a symmetrical bandpass filter), $G_n(f + f_0) = G_n(f - f_0)$, and

$$G_x(f) = 2G_n(f + f_0) \qquad (1\text{-}7\text{-}18)$$

The asymmetrical case is pictured in Fig. (1-7-3) with the folding over of the term $G_n(f - f_0)$ shown.

As a check, note either from Eqs. (1-7-17) and (1-7-18) or from Fig.

[1] Arens, *op. cit.*, p. 205.

1-7-3 that the mean-squared value of x is the same as that of n. Thus

$$\langle x^2 \rangle = \int_{-\infty}^{\infty} G_x(f)\, df = N = \langle n^2 \rangle = \int_{-\infty}^{\infty} G_n(f)\, df \qquad (1\text{-}7\text{-}19)$$

But $\langle x^2 \rangle = R_x(0) = R_n(0)$ from Eq. (1-7-15). Also, from Eq. (1-7-8), we have $\langle x^2 \rangle = \langle n^2 \rangle/2 + \langle \hat{n}^2 \rangle/2 = N$, using the fact that $\langle n\hat{n} \rangle = 0$, and that $\langle n^2 \rangle = \langle \hat{n}^2 \rangle = N$.

Specific examples will be considered in Chap. 3.

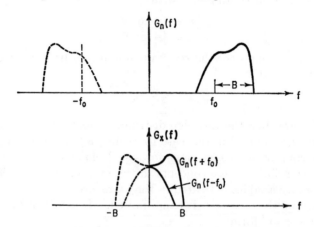

Fig. 1-7-3. Spectral densities of band-limited noise.

We showed in Sec. 1.4, using the Fourier-series representation of noise, that $x(t)$ and $y(t)$ were uncorrelated: $\langle xy \rangle = 0$. The correlation between $x(t)$ and $y(t + \tau)$ is, more generally, not equal to zero, as can also be demonstrated using the Fourier-series approach. Alternatively, we may use our Hilbert-transform relations to show that

$$R_{xy}(\tau) \equiv \langle x(t)y(t + \tau) \rangle = \hat{R}_n(\tau) \cos \omega_0 \tau - R_n(\tau) \sin \omega_0 \tau \qquad (1\text{-}7\text{-}20)$$

[This is again readily demonstrated with the use of Eqs. (1-7-8) and (1-7-9).]

Letting $\tau = 0$, we have

$$R_{xy}(0) = 0 = \langle x(t)y(t) \rangle \qquad (1\text{-}7\text{-}21)$$

as expected.

Writing $R_n(\tau)$ and $\hat{R}_n(\tau)$ in terms of the one-sided noise spectral density $2G_n(f)$, it is readily shown that $R_{xy}(\tau)$ can be written in the alternative form

$$R_{xy}(\tau) = \int_0^{\infty} 2G_n(f) \sin (\omega - \omega_0)\tau\, df \qquad (1\text{-}7\text{-}22)$$

Similarly, the autocorrelation functions $R_x(\tau)$ and $R_y(\tau)$ can be written in the form

$$R_x(\tau) = R_y(\tau) = \int_0^{\infty} 2G_n(f) \cos (\omega - \omega_0)\tau\, df \qquad (1\text{-}7\text{-}23)$$

These expressions will be useful in some of the material of Chap. 3.

Now assume two stationary Gaussian-noise variables $n_1(t)$ and $n_2(t)$. Assume they have some cross-correlation $\langle n_1 n_2 \rangle = R_{n_1 n_2}(0)$ $(\tau = 0)$. The two variables thus have a certain amount of dependence at a given sampling time. The following relations can be derived easily (they will again be utilized in later chapters):

1. $\langle \hat{n}_1 \hat{n}_2 \rangle = \langle n_1 n_2 \rangle = R_{n_1 n_2}(0)$ (1-7-24)
2. $\langle \hat{n}_1 n_2 \rangle = -\langle n_1 \hat{n}_2 \rangle$ $(\tau = 0)$ (1-7-25)
3. $\langle x_1 x_2 \rangle = \langle n_1 n_2 \rangle = \langle y_1 y_2 \rangle$ (1-7-26)
4. $\langle x_1 y_2 \rangle = \langle n_1 \hat{n}_2 \rangle = -\langle x_2 y_1 \rangle$ (1-7-27)

The first two relations are proved by expressing $\hat{n}_1$ and $\hat{n}_2$ as convolutions of n_1 and n_2 with the impulse response of the 90° network and ensemble-averaging. Relations 3 and 4 are corresponding relations between in-phase and quadrature components of the noises in their "narrowband" representations:

$$n_1(t) = x_1 \cos \omega_0 t - y_1 \sin \omega_0 t \qquad (1\text{-}7\text{-}28)$$
$$n_2(t) = x_2 \cos \omega_0 t - y_2 \sin \omega_0 t \qquad (1\text{-}7\text{-}29)$$

There is thus in general correlation $\langle x_1 x_2 \rangle$ and $\langle x_1 y_2 \rangle$. These are the same, to within a minus sign in the latter case, as $\langle y_1 y_2 \rangle$ and $\langle x_2 y_1 \rangle$.

1-8. Low-pass Equivalents of Bandpass Signals

In discussing linear filtering of bandpass signals it is frequently desirable (and computationally simpler) to deal instead with their envelopes and the equivalent low-pass filtering of these. This technique will be utilized in later chapters.

Consider, for example, a bandpass signal $s(t)$ transmitted through the linear filter of Fig. 1-8-1a. Then, as noted in the past sections, $s(t)$ can be represented in the phasor form

$$s(t) = \text{Re} [z(t)] = \text{Re} [u(t)e^{j\omega_0 t}] \qquad (1\text{-}8\text{-}1)$$

The preenvelope or analytic signal $z(t)$ has as its magnitude $|u(t)|$, the envelope of $s(t)$. The only restriction on this usage is that the function $u(t)$ is band-limited to $B \leq f_0$. This ensures that $z(t)$ has positive-frequency components only and is an analytic signal in the sense discussed in previous sections.

If the bandpass filter has an impulse response $g(t)$, with a typical frequency response as shown in Fig. 1-8-1, the filter output $q(t)$ is given by the usual convolution integral

$$q(t) = \int_{-\infty}^{\infty} g(t - \tau)s(\tau) \, d\tau \qquad (1\text{-}8\text{-}2)$$

If we now write the output $q(t)$ in its bandpass form

$$q(t) = \text{Re} \left[v(t)e^{j\omega_0 t} \right] \qquad (1\text{-}8\text{-}3)$$

$[|v(t)|$ is then the envelope of $q(t)$ since it is also band-limited to $B \leq f_0]$, we shall show that the linear filtering can equally well be represented in terms of a hypothetical low-pass filter $h(t)$, such that

$$v(t) = \int_{-\infty}^{\infty} h(t - \tau)u(\tau)\, d\tau \qquad (1\text{-}8\text{-}4)$$

The frequency response of this generally unrealizable low-pass filter is found by shifting the positive-frequency component of $G(\omega)$ down to the zero-frequency axis:

$$H(\omega - \omega_0) = \begin{cases} G(\omega) & f \geq 0 \\ 0 & f < 0 \end{cases} \qquad (1\text{-}8\text{-}5)$$

[Note that if $G(\omega)$ is unsymmetrical about f_0, $H(\omega)$ will likewise be unsymmetrical about $f = 0$ and $h(t)$ will be a *complex* function of time.]   An example is shown in Fig. 1-8-1.

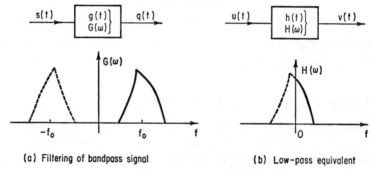

(a) Filtering of bandpass signal   (b) Low-pass equivalent

FIG. 1-8-1. Low-pass equivalent of bandpass signal.

The validity of Eq. (1-8-4) is easily demonstrated as follows: Recall, from our discussion of Hilbert transforms, that the Fourier transforms of $z(t)$, $s(t)$, and $u(t)$ are related by the simple property

$$Z(\omega) = 2S(\omega) = \begin{cases} U(\omega - \omega_0) & f \geq 0 \\ 0 & f < 0 \end{cases} \qquad (1\text{-}8\text{-}6)$$

Now consider the bandpass-filter impulse response $g(t)$.   This can also be written in the narrowband form

$$g(t) = \text{Re} \left[k(t) \right] = \text{Re} \left[2h(t)e^{j\omega_0 t} \right] \qquad (1\text{-}8\text{-}7)$$

where the factor of 2 has been included to simplify the form of the equations that follow.   Again assuming $h(t)$ has a bandwidth $< f_0$, $k(t)$ is also an analytic signal and we can write

$$K(\omega) = \begin{cases} 2G(\omega) = 2H(\omega - \omega_0) & f \geq 0 \\ 0 & f < 0 \end{cases} \qquad (1\text{-}8\text{-}8)$$

The relation between K and $2H$ follows from the form of Eq. (1-8-7).

Since $s(t)$, $g(t)$, and $q(t)$ are real functions of time [this is not necessarily true for $u(t)$ and $v(t)$], Eq. (1-8-2) can be written

$$q(t) = \int_{-\infty}^{\infty} g(t - \tau)\, \text{Re}\,[z(\tau)]\, d\tau$$

$$= \text{Re}\left[\int_{-\infty}^{\infty} g(t - \tau)z(\tau)\, d\tau\right]$$

$$= \text{Re}\left[\int_{-\infty}^{\infty} e^{j\omega t}G(\omega)Z(\omega)\, df\right]$$

$$= \text{Re}\left[\int_{0}^{\infty} e^{j\omega t}G(\omega)Z(\omega)\, df\right] \qquad (1\text{-}8\text{-}9a)$$

since $Z(\omega) = 0$, $f < 0$. Replacing $G(\omega)$ and $Z(\omega)$ in the positive-frequency range by $H(\omega - \omega_0)$ and $U(\omega - \omega_0)$, respectively, and introducing the new dummy variable $x = \omega - \omega_0$, we get

$$q(t) = \text{Re}\left[e^{j\omega_0 t}\frac{1}{2\pi}\int_{-\omega_0}^{\infty} e^{jxt}H(x)U(x)\, dx\right]$$

$$= \text{Re}\left[e^{j\omega_0 t}\frac{1}{2\pi}\int_{-\infty}^{\infty} e^{jxt}H(x)U(x)\, dx\right] \qquad (1\text{-}8\text{-}9b)$$

since H and $U = 0$, $f < -f_0$, by hypothesis. But note that the integral in Eq. (1-8-9b) is just the Fourier-transform formulation of Eq. (1-8-4). We thus get, finally,

$$q(t) = \text{Re}\,[v(t)e^{j\omega_0 t}] \qquad (1\text{-}8\text{-}3)$$

with

$$v(t) = \frac{1}{2\pi}\int_{-\infty}^{\infty} e^{j\omega t}H(\omega)U(\omega)\, d\omega$$

$$= \int_{-\infty}^{\infty} h(t - \tau)u(\tau)\, d\tau \qquad (1\text{-}8\text{-}4)$$

as was to be proven.

Application to Narrowband Noise. Most of the relations in Sec. 1-7 involving correlation functions can be rewritten in particularly succinct form by using phasor representations. They then take on forms analogous to the low-pass-bandpass representations of this section. For example, consider a narrowband noise wave $n(t)$ written in the form

$$n(t) = \text{Re}\,[z(t)] = \text{Re}\,[u(t)e^{j\omega_0 t}] \qquad (1\text{-}8\text{-}10)$$

Again the only stipulation is that the bandwidth of $u(t)$ is $B \leq f_0$. Note again that $z(t)$ plays the role of an analytic signal here. The function $u(t)$ in this case is the complex quantity

$$u = x + jy \qquad (1\text{-}8\text{-}11)$$

Then we showed in Sec. 1.7, by actually performing the indicated average, that $\langle x(t)x(t + \tau)\rangle$ is given by

$$R_x(\tau) = R_y(\tau) = R_n(\tau)\cos\omega_0\tau + \hat{R}_n(\tau)\sin\omega_0\tau \qquad (1\text{-}8\text{-}12)$$

Here

$$R_n(\tau) \equiv \langle n(t)n(t + \tau)\rangle \qquad (1\text{-}8\text{-}13)$$

is the autocorrelation function of the noise $n(t)$.

As an alternative approach, we have, by writing $z(t) = n(t) + j\hat{n}(t)$ directly, that

$$R_z(\tau) \equiv \langle z^*(t)z(t + \tau) \rangle = 2[R_n(\tau) + jR_{n\hat{n}}(\tau)] \qquad (1\text{-}8\text{-}14)$$

Then

$$R_n(\tau) = \tfrac{1}{2} \operatorname{Re} [R_z(\tau)] = \tfrac{1}{2} \operatorname{Re} [R_u(\tau)e^{j\omega_0\tau}] \qquad (1\text{-}8\text{-}15)$$

from Eq. (1-8-10). Here $R_u(\tau) \equiv \langle u^*(\tau)u(t + \tau) \rangle$ is the (complex) auto-correlation function of $u(t)$. Defining the correlation function $R(\tau)$ as

$$R(\tau) \equiv \tfrac{1}{2}R_u(\tau) = \tfrac{1}{2}\langle u^*(t)u(t + \tau) \rangle \qquad (1\text{-}8\text{-}16)$$

we also have

$$R_n(\tau) = \operatorname{Re} [R(\tau)e^{j\omega_0\tau}] \qquad (1\text{-}8\text{-}17)[1]$$

Note that this is exactly the representation of a bandpass signal. Since we have previously assumed $n(t)$ to have a bandwidth $B \leq f_0$, its spectral density must be band-limited to $B \leq f_0$ cps, and $R(\tau)$ is in turn also band-limited to $B \leq f_0$.

As a check, because of the form of Eq. (1-8-17), we must have

$$\hat{R}_n(\tau) = \operatorname{Im} [R(\tau)e^{j\omega_0\tau}] = R_{n\hat{n}}(\tau) \qquad (1\text{-}8\text{-}18)$$

Then
$$R(\tau) = [R_n(\tau) + j\hat{R}_n(\tau)]e^{-j\omega_0\tau} \qquad (1\text{-}8\text{-}19)$$
and
$$\operatorname{Re} [R(\tau)] = R_n(\tau) \cos \omega_0\tau + \hat{R}_n(\tau) \sin \omega_0\tau = R_x(\tau) \qquad (1\text{-}8\text{-}20)$$

as in Eq. (1-8-12).

But
$$\begin{aligned} R(\tau) &= \tfrac{1}{2}\langle u^*(t)u(t + \tau) \rangle \\ &= \tfrac{1}{2}\langle \{[x - jy][x(t + \tau) + jy(t + \tau)] \rangle \\ &= R_x(\tau) + jR_{xy}(\tau) \end{aligned} \qquad (1\text{-}8\text{-}21)$$

after performing the indicated averages. Equations (1-8-12), (1-8-20), and (1-8-21) thus agree with one another.

It is apparent from the form of Eq. (1-8-17) that in calculations dealing with noise through linear filters it suffices to deal with the (complex) correlation function $R(\tau)$, and low-pass equivalents of filters. Using Eqs. (1-8-17) and (1-8-21) the other correlation functions can readily be found.

Cross-correlation of Narrowband Noise Terms. We indicated at the end of Sec. 1-7 some simple properties relating correlation functions of two narrowband noise terms $n_1(t)$ and $n_2(t)$. (Again the term narrowband means specifically $B \leq f_0$.) We can now extend these in a more general sense, and indicate specifically how the correlation can be calculated in the case of a given noise term $n(t)$ applied to the inputs of two different filters. This will be useful in later chapters.

Consider then two narrowband noise waves $n_1(t)$ and $n_2(t)$, with a cross-correlation function defined as

$$R_{n_1n_2}(\tau) \equiv \langle n_1(t)n_2(t + \tau) \rangle \qquad (1\text{-}8\text{-}22)$$

Using the phasor representations

$$n_1 = \operatorname{Re} [u_1e^{j\omega_0t}] \qquad n_2 = \operatorname{Re} [u_2e^{j\omega_0t}] \qquad (1\text{-}8\text{-}23)$$

---

[1] In much of the literature $R(\tau)$ is defined directly as the correlation function of $u(t)$. We choose to use $R_u(\tau)$ also to be consistent with our previous definitions.

we can also write

$$R_{n_1 n_2}(\tau) = \text{Re}\ [R_{12}(\tau)e^{j\omega_0\tau}] \tag{1-8-24}$$

with
$$R_{12}(\tau) \equiv \tfrac{1}{2}\langle u_1^*(t)u_2(t+\tau)\rangle \tag{1-8-25}$$

The correlation function $R_{12}(\tau)$ is thus the low-pass equivalent of $R_{n_1 n_2}(\tau)$. As in the previous paragraph, it is then readily shown that the following correlation terms are found from $R_{12}(\tau)$.

$$\rho_c(\tau) \equiv \langle x_1(t)x_2(t+\tau)\rangle = \langle y_1(t)y_2(t+\tau)\rangle = \text{Re}\ [R_{12}(\tau)] \tag{1-8-26}$$

and
$$\rho_s(\tau) \equiv \langle x_1(t)y_2(t+\tau)\rangle = -\langle y_1(t)x_2(t+\tau)\rangle = \text{Im}\ [R_{12}(\tau)] \tag{1-8-27}$$

This is a generalization of Eqs. (1-7-24) to (1-7-27) in Sec. 1-7.

As an example of the calculation of cross-correlation between two noise terms and the use of low-pass equivalents in this determination, consider noise appearing at the output of two bandpass filters with the same noise $n(t)$ applied at the input. It suffices to discuss the low-pass equivalents only. Thus, if $n(t) = \text{Re}\ [u(t)e^{j\omega_0 t}]$ is the input noise to both filters, the output noises are, respectively,

$$u_1(t) = \int_{-\infty}^{\infty} h_1(\tau)u(t-\tau)\ d\tau \tag{1-8-28}$$

and
$$u_2(t) = \int_{-\infty}^{\infty} h_2(\tau)u(t-\tau)\ d\tau \tag{1-8-29}$$

with $h_1(t)$ and $h_2(t)$ the low-pass equivalents of the filter impulse responses. The cross-correlation function at the output is thus

$$R_{12}(\tau) = \tfrac{1}{2}\langle u_1^*(t)u_2(t+\tau)\rangle$$
$$= \int_{-\infty}^{\infty}\int_{-\infty}^{\infty} h_1^*(\tau_1)h_2(\tau_2)R(\tau-\tau_2+\tau_1)\ d\tau_1\ d\tau_2 \tag{1-8-30}$$

with $R(\tau) = \tfrac{1}{2}\langle u^*(t)u(t+\tau)\rangle$ the low-pass autocorrelation function of the input noise. Defining $G(f)$ as the Fourier transform of $R(\tau)$, or the "low-pass equivalent" spectral density of the noise, we have

$$\int_{-\infty}^{\infty} h_2(\tau_2)R(\tau-\tau_2+\tau_1)\ d\tau_2 = \int_{-\infty}^{\infty} H_2(\omega)G(f)e^{j\omega(\tau_1+\tau)}\ df \tag{1-8-31}$$

Then
$$R_{12}(\tau) = \int_{-\infty}^{\infty} e^{j\omega\tau}H_2(\omega)G(f) \underbrace{\left[\int_{-\infty}^{\infty} h_1^*(\tau_1)e^{j\omega\tau_1}\ d\tau_1\right]}_{H_1^*(\omega)} \tag{1-8-32}$$

$$= \int_{-\infty}^{\infty} e^{j\omega\tau}H_1^*(\omega)H_2(\omega)G(f)\ df$$

The output complex cross-correlation function thus appears in terms of the two low-pass equivalent filters and the low-pass equivalent power spectral density of the input noise.

As an example, if the input noise is white, with two-sided spectral density $n_0/2$, $G(f) = n_0/2$ also, and

$$R_{12}(\tau) = \frac{n_0}{2}\int_{-\infty}^{\infty} H_1^*(\omega)H_2(\omega)e^{j\omega\tau}\ df \tag{1-8-33}$$

If the two filters are orthogonal, in the sense that the integral is zero, $R_{12}(\tau) = 0$, and there is no correlation. (An obvious example is the one in which the two filters occupy separate and *nonoverlapping* frequency ranges.) As a special case we have the cross-correlation at $\tau = 0$:

$$R_{12}(0) = \frac{n_0}{2}\int_{-\infty}^{\infty} H_1^*(\omega)H_2(\omega)\ df \tag{1-8-34}$$

CHAPTER 2

STATISTICAL COMMUNICATION THEORY AS APPLIED TO DIGITAL COMMUNICATIONS

2-1. Statistical Decision Theory

In Chap. 1 some examples of the use of the statistical distributions of noise and of signal plus noise in evaluating error probabilities were chosen from the field of simple binary transmission. In the examples discussed we relied primarily on intuition in setting up and evaluating criteria for detecting the presence of signals.

We shall now generalize somewhat and put the analysis on a more secure theoretical basis by utilizing the tools of statistical decision theory.[1] For it is obvious that many of the problems of signal detection are statistical in nature. The material in Chap. 1 indicated that received signals are corrupted by additive fluctuation noise and can therefore only be *estimated*. Multipath interference leading to signal fading, and reception in scatter communications systems can also only be described statistically (see Chap. 9). So the problems normally encountered in communications involve deciding on a particular signal transmitted or estimating signal amplitudes, phases, and/or wave shapes in a statistical sense. The techniques of statistical decision and estimation theory will enable us in

---

[1] The statistical theory can be found in a variety of books. See, e.g., A. M. Mood and F. A. Graybill, "Introduction to the Theory of Statistics," 2d ed., McGraw-Hill Book Company, New York, 1963; H. Cramer, "Mathematical Methods of Statistics," Princeton University Press, Princeton, N.J., 1946. The Wiley series on Probability and Statistics, John Wiley & Sons, Inc., New York, contains many specialized books in this area.

Applications of the theory to the field of Communications may be found in V. A. Kotel'nikov, "Theory of Optimum Noise Immunity," McGraw-Hill Book Company, New York, 1960, a particularly well-written, well-organized book with many specific examples; C. W. Helstrom, "Statistical Theory of Signal Detection," Pergamon Press, New York, 1960; D. Middleton, "Introduction to Statistical Theory of Communication," McGraw-Hill Book Company, New York, 1960; E. Baghdady, (ed.) "Lectures on Communication System Theory," McGraw-Hill Book Company, New York, 1961; W. B. Davenport and W. L. Root, "An Introduction to the Theory of Random Signals and Noise," McGraw-Hill Book Company, New York, 1958; W. W. Harman, "Principles of the Statistical Theory of Communication," McGraw-Hill Book Company, New York, 1963. All these books contain extensive references to the literature.

some cases to find the "best" way to perform these estimates. We shall find that all of the cases considered will involve some form of a likelihood ratio, or probability ratio test, as an extension of the Bayes' decision procedure to be described in the next paragraph.

Two-level Signals; Alternative Hypotheses. The simplest problem we can treat is that of detecting the absence or presence of a signal pulse or estimating the polarity of a bipolarity signal.

In statistical terminology, given the value of a statistical sample (or group of samples) we must select between either one of two alternative hypotheses. Call these H_0 and H_1. Our sample will be the value of a voltage v at a given instant of time or a sequence of such voltages if several samples are considered. Hypothesis H_0 may correspond to saying the voltage v measured represents noise, or a 0 transmitted, or -1, in the bipolarity case. Hypothesis H_1, the alternative hypothesis, then corresponds to saying a signal, or a 1, is present.

Either choice on our part could be in error. Thus, assuming H_0 to be correct, H_1 may turn out to be true; assuming H_1 to be correct, H_0 may actually be true.

Assume first that these two different kinds of error are equally important. The received voltage v theoretically can take on all values in the range $-\infty < v < \infty$ (or the range of positive values if the envelope-detected case is considered). How do we "best" break up this range of v into regions corresponding to a choice of H_0 assumed correct or of H_1 assumed correct?

We define as our criterion of "best" the choice of mutually exclusive regions of H_0 and H_1 that provides a minimum overall probability of error. Thus, let region V_0 correspond to the choice of H_0, V_1 to the choice of H_1. Then $V_0 + V_1$ comprises the entire one-dimensional space of v. We are then to choose V_0 (or V_1) to minimize the overall probability of error.

We assume here we are given the a priori probabilities P_0 and P_1 of transmitting a 0 and a 1, respectively, $(P_0 + P_1 = 1)$. We are also given the conditional probability densities $p_1(v)\,dv$ and $p_0(v)\,dv$, corresponding, respectively, to the probability of receiving voltage v, given a 1 transmitted, or a 0 transmitted. For Gaussian noise and signal of values 0 and A, or $\pm A/2$, these are just the probability densities of Fig. 1-3-2.

With the defined probability densities the error probability that v will fall in V_0 even though a 1 is transmitted is

$$\int_{V_0} p_1(v)\,dv,$$

while the probability that v may fall in V_1, even though a 0 was sent, is given by

$$\int_{V_1} p_0(v)\,dv.$$

The overall error probability P_e that is to be minimized by the appropriate choice of V_0 is given by

$$P_e = P_1 \int_{V_0} p_1(v) \, dv + P_0 \int_{V_1} p_0(v) \, dv \qquad (2\text{-}1\text{-}1)$$

Since $V_0 + V_1$ covers all of the possible values of v, we have

$$\int_{V_0 + V_1} p_0(v) \, dv = 1,$$

and the equation can be written to eliminate V_1, giving

$$P_e = P_0 + \int_{V_0} [P_1 p_1(v) - P_0 p_0(v)] \, dv \qquad (2\text{-}1\text{-}2)$$

Since P_0 is a specified number and assumed known, P_e is minimized by choosing the region V_0 to minimize the integral. This can be done by picking V_0 to be the region in which

$$P_0 p_0(v) > P_1 p_1(v) \qquad (2\text{-}1\text{-}3)$$

This will ensure the integral is always negative (probabilities are always positive numbers), so that P_e is made as small as possible.

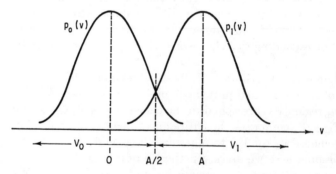

FIG. 2-1-1. Choice of decision regions.

Hypothesis H_0 will thus be chosen (assumed correct) if v falls in the range where the inequality

$$\frac{p_0(v)}{p_1(v)} > \frac{P_1}{P_0} \qquad (2\text{-}1\text{-}4)$$

is satisfied.

As an example, let $P_0 = P_1 = \frac{1}{2}$, and consider the two similar Gaussian density functions of Fig. 2-1-1. Then region V_0 corresponds to all values of $v < A/2$, V_1 to all values of $v > A/2$. A threshold level b would then be chosen at $b = A/2$, such that all values of v above this value are assumed due to a 1 signal, all values below to be a 0 signal. This ensures minimum overall probability of error. Note that this agrees with our intuitive reasoning in Chap. 1, as indicated by Fig. 1-3-2.

If $P_1 > P_0$, however, this biases us in favor of H_1, so that the V_0 region should be decreased, with the threshold level shifted to the left.

A different example, involving two other (arbitrarily chosen) distributions, is shown in Fig. 2-1-2. For $P_0 = P_1 = \frac{1}{2}$ again, the optimum regions of V_0 and V_1 are as indicated.

The rule for choosing H_0, given by Eq. (2-1-4), and developed on the basis of minimum overall probability of error, is called the *Bayes decision rule*. We can state it alternatively by saying we shall pick H_1 if v falls in a region V_1 given by

$$\frac{p_1(v)}{p_0(v)} > \frac{P_0}{P_1} \qquad (2\text{-}1\text{-}5)$$

The ratio of probability densities $p_1(v)/p_0(v)$ is called the likelihood ratio $l(v)$ and appears in all statistical estimation tests.

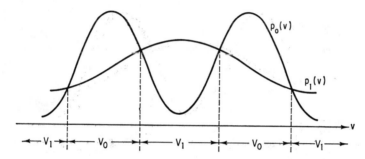

FIG. 2-1-2. Another example of decision regions.

It is of interest to consider another interpretation of the "optimum" test procedure just developed. This will be useful when we consider the case of multiple hypotheses in section 2-7.

Let $P(1,v)$ be the joint probability of transmission of a 1 and reception, including noise, of a value of v within the range $v \pm dv/2$. Then, in terms of our previously defined probabilities,

$$P(1,v) = P_1 p_1(v)\, dv \qquad (2\text{-}1\text{-}6)$$

But we can also write the joint probability as

$$P(1,v) = p(v)\, dv\, P(1|v) \qquad (2\text{-}1\text{-}7)$$

with $p(v)\, dv$ the probability of having v fall in the range $v \pm dv/2$, and $P(1|v)$ the probability that given a particular value of v, a 1 was sent. From the two equations, we get

$$P(1|v) = \frac{P_1 p_1(v)}{p(v)} \qquad (2\text{-}1\text{-}8)$$

Similarly,

$$P(0|v) = \frac{P_0 p_0(v)}{p(v)} \qquad (2\text{-}1\text{-}9)$$

These two equations are examples of Bayes' rule, involving the a posteriori probabilities $P(1|v)$ and $P(0|v)$.

Given a specified value of v we use Eqs. (2-1-8) and (2-1-9) to calculate the probabilities $P(1|v)$ and $P(0|v)$. Our decision procedure then simply involves the choice of H_1 if $P(1|v) > P(0|v)$, or H_0 if reversed. This will ensure a minimum number of errors over a large number of trials and resultant minimum penalty if H_0 and H_1 are of equal importance.

Note, however, that this rather simple rule of assuming as correct the hypothesis corresponding to the larger of the two conditional probabilities is exactly the Bayes' decision rule developed previously;

$$\frac{P(1|v)}{P(0|v)} = \frac{P_1 p_1(v)}{P_0 p_0(v)} > 1 \tag{2-1-10}$$

gives the range of values corresponding to the region V_1, or hypothesis H_1.

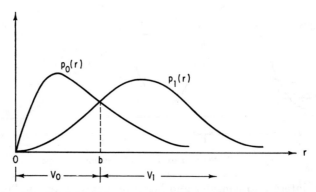

FIG. 2-1-3. Decision procedure after envelope detection.

For the case of multiple hypotheses, to be considered briefly in section 2-7, we shall use the rule of selecting the one corresponding to the largest a posteriori probability. Such a detection procedure is referred to as a maximum a posteriori probability detection procedure.

Application to Envelope Detection. As another application of the Bayes' likelihood ratio approach to statistical decision we consider again the case of noncoherent on-off binary signals after envelope detection, discussed in Chap. 1. We again assume the transmission of either signal to be equally likely.

The appropriate probability density functions are shown in Fig. 2-1-3. For the equally likely case, Eq. (2-1-10) indicates that the threshold b should be chosen at the point $p_1(r) = p_0(r)$, as shown in the figure. The region V_1 corresponding to the decision that H_1 is correct (an "on" signal sent) is then given by all values of $r > b$. This particular choice of threshold will then ensure a minimum overall probability of error or the minimum number of errors in a large number of trials (large number of bits transmitted). This contrasts with the various other possible threshold locations noted in Chap. 1; halfway between the peaks of the two distributions, at the point where the two types of error are equal (equal areas under the curves), at the point where the slopes are equal, etc. (For large signal-to-noise ratio, frequently necessary to ensure tolerable error probabilities, however, it must again be noted that these different possibilities provide about the same threshold location.)

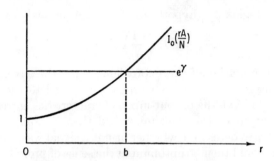

FIG. 2-1-4. Threshold determination.

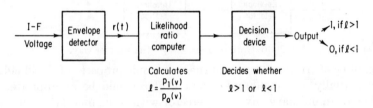

FIG. 2-1-5. Optimum decision circuitry—the hard way.

Using the appropriate density functions obtained and discussed in Chap. 1, the threshold b in this case is given by

$$\frac{p_1(b)}{p_0(b)} = 1 = e^{-\gamma} I_0\left(\frac{bA}{N}\right) \tag{2-1-11}$$

with $\gamma = A^2/2N$, the mean power signal-to-noise (S/N) ratio. A solution for b requires solving the equation

$$I_0\left(\frac{bA}{N}\right) = e^{\gamma} \tag{2-1-12}$$

as depicted in Fig. 2-1-4.

The brute-force way of implementing the solution of the equation is by means of the decision circuitry of Fig. 2-1-5.

This complicated-looking system is actually not necessary in this particular case. (Note that the computer would have to have stored in it the signal-to-noise ratio γ. Any changes in either the peak signal A or rms noise $\sqrt{N}$ would then require changes in γ.) As a matter of fact we can show quite simply that all that is really required is a "run of the mill" envelope detector (diode plus filter) and an appropriate voltage selector following! (A transistor normally biased off, with an applied voltage of b volts or greater necessary to turn it on, will do.)

To show this we take the natural log of the likelihood ratio

$$l = \frac{p_1(r)}{p_0(r)}$$

and get for the region V_1 (hypothesis H_1) in this special case

$$\log I_0\left(\frac{rA}{N}\right) > \gamma \qquad (2\text{-}1\text{-}13)$$

The initial interpretation of this expression is that the envelope detector instead of being linear (output linearly proportional to the envelope of the input) should have the output-input characteristics corresponding to $\log I_0$. The output of this detector would then be compared with the stored value of γ to determine whether or not a signal was present. This $\log I_0$ detector would then be optimum in the sense of providing minimum

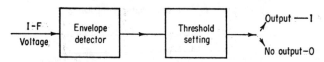

Fig. 2-1-6. Optimum circuitry—the simpler way.

probability of error. Because of the monotonic property of the likelihood ratio, actually any monotone function of r would be appropriate. In particular an ordinary envelope detector with some quadratic curvature for small inputs and linear response for large inputs would most appropriately be used, as shown in Fig. 2-1-6.

This type of detector is actually contained within the $\log I_0$ representation of Eq. (2-1-13). For we can show that for small γ it reduces to a quadratic detector and for large γ to the linear detector. It is useful to demonstrate this property at this point, since it will be appropriate in dealing with multiple signal samples in the next section, in which case we shall find ourselves considering sums of logarithms of likelihood ratios. Consider, then, two extreme cases:

1. $\gamma \ll 1$: then r is likely to be small also, and

$$I_0\left(\frac{rA}{N}\right) \doteq 1 + \left(\frac{rA}{2N}\right)^2 \doteq e^{r^2\gamma/2N} \qquad \frac{rA}{N} \ll 1 \qquad (2\text{-}1\text{-}14)$$

Taking the natural log, as in Eq. (2-1-13),

$$\frac{r^2\gamma}{2N} > \gamma$$

or

$$r^2 > 2N \qquad (2\text{-}1\text{-}15)$$

Thus, for small γ the likelihood test reduces to that of using a quadratic envelope detector, and the output must exceed twice the mean-squared noise at the input. (The detector constant is here taken to be 1.)

2. $\gamma \gg 1$: then, with signal present, r will normally be large, and $rA/N \gg 1$.

$$I_0\left(\frac{rA}{N}\right) \doteq \frac{e^{rA/N}}{\sqrt{2\pi rA/N}} \qquad \frac{rA}{N} \gg 1 \qquad (2\text{-}1\text{-}16)$$

Again taking the natural log and neglecting the small square-root term, the likelihood test reduces to

$$\frac{rA}{N} > \gamma = \frac{A^2}{2N}$$

or

$$r > \frac{A}{2} \qquad (2\text{-}1\text{-}17)$$

So in this case of large S/N, a *linear* envelope detector plus threshold set at half the signal amplitude provides appropriate detection.

The composite detector characteristic appropriate for all values of r is shown in Fig. 2-1-7. For small r and γ it would be quadratic, for large r

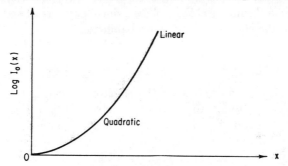

FIG. 2-1-7. Optimum detector characteristic.

and γ linear, as is the case for ordinary envelope detectors. A good approximation to Eq. (2-1-13) useful for analysis purpose is given by $r/\sqrt{N} > \sqrt{2 + \gamma/2}$. Note that it reduces to Eqs. (2-1-15) and (2-1-17) in the two extremes of $\gamma \ll 1$ and $\gamma \gg 1$.

Weighted Losses. The simple decision rule for choosing between two hypotheses was developed on the assumption that the two kinds of error possible were equally important. In the event that the two types of error have different significance, the rule requires some modification.[1]

One possible procedure is to assign some loss values to the different types of error and minimize average loss.[2]

[1] In radar, for example, noise mistaken for a signal may be less significant than the loss of a signal.

[2] See, e.g., Davenport and Root, *op. cit.*; Harman, *op. cit.*; Helstrom *op. cit.*; Middleton, *op. cit.* These books generalize by including the possibility of weighting a correct decision and use cost matrices for this purpose.

Thus, let L_{10} represent the loss involved in mistaking a 1 for a 0 and L_{01} the loss in mistaking a 0 for a 1. The *average loss* is then

$$\bar{L} = L_{10}P_1 \int_{V_0} p_1(v) \, dv + L_{01}P_0 \int_{V_1} p_0(v) \, dv \qquad (2\text{-}1\text{-}18)$$

and the problem is to choose region V_0 so as to minimize $\bar{L}$. Comparing this equation with Eq. (2-1-1) for the error probability P_e, the region V_0, corresponding to the choice of hypothesis H_0, will be given by

$$L_{01}P_0 p_0(v) > L_{10}P_1 p_1(v) \qquad (2\text{-}1\text{-}19)$$

The condition for the choice of hypothesis H_1 in terms of the likelihood ratio l is then

$$l = \frac{p_1(v)}{p_0(v)} > \frac{P_0 L_{01}}{P_1 L_{10}} \qquad (2\text{-}1\text{-}20)$$

The effect of introducing loss values is thus simply to weight the likelihood ratio in favor of one hypothesis or the other. As an extreme case, if $L_{01} = 0$ (no penalty is incurred if a 0 is mistaken for a 1), $p_1(v) > 0$, and all possible values of v correspond to the choice of H_1. We shall not refer to loss values in the material that follows, since they correspond essentially to modifying the choice of a priori probabilities.

2-2. Decision Theory in the Case of Binary-signal Repetition

As in Chap. 1 we now consider the effect of repeating a given binary signal n times to attempt to improve its detectability. The two signals are again assumed to have a priori probabilities P_0 and P_1.

The signal plus additive noise at the receiver will result in a random voltage v. This voltage will be sampled n times, and the problem here is how to "best" process the n samples, $v_1, v_2, \ldots, v_n$, in the sense of minimizing the overall probability of error in deciding between hypotheses H_0 and H_1.

The n samples of v can be visualized as representing one point in an n-dimensional space. The statistical problem is then to choose surfaces in this space which optimumly divide it into two regions V_0 and V_1. Just as before in the case of a one-dimensional space, we proceed by setting up the expression for the probability of error P_e and adjust the regions V_0 and V_1 to minimize P_e. Because of the n samples, however, we now have nth-order joint-probability-density functions, $p_0(v_1, v_2, \ldots, v_n)$ and $p_1(v_1, v_2, \ldots, v_n)$, appearing in the expression for the probability of error in place of the first-order density functions of Eq. (2-1-1).

By using the same procedure as before, it then follows that the optimum region of choice of hypothesis H_1 is given by a more general Bayes' likelihood test,

$$l = \frac{p_1(v_1, v_2, \ldots, v_n)}{p_0(v_1, v_2, \ldots, v_n)} > \frac{P_0}{P_1} \qquad (2\text{-}2\text{-}1)$$

The likelihood ratio l is now defined in a more general way as the ratio of the nth-order joint probability functions.

Alternatively, we could evaluate the conditional probabilities $P(1|v_1,v_2, \ldots ,v_n)$ and $P(0|v_1,v_2, \ldots ,v_n)$ as an extension of the approach leading to Eq. (2-1-8) and (2-1-9). We would then base our decision on the larger of the two, leading of course to the likelihood-ratio test of Eq. (2-2-1).

In the special case where the successive samples of v are statistically independent, the joint-probability-density functions become the product of their respective first-order density functions. The likelihood test for choosing hypothesis H_1 then becomes

$$l = \frac{p_1(v_1)p_1(v_2) \cdot \cdot \cdot p_1(v_n)}{p_0(v_1)p_0(v_2) \cdot \cdot \cdot p_0(v_n)} > \frac{P_0}{P_1} \qquad (2\text{-}2\text{-}2)$$

This is the case of most interest to us and the one for which we shall consider some specific examples.

First Example—Coherent Binary Transmission. Assume, as the first example, that the binary signal is repeated at intervals far enough apart in time so that the noise samples added at the receiver are effectively independent. (Recall from Chap. 1 that this implies that the sampling interval $\tau > 1/B$, with B the system bandwidth in cps.) To generalize our previous discussion a bit, assume the received signal may have either of two fixed amplitudes A_0 or A_1 volts. The noise added is again Gaussian, and coherent transmission and reception is assumed.

The jth sample of voltage v will then have the probability distributions

$$p_0(v_j) = \frac{e^{-(v_j - A_0)^2/2N}}{\sqrt{2\pi N}} \qquad j = 1, 2, \ldots , n \qquad (2\text{-}2\text{-}3)$$

or

$$p_1(v_j) = \frac{e^{-(v_j - A_1)^2/2N}}{\sqrt{2\pi N}} \qquad j = 1, 2, \ldots , n \qquad (2\text{-}2\text{-}4)$$

depending on which binary signal was transmitted.

Using the likelihood ratio criterion of Eq. (2-2-2) to determine the condition for deciding on hypothesis H_1 and taking natural logarithms of both sides to simplify the calculations, we get

$$\sum_{j=1}^{n} [(v_j - A_0)^2 - (v_j - A_1)^2] > 2N \log_e \frac{P_0}{P_1} \qquad (2\text{-}2\text{-}5)$$

This can be given an interesting geometric interpretation in the case of equiprobable signals.[1] With $P_0 = P_1 = \frac{1}{2}$, we choose H_1 if

$$\sum_{j=1}^{n} (v_j - A_1)^2 < \sum_{j=1}^{n} (v_j - A_0)^2 \qquad (2\text{-}2\text{-}6)$$

The quantity $\sum_{n} (v_j - A_1)^2$ is just the square of the distance between the

[1] Kotel'nikov, *op. cit.*, pp. 22, 24.

n-dimensional point $v = v_1, v_2, \ldots, v_n$ and A_1. We thus assume H_1 correct if the point v lies closer to A_1 than to A_0. Unequal a priori probabilities (or loss values if introduced) serve to shift the boundary between the regions V_0 and V_1 one way or the other. But note that this rather simple result is valid only because of the Gaussian distributions assumed. Other distributions, as in the example to follow, do not provide as intuitively satisfying results.

Equation (2-2-5) can be further simplified by expanding the squares to give

$$\sum_{j=1}^{n} v_j > \frac{n(A_1 + A_0)}{2} + \frac{N}{A_1 - A_0} \log_e \frac{P_0}{P_1} \qquad A_1 > A_0 \qquad (2\text{-}2\text{-}7)$$

The optimum way of processing the n independent samples of signal plus Gaussian noise in the sense of minimizing the overall probability of error is thus to *add* the samples and require them to either exceed or drop below a specified threshold level[1]

$$b = \frac{n(A_1 + A_0)}{2} + \frac{N}{A_1 - A_0} \log_e \frac{P_0}{P_1} \qquad (2\text{-}2\text{-}8)$$

This of course agrees with the intuitive result noted in Fig. 1-3-2a for the special case $P_0 = P_1 = \frac{1}{2}$, $A_1 = A$, $A_0 = 0$.

Second Example—Incoherent Binary Transmission; Envelope Detection. For the second example we again consider the case in which envelope detection is required (incoherent transmission). The binary signals transmitted again consist, respectively, of "on" pulses of received amplitude A volts and "off" intervals with no signal transmitted. Each particular bit is however repeated n times in succession, at intervals far enough apart so as to ensure independent noise samples.

The jth sample of received voltage then has as its two possible probability distributions

$$p_1(r_j) = \frac{r_j e^{-\gamma} e^{-r_j^2/2N}}{N} I_0 \left(\frac{r_j A}{N} \right) \qquad \gamma \equiv A^2/2N \qquad (2\text{-}2\text{-}9)$$

and
$$p_0(r_j) = \frac{r_j e^{-r_j^2/2N}}{N} \qquad (2\text{-}2\text{-}10)$$

The likelihood ratio for n independent samples becomes in this case

$$l = \frac{\prod_j p_1(r_j)}{\prod_j p_0(r_j)} = e^{-n\gamma} \prod_{j=1}^{n} I_0 \left(r_j \frac{A}{N} \right) \qquad (2\text{-}2\text{-}11)[2]$$

---

[1] The direct addition of the samples is due specifically to the Gaussian statistics, with unknown means, chosen. Other distributions lead to other optimum processing procedures.

[2] Note that the case of known but varying signal amplitude could be handled by using the value A_j for the jth sample.

Taking natural logs again, the Bayes decision rule for choosing H_1 gives

$$\sum_{j=1}^{n} \log_e I_0 \left(\frac{r_j A}{N}\right) > n\gamma + \log_e \frac{P_0}{P_1} \qquad (2\text{-}2\text{-}12)$$

The interpretation of this result is quite simple: use a $\log I_0$ envelope detector, add or integrate the successive n samples at the output of this detector and then require the integrated output at the end of the n intervals of repetitive transmission to exceed a specified threshold level. As pointed out previously, however, the optimum $\log I_0$ detector is not really necessary and can be replaced by an ordinary envelope detector. The decision circuitry required is shown in Fig. 2-2-1. The setting of the

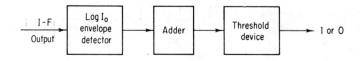

(a) Optimum decision procedure

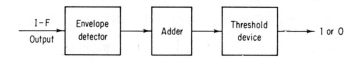

(b) Practical circuitry

FIG. 2-2-1. Decision circuitry for repetitive signals.

threshold depends, as previously, on the S/N ratio γ, P_0, P_1, and n, the number of samples integrated.

2-3. Neyman-Pearson Theory of Testing Hypotheses with Application to Radar

Implicit in the previous discussion of optimum testing procedures for choosing between two alternative hypotheses H_0 and H_1 has been the assumption that the a priori probabilities P_0 and P_1 were known. This may not always be the case, however. In a search radar, for example, there is no way of telling in advance whether or not a target will appear. Most of the time the voltages registered on a scope or meter will be those due to noise. How do we "best" process the information in this case?

A procedure minimizing the overall probability of error in this case is clearly not possible since the a priori probabilities either are unknown or have no significance. The testing procedure developed by Neyman and

Pearson in 1930,[1] and since widely adopted by statisticians, is particularly appropriate in this case. It also involves, as we shall see, the use of the likelihood ratio and a Bayes-type decision rule.

Assume as previously that n independent samples of a randomly varying voltage are available upon which to base the choice between the alternative hypotheses H_0 and H_1.

Although the overall probability of error can no longer be evaluated because P_0 and P_1 are not known, the two possible types of error can be calculated. As in Sec. 2-1, they will be (using statistical terminology),

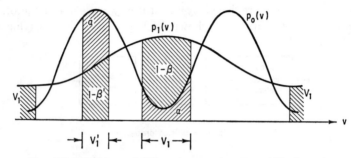

FIG. 2-3-1. Regions of different power (portion of V_1 shown).

1. Error of the first kind—H_0 rejected although true. The probability of this happening is

$$\alpha = \int_{V_1} \cdots \int p_0(v_1)p_0(v_2) \cdots p_0(v_n)\, dv_1 \cdots dv_n \qquad (2\text{-}3\text{-}1)$$

2. Error of the second kind—H_0 accepted although H_1 true. The error probability in this case is

$$\beta = \int_{V_0} \cdots \int p_1(v_1) \cdots p_1(v_n)\, dv_1 \cdots dv_n \qquad (2\text{-}3\text{-}2)$$

$V_0 + V_1$ again correspond to the entire n-dimensional space of v.

It is apparent that V_1 (or V_0) cannot be chosen to simultaneously make α and β as small as possible. The Neyman-Pearson procedure instead fixes the error of the first kind α at some tolerable value and then, for this given value, finds the region V_1 that serves to minimize β.

In statistical terminology α is frequently called the significance level or "size" of a test, $1 - \beta$ the power of the test, and V_1 the critical region or the region of rejection of the H_0 (null) hypothesis. The "most powerful" test is the one which maximizes the power for a given size α.

As an example consider the one-dimensional case of Fig. 2-3-1. Two

[1] J. Neyman and E. S. Pearson, On the Problem of the Most Efficient Tests of Statistical Hypotheses, *Phil. Trans. Roy. Soc. London, Ser. A*, No. 231, pp. 289–337, 1931. See also any one of most books on statistics. The books by Mood and Cramer have already been cited. A particularly succinct summary appears in A. Wald, "Sequential Analysis," John Wiley & Sons, Inc., New York, 1947.

possible regions V_1 and V_1' are shown, chosen so that α is the same in both. Then V_1 is a more powerful region since $1 - \beta > 1 - \beta'$. It is not too hard to show that the optimum choice of V_1, in the Neyman-Pearson sense in this one-dimensional case, corresponds to all values of v such that $p_1(v) > kp_0(v)$, with k a constant depending on the choice of α.[1] For if a small strip of V_1 satisfying this relation is replaced by a strip elsewhere, with the widths adjusted to keep α constant, the area under the $p_1(v)$ curve, or $1 - \beta$, will necessarily decrease. This is apparent from Fig. 2-3-1.

In the general n-dimensional case, with n independent samples considered, a necessary and sufficient condition for a most-powerful region can be shown to be just the extension of the one-dimensional case:[2]

$$l = \frac{p_1(v_1) \; \cdots \; p_1(v_n)}{p_0(v_1) \; \cdots \; p_0(v_n)} > k(\alpha) \tag{2-3-3}$$

with k a constant depending on the choice of α. Note that the likelihood ratio l again appears.

The Neyman-Pearson procedure thus leads to an extension of the Bayes decision rule, with the constant k replacing the a priori probabilities P_0/P_1.

As an example, we choose again the on-off binary transmission case, with a received signal of A volts amplitude. Then, as previously,

$$p_0(v) = \frac{e^{-v^2/2N}}{\sqrt{2\pi N}} \qquad p_1(v) = \frac{e^{-(v-A)^2/2N}}{\sqrt{2\pi N}}$$

The critical region, or the region of acceptance of H_1, is then given by

$$l = \frac{p_1(v)}{p_0(v)} > k(\alpha)$$

Taking natural logs and simplifying, we again get a single threshold level b separating the two regions V_0 and V_1, as expected:

$$v > b = \frac{N \log k}{A} + \frac{A}{2}$$

Assume in particular that $\alpha = 0.05$. (This implies that noise will be mistaken for signal on the average of 5 per cent of the times during which no signal is transmitted.) Then

$$\alpha = \int_b^\infty \frac{e^{-v^2/2N}}{\sqrt{2\pi N}} \, dv = 0.05$$

[1] A. M. Mood and F. A. Graybill, "Introduction to the Theory of Statistics," 2d ed., McGraw-Hill Book Company, New York, 1963.

[2] See Neyman and Pearson, op. cit., for proof.

From the tables of the error function we get

$$b = 1.65 \sqrt{N}$$

as the threshold level.

A different choice of α would have changed b. Reducing α increases b, and vice versa.

Note that in this example the threshold level is independent of the signal amplitude A. This is apparent from Fig. 2-3-2. The particular value of A will determine the power $1 - \beta$, or the probability of signal detection. As $A/\sqrt{N}$ increases, this probability of detection increases also. The threshold level b remains fixed, however, in this case once α is specified.

The fact that the critical region is independent of the parameter A indicates that the Neyman-Pearson test used is *uniformly most powerful*.[1]

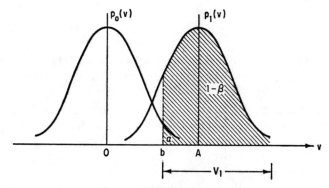

FIG. 2-3-2. Example of the Neyman-Pearson test.

With α fixed, the power of any other test will be less than the power found for this test.

The concept "uniformly most powerful" arises from the possibility that the probability function for hypothesis H_1 depends on a parameter which can take on a range of values. For example, $p_1(v)$ in the case just considered depends on the signal amplitude A. In general A may not be known exactly, because of signal fading, distance changing between transmitter and receiver, etc. The hypotheses to be tested then consist of determining whether the voltage v is due to noise only ($A = 0$) or *any* value of $A > 0$.

In statistical terms we test a hypothesis H_0 with associated probability $p_0(v_j, \theta_0)$ against a hypothesis H_1 with probability $p_1(v_j, \theta)$, $\theta \neq \theta_0$. The parameter θ may in general take on all possible values different from θ_0. For any particular value of θ we can utilize the Neyman-Pearson testing procedure to determine the critical region V_1. In general V_1, and therefore the power $1 - \beta$, will vary with θ. The most powerful test for one

[1] Mood and Graybill, *ibid.*

particular value of θ may not be most powerful for another value. If the test results in a region V_1 independent of θ, however, as in the simple example discussed, the test is *uniformly most powerful*.

Application to Radar. The radar-detection problem was the first in the general area of communications to which the Neyman-Pearson procedure was applied.[1,2,3]

The two alternative hypotheses in this application are, as previously,

1. Noise present, signal absent (the H_0 hypothesis)
2. Signal present (H_1 hypothesis).

The two types of error are again

1. The error of the first kind α, the chance that H_0 will be rejected although true.

2. The error of the second kind β, the probability that H_1 will be rejected although true.

We shall choose to use somewhat different symbols, however, that are more in keeping with the specific problem. Thus, instead of α we shall use P_n, the probability that noise is erroneously called signal, and P_s, equivalent to $1 - \beta$, the probability of detection of a signal when it appears.

Since radar return pulses are in general incoherent in phase with the transmitter, envelope detection is normally used. The optimum processing of n returned pulses, spaced at large enough time intervals to ensure independent noise samples, then corresponds essentially to that derived using the Bayes decision rule as outlined in Sec. 2-2 and given by Eq. (2-2-12). The only difference in this case is that with the a priori probabilities unknown, the critical region chosen will depend on the choice of P_n, rather than on P_0/P_1. (The a priori probabilities of a signal present or absent make no sense in the radar case.)

Interpreting Eq. (2-2-12) in the Neyman-Pearson sense, the detection procedure developed consists of requiring the sum of n envelope-detected voltage pulses to exceed a specified threshold level.[4] This level is determined by the allowable probability P_n that noise in the absence of signal may exceed the level and be erroneously detected as a signal. The probability P_s that signal plus noise will exceed the level (after summing or integration) and be identified correctly as signal then depends on the signal-to-noise ratio.

[1] M. Schwartz, "Statistical Approach to the Automatic Search Problem," Ph.D. dissertation, Harvard University, 1951.

[2] H. V. Hance, "The Optimization and Analysis of Systems for the Detection of Pulsed Signals in Random Noise," Sc.D. dissertation, MIT, 1951.

[3] J. I. Marcum, A Statistical Theory of Target Detection by Pulsed Radar, *Rand. Res. Memo* RM-754, December, 1947, reprinted in *IRE Trans. Inform. Theory*, vol. IT-6, April, 1960.

[4] The optimum log I_0 detector again can be approximated very satisfactorily by either a linear or quadratic envelope detector.

This test procedure is uniformly most powerful in the sense indicated in the previous paragraph, since it applies independent of the actual signal amplitude or signal-to-noise ratio. It is then presumably optimum in the sense that it requires minimum signal-to-noise ratio for given P_n and P_z.

Using this Neyman-Pearson threshold procedure, radar performance curves for the case of a constant amplitude signal return can be constructed. One such curve is shown in Fig. 2-3-3 for the special case of $P_n = 10^{-10}$ and $P_s = 50$ per cent and 99 per cent. These curves relate

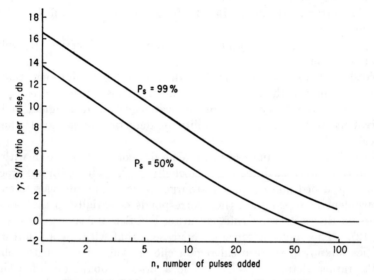

Fig. 2-3-3. Radar performance curves, $P_n = 10^{-10}$.

the signal-to-noise ratio $\gamma = A^2/2N$ at the input to the envelope detector to P_s, P_n, and n, the number of pulses added.[1]

Note that although the integration reduces the required S/N per pulse, the decrease in γ with increase in n is less than linear, as would be the case if the pulses could be added coherently. Envelope detection and integration is thus again not as efficient as coherent detection and integration, as noted in Chap. 1.[2]

The extension of these results for constant signal amplitude to include the effect of signal amplitude fluctuations is considered in a paper by

[1] See the references cited at the beginning of this paragraph for extensive collections of curves for various combinations of the variables.

[2] Further discussion, including the relation between P_n and the often-used concept of false-alarm time, can be found in the references cited at the beginning of this paragraph, as well as in the books by Schwartz, op. cit., pp. 403–410, 419–422, and Helstrom, op. cit., Chaps. 5 and 6.

M. Schwartz.[1] A nonoptimum detection procedure, which is found to perform about 1.5 db worse than the Neyman-Pearson procedure, is also discussed in the literature.[2]

2-4. Signal Shape and Matched Filters

In our discussion of signal detection thus far we have said nothing about signal shape, system bandwidth, and filtering characteristics. In the case of yes-no or on-off binary detection the particular shape of the signal is obviously unimportant; the peak signal-to-noise ratio $A/\sqrt{N}$ measured at the time at which a voltage is used in making the decision is decisive in determining the probability of error. But both A and $\sqrt{N}$, measured at the same point in the system (in our examples, at the output of the i-f strip), depend on the system transfer function and on the signal shape. Is it possible, for a given signal shape, to choose a transfer function to maximize $A/\sqrt{N}$? The answer is yes, and the result called for is termed a *matched filter*.[3]

To demonstrate this qualitatively, assume a rectangular pulse signal of width τ embedded in noise. Assume we start with a very narrow system bandwidth B and increase this systematically. The rectangular signal has a $(\sin x)/x$ frequency dependence. For small B the amplitude A of the signal at its peak increases linearly with B as more of the spectral components of the signal appear at the output. Most of the signal energy lies within the bandwidth $1/\tau$, however, so that at about the bandwidth $B = 1/\tau$, the signal amplitude will reach a maximum value. Further increases in B reproduce the fine detail of the signal (the rise time in particular becomes steeper) but with no further increase in the peak amplitude A. This is shown pictorially in Fig. 2-4-1, for an idealized rectangular filter. (Fig. 2-4-1 is drawn for the low-frequency case. A bandpass filter with the same characteristics would produce the same effect on the *envelope* of a pulsed sinusoidal signal.)

Since the rms noise passing through the filter varies as $\sqrt{B}$, the ratio $A/\sqrt{N}$ will tend to increase at first with increasing B. In the vicinity

[1] M. Schwartz, Effect of Signal Fluctuation on the Detection of Pulsed Signals in Noise, *IRE Trans. Inform. Theory*, vol. IT-2, pp. 66–71, June, 1956.

[2] M. Schwartz, A Coincidence Procedure for Signal Detection, *IRE Trans. Inform. Theory*, vol. IT-2, December, 1956.

[3] D. O. North, Analysis of the Factors Which Determine Signal/Noise Discrimination in Radar, *RCA Tech. Rept.* PTR-6-C, June, 1943, reprinted in *Proc. IRE*, vol. 51, pp. 1016–1028, July, 1963; J. H. Van Vleck and David Middleton, A Theoretical Comparison of Visual, Aural, and Meter Reception of Pulsed Signals in the Presence of Noise, *J. Appl. Phys.*, vol. 17, pp. 940–971, November, 1946; George L. Turin, An Introduction to Matched Filters, *IRE Trans. Inform. Theory*, vol. IT-6, June, 1960 (this issue of the transactions is devoted entirely to the subject of matched filters).

Among the books previously cited in which the matched filter is discussed are Davenport and Root, V. A. Kotel'nikov, C. Helstrom, D. Middleton, and M. Schwartz.

of $B = 1/\tau$, close to the point where the amplitude A reaches its maximum value, $A/\sqrt{N}$ will peak also. But for $B > 1/\tau$, $A/\sqrt{N}$ will steadily decrease with B as more noise is allowed through and A will remain the same. An optimum *bandwidth* for maximizing $A/\sqrt{N}$ thus exists and is of the order of $1/\tau$ for a rectangular pulse passed through a rectangular filter. Other signal pulse shapes give essentially the same result.

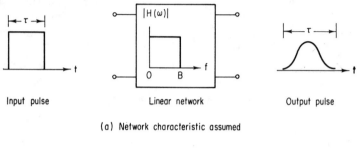

Input pulse   Linear network   Output pulse

(a) Network characteristic assumed

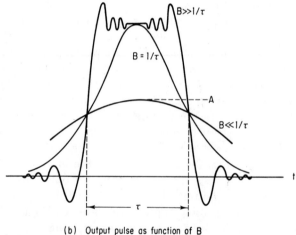

(b) Output pulse as function of B

FIG. 2-4-1. Effect of bandwidth limiting.

The system bandwidth is thus expected to play an important role in maximizing $A/\sqrt{N}$ and hence signal detectability in the presence of noise. We shall also show that system filter *shape* plays a role, although not as decisively. The optimum filter for maximizing $A/\sqrt{N}$, the ratio of the *peak* value of the signal amplitude to the rms noise, at a point in the receiver just prior to detection, will be found to be one whose impulse response is matched to the signal pulse shape.[1]

---

[1] We consider here the effect of white noise only. See Helstrom, *op. cit.*, and V. A. Kotel'nikov, *op. cit.*, for a discussion of the case of signal plus "colored" noise.

To demonstrate these ideas more quantitatively, consider a signal $f(t)$ passed through a linear filter with transfer function $H(\omega)$ and impulse response $h(t)$. This filter represents the entire system, assumed linear, between the point at which white noise is introduced, and the point at which $A/\sqrt{N}$ is measured.

The output $g(t)$ of the filter at some time t is given by either the convolution integral or Fourier transform:[1]

$$g(t) = \int_{-\infty}^{\infty} f(\tau)h(t - \tau)\, d\tau = \frac{1}{2\pi} \int_{-\infty}^{\infty} e^{j\omega t}F(\omega)H(\omega)\, d\omega \qquad (2\text{-}4\text{-}1)$$

with $F(\omega)$ the Fourier transform of $f(t)$.

The mean-squared noise output at this same point, due to white noise of two-sided spectral density $n_0/2$ applied at the filter input, is

$$N = \frac{n_0}{2} \int_{-\infty}^{\infty} |H(\omega)|^2\, df$$

$$= \frac{n_0}{2} \int_{-\infty}^{\infty} h^2(\tau)\, d\tau \qquad (2\text{-}4\text{-}2)$$

using Parseval's theorem.

Note that $h(t)$ [or $H(\omega)$] appears in the equations for both $g(t)$ and N. The problem here is to find the form of $h(t)$ that maximizes the ratio $g(t_0)/\sqrt{N}$, with t_0 defined to be the time at which $g(t)$ has its peak value A. It is simpler to consider the *square* of the ratio, or the ratio of signal squared to mean noise power at time t_0:

$$\frac{g^2(t_0)}{N} \equiv S/N = \frac{\left[\int_{-\infty}^{\infty} f(\tau)h(t_0 - \tau)\, dt\right]^2}{n_0/2 \int_{-\infty}^{\infty} h^2(\tau)\, d\tau} \qquad (2\text{-}4\text{-}3)$$

To maximize this ratio by the proper choice of $h(t)$ we employ a simple artifice. The signal $f(t)$ is assumed known, so that its energy E is a known *constant* given by

$$E = \int_{-\infty}^{\infty} f^2(t)\, dt = \int_{-\infty}^{\infty} |F(\omega)|^2\, df \qquad (2\text{-}4\text{-}4)$$

Dividing Eq. (2-4-3) through by the constant E does not affect the maximization process but leads to the following symmetrical-looking expression to be maximized:

$$\frac{\left[\int_{-\infty}^{\infty} f(\tau)h(t_0 - \tau)\, d\tau\right]^2}{\int_{-\infty}^{\infty} f^2(t)\, dt \int_{-\infty}^{\infty} h^2(\tau)\, d\tau}$$

By Schwarz's inequality

$$\left[\int_{-\infty}^{\infty} f(\tau)h(t_0 - \tau)\, d\tau\right]^2 \leq \int_{-\infty}^{\infty} f^2(t)\, dt \int_{-\infty}^{\infty} h^2(\tau)\, d\tau \qquad (2\text{-}4\text{-}5)$$

[1] Schwartz, "Information Transmission, Modulation, and Noise," chap. 2.

with the equality holding if

$$f(\tau) = h(t_0 - \tau) \qquad \text{or} \qquad h(t) = f(t_0 - t) \qquad (2\text{-}4\text{-}6)$$

This provides the maximum value of the peak signal-to-noise ratio. A filter with this impulse response is said to be *matched* to the signal. In the frequency domain this corresponds to having

$$H(\omega) = F^*(\omega)e^{-j\omega t_0} \qquad (2\text{-}4\text{-}7)$$

with $F^*(\omega)$ the complex conjugate of $F(\omega)$. The time of occurrence t_0 of the peak value of the signal represents essentially a time delay term

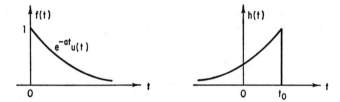

FIG. 2-4-2. An unrealizable matched filter.

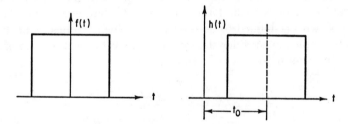

FIG. 2-4-3. A realizable matched filter.

which can be varied at will by adjusting the $e^{-j\omega t_0}$ phase term in the matched-filter characteristic.

Unfortunately, in many cases of interest the filter called for is physically unrealizable. As an example, let $f(t) = e^{-at}U(t)$, as shown in Fig. 2-4-2. Then

$$h(t) = f(t_0 - t) = e^{-a(t_0 - t)}U(t_0 - t)$$

as shown in Fig. 2-4-2. The impulse response in this case is nonvanishing for negative t, an obvious physical impossibility.

If $f(t)$ is a symmetrical pulse of *finite* duration, however, $h(t)$ is symmetrical also, and may correspond to a realizable filter. An example is shown in Fig. 2-4-3. Obviously, in the example above, realizability could also be obtained by regarding the exponential as truncated for some large value of the argument and choosing t_0 large enough.

The maximum S/N attainable using the matched filter can be readily calculated by substituting Eq. (2-4-6) into Eq. (2-4-3). This gives

$$S/N]_{\max} = \frac{\int_{-\infty}^{\infty} f^2(t)\, dt}{n_0/2} = \frac{2E}{n_0} \tag{2-4-8}$$

The maximum value of the peak signal-to-noise ratio thus depends only on the signal *energy* and the white-noise spectral density, *independent of pulse shape*. The peak detectability of a given signal pulse is thus independent of the signal shape if a matched filter is used in the receiver. (This will be generalized further in the binary decision case of deciding between two signals of arbitrary shape considered in the next section.)

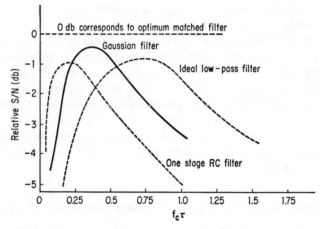

FIG. 2-4-4. Peak S/N for various filters, compared with matched filter (rectangular-pulse input).

In actual practice the exact shape of the matched filter is frequently of secondary importance, as noted previously, the proper system bandwidth being the crucial quantity. This has been shown for the case of a rectangular signal pulse embedded in white noise.[1] The matched filter then has the rectangular-pulse impulse response of Fig. 2-4-3, while its frequency-transfer function is of the (sin x)/x type.

Calculations of the output S/N ratio for a single RC network (the low-frequency equivalent of a single tuned circuit), a Gaussian filter (this corresponds to a large number of synchronously tuned amplifier stages), and an ideal rectangular filter indicate that there is little difference between these filters and the matched filter if the bandwidth is chosen properly. The results of these calculations are shown plotted in Fig. 2-4-4. The parameter f_c is the 3-db video bandwidth for each filter and corresponds to one-half of the r-f bandwidth. The quantity τ is the rectangular-pulse width. Note that all of these filters provide a peak

[1] Schwartz, *ibid.*, pp. 288–291.

signal-to-noise ratio within 1 db of that obtainable in the matched-filter case. The optimum r-f bandwidths are found to range from $0.5/\tau$ to $1.5/\tau$.

The Gaussian-shaped filter characteristic, corresponding to several cascaded and isolated synchronously tuned amplifier stages, can be seen to approach the optimum matched filter result to within 0.5 db. A rectangular pulse passed through such a filter emerges as a pulse of approximately cosinusoidal shape. This filter characteristic has been used in an experimental pulse-code modulation (PCM) system designed at the Bell Telephone Laboratories.[1]

A bandwidth choice of $1/\tau$ is also common practice in the design of pulse-search radars, where peak pulse detectability rather than pulse shape is the significant quantity.

The matched filter and practical approximations to it ensure maximum signal-to-noise ratio at the point of voltage sampling. However, in communications with strings of bits representing information transmitted, interference between successive bits or symbols presents an additional problem unless the filter responses decay quickly enough. A compromise may sometimes be necessary between a bandwidth chosen for optimum matched-filter detection on an individual-bit basis, and a bandwidth large enough to keep interference to a tolerable level. This point is discussed further in Chap. 7.[2]

2-5. Transmission of Two Known Messages of Arbitrary Shape[3]

We have discussed thus far in this chapter optimum decision procedures for binary transmission in the case where the signal is essentially a pulse of either one of two amplitudes or a repeated sequence of pulses of fixed amplitude. Alternatively, the material presented applies to samples of a given signal, sampled at prescribed times.

The discussion in the previous section has shown that the actual shape of a transmitted pulse carrying binary information is unimportant, providing a matched filter is used before the signal (plus noise) is sampled at its expected peak value, the decision circuitry in the receiver then basing its decision on the sampled voltage.

Now assume the binary information is to be carried by either one of two signals $s_1(t)$ and $s_2(t)$ of arbitrary and different shape. Examples

[1] L. A. Meacham and E. Peterson, An Experimental Multichannel PCM System of Toll Quality, *Bell System Tech. J.*, vol. 27, pp. 1–43, January, 1948.

[2] The problem of designing filters to minimize intersymbol interference is a significant one in the case of data transmission over telephone lines. A thorough discussion appears in W. R. Bennett and J. R. Davey, "Data Transmission," chap. 5, McGraw-Hill Book Company, New York, 1965.

[3] Kotel'nikov, *op. cit.*, chaps. 3 and 4; Helstrom, *op. cit*, chap. 4; Baghdady, *op. cit.*, chaps. 8 and 9; Davenport and Root, *op. cit.*, pp. 338–345.

would include phase-shift-keyed (PSK) and frequency-shift-keyed (FSK) signals commonly used in binary transmission. The PSK signal represents the r-f equivalent of bipolarity pulse transmissions. (Systems utilizing these signals are discussed in detail in Chap. 7.)

How do we "best" distinguish between the two signals if they appear embedded in Gaussian noise? Does any particular type of signal processing (PSK, FSK, on-off carrier, etc.) provide the best signal detectability, in the sense of minimum probability of error for given signal-to-noise ratio?

We shall find that the extension of the likelihood-ratio decision procedure to this case leads to results analogous to those of the previous sections. For simplicity's sake we shall treat in detail the case of white Gaussian noise only. The detection of binary signals in the presence of nonwhite Gaussian noise, considered in the references cited, leads to similar results.

The basic problem then is to find the optimum way to distinguish between either of two wave shapes $s_1(t)$ and $s_2(t)$, each defined over the bit interval T sec in length. The same interval length is used for processing at the receiver.

Since both signals are defined over the interval $0 < t < T$, we can expand each in terms of an orthonormal series, as discussed in Sec. 1-2. Either expansion then has the form

$$s_i(t) = \sum_{l=1}^{\infty} s_{l_i} \phi_l(t) \qquad i = 1, 2 \tag{2-5-1}$$

with the coefficients given by

$$s_{l_i} = \int_0^T s_i(t) \phi_l(t) \, dt \qquad i = 1, 2 \tag{2-5-2}$$

and orthonormality implying

$$\int_0^T \phi_l(t) \phi_j(t) = \delta_{lj} \tag{2-5-3}$$

We shall refer to the coefficients in the orthonormal expansion as Fourier coefficients for convenience sake, although the Fourier series is but one example of an orthonormal series.

The noise $n(t)$ can also be expanded in terms of an orthonormal expansion as in Sec. 1-2.

Thus

$$n(t) = \sum_{l=1}^{\infty} n_l \phi_l(t) \, dt \tag{2-5-4}$$

with

$$n_l = \int_0^T n(t) \phi_l(t) \, dt \tag{2-5-5}$$

Since $n(t)$ is assumed Gaussian, the Fourier coefficients n_l are Gaussian also. By proper choice of the orthonormal functions the coefficients can be made statistically uncorrelated and hence independent. As shown in Sec. 1-2, the condition for statistically independent Fourier coefficients in the case of Gaussian noise is given by the solution of the integral equation

$$\int_0^T R(t - s)\phi_l(t)\, dt = \sigma_l{}^2 \phi_l(s) \qquad (2\text{-}5\text{-}6)$$

Here $R(\tau)$ is the autocorrelation function of the noise $n(t)$, and $\sigma_l{}^2$ is $\langle n_l{}^2 \rangle$, the ensemble average of $n_l{}^2$.

In particular, as shown in Sec. 1-2, any set of orthogonal functions would be appropriate in the case of white noise, while for band-limited white noise the orthogonal set of $(\sin x)/x$ functions turns out to have statistically independent coefficients in the expansion, if $BT \gg 1$, with B the noise bandwidth. These coefficients are in fact obtained by sampling the noise $n(t)$ at intervals $1/2B$ sec apart.

The representation of both signal and noise by their respective orthogonal series enables us to replace the problem of comparing two *analogue-* type signals by their discrete representations in terms of the Fourier coefficients.

We now specialize to the case of white Gaussian noise, with two-sided spectral density $n_0/2$. The correlation function is $R(\tau) = (n_0/2)\delta(\tau)$, so that $\sigma_l{}^2 = n_0/2$, using Eq. (2-5-6). The ensemble mean-squared average of each noise Fourier coefficient is then just $n_0/2$. The probability density of each coefficient is given by

$$p(n_l) = \frac{e^{-n_l{}^2/n_0}}{\sqrt{\pi n_0}} \qquad (2\text{-}5\text{-}7)$$

Using the orthonormal representation over the T-sec interval of both the binary signal and the noise, we are now in a position to consider an optimum decision procedure in the receiver. For instead of dealing with the continuous time functions $s_1(t)$, $s_2(t)$, and $n(t)$ defined over $0 < t < T$, we can represent each by its Fourier coefficients. This will enable us to apply the Bayes likelihood test of Sec. 2-1.

Thus, with either $s_1(t)$ or $s_2(t)$ transmitted, the receiver voltage is given by

$$v(t) = s_i(t) + n(t) \qquad i = 1, 2 \qquad (2\text{-}5\text{-}8)$$

The receiver measures $v(t)$ over the specified interval $0 < t < T$ and is asked to make the "best" decision as to whether $s_1(t)$ or $s_2(t)$ was transmitted. (Note again the distinction between this case and that treated in the previous sections. There the receiver based its decision on the amplitude of the voltage sampled at n specified instants of time. The n numbers obtained were to be then processed in an optimum fashion. Here the decision is to be based on a knowledge of the voltage measured over the entire interval T, rather than at one specified instant of time or n such instants.)

With $v(t)$ given over the interval $0 < t < T$ the expression also can be expanded in the orthonormal Fourier series

$$v(t) = \sum_l v_l \phi_l(t) \tag{2-5-9}$$

All the information available about $v(t)$ is thus equally well contained in the Fourier coefficients. These are given by

$$v_l = s_{li} + n_l \qquad i = 1, 2 \tag{2-5-10}$$

depending upon whether $s_1(t)$ or $s_2(t)$ was transmitted. Since the noise coefficients n_l are Gaussian-distributed and independent, the v_l coefficients are also Gaussian-distributed and independent with density functions given by

$$p_i(v_l) = \frac{e^{-(v_l - s_{li})^2/n_0}}{\sqrt{\pi n_0}} \qquad i = 1, 2 \tag{2-5-11}$$

The statistical independence of the random Fourier coefficients v_l enables us to apply the Bayes likelihood test of previous sections. Thus, assume the a priori probability of sending signal $s_1(t)$ to be P_1, and that of $s_2(t)$, P_2. The receiver measures the voltage $v(t)$ over the interval $0 < t < T$ and from this measurement generates the Fourier coefficients v_l. It then decides that $s_1(t)$ was sent if

$$\frac{\prod_l p_1(v_l)}{\prod_l p_2(v_l)} > \frac{P_2}{P_1} \tag{2-5-12}$$

This decision procedure is guaranteed to result in the smallest chance of error, or the lowest error rate in the reception of $s_1(t)$ and $s_2(t)$.

The actual implementation of the decision is again best determined by taking the log of both sides of Eq. (2-5-12). This produces, with the use of Eq. (2-5-11), the following inequality:

$$\sum_l [v_l - s_{l_1}]^2 - \sum_l [v_l - s_{l_2}]^2 < n_0 \ln \frac{P_1}{P_2} \tag{2-5-13}$$

Note that because of the expansion of the signals and noise into their respective orthogonal series, with the noise coefficients *independent* Gaussian variables, we have been able to replace the seemingly difficult problem of decision between two arbitrary wave shapes by the likelihood-ratio procedure of the previous sections.

[If the a priori probabilities are not known, P_2/P_1 again can be replaced by the Neyman-Pearson parameter $k(\alpha)$.]

The geometric interpretation of this equation is again interesting: Assume n terms in the orthogonal series are significant. We represent the n Fourier coefficients of $s_1(t)$ and $s_2(t)$ by two points in an n-dimensional space.   The receiver voltage $v(t)$ is then expanded in an orthogonal series, and the n coefficients thus derived represent another point in this space.   If the a priori probabilities are equal, the decision is to pick as the signal the one lying closest to the measured receiver voltage.

An additional interpretation of the likelihood-ratio test, leading directly to a matched-filter method of instrumenting the decision procedure, is of interest: Recall that

$$v(t) = \sum_l v_l \phi_l(t) \tag{2-5-9}$$

and

$$s_i(t) = \sum_l s_{l_i} \phi_l(t) \qquad i = 1, 2 \tag{2-5-1}$$

Then

$$[v - s_i(t)] = \sum_l [v_l - s_{l_i}] \phi_l(t) \qquad i = 1, 2 \tag{2-5-14}$$

Squaring and averaging in time,

$$\int_0^T [v - s_i]^2 \, dt = \sum_l [v_l - s_{l_i}]^2 \qquad i = 1, 2 \tag{2-5-15}^1$$

We can thus replace the sums in Eq. (2-5-13) by the appropriate integrals, so that the likelihood-ratio test becomes

$$\int_0^T [v - s_1]^2 \, dt - \int_0^T [v - s_2]^2 \, dt < n_0 \ln \frac{P_1}{P_2} \tag{2-5-16}$$

For equal a priori probabilities, we then decide $s_1(t)$ was transmitted, with the smallest probability of being in error, if the difference between the measured voltage $v(t)$ and the known wave shape $s_1(t)$ is smaller than the corresponding difference between $v(t)$ and $s_2(t)$ in the mean-square sense.   This is one of the reasons for the great interest in least-mean-square error filtering.

We can now demonstrate that the actual decision procedure can be implemented by using two matched filters.   Expanding the squares in Eq. (2-5-16) and integrating term by term, we get

$$\int_0^T [s_2 - s_1] v(t) \, dt < \frac{n_0}{2} \ln \frac{P_1}{P_2} + \frac{E_2 - E_1}{2} \tag{2-5-17}$$

with E_1 and E_2 the energy in each signal.

$$E_i \equiv \int_0^T s_i^2(t) \, dt = \sum_l s_{l_i}^2 \qquad i = 1, 2 \tag{2-5-18}$$

We now construct two matched filters, one matched to $s_1(t)$ and the other

---

[1] We ignore questions of the existence of this integral and similar ones that follow. For white noise $\langle v^2(t) \rangle$ is infinite.   Limiting arguments may be used, or, as noted later, $v(t)$ may be assumed essentially band-limited.   See Davenport and Root for references on this subject.

to $s_2(t)$ so that

$$\begin{cases} h_1(T - t) = s_1(t) & h_2(T - t) = s_2(t) \\ h_1(t) \;\;\;\;\;\;= s_1(T - t) & h_2(t) \;\;\;\;\;\;= s_2(T - t) \end{cases} \quad (2\text{-}5\text{-}19)$$

Equation (2-5-17) then simply says that $v(t)$ is fed into both filters beginning at time $t = 0$ and that the outputs are compared at time $t = T$. If the output of filter h_2 is smaller than that of h_1 plus a given constant (or threshold), $s_1(t)$ is assumed to have been transmitted. Otherwise $s_2(t)$ is assumed to have been transmitted. The decision circuitry in this case is shown in Fig. 2-5-1.

Alternatively, the two filters can be combined into one, given by

$$h(t) = s_1(T - t) - s_2(T - t) \quad (2\text{-}5\text{-}20)$$

and the output of this filter compared with a threshold value given by

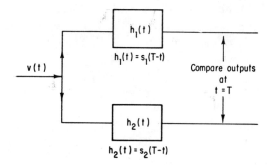

FIG. 2-5-1. Waveshape decision circuitry using matched filters.

the right-hand side of Eq. (2-5-17). In the special case of equal-energy signals, with $E_1 = E_2$ and equal a priori probabilities, the threshold level is zero. Positive outputs of the filter at $t = T$ imply $s_1(t)$ was transmitted, negative outputs imply $s_2(t)$ was transmitted. For the two filters of Fig. 2-5-1, the decision in this case goes simply to the one with the larger output.

The term correlation detection is also used for this type of optimum detector, since the filter operation corresponds to a correlation of $v(t)$ with both $s_1(t)$ and $s_2(t)$.

The analysis leading to a matched filter plus threshold decision procedure has assumed that the additive Gaussian noise is white, i.e., that it has a constant or flat spectral density over all frequencies of interest. As noted previously, the analysis can be extended to the more general case of colored noise by choosing an appropriate set of orthogonal functions for expansion. Alternatively, and more simply, the colored noise case can be handled by passing signal plus noise through a "whitening" or equalizing filter, which corrects the noise to white noise, and then carrying out the matched-filter decision procedure.[1] This leads to an overall matched filter of the Dwork type.[2] The orthogonal function approach also can be shown to lead to the Dwork-type matched filter.[3]

One previously noted special case whose analysis follows almost exactly that for the case of white noise is the case of band-limited white noise. Here the noise spectral density is flat over a range B cps wide and zero elsewhere. Thus, the one-sided spectral density is

$$2G_n(f) = \begin{cases} n_0 & 0 < f < B \\ 0 & \text{elsewhere} \end{cases} \tag{2-5-21}$$

The total mean-squared noise is $N = n_0 B$. As noted in Sec. 1-2 the orthogonal prolate spheroidal functions giving rise to independent Fourier coefficients in this case approach the $(\sin x)/x$ functions, if $BT \gg 1$, and the coefficients turn out to be related to the samples of $n(t)$ spaced $1/2B$ sec apart. If we assume both noise and signals over the interval T sec long to be band-limited to B cps, only $2BT$ terms are needed in the orthogonal expansions. The parameter l in the previous summation need therefore only range from 1 to $2BT$. We thus have as the expansion for $n(t)$ in this case, as noted in Sec. 1-2,

$$n(t) = \sum_{l=1}^{2BT} \frac{1}{\sqrt{2B}} n\left(\frac{l}{2B}\right) \phi_l(t) \tag{2-5-22}$$

with similar expansions for $s_1(t)$, $s_2(t)$, and $v(t)$.[4] The ensemble mean-squared values of the Fourier coefficients of the noise are again given by

$$\frac{1}{2B} \left\langle \left[n\left(\frac{l}{2B}\right) \right]^2 \right\rangle = \frac{n_0}{2} \tag{2-5-23}$$

The probability distribution of each Fourier coefficient

$$v_l = \frac{1}{\sqrt{2B}} v\left(\frac{l}{2B}\right)$$

of $v(t) = s_i + n$, $i = 1, 2$, is again given by Eq. (2-5-11); Eqs. (2-5-12) through (2-5-17) follow in identical manner, and we again arrive at a matched-filter decision procedure as the optimum one. This is almost an obvious conclusion, since by assuming band-limited signals we need only consider frequencies in the range B cps wide. Whether the noise also cuts off at B cps or continues on indefinitely therefore makes no difference in the result.

As a check in this case, it can be shown, upon time- and ensemble-

[1] Kotel'nikov, op. cit., pp. 42–43.
[2] B. M. Dwork, The Detection of a Pulse Superimposed on Fluctuation Noise, Proc. IRE, vol. 38, p. 771, 1950.
[3] Helstrom, op. cit., pp. 95–109.
[4] As noted in Chap. 1, $n(t)$ is constrained to have zero value at the sampling points $t = l/2B$ outside the range of interest $0 < t < T$.

averaging n^2 and using Eqs. (2-5-22) and (2-5-23), that

$$\langle n^2 \rangle = N = Bn_0 \tag{2-5-24}$$

as expected.

Probability of Error. The optimum procedure for distinguishing between two known signals $s_1(t)$ and $s_2(t)$, in the sense of minimum probability of error, has been discussed above. For band-limited signals and flat-frequency Gaussian noise, the decision procedure consists of passing the received voltage (signal plus noise) through two matched filters and comparing the output voltages at time $t = T$.

We would now like to evaluate the probability that an error will be made in such a decision process.

Assume for example that $s_1(t)$ is transmitted. What is the probability that the received voltage $v(t) = n(t) + s_1(t)$ will be mistaken for $s_2(t)$? This is just the probability that the inequality of Eq. (2-5-16) is *not* satisfied. The probability of an error occurring thus corresponds to values of v such that

$$\int_0^T [v - s_1]^2 \, dt - \int_0^T [v - s_2]^2 \, dt > n_0 \ln \frac{P_1}{P_2} \tag{2-5-25}$$

Since $v(t) = s_1(t) + n(t)$, this last inequality can be rewritten as

$$\int_0^T n^2(t) \, dt - \int_0^T [s_1 - s_2 + n]^2 \, dt > n_0 \ln \frac{P_1}{P_2} \tag{2-5-26}$$

Expanding the quadratic term and rearranging terms, we get

$$\int_0^T n(s_1 - s_2) \, dt < \frac{n_0}{2} \ln \frac{P_2}{P_1} - \int_0^T \frac{(s_1 - s_2)^2 \, dt}{2} \tag{2-5-27}$$

The probability of error is given by the chance that the noise $n(t)$ will satisfy this inequality. The integral to the left of the inequality is a Gaussian-distributed variable, since its value depends on the function $n(t)$ in any particular interval $0 < t < T$. Since $n(t)$ is Gaussian, the integral will be Gaussian also. (Any linear operation on a Gaussian variable, in this case multiplication by the known function $s_1(t) - s_2(t)$, and integration over the specified interval, produces a Gaussian variable also.)

This can be demonstrated quite simply by expanding both $n(t)$ and $s_1(t) - s_2(t)$ in their respective Fourier representations:

$$n(t) = \sum_l n_l \phi_l(t) \tag{2-5-28}$$

$$s_1 - s_2 = \sum_l [s_{l_1} - s_{l_2}] \phi_l(t) \tag{2-5-29}$$

Then, by virtue of the orthogonality of the Fourier functions,

$$\int_0^T n(t)(s_1 - s_2) \, dt = \sum_l n_l (s_{l_1} - s_{l_2}) \tag{2-5-30}$$

Since each n_l is Gaussian with zero average value, the weighted sum shown is Gaussian with zero average value also. Call this resultant Gaussian variable G. Its variance $\sigma_G{}^2$ is the sum of the individual variances and is given by

$$\sigma_G{}^2 = \langle G^2 \rangle = \sum_l \langle n_l{}^2 \rangle (s_{l_1} - s_{l_2})^2$$

$$= \frac{n_0}{2} \int_0^T (s_1 - s_2)^2 \, dt \qquad (2\text{-}5\text{-}31)^1$$

with $\langle n_l{}^2 \rangle = n_0/2$ and the sum replaced by the equivalent integral.

The probability distribution in G thus becomes

$$p(G) = \frac{e^{-G^2/2\sigma_G{}^2}}{\sqrt{2\pi\sigma_G{}^2}} \qquad (2\text{-}5\text{-}32)$$

From Eq. (2-5-27) an error will occur if

$$G < G_1 \equiv \frac{n_0}{2} \ln \frac{P_2}{P_1} - \int_0^T \frac{(s_1 - s_2)^2}{2} \, dt \qquad (2\text{-}5\text{-}33)$$

The probability of this occurring is then

$$\alpha = \int_{-\infty}^{G_1} p(G) \, dG \qquad (2\text{-}5\text{-}34)$$

This can be written in a normalized and instructive fashion by defining a parameter

$$a^2 \equiv \int_0^T \frac{(s_1 - s_2)^2 \, dt}{n_0/2} \qquad (2\text{-}5\text{-}35)$$

The probability of mistaking $s_1(t)$ for $s_2(t)$ then becomes

$$\alpha = \int_{-\infty}^{-Q_1} \frac{e^{-x^2/2} \, dx}{\sqrt{2\pi}} = \frac{1}{2} \operatorname{erfc} \frac{Q_1}{\sqrt{2}} \qquad (2\text{-}5\text{-}36)$$

with $\qquad Q_1 \equiv \frac{-G_1}{\sigma_G} = \left(\frac{a}{2} + \frac{\ln P_1/P_2}{a} \right) \qquad (2\text{-}5\text{-}37)$

The probability of mistaking $s_2(t)$ when transmitted for $s_1(t)$ can be written by analogy as

$$\beta = \int_{-\infty}^{-Q_2} \frac{e^{-x^2/2} \, dx}{\sqrt{2\pi}} = \frac{1}{2} \operatorname{erfc} \frac{Q_2}{\sqrt{2}} \qquad (2\text{-}5\text{-}38)$$

with $\qquad Q_2 = \left(\frac{a}{2} + \frac{\ln P_2/P_1}{a} \right) \qquad (2\text{-}5\text{-}39)$

---

[1] Alternatively, and more simply, we have $\langle G \rangle = \int_0^T \langle n(t) \rangle (s_1 - s_2) \, dt = 0$ and $\langle G^2 \rangle = \int_0^T \int_0^T [s_1(\tau) - s_2(\tau)][s_1(t) - s_2(t)] \langle n(\tau)n(t) \rangle \, d\tau \, dt$. For white noise, as assumed here, $\langle n(\tau)n(t) \rangle = R_n(t - \tau) = (n_0/2)\delta(t - \tau)$. Equation (2-5-31) follows directly.

The *overall* probability of error is then given by

$$P_e = P_1\alpha + P_2\beta \qquad (2\text{-}5\text{-}40)$$

as in Sec. 2-1.

Because of the symmetrical form of α and β, it is apparent that P_e depends only on P_1/P_2 and a^2. Some typical curves for the cases $P_1/P_2 = 1$ (then $\alpha = \beta$ and $Q = a/2$) and $P_1/P_2 = 0.1$ or 10 are plotted in Fig. 2-5-2.[1] Note that the curve for $P_1/P_2 = 1$ is identical with that of Fig. 1-3-3, relating probability of error in binary transmission to $A/\sqrt{N}$, the ratio peak of signal to rms noise. It is thus apparent that the parameter a, defined by Eq. (2-5-35), must reduce to the previously

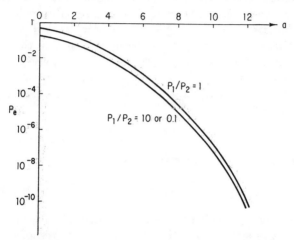

Fig. 2-5-2. Probability of error in decision between binary signals. (*From V. A. Kotel'nikov, "Theory of Optimum Noise Immunity," McGraw-Hill Book Company, New York, 1960. Fig. 4-1.*)

used parameter $A/\sqrt{N}$ in the case of sampling at one prescribed instant of time.

As a matter of fact, we shall show shortly that a^2 is expressible as a signal-to-noise ratio at the output of a matched filter and does reduce to A^2/N in the special case where the binary decision is based on one sample of a voltage as treated previously.

As noted previously the material of this section *extends* the previous results to the case of deciding between two arbitrary wave shapes, so that it should come as no surprise that Fig. 1-3-3 is contained as a special case of Fig. 2-5-2. Just as in previous sections where we considered detection on the basis of samples of known pulse-type signals only, various types of signals that could be used for binary transmission will result in the same

---

[1] These have been reproduced from Kotel'nikov, *op. cit.*, Fig. 4-1, p. 29. His parameter α corresponds to our $a/2$. Kotel'nikov discusses this material in detail on pp. 26–30.

performance, provided they have the same parameter a^2 and matched filter detection is used. (All of this is of course true only for Gaussian noise and should not be carried over to systems where other types of noise—burst-type or impulse noise being one important example—play a predominant role.)

The use of nonoptimum filters in place of the matched filters called for will result in some degradation of transmission in the sense of increased error probability. As noted in Sec. 2-4, however, this degradation normally will be small if the filters used are designed to have the proper bandwidths to accommodate the known signals.

Interpretation of Results. We have alluded to the fact that the key parameter a^2 can be shown to be related to a signal-to-noise ratio at the output of the matched filters. We shall now proceed to demonstrate this, tying this interpretation of the parameter in with the discussion of matched filters in Sec. 2-4.

Consider the signal $s_1(t)$ or $s_2(t)$, noise assumed absent, to be passed through a linear filter with impulse response $h(t)$. If the signal is s_1, the response at time $t = T$ is

$$\int_0^T s_1(t)h(T - t)\, dt$$

while if the signal is $s_2(t)$, the response is

$$\int_0^T s_2(t)h(T - t)\, dt$$

Since we are to distinguish between the two signals it would seem intuitively obvious to try to make the difference in the responses as large as possible. This is of course just $\int_0^T (s_1 - s_2)h(T - t)\, dt$.

The noise actually present produces at the output a mean-squared noise voltage given by

$$\frac{n_0}{2} \int_0^T h^2(t)\, dt$$

if white noise of spectral density $n_0/2$ is again assumed at the input.

Since we would like to distinguish between the two signals in the presence of this noise as effectively as possible, we should choose filter $h(t)$ to maximize the ratio of the difference in the signal responses to the rms noise at the output. Calling the square of this ratio the "effective" signal-to-noise ratio S/N we get

$$\frac{S}{N} \equiv \frac{\left[\int_0^T (s_1 - s_2)h(T - t)\, dt\right]^2}{n_0/2 \int_0^T h^2(t)\, dt} \tag{2-5-41}$$

But this is exactly the form of the signal-to-noise ratio of Eq. (2-4-3), so that using the matched-filter results of Sec. 2-4, the appropriate choice of

$h(t)$ to maximize S/N here is

$$h(t) = s_1(T - t) - s_2(T - t) \qquad (2\text{-}5\text{-}20)$$

The maximum value of S/N, assuming this matched filter, is just the parameter a^2:

$$a^2 = 2 \int_0^T \frac{(s_1 - s_2)^2 \, dt}{n_0} \qquad (2\text{-}5\text{-}42)$$

The matched filter obtained here is of course just the one obtained previously using the likelihood-ratio criterion [Eq. (2-5-20)].

The parameter a^2 can thus be interpreted as being the maximum possible S/N in the case of distinguishing between two known signals in the presence of Gaussian white noise.

It is also interesting that this matched-filter solution corresponds to minimum error probability and to the least-mean-squared error [Eq.

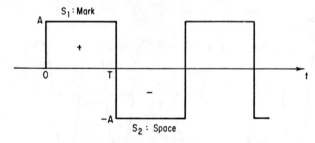

FIG. 2-5-3. Bipolarity pulse transmission.

(2-5-16)] as well as to the maximum S/N defined. In the particular case of Gaussian white noise all three criteria for distinguishing between the two signals in the presence of the noise lead to exactly the same type of decision procedure.

Examples and Applications. Consider the parameter a^2, upon which the probability of error depends, in more detail. Expanding Eq. (2-5-42), we get

$$\frac{a^2}{2} = \frac{E_1 + E_2 - 2 \int_0^T s_1 s_2 \, dt}{n_0} \qquad (2\text{-}5\text{-}43)$$

where $E_i \equiv \int_0^T s_i^2 \, dt$, $i = 1, 2$, represents the energy in either signal. Several cases are of interest.

1. Assume $E = E_1 = E_2$; $s_1(t) = -s_2(t)$

Then

$$a^2 = \frac{8E}{n_0} \qquad (2\text{-}5\text{-}44)$$

Note that this gives the largest possible value of a^2 and is the best we can do with fixed signal energies. As simple examples of such signals we have the bipolarity pulse train of Fig. 2-5-3 and its r-f equivalent, the phase-shift-keyed (PSK) signal of Fig. 2-5-4.[1] The PSK signal is given as

$$s(t) = P \cos(\omega_0 t + \theta) \qquad 0 < t < T$$

with $\theta = 0$ for a Mark (s_1) and $\theta = \pi$ for a Space (s_2).

For the bipolarity video pulse train of amplitude A, $E = A^2 T$, and for the PSK signal $E = P^2 T/2$ if $f_0 T \gg 1$.

2. Assume $s_2 = 0$, $E_2 = 0$.

This is then an on-off binary transmission system. An example is of course the on-off rectangular-pulse train of Chap. 1 and its r-f equivalent, the pulsed (on-off) carrier. In this case,

$$a^2 = \frac{2E}{n_0} \tag{2-5-45}$$

so that for the same signal energy E in the Mark interval, the on-off

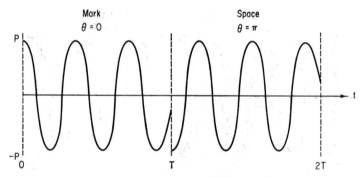

Fig. 2-5-4. PSK signal.

matched-filter system has an a^2 6 db less than the bipolarity system. Its probability of error is correspondingly greater, as is apparent from Fig. 2-5-2.

Alternatively, if the error probability is to be the same in both cases, the on-off matched-filter case requires 6 db more peak power than the bipolar signal in the Mark position and the average power required is 3 db more. This is of course consistent with the discussion in Sec. 1-3, in which on-off pulses of amplitude A and bipolarity pulses of amplitude $\pm A/2$ were shown to have the same error probability.

Both the bipolarity and on-off cases assume coherent detection and matched filtering. (Recall that the assumption of Gaussian noise requires coherent or synchronous detection.) Although the PSK system is thus 3 db better on an average power basis than the pulsed-carrier system, coherent detection is always necessary for recovery of the trans-

---

[1] The discontinuity shown at the end of the bit interval could be eliminated by choosing $\omega_0 T$ some multiple of 2π. The system filtering would also make the successive symbols blend smoothly into one another.

mitted information (Fig. 2-5-5). Envelope detection of the pulsed r-f (on-off) carrier is also possible, as noted in Sec. 1-5, although an additional loss of about 1 db, is encountered here (see Fig. 1-5-2).

3. $E_1 = E_2$, $s_1(t)$ and $s_2(t)$ orthogonal.

Then
$$\int_0^T s_1 s_2 \, dt = 0 \qquad \text{and} \qquad a^2 = \frac{4E}{n_0} \qquad (2\text{-}5\text{-}46)$$

This case is then intermediate between the two previous cases. One approximation to the orthogonal-signal case is the system of *frequency-shift keying* (FSK). (In practice noncoherent, or envelope, detection is used with FSK.) Here

$$s_1(t) = A \cos \omega_1 t \qquad 0 < t < T$$
$$s_2(t) = A \cos \omega_2 t \qquad 0 < t < T$$

with ω_1, $\omega_2 \gg 2\pi/T$.

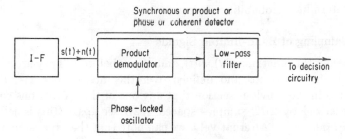

FIG. 2-5-5. Synchronous detection.

The carrier frequency is deviated between frequencies f_1 and f_2 every T sec, in accordance with the binary modulating intelligence. This can be visualized as a rudimentary form of FM signal, with $f_2 - f_1$ corresponding to the frequency deviation and $1/T$ the modulating frequency. The modulation index β is thus

$$\beta = (f_2 - f_1)T \qquad (2\text{-}5\text{-}47)$$

Actually in an FSK system $s_1(t)$ and $s_2(t)$ are not orthogonal unless f_1 and f_2 are both multiples of $1/T$. In that case $a^2 = 4E/n_0$, as noted above. It is possible, however, to obtain a somewhat larger value for a^2 (and hence smaller error probability) by choosing f_1 and f_2 appropriately.[1]

Thus, actually performing the integration called for by Eq. (2-5-42) and assuming $\omega_1 T$ and $\omega_2 T \gg 1$, we get

$$a^2 = \frac{4E}{n_0} \left[1 - \frac{\sin (\omega_1 - \omega_2) T}{(\omega_1 - \omega_2) T} \right] \qquad (2\text{-}5\text{-}48)$$

[1] Kotel'nikov, *op. cit.*, pp. 39–42.

The bracketed quantity has a maximum value of 1.2 for $(f_1 - f_2)T = 0.7$.[1] The "best" value of a^2 for the FSK case is thus

$$a^2 = \frac{4.8E}{n_0} \qquad (2\text{-}5\text{-}49)$$

and the corresponding modulation index is

$$\beta = 0.7 \qquad (2\text{-}5\text{-}50)$$

The three cases considered above, corresponding to three different types of binary transmission systems, with matched-filter coherent detection, indicate that most binary transmission systems would be expected to perform within a few db of each other if constant amplitude signals and Gaussian-type white noise could be assumed. (The extremely important cases of signal fading due to propagation vagaries and/or scatter phenomena and impulse-type noise are thus excluded.) With matched filtering or a practical approximation to this incorporated in the decision circuitry, it is the signal *energy*, rather than signal wave shape, that determines probability of error.

2-6. Sampling of Band-limited Signals

Consider the functions $s_1(t)$, $s_2(t)$, and $n(t)$ as before. They are assumed band-limited to B cps and defined over the interval $0 < t < T$. We indicated in the previous section that any one of these functions could be characterized by $2BT$ samples spaced $1/2B$ sec apart (this is called the *Nyquist interval*). Alternatively, we can note that the expansion of these functions into their respective Fourier sine series with $1/T$ as the fundamental frequency and B cps as the maximum frequency requires BT sine and BT cosine terms in the general expansion. Therefore the functions also can be characterized by $2BT$ unique Fourier-sine-series coefficients. The samples spaced $1/2B$ seconds apart are in effect the time-domain dual of these Fourier coefficients.

Both of these are examples of the very general statement that a band-limited time function defined over an interval T sec long can be completely characterized by $2BT$ independent numbers of pieces of information.[2]

---

[1] It may appear from Eq. (2-5-48) that a frequency spacing $f_1 - f_2 = 1/2T$ would provide orthogonal signals, in contradiction to the statement that f_1 and f_2 are both multiples of $1/T$. It can easily be shown that this rather peculiar result is critically dependent on the zero phase condition implied in the expressions assumed for $s_1(t)$ and $s_2(t)$. Letting $s_1(t) = A \cos(\omega_1 t + \theta)$ and $s_2(t) = A \cos \omega_2 t$ and then evaluating a^2, it is found that $a^2 = 4E/n_0$ only for $f_1 - f_2 = n/T$, n an integer, independent of θ. In practice, then, the frequencies would be chosen a multiple of $1/T$ cps apart if orthogonality were desired.

[2] Strictly speaking, a band-limited signal confined to an interval T sec long is physically impossible to attain. By proper filtering we can approach this condition as closely as we like. See the series of papers by D. Slepian, H. O. Pollak, and H. J. Landau, *Bell System Tech. J.*, 1961–1962, for detailed discussions.

The statement that $2B$ independent samples per sec will completely characterize a band-limited signal is often called the sampling theorem.[1] We shall demonstrate this theorem for the special case of a low-frequency signal confined to the range of 0-B cps. (See Black, *op. cit.*, and D. Linden, A Discussion of Sampling Theorems, *Proc. IRE*, vol. 47, pp. 1219–1226, July, 1959, for more general discussions.)

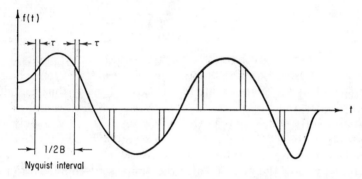

FIG. 2-6-1. Nyquist interval sampling.

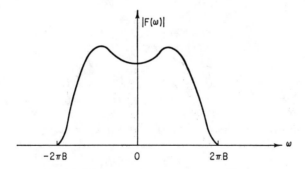

FIG. 2-6-2. Frequency representation of $f(t)$.

Thus, consider such a function $f(t)$ as in Fig. 2-6-1. Since $f(t)$ is assumed band-limited, its Fourier integral representation has the form

$$f(t) = \frac{1}{2\pi} \int_{-2\pi B}^{2\pi B} F(\omega)e^{j\omega t}\, d\omega \qquad (2\text{-}6\text{-}1)$$

$$(F(\omega) = 0,\ |\omega| > 2\pi B)$$

The Fourier transform $F(\omega)$, confined to the frequency range $\pm 2\pi B$, can be represented within this range by a Fourier series of base period

[1] H. Black, "Modulation Theory," chap. 4, D. Van Nostrand Company, Inc., Princeton, N.J., 1953. See also Schwartz, "Information Transmission, Modulation, and Noise," chap. 4.

$4\pi B$ (Fig. 2-6-2).   Thus

$$F(\omega) = \frac{1}{4\pi B} \sum_{k=-\infty}^{\infty} c_k e^{jk\omega/2B} \qquad (2\text{-}6\text{-}2)$$

where

$$c_k = \int_{-2\pi B}^{2\pi B} F(\omega) e^{-jk\omega/2B}\, d\omega \qquad (2\text{-}6\text{-}3)$$

Comparing Eqs. (2-6-1) and (2-6-3),

$$c_k = f\left(\frac{-k}{2B}\right) \qquad (2\text{-}6\text{-}4)$$

This indicates that given $f(k/2B)$, or $f(t)$ at the sampled points, we can construct $F(\omega)$ using Eq. (2-6-2) and from this reconstruct $f(t)$.   Samples of $f(t)$ spaced at the Nyquist interval ($1/2B$ sec apart) thus completely characterize the function $f(t)$.   This proves the desired theorem.

Note that if $f(t)$ is defined over the finite interval $0 < t < T$ only and is zero elsewhere,[1] only $2BT$ samples of $f(t)$ are required and only $2BT$ terms appear in the Fourier series for $F(\omega)$, as expected.

To actually show the way in which the samples are combined to reconstruct $f(t)$, we simply replace $F(\omega)$ in Eq. (2-6-1) by its series representation of Eq. (2-6-2) and integrate term by term.   This gives

$$\begin{aligned} f(t) &= \frac{1}{2\pi} \int_{-2\pi B}^{2\pi B} F(\omega) e^{j\omega t}\, d\omega \\ &= \frac{1}{2\pi} \int_{-2\pi B}^{2\pi B} \left(\sum_k c_k e^{jk\omega/2B} \right) e^{j\omega t}\, d\omega \\ &= \sum_k f\left(\frac{k}{2B}\right) \frac{\sin 2\pi B(t - k/2B)}{2\pi B(t - k/2B)} \end{aligned} \qquad (2\text{-}6\text{-}5)$$

If $f(t)$ is defined over the interval $0 < t < T$ only, we get the finite series

$$f(t) = \sum_{k=1}^{2BT} f\left(\frac{k}{2B}\right) \frac{\sin 2\pi B(t - k/2B)}{2\pi B(t - k/2B)} \qquad (2\text{-}6\text{-}5a)[2]$$

Note that the $\sin x/x$ series, mentioned in Sec. 1-2 as an example of an orthogonal series, appears here in a very natural way.

There is an interesting interpretation of this series representation of $f(t)$.   We shall show quite simply that we can instrument this reconstruc-

---

[1] This again violates the condition of a band-limited function, but we ignore this point. See the papers by Slepian et al., *op. cit.*, for a detailed discussion.

[2] $f(t)$ is then zero at the *sampling points* $t = k/2B$ outside the integral $0 < t < T$, but has nonzero values at other points outside the interval.   This is again due to the fact that both the band-limiting of $f(t)$ and limiting it in time to $0 < t < T$ are inconsistent.   However, as noted in Chap. 1, if $2BT \gg 1$, $f(t)$ will be expected to be small at all values of time outside the expansion interval $0 < t < T$.   See also the papers referred to previously by Slepian et al.

tion of $f(t)$ from its Nyquist samples by simply passing the successive samples through an ideal rectangular low-pass filter of B cps bandwidth.

Thus consider a typical sample $f(k/2B)$. Assume it has a finite width $\tau \ll 1/2B$ (Fig. 2-6-1). Its spectral representation is then very nearly that of an impulse of amplitude $\tau f(k/2B)$ and is given by

$$\tau f\left(\frac{k}{2B}\right) e^{-j\omega k/2B}$$

(The phase term results from the time delay $k/2B$.)

The impulse response $h(t)$ of an ideal rectangular low-pass filter of B cps bandwidth is given by

$$h(t) = 2B\frac{\sin 2\pi Bt}{2\pi Bt}$$

so that the response to the sample at $t = k/2B$ is

$$2B\tau f\left(\frac{k}{2B}\right) \frac{\sin 2\pi B(t - k/2B)}{2\pi B(t - k/2B)}$$

The total response to the $2BT$ samples is then

$$2B \sum_{k=1}^{2BT} f\left(\frac{k}{2B}\right) \frac{\sin 2\pi B(t - k/2B)}{2\pi B(t - k/2B)} = 2B\tau f(t)$$

from Eq. (2-6-5).

We have thus shown that $f(t)$ is uniquely represented by the $2BT$ samples and that it can be obtained from these by passing them through a low-pass filter.

As noted previously the $\sin x/x$ series of Eq. (2-6-5) happens to be an example of an orthogonal series. In particular, as noted in section 1-2, we have

$$\int_{-\infty}^{\infty} \frac{\sin \pi(2Bt - k)}{\pi(2Bt - k)} \frac{\sin \pi(2Bt - m)}{\pi(2Bt - m)} \, dt = \begin{cases} 0 & m \neq k \\ \dfrac{1}{2B} & m = k \end{cases} \qquad (2\text{-}6\text{-}6)$$

2-7. Decision-theory Approach to M-ary Signal Transmission

The principles of statistical decision theory were applied in Secs. 2-1 and 2-5 to the problem of binary transmission in the presence of white Gaussian noise. Specifically, we found in Sec. 2-5, using a minimum-probability-of-error criterion, that matched-filter or cross-correlation detection was the optimum way to choose between two wave shapes $s_1(t)$ and $s_2(t)$ defined over an interval T sec long. Intersymbol interference and possible signal amplitude fading or fluctuation were ignored (these are considered in Chaps. 7-9) and phase coherence was assumed to be maintained. (If a coherent phase reference is not available at the receiver, envelope detection is commonly resorted to. This too was discussed in previous sections. In the case of on-off carrier transmission, for example, the degradation in signal-to-noise ratio due to envelope detection as contrasted to phase coherent or synchronous detection is only of the order of 1 db. If phase stability between two successive binary intervals can be maintained, a prior symbol can serve as the phase reference for the one following. Differential phase-shift keying (DPSK), an example of such a scheme, is discussed in detail in Chaps. 7 and 8.)

It is also possible to use M-level or M-ary signal transmission. The M-level PCM system is an example of an M-level amplitude scheme.[1] The transmission of any one of M discrete frequencies (M-ary FSK) and any one of M phase positions (M-ary PSK) are other examples. If all the M levels are equally likely, it is apparent that $\log_2 M$ bits are being transmitted in the T-sec time interval, and it is thus possible to transmit correspondingly more information per unit time. However, the result may be a deterioration in signal-to-noise ratio (assuming a peak or average power limitation) and a corresponding increase in error rate. This is found to be the case for example for M-ary PSK and M-ary AM. In the case of M-level FSK the error rate can be decreased but at the expense of increased transmission bandwidth. We shall discuss these points in more detail later.

A geometric approach is frequently helpful in comparing these various systems analogous to the intuitive geometric items invoked in earlier sections. The M-level AM system can be visualized as a one-dimensional system, with signal points directly spaced along a line. For fixed average or peak powers, increasing M results in closer packing of these points and a corresponding increase in probability of error, as already noted. The M-ary PSK scheme corresponds to a two-dimensional system, with M points distributed over the 2π-radian range. (Combined amplitude and phase systems are also two-dimensional.[2] These are equivalent to simultaneous amplitude modulation of two carriers in phase quadrature with one another.[3]) It is apparent that closer packing of the signal points and hence increased probabilities of error are incurred when

[1] Schwartz, "Information Transmission, Modulation, and Noise," chap. 6.

[2] C. R. Cahn, Combined Digital Phase and Amplitude Modulation Communication Systems, *IRE Trans. Commun. Systems*, vol. CS-8, pp. 150–155, September, 1960; J. R. Hancock and R. W. Lucky, Performance of Combined Amplitude and Phase-modulated Communication Systems, *IRE Trans. Commun. Systems*, vol. CS-8, pp. 232–237, December, 1960. See also their later paper, On the Optimum Performance of N-ary systems Having Two Degrees of Freedom, *IRE Trans. Commun. Systems*, vol. CS-10, ˻ p. 177-184, June, 1962.

[3] C. N. Campopiano and B. G. Glazer, A Coherent Digital Amplitude and Phase Modulation Scheme, *IRE Trans. Commun. Systems*, vol. CS-10, pp. 90–95, March, 1962.

M increases here. The M-level FSK system, on the other hand, is M-dimensional and the points can be maintained at equal spacings as M increases.

To generalize the approach to M-ary transmission, we shall assume, by analogy with the binary case, M arbitrary signals $s_1(t)$ · · · $s_M(t)$, with a priori transmission probabilities P_1 · · · P_M, respectively. Any one of these is transmitted in a T-sec interval and is received in the presence of white Gaussian noise. We shall then find, just as in the previous case of binary transmission, that a matched-filter detection procedure is optimum in the sense of smallest probability of error. This extension to M-ary systems of the binary-transmission result, and the resultant probabilities of error calculated in certain special cases have been demonstrated frequently in the literature.[1]

To develop the optimum procedure for M-ary transmission we employ a generalized form of the Bayes procedure used in Sec. 2-1.

Recall that in the binary case with signals $s_1(t)$ or $s_2(t)$ we considered two a posteriori probabilities. For one sample of s_1 or s_2

$$P(1|v) = \frac{P_1 p_1(v)}{p(v)} \quad \text{and} \quad P(2|v) = \frac{P_2 p_2(v)}{p(v)}$$

Here v represents the voltage measured at the receiver. To minimize the long-run average error rate, we chose the higher probability. We thus decided to choose s_1 if

$$\frac{P(1|v)}{P(2|v)} = \frac{P_1 p_1(v)}{P_2 p_2(v)} > 1 \qquad (2\text{-}7\text{-}1)$$

This gave us the simplest form of the likelihood ratio.

Now consider the M signals $s_1(t)$ · · · $s_M(t)$, with a priori probabilities P_1 · · · P_M. At the receiver the voltage $v(t)$, consisting of one of the transmitted signals plus noise, is sampled and measured. Using the sampled value of v the a posteriori probabilities

$$P(s_j|v) = \frac{P_j p_j(v)}{p(v)} \qquad (2\text{-}7\text{-}2)$$

are calculated for *all* $j = 1$ · · · M. The decision as to which of the M signals was transmitted then goes to the $s_j(t)$ with the highest a posteriori probability. This again will ensure the smallest average error rate. This procedure is also equivalent to comparing all possible likelihood ratios and so is also called a maximum-likelihood procedure.

---

[1] Kotel'nikov, *op. cit.*, chap. 5; S. Rieger, Error Rates in Data Transmission, *Proc. IRE*, vol. 46, p. 919, May, 1958. An excellent tutorial discussion using a somewhat different viewpoint appears in E. Arthurs and H. Dym, On the Optimum Detection of Digital Signals in the Presence of White Gaussian Noise, *IRE Trans. Commun. Systems*, vol. CS-10, pp. 336–372, December, 1962. See also, S. W. Golomb (ed.), "Digital Communications with Space Applications," chap. 7, Prentice-Hall, Inc., Englewood Cliffs, N.J., 1964. Other references are given further in this section.

Assume each of the M signals lasts for T sec when transmitted. White noise of one-sided spectral density n_0 is again introduced during transmission and at the receiver. Repeating the procedure of Sec. 2-5 we expand each of the M signals, the noise $n(t)$, and the received voltage in its respective Fourier series of orthogonal functions; replace each continuous voltage by its Fourier components; and set up the multidimensional likelihood test as in Eq. (2-5-12) on all possible pairs of transmitted signals. Since the noise is Gaussian and the Fourier components of the noise are independent, a typical likelihood-ratio test reduces to the inequality of Eq. (2-5-13). The sums again can be replaced by integrals, and we finally arrive at the more general result that the signal $s_1(t)$ is assumed to have been transmitted, as an example, if the following inequality is satisfied for *all* other values of $j = 2 \cdots M$:

$$\int_0^T [v - s_1(t)]^2 \, dt - n_0 \ln P_1 < \int_0^T [v - s_j(t)]^2 \, dt - n_0 \ln P_j \qquad (2\text{-}7\text{-}3)$$

The same procedure can be applied to band-limited white noise, with the sampled voltages used in place of the Fourier coefficients and the $\sin x/x$ series as a particular set of orthogonal functions. The results are of course the same.

Expanding Eq. (2-7-3) we get as the rule for the decision that $s_1(t)$ was transmitted

$$\int_0^T v(t) s_1(t) \, dt + b_1 > \int_0^T v(t) s_j(t) \, dt + b_j \qquad (2\text{-}7\text{-}4)$$

for all $j > 1$ $(j = 2 \cdots M)$.

Here b_j is a constant bias given by

$$b_j = \frac{n_0}{2} \ln P_j - \frac{E_j}{2}$$

with $E_j = \int_0^T s_j{}^2 \, dt$ the energy in the jth signal. It is apparent that the implementation of Eq. (2-7-4) corresponds to using M matched filters, with impulse responses $h_j(t) = s_j(T - t)$. This is shown in Fig. 2-7-1. The outputs of these filters, with a constant bias b_j added in each case, are compared at time $t = T$, and the largest is chosen as the one corresponding to the transmitted signal. (The actual number of matched filters used can be reduced considerably depending on the signals $s_j(t)$ chosen. For example, in the case of M-ary AM, the signals are identical in shape, differing only in their amplitudes, or in the energy E_j.)

If all M signals are available at the receivers, the received voltage $v(t)$ can be cross-correlated against each $s_j(t)$ simultaneously [multiplying by $s_j(t)$ and integrating over the T-sec interval] and the outputs compared. This is of course formally identical to matched filtering.

As in Sec. 2-5 the probability of error P_e can be evaluated in a rather straightforward way. The resultant expression normally appears in the form of multiple integrals of correlated Gaussian variables and is of little help in obtaining numerical answers. We shall, however, consider some special cases for which results have been obtained. We shall refer interchangeably to either P_e or $P_c = 1 - P_e$, the probability of a *correct* decision. Since $\log_2 M$ bits are transmitted per baud (or base interval T sec long) in the case of equiprobable levels, it is apparent that the probability of error P_e in this section is *not* the same as the binary error probability discussed previously. We call P_e a *character* error, any one of

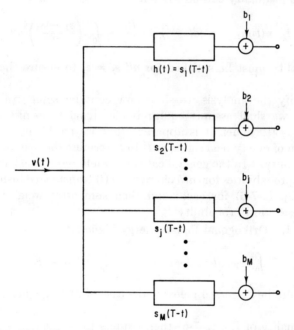

Fig. 2-7-1. M matched filters to implement decision procedure.

the M characters $s_j(t)$ corresponding to a string of bits. The relation between the character error P_e and the binary error P_b depends in general on the type of coding or character-bit transformation used. Arthurs and Dym[1] have however obtained the following bounds relating P_b to P_e:

$$\frac{P_e}{\log_2 M} \leq P_b \leq P_e \tag{2-7-5}$$

To find P_e, the chance of a character error occurring, we follow the procedure used in Sec. 2-5. Assuming $s_1(t)$ transmitted, an error will occur if any one of the $(M - 1)$ inequalities of Eq. (2-7-4) is not satisfied. Conversely the probability of a *correct* decision, given $s_1(t)$ transmitted,

[1] Arthurs and Dym, *op. cit.*, p. 359.

is the probability that the inequality of Eq. (2-7-4) is satisfied for *all* $j > 1$. This is readily found by writing $v(t) = s_1(t) + n(t)$. The inequality then appears in the form

$$\int_0^T n(t)(s_1 - s_j)\, dt > \int_0^T s_1 s_j\, dt + \frac{n_0}{2} \ln \frac{P_j}{P_1} - \left(\frac{E_1 + E_j}{2} \right) \quad (2\text{-}7\text{-}6)$$

Here $\int_0^T s_1 s_j\, dt$ represents the cross-correlation between the signals $s_1(t)$ and $s_j(t)$. Combining this term with the energy term a more compact form for the inequality can be written:

$$\int_0^T n(t)(s_1 - s_j)\, dt > \frac{n_0}{2} \ln \frac{P_j}{P_1} - \int_0^T \left(\frac{s_1 - s_j}{2} \right)^2 dt \quad (2\text{-}7\text{-}6a)$$

This inequality must be satisfied for *all* $s_j \neq s_1$ to ensure that no error will occur.

To simplify the analysis we shall now consider some examples. In these cases we shall assume equiprobable signal transmission so that $P_1 = P_j = 1/M$. Then it is apparent that we need only consider the transmission of one typical signal $s_1(t)$ to determine the overall character-error probability. In the general case one would have to calculate conditional error probabilities for *each* character $s_j(t)$ transmitted [using inequalities like Eq. (2-7-6) for each] and then sum after weighting by the appropriate a priori probability P_j.

Example 1. Orthogonal Equal-energy Signals.[1]

Here $\int_0^T s_1 s_j\, dt = 0$ and $\int_0^T s_j^2\, dt = E$

An example to be discussed below is the case of M frequencies spaced by $1/T$ cps.

The inequality of Eq. (2-7-6) then reduces to

$$\int_0^T n(t)[s_1(t) - s_j(t)]\, dt > -E \quad (2\text{-}7\text{-}7)$$

and this must be satisfied for *all* s_j if no error is to occur. [Compare with Eq. (2-5-27). Note that $-E$ is equivalent to the parameter G_1 used previously and defined in Eq. (2-5-33).]

The chance that this inequality is satisfied for *all* s_j can be determined by extending the analysis of Sec. 2-5. Thus consider the function

$$x_j \equiv \int_0^T n(t) s_j(t)\, dt \quad (2\text{-}7\text{-}8)$$

As in Sec. 2-5 this is a Gaussian variable with zero average value and

[1] Kotel'nikov; *op. cit.*, pp. 46, 47.

variance given by

$$\sigma_j{}^2 = \langle x_j{}^2 \rangle = \frac{n_0}{2} \int_0^T s_j{}^2(t)\, dt = \frac{n_0}{2} E \qquad (2\text{-}7\text{-}9)\,[1]$$

Thus

$$p(x_j) = \frac{e^{-x_j{}^2/n_0 E}}{\sqrt{\pi n_0 E}} \qquad (2\text{-}7\text{-}10)$$

Rewriting Eq. (2-7-7) in terms of x_j, no error will occur if

$$x_j - x_1 < E \qquad (2\text{-}7\text{-}11)$$

Assume x_1 has a value within the range $x < x_1 < x + dx$. The probability of this is just

$$\frac{e^{-x^2/n_0 E}}{\sqrt{\pi n_0 E}}\, dx$$

The probability that $x_j < x + E$ is

$$\int_{-\infty}^{x+E} \frac{e^{-x_j{}^2/n_0 E}}{\sqrt{\pi n_0 E}}\, dx_j = \frac{1}{2} \left[1 + \operatorname{erf} \left(y + \sqrt{\frac{E}{n_0}} \right) \right]$$

with

$$\operatorname{erf} x \equiv \frac{2}{\sqrt{\pi}} \int_0^x e^{-x^2}\, dx$$

and

$$y \equiv \frac{x}{\sqrt{n_0 E}}$$

The probability that the inequality is satisfied for *all* $(M - 1)$ values of j is then

$$\left(\frac{1}{2} \right)^{M-1} \left[1 + \operatorname{erf} \left(y + \sqrt{\frac{E}{n_0}} \right) \right]^{M-1}$$

Summing over all possible values of y (corresponding to all values of x_1), we finally get for the probability that s_1 is chosen correctly *when transmitted*

$$P_c = \frac{1}{\sqrt{\pi}} \int_{-\infty}^{\infty} e^{-y^2} \left[\frac{1}{2} + \frac{1}{2} \operatorname{erf} \left(\sqrt{\frac{E}{n_0}} + y \right) \right]^{M-1} dy \qquad (2\text{-}7\text{-}12)$$

In this particular example (equiprobable, equal-energy, orthogonal signals) this will be the same for any signal transmitted. The error probability is $P_e = 1 - P_c$.

As expected this result reduces to the one found previously in the binary case if $M = 2$ (Sec. 2-5). Note again that the error probability depends solely on the ratio of signal energy E to noise spectral density n_0. Numerical integration must be utilized to obtain curves relating P_c or $P_e = 1 - P_c$ to E/n_0. The integral of Eq. (2-7-12) has been tabulated for various

[1] See Eq. (2-5-31). We are again assuming white noise with one-sided spectral density n_0.

values of M and E/n_0 by R. H. Urbano, A. Viterbi, and others.[1] Curves relating P_e to E/n_0 can be found in Balakrishnan and Taber.[2] Other tabulations are referenced by A. H. Nuttall.[3] The following bounds on $P_e = 1 - P_c$, useful for computational purposes, have been obtained by Arthurs and Dym:[4]

$$\frac{1}{2} \operatorname{erfc} \sqrt{\frac{E}{2n_0}} \leq P_e \leq \frac{(M-1)}{2} \operatorname{erfc} \sqrt{\frac{E}{2n_0}} \qquad (2\text{-}7\text{-}13)$$

For $M = 2$, the binary orthogonal signal case, this reduces to

$$P_e = \frac{1}{2} \operatorname{erfc} \sqrt{\frac{E}{2n_0}} \qquad (2\text{-}7\text{-}14)$$

as in Eq. (2-5-36), with Eqs. (2-5-46) and (2-5-37) introduced, and assuming $P_1 = P_2$. [As noted in Sec. 2-4, E/n_0 represents the power signal-to-noise ratio γ at the output of a matched filter. See Eq. (2-4-8), where S/N is the *peak* signal-to-noise ratio, or 2γ. Then, for the binary orthogonal case, with orthogonal FSK as an example, we can write

$$P_e = \frac{1}{2} \operatorname{erfc} \sqrt{\frac{\gamma}{2}} \qquad (2\text{-}7\text{-}14a)$$

This result, as well as comparable ones for binary PSK and binary AM, is of course similar to those obtained in a more intuitive way in Chap. 1 for coherent or synchronous detection of binary signals. A further detailed discussion is presented in Chaps. 7 and 8.]

It would appear from the bounds of Eq. (2-7-13) that M-ary transmission of orthogonal signals results in an increased probability of error as contrasted with the binary case. As noted earlier however, the M-ary error probability refers to character error rather than bit error as in the binary case. As pointed out by Viterbi,[5] a meaningful comparison of M-ary transmission with the equivalent binary-transmission scheme indicates a *reduction* in overall message probability of errors as M increases. In particular, as M increases beyond bound, the overall probability of error can be shown to approach zero (assuming channel capacity is not

[1] R. H. Urbano, Analysis and Tabulation of the M Positions Experiment Integral and Related Error Function Integrals, AF Cambridge Res. Ctr., Bedford Mass., Rept. No. AFCRC-TR-55-100, April, 1955. A. Viterbi, in S. W. Golomb (ed.), "Digital Communications with Space Applications," chap. 7, p. 120.

[2] Error Rates in Coherent Communication Systems, *IRE Trans. Commun. Systems*, vol. CS-10, pp. 86–89, March, 1962.

[3] A. H. Nuttall, Error Probabilities for Equicorrelated M-ary Signals under Phase-coherent and Phase-incoherent Reception, *IRE Trans. Inform. Theory*, vol. IT-8, p. 308, July, 1962. (See his references [26], [52]–[55].)

[4] Arthurs and Dym, *op. cit.*, p. 350. Note that their N_0 is the two-sided spectral density, equivalent to our $n_0/2$.

[5] Viterbi, in "Digital Communications," chap. 7.

exceeded); but there is a delay at both transmitter and receiver proportional to M while the transmission bandwidth increases as $M/\ln M$. A curve of the character error P_e versus $\sqrt{E/n_0}$ for the special case of $M = 32$ is sketched as curve 1, Fig. 2-7-4[1] and is there compared with an equivalent binary scheme transmitting the same five bits in a given time interval. Note the improvement shown by the M-ary scheme. It is of interest to compare orthogonal M-ary with various types of binary transmission in more detail. This discussion follows. In large part we follow Kotel'nikov's approach.

As a specific example, Kotel'nikov considers the case of transmitting 32 equiprobable symbols or 5 bits of information in T sec. (This is just

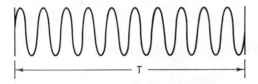

(a) One frequency of 32, signal lasts T seconds

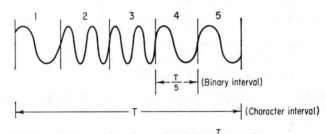

(b) Binary FSK: one of two frequencies, lasting $\frac{T}{5}$ seconds

Fig. 2-7-2. Equal-data-rate signals.

the telegraph problem.) The comparison is to be made on the basis of equal signal-transmission rates. Different methods of transmission will then be compared on the basis of bandwidth and signal-to-noise ratio (or probability of error). We shall have more to say about this later. Two methods are to be compared:

1. Use $M = 32$ orthogonal equal-energy signals. A specific example is the case of 32 different frequencies. The signals will be orthogonal if the frequencies are separated by integral multiples of $1/T$ and if $f_jT \gg 1$, with f_j the frequency (in cps) of any of the signals.

2. Break T up into 5 segments and transmit either of 2 binary orthogonal signals in each $T/5$-sec interval. A specific example is the use of binary FSK (Fig. 2-7-2).

[1] Kotel'nikov, *op. cit.*, p. 49, curve 1, Fig. 5-1.

Note that the 32 frequencies, each lasting T sec, require $16\!/\!_5 \doteq 3$ times the bandwidth of the two FSK frequencies, each lasting $T/5$ sec. (Fig. 2-7-3).

The analysis of the second (binary FSK) method follows directly from Sec. 2-5. Assume each of the two signals has the same amplitude. The average power will then remain constant and the energy will be equally distributed over the 5 subintervals in the T-sec period. The energy in any one subinterval will then be $E/5$ if the *total* energy over the T-sec

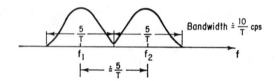

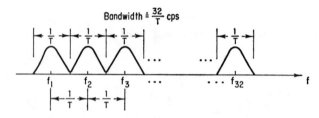

(a) Binary FSK: signal pulses last $\dfrac{T}{5}$ seconds

(b) 32-ary FSK: signal pulses last T seconds

FIG. 2-7-3. Comparison of required bandwidths, binary and M-ary FSK signals, equal data rates.

period is E. From Eq. (2-7-14), the probability that a signal in any *one* subinterval will be received *correctly* is

$$1 - \frac{1}{2}\operatorname{erfc}\sqrt{\frac{E}{10n_0}} = \int_{-\sqrt{E/10n_0}}^{\infty} \frac{e^{-x^2}\,dx}{\sqrt{\pi}}$$

The probability of error in the T-sec interval is then

$$P_e = 1 - \left(\int_{-\sqrt{E/10n_0}}^{\infty} \frac{e^{-x^2}\,dx}{\sqrt{\pi}} \right)^5 \qquad (2\text{-}7\text{-}15)$$

This is plotted as curve 2 in Fig. 5-1, p. 49, of Kotel'nikov and is reproduced here as curve 2 of Fig. 2-7-4. Note that for the same probability of error the 5-interval binary code requires 3.5 times the energy of the 32-orthogonal-signal case. There is thus an exchange of S/N and bandwidth. Here the exchange is about equal, the signal with one-third the bandwidth requiring 3.5 times the energy.

It is of interest to include in the comparison of equal-data rate signals, transmission via a 32-level PCM (32-level AM) system.[1] In the baseband case a variable-amplitude pulse, with the amplitude chosen from 1 of 32 possible values, is transmitted every T sec. In the high-frequency case a fixed carrier frequency is used and the amplitude is changed every T sec. It is apparent that the bandwidth required is approximately $1/T$ cps. Assume bipolarity signals are used with equal amplitude spacing to minimize the power requirements. In the baseband case the 32 levels are then equally spaced in the positive and negative direction. (The equivalent carrier is then actually a combined binary PSK 16-level AM signal.)

We shall compare this transmission scheme with the two FSK schemes considered above by first comparing it to a binary PSK system transmitting the same 5 bits/T sec. As noted in Sec. 2-5, binary PSK transmission ideally requires only half the signal energy and half the bandwidth

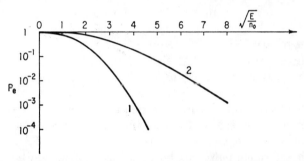

Fɪɢ. 2-7-4. Probability of character error for optimum transmission of 32 equiprobable signals. Curve 1—orthogonal signals. Curve 2—five binary signals. (*From V. A. Kotel'nikov, "Theory of Optimum Noise Immunity," McGraw-Hill Book Company, New York, 1960, Fig. 5-1, p. 49*).

of the coherent binary FSK method. The connection between these two then enables us to relate the M-ary AM to the M-ary FSK system.

To be specific assume the character-error probability, defined for the T-sec interval, is 10^{-5}. If the spacing of the levels in the M-level AM scheme is wide enough, errors will almost always be caused by (mistaken) transitions between adjacent levels only. Assume the spacing between levels to be given by $K\sqrt{N}$ ($K \gg 1$), with N the mean-squared noise. For equally likely levels divided evenly between positive and negative values, as assumed here, it is then readily shown that the average signal power is given by

$$S = K^2 N(M^2 - 1)/12 \qquad (2\text{-}7\text{-}16)^2$$

With fixed level spacing, the signal power increases, as expected, as the square of the number of levels.

[1] M. Schwartz, *op. cit.*, chap. 6.

[2] B. M. Oliver, J. R. Pierce, and C. E. Shannon, The Philosophy of PCM, *Proc. IRE*, vol. 36, p. 1324, November, 1948.

The chance of an error occurring, with $K \gg 1$, is exactly the same as that calculated in Sec. 1-3 when considering the transmission of on-off pulse sequences. In particular K corresponds to $A/\sqrt{N}$ in that section, with A the "on" pulse amplitude. From Fig. 1-3-3, then, $K = 8.5$ for $P_e = 10^{-5}$, and, from Eq. (2-7-16), $S \doteq 6100N$ for the $M = 32$-level bipolar case. For the equivalent binary bipolar case (signals lasting $T/5$ sec), with the same character error P_e, we have

$$P_e = 10^{-5} = 1 - [1 - P_b]^5 \doteq 1 - 5P_b$$
and
$$P_b = 0.2 \times 10^{-5}$$

Here P_b is the binary-error probability in any $T/5$ sec bit interval. For this binary-error probability we find the peak voltage/rms noise to be $A/\sqrt{N} = 9.3$ (Fig. 1-3-3). (Note that there isn't much change from $A/\sqrt{N} = 8.5$ for $P_b = 10^{-5}$.) The mean signal-to-noise power ratio is therefore $\frac{1}{4}(9.3)^2 \doteq 22$.

Since the binary PSK signals require $5/T$ cps bandwidth, or 5 times the bandwidth of the 32-level AM signals, the ratio of the average *signal powers* in the two cases is $6100/(5 \times 22) \doteq 55$. Here an increase of 5 in the bandwidth, in going from the 32-level AM case to the equivalent binary case, decreases the required signal power by a factor of 55. (This is an example of the *exponential* exchange between S/N and bandwidth common in wideband coded systems.) Using binary FSK signals, the bandwidth and signal power are both increased by an additional factor of 2 over the binary PSK case. Using 32-level FSK the required signal power can be reduced by a factor 3.5 over the binary FSK case, but with an additional threefold increase in bandwidth.

These results for this specific case of equal-data-rate transmission and for the given character error probability $P_e = 10^{-5}$ are summarized in the following table:

System	Bandwidth	Relative signal power
32-level AM	$1/T$	S_o
binary PSK	$5/T$	$\dfrac{S_o}{55}$
binary FSK	$10/T$	$\dfrac{2S_o}{55}$
32-ary FSK	$32/T$	$\dfrac{\frac{2}{3}S_o}{55}$

Example 2. Equicorrelated M-ary Signals.[1] As was pointed out earlier the optimum detection of M-ary signals embedded in additive

[1] Nuttall, *op. cit.*

Gaussian white noise is easily handled. The optimum detection procedure is given by the bank of matched filters in Fig. 2-7-1. Useful evaluations of the probability of error have, however, been obtained in only a few special cases. The second case to be considered (as a generalization of the orthogonal-signal case) is one in which all M signals are equally correlated. By correlation coefficient we mean the term

$$\int_0^T s_i(t)s_j(t)\, dt$$

defined for real signals. Specifically, then, we assume in this example

$$\int_0^T s_i(t)s_j(t)\, dt = \lambda E \qquad i \neq j \qquad (2\text{-}7\text{-}17)$$

and

$$\int_0^T s_i{}^2\, dt = E \qquad (2\text{-}7\text{-}18)$$

again assuming equal-energy signals.

Although this example is a rather artificial one normally (the common cases of PSK, FSK, and AM do not fit in), it at least represents a first approach to determining the effect of correlation on signal detection.[1] From Eq. (2-7-6) the probability of a correct decision in this case is

$$\int_0^T n(t)s_1(t)\, dt > \int_0^T n(t)s_j(t)\, dt - E(1 - \lambda) \qquad (2\text{-}7\text{-}19)$$

for all $j > 1$.

Note that the effect of λ here is to modify the energy E. [(Compare this with Eq. (2-7-7).] In fact the results obtained by Nuttall bear this out precisely.

The function

$$x_j \equiv \int_0^T n(t)s_j(t)\, dt \qquad (2\text{-}7\text{-}8)$$

is again a zero-mean Gaussian variable with variance

$$\langle x_j{}^2 \rangle = \frac{n_0}{2} E \qquad (2\text{-}7\text{-}9)$$

But there is correlation between the variables given by

$$\langle x_i x_j \rangle = \left\langle \int_0^T n(t)s_i(t)\, dt \int_0^T n(z)s_j(z)\, dz \right\rangle$$
$$= \int_0^T \int s_i(t)s_j(z) R_n(z - t)\, dz\, dt \qquad (2\text{-}7\text{-}20)$$

Since we are assuming white noise, $R_n(\tau) = (n_0/2)\, \delta(\tau)$ and

$$\langle x_i x_j \rangle = \frac{n_0}{2} \int_0^T s_i(t)s_j(t)\, dt = \frac{n_0 \lambda E}{2} \qquad i \neq j \qquad (2\text{-}7\text{-}21)$$

as might have been expected. As previously, the probability of a correct

[1] *Ibid.*, p. 312.

decision is then given by

$$P_c = \text{prob } [x_1 + E(1 - \lambda) > x_2, x_3, \ldots, x_M] \qquad (2\text{-}7\text{-}22)$$

It is apparent that the more negative we can make λ the greater this probability.

Without going through the detailed analysis suffice it to say that by appropriate coordinate transformations one may rotate the M-dimensional axes to produce a set of M *uncorrelated* Gaussian variables. It then turns out the resultant expression is identical with the one obtained for uncorrelated variables with $E(1 - \lambda)$ replacing E. The final expression for P_c is thus given by[1]

$$P_c = \frac{1}{\sqrt{\pi}} \int_{-\infty}^{\infty} e^{-y^2} \left[\frac{1}{2} + \frac{1}{2} \text{ erf} \left(\sqrt{\frac{E(1 - \lambda)}{n_0}} + y \right) \right]^{M-1} dy \qquad (2\text{-}7\text{-}23)$$

[(Compare with Eq. (2-7-12)] and all the comments made previously apply, with E replaced by $E(1 - \lambda)$.

It is of interest to find the *minimum* value of λ. (For $M = 2$ it will of course be -1.) Following Nuttall (*op. cit.*, p. 306), we note that

$$\int_0^T \left[\sum_{i=1}^M s_i(t) \right]^2 dt \geq 0 \qquad (2\text{-}7\text{-}24)$$

because of the square in the integrand. Expanding, we get

$$\int_0^T \left[\sum_{i=1}^M s_i(t) \right] \left[\sum_{j=1}^M s_j(t) \right] dt = ME + M \left(\sum_{j=2}^M \int_0^T s_j s_1 \, dt \right)$$
$$= ME + M(M - 1)\lambda E \geq 0 \qquad (2\text{-}7\text{-}25)$$

Then
$$1 \geq \lambda \geq -\frac{1}{M - 1} \qquad (2\text{-}7\text{-}26)$$

The minimum value of λ is thus $-1/(M - 1)$ $(= -1$ for $M = 2$ as a check), and this will give minimum error probability for this case of equicorrelated M-ary signals. It is apparent that for $M \gg 1$, there is no substantial difference between this case and the uncorrelated case treated previously.

The examples considered thus far have been those in which synchronous (coherent) detection is possible at the receiver. The noncoherent case can be handled similarly and leads, as might be expected, to matched filters followed by envelope detectors.[2] Various examples of M-ary systems, of both the coherent and noncoherent types, have been considered in the literature and the evaluation of probability of error versus

[1] *Ibid.*, p. 308.

[2] S. Reiger, Error Rates in Data Transmission, *Proc. IRE*, vol. 46, p. 919, May, 1958.

E/n_0 (or signal-to-noise ratio) carried out. Representative types with references following include:

1. M-level coherent PSK (Arthurs and Dym, *op. cit.*).
2. M-level differential PSK (Arthurs and Dym).
3. M-level noncoherent FSK (Arthurs and Dym).
4. M-level AM, coherent and noncoherent cases (Arthurs and Dym).
5. M-level equicorrelated signals, noncoherent case (Nuttall, *op. cit.*).
6. Combined AM and PSK M-ary systems (Cahn, *op. cit.*, and Hancock and Lucky, *op. cit.*).

Arthurs and Dym show curves indicating that increasing M introduces the most degradation in the M-level AM cases, with somewhat less degradation in the PSK cases. They consider system comparisons based on fixed signaling rate. (This is similar to Kotel'nikov's telegraph signal example considered earlier.) They also compare M-ary systems on the basis of bandwidth, noting that M-level FSK requires much larger bandwidths than the corresponding M-level PSK and AM.

Similar system comparisons on the basis of bandwidths or equal rates of transmission have been carried out by C. W. Helstrom in his paper, Comparison of Digital Communication Systems, *IRE Trans. Commun. Systems*, vol. CS-8, pp. 141–150, September, 1960. Various types of binary and M orthogonal signal systems are considered, and the effect of redundant coding is taken into account.

The Hancock and Lucky paper noted earlier, On the Optimum Performance of N-ary Systems Having Two Degrees of Freedom, *IRE Trans. Commun. Systems*, vol. CS-10, pp. 177–184, June, 1962, considers the optimum location of signal points in a two-dimensional space subject to a fixed power constraint.

Four level differential phase-shift keying techniques have been utilized by Collins Radio Company in their Kineplex data-transmission system[1] and by Bell Telephone Laboratories in their Dataphone system. Examples of M-level FSK systems developed for teletype use are given in a paper by D. B. Jordan, H. Greenberg, et al.[2]

[1] M. L. Doelz, E. T. Heald, and D. L. Martin, Binary Data Transmission Techniques for Linear Systems, *Proc. IRE*, vol. 45, pp. 656–661, May, 1957.

[2] D. B. Jordan, H. Greenberg, E. E. Eldrege, and W. Serniuk, Multiple Frequency Shift Teletype Systems, *Proc. IRE*, vol. 43, pp. 1647–1655, November, 1955.

CHAPTER 3

CW COMMUNICATIONS: COMPARISON OF
AM AND FM[1]

3-1. S/N Ratios in AM

Introduction. When comparing continuous-wave (CW) systems such as AM and FM it is difficult to set up and give meaning to the concepts of probability of detection and error rate, as has been possible with the binary systems and multilevel systems treated thus far. (The calculation of probabilities of error requires quantization or discrete levels of transmission.)

Instead we shall use here a less satisfactory although still useful approach: CW systems will be compared on the basis of S/N ratios at the receiver input and output. This will essentially hinge on a comparative discussion of the detection process: the envelope detector in the normal AM case, and the discriminator in the FM case. By comparing S/N ratios at the input and output of the detector in the two cases, we shall find that the wideband FM system of modulation produces the well-known S/N improvement with bandwidth, while in the AM system the input and output S/N ratios can at best be the same.[2]

This improvement with bandwidth in the FM case is characteristic of wideband communication systems, but the improvement obtained will be found proportional to bandwidth in the FM case (this holds true for

---

[1] D. Middleton, "Introduction to Statistical Communication Theory," McGraw-Hill Book Company, New York, 1960 and, J. L. Lawson and G. E. Uhlenbeck, "Threshold Signals," McGraw-Hill Book Company, New York, 1950, contain extensive discussions of both AM and FM.

[2] In the material to follow the reader is assumed to have a basic knowledge of AM and FM circuitry, bandwidth, and power requirements, etc. The S/N aspects at the input and output of the detector only will be stressed here. Those desiring a more detailed knowledge of the actual techniques of modulation and demodulation are referred to the literature. See, e.g., H. S. Black, "Modulation Theory," D. Van Nostrand Company, Inc., Princeton, N.J., 1953, or M. Schwartz, "Information Transmission, Modulation, and Noise," McGraw-Hill Book Company, New York, 1959. Both of these books also have a comparative S/N analysis of AM and FM but for the high S/N case only. Other aspects of AM and FM will be considered in Chaps. 4 and 5.

PPM and other analogue-type systems as well), rather than exponentially proportional as is the case with PCM digital wideband systems.[1]

The detection process in the FM case (limiter-discriminator combination) will be found to introduce an S/N threshold characteristic of wideband noise-improvement systems. Above this threshold the noise improvement is proportional to bandwidth as noted. Below this threshold the output S/N ratio deteriorates rapidly. The corresponding threshold effect in the case of binary transmission was noted in Fig. 1-3-3. There the analogue of output S/N was probability of error. Above a peak pulse-to-rms noise ratio of $A/\sqrt{N} = 8$, the error probability decreases rapidly. Below this value it increases prohibitively.

The S/N approach used here and in most of the literature is less general than the probability-of-error approach since the mean signal-and-noise power to be evaluated are determined from the second moments of the probability distributions. The approach will be even more restrictive in those cases where we are forced to consider the rather unrealistic situations of noise plus unmodulated carrier or a sinusoidally modulated carrier. The results obtained do bear out, at least qualitatively, known experimental results for CW systems. (We shall reference some work by Rice that considers both deterministic and random-type modulating signals in the FM case.)

Several alternative methods of analysis for both AM and FM detection will be considered, since the purpose here is also to provide some further insight into the handling of signal-and-noise problems.

The starting point of the analysis is based on the equations of narrow-band noise plus an unmodulated sinusoidal carrier at the i-f output, discussed in Secs. 1-4 and 1-7 and represented by Eqs. (1-4-4), (1-4-23), and (1-7-14). Thus the instantaneous voltage $v(t)$ measured at the narrow-band i-f output can be written

$$
\begin{aligned}
v(t) &= A \cos \omega_0 t + n(t) \\
&= (x + A) \cos \omega_0 t - y(t) \sin \omega_0 t \\
&= r(t) \cos [\omega_0 t + \theta(t)]
\end{aligned}
\tag{3-1-1}
$$

The in-phase and quadrature noise terms $x(t)$ and $y(t)$ are slowly varying Gaussian variables with spectral densities and cross-correlation functions given by

$$
G_x(f) = G_y(f) = \begin{cases} G_n(f + f_0) + G_n(f - f_0) & -f_0 < f < f_0 \\ 0 & \text{elsewhere} \end{cases}
\tag{3-1-2}
$$

[see Eq. (1-7-17)], and

$$
R_{xy}(\tau) = \int_0^\infty 2G_n(f) \sin (\omega - \omega_0)\tau \, df
\tag{3-1-3}
$$

[see Eq. (1-7-22)].

---

[1] Black, *op. cit.*; Schwartz, *op. cit.*

Here $G_n(f)$ is the two-sided spectral density of the noise $n(t)$ at the i-f output. As noted previously, $x(t)$ and $y(t)$ are independent Gaussian variables, since $R_{xy}(0) = 0$.

The envelope $r(t)$ and phase angle $\theta(t)$ are given, respectively, by

$$r = \sqrt{(x + A)^2 + y^2} \tag{3-1-4}$$

and
$$\theta = \tan^{-1}\frac{y}{x + A} \tag{3-1-5}$$

The AM analysis to be considered here will be concerned primarily with studying the properties of the envelope r: its moments, spectral distribution, etc. (Fig. 3-1-1a). This will enable us to study the effect of filtering at the detector output on the properties of both signal and noise. Some of this material has already been handled in Sec. 1-4 in discussing the probability distribution of the envelope [Eq. (1-4-26)].

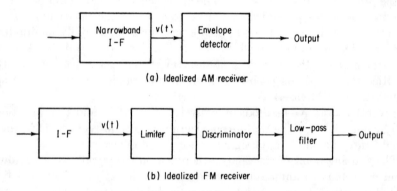

(a) Idealized AM receiver

(b) Idealized FM receiver

Fig. 3-1-1. Idealized AM and FM receiver.

In its most idealized form the FM-discriminator output will be considered to reproduce $d\theta/dt$, with $\theta(t)$ as defined in the simple case of Eqs. (3-1-1) and (3-1-5). This corresponds to ideal limiting at all signal levels and to the use of a perfect discriminator (Fig. 3-1-1b). Here too we shall discuss the spectral distribution of the noise at the discriminator output, mean S/N ratios at the output, etc. Alternatively, we shall consider the discriminator to be a zero-crossing counter, and show this apparently different interpretive model leads to essentially the same results.

In Sec. 3-8 we shall discuss a simplified analysis of S/N phenomena in FM receivers, due to S.O. Rice and based on a study of impulsive changes of $d\theta/dt$, that leads to a relatively simple understanding of threshold effects in FM. In Sec. 3-9 we consider FM threshold-extension schemes such as the phase-locked loop and the FM receiver with feedback.

Ideal AM Detector, Unmodulated Carrier. We assume the ideal AM detector to be an envelope-detection device whose output z is proportional to some power of $r(t)$:

$$z = r^n(t) \qquad (3\text{-}1\text{-}6)^1$$

The physical embodiment of this detector consists of a nonlinear device (usually a diode) followed by a low-pass filter. A common envelope detector is shown in Fig. 3-1-2. In a later paragraph we shall separate the two processes of detection and filtering to focus attention on the spectral distribution of noise at the detector output. The results obtained will of course be the same as those obtained in this paragraph.

The concept of S/N is of necessity ambiguous at the output of a nonlinear device because of the mixing of signal and noise terms. Almost any reasonably consistent definition of S/N will, however, lead to similar results, as will be noted later. For the time being we shall define the output S/N ratio S_0/N_0 as the ratio of mean-squared signal out, with the *noise set equal to zero*, to the mean-squared noise at the output. For the case of an unmodulated carrier of amplitude A [Eq.

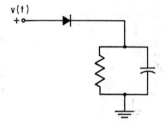

FIG. 3-1-2. AM detector.

(3-1-1)], the mean signal at the output of the envelope detector is just

$$S_0 = A^{2n} \qquad (3\text{-}1\text{-}7)$$

The mean noise power N_0 will in general have two components:
1. $n \times n$ terms—those due to the noise nonlinearly beating with itself.
2. $s \times n$ terms—those due to the noise nonlinearly mixing with the carrier (and signal when a modulating signal is present).

Because of the $s \times n$ terms we shall find the noise at the output to be in general greater than that at the input. This is a well-known characteristic of AM detection. The output S_0/N_0 will in general be a rather complicated function of the input carrier-to-noise ratio

$$\frac{S_i}{N_i} \equiv A^2/2N = \gamma$$

(N is again the mean noise power $\langle n^2 \rangle$ at the detector input). But we shall see that

$$\frac{S_0}{N_0} = \begin{cases} a_n \left(\dfrac{S_i}{N_i}\right)^2 & \dfrac{S_i}{N_i} \ll 1 & (3\text{-}1\text{-}8) \\[3mm] b_n \left(\dfrac{S_i}{N_i}\right) & \dfrac{S_i}{N_i} \gg 1 & (3\text{-}1\text{-}9) \end{cases}$$

The parameters a_n and b_n are constants of the particular detector [Eq. (3-1-6)] assumed.

---

[1] The proportionality, or detector, constant has been arbitrarily taken as 1. In the ratio of signal to noise to be taken later the detector constant cancels out.

In the small carrier-to-noise case the $n \times n$ noise terms will be found to dominate, leading to the quadratic relation shown, while for the large carrier-to-case the $s \times n$ noise terms dominate, leading to the linear relation.

The small S/N case demonstrates the so-called *suppression characteristic* of envelope detection:[1] for $S_i/N_i < 1$, the output S_0/N_0 drops more rapidly (quadratically in fact) with decreasing S_i/N_i. The S_i/N_i versus S_0/N_0 characteristic is thus asymptotic to the two lines shown in Fig. 3-1-3. The exact intersection of these lines will depend on the detector law assumed, but the slopes, or shape of the detector S/N characteristic, will be the same for all detector laws.

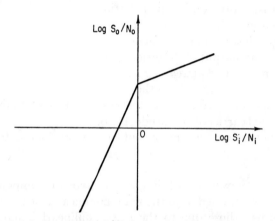

Fig. 3-1-3. Asymptotic S/N characteristics, envelope detector.

The high S/N result for an unmodulated carrier can be shown quite simply. The mean-squared envelope-detector output is

$$\langle z^2 \rangle = \langle r^{2n} \rangle = \langle [(x + A)^2 + y^2]^n \rangle$$
$$= A^{2n} \left\langle \left[1 + \frac{2x}{A} + \frac{x^2 + y^2}{A^2} \right]^n \right\rangle \qquad (3\text{-}1\text{-}10)$$

Expanding by the binomial theorem, assuming $A^2 \gg \langle x^2 \rangle$, $\langle y^2 \rangle = N$, averaging as indicated, and retaining just the largest terms, we find

$$\langle r^{2n} \rangle / A^{2n} \doteq 1 + \frac{2n^2 N}{A^2} \qquad (3\text{-}1\text{-}11)$$

(Recall that $\langle x \rangle = \langle y \rangle = 0$ and that x and y are independent.)

This says that with the magnitude assumed here ($A^2 \gg N$ or $S_i/N_i \gg 1$), r^{2n} has two terms: the signal term A^{2n} and the $s \times n$ noise term $2n^2NA^{2n-2}$.

---

[1] Middleton, *op. cit.*; W. B. Davenport, Jr., and W. L. Root, "Introduction to Random Signals and Noise," McGraw-Hill Book Company, New York, 1958.

The output S_0/N_0 is then

$$S_0/N_0 = A^{2n}/2n^2NA^{2n-2} = \frac{1}{n^2}\frac{S_i}{N_i} \tag{3-1-12}$$

For example, with $n = 1$ (linear envelope detector),

$$\frac{S_0}{N_0} = \frac{S_i}{N_i}$$

With $n = 2$ (quadratic envelope detector),

$$\frac{S_0}{N_0} = \frac{1}{4}\frac{S_i}{N_i} \tag{3-1-13}$$

The constant b_n of Eq. (3-1-9) is thus $1/n^2$.

The small S_i/N_i result is rather difficult to demonstrate straightforwardly, except for the quadratic envelope detector. We shall therefore resort specifically to ensemble-averaging, using the known probability distribution of the envelope to obtain the desired result. In the next section we shall repeat this using the spectrum approach.

From Eq. (1-4-26) the probability density of the envelope r is

$$p(r) = \frac{re^{-r^2/2N}e^{-S_i/N_i}}{N} I_0\frac{(rA)}{N} \tag{3-1-14}$$

First consider a quadratic detector, with $n = 2$ in Eq. (3-1-6), for simplicity's sake.

The second moment or mean-squared value cf the output of this detector is just $m_2 \equiv \langle r^4 \rangle$ and can be shown by integration to be[1]

$$m_2 = \sigma^2 + m_1{}^2 = \underbrace{8N^2}_{n \times n} + \underbrace{8NA^2}_{s \times n} + \underbrace{A^4}_{s \times s} \tag{3-1-15}$$

The $n \times n$ and $s \times n$ noise terms are those indicated, while the $s \times s$ term A^4 represents the mean signal output. Note that this detector provides particularly simple results, with the $n \times n$, $s \times n$, and $s \times s$ terms easily interpreted as such. Note the effect mentioned previously of an *increase* in noise power at the output when an unmodulated carrier is added to the noise. This is easily noticed on commercial AM receivers and as mentioned, is caused by the additional $s \times n$ noise term. (The $s \times s$ term shown here is a dc term and is normally suppressed in ac-coupled receivers.)

The entire S_0/N_0 characteristic, including the two asymptotes of Fig. 3-1-3, is readily obtained from Eq. (3-1-15). Thus, defining S_0/N_0, as previously, as the ratio of A^4 to the sum of the two noise terms,

$$S_0/N_0 \equiv \frac{A^4}{N_0} = \frac{A^4}{8N^2 + 8NA^2} = \frac{1}{2}\frac{(S_i/N_i)^2}{(1 + 2S_i/N_i)} \tag{3-1-16}$$

[1] Schwartz, *op. cit.* pp. 452–453.

For $S_i/N_i \gg 1$, $S_0/N_0 \doteq \frac{1}{4} S_i/N_i$, checking the result of Eq. (3-1-13). For $S_i/N_i \ll 1$, $S_0/N_0 = \frac{1}{2}(S_i/N_i)^2$, demonstrating the suppression effect. (These expressions will be rederived in the next section using a spectral approach.)

For any other detector type, with $S_i/N_i \ll 1$, the meaning of output S_0/N_0 becomes quite ambiguous and must be defined according to the particular application. For example, the output signal *voltage* might be defined to be the shift in dc level with the appearance of signal. Since the rms output voltage or standard deviation σ does not change too much in the presence of a small signal $(S_i/N_i \ll 1)$, the output signal-to-noise ratio can be defined in this case as

$$\frac{S_0}{N_0} \equiv \frac{(\langle r^n \rangle_{S+N} - \langle r^n \rangle_N)^2}{\sigma^2} \tag{3-1-17}$$

Here $\langle r^n \rangle$ represents the dc value or first moment for the nth-law detector. The subscripts refer to the signal-plus-noise and noise-only cases, respectively.

Alternatively, in the case of the linear detector the output signal voltage could be defined as proportional to the shift in the peak of the probability distribution due to the appearance of signal. Other definitions of output signal-to-noise ratio are possible. All, if interpreted, will show

$$\frac{S_0}{N_0} \propto \left(\frac{S_i}{N_i}\right)^2$$

for small S_i/N_i. This suppression effect, as noted previously, occurs because at low S_i/N_i the predominant noise terms are the $n \times n$ terms and these are *quadratically* larger than the signal term. (The $s \times n$ terms are linearly proportional to the input noise. These predominate at large S_i/N_i, giving rise to the linear relation between input and output S/N at high input signal-to-noise ratios.)

Mathematically, the quadratic variation shows up in the modified Bessel function $I_0(x)$ appearing in the probability distribution of the envelope of signal plus narrowband noise. The Bessel function is a quadratic in x for small values of x.

To demonstrate the suppression effect for any nth-law detector, consider the average value definition of Eq. (3-1-17):

$$m_1 \equiv \langle r^n \rangle = \frac{1}{N} \int_0^\infty r^{n+1} e^{-A^2/2N} e^{-r^2/2N} I_0 \left(\frac{rA}{N}\right) dr \tag{3-1-18}$$

$$= 2e^{-\gamma}(2N)^{n/2} \int_0^\infty x^{n+1} e^{-x^2} I_0(2\sqrt{\gamma}x) \, dx$$

by making a simple change of variables and defining $\gamma \equiv A^2/2N \equiv S_i/N_i$. The integral appearing can be evaluated directly in terms of the confluent hypergeometric function[1] and its properties investigated for various values of γ if desired.

For small γ, however, the desired suppression effect can be demonstrated readily by expanding the modified Bessel function. Thus,

$$I_0(2\sqrt{\gamma}\,x) \doteq 1 + \frac{(2\sqrt{\gamma}\,x)^2}{4} \doteq e^{\gamma x^2} \qquad \sqrt{\gamma}\,x \ll 1 \qquad (3\text{-}1\text{-}19)$$

For the small-signal-plus-noise case

$$m_1\Big|_{S+N} \doteq 2(2N)^{n/2} \int_0^\infty x^{n+1} e^{-x^2(1-\gamma)} e^{-\gamma}\, dx \qquad (3\text{-}1\text{-}20)$$

The *change* Δm_1 in first moments is then

$$\Delta m_1 \equiv m_1\Big|_{S+N} - m_1\Big|_N = 2(2N)^{n/2} \int_0^\infty x^{n+1} e^{-x^2} [e^{\gamma(x^2-1)} - 1]\, dx \qquad (3\text{-}1\text{-}21)$$

But for $\gamma \ll 1$, $[e^{\gamma(x^2-1)} - 1] \doteq \gamma(x^2 - 1)$

The change in dc level is then of the form

$$\Delta m_1 = c_n \gamma (N)^{n/2} \qquad (3\text{-}1\text{-}22)$$

with c_n a constant depending on the value of the remaining integral in x. Note the quadratic variation already appearing for $S_0 \equiv (\Delta m_1)^2 \propto \gamma^2$ or $(S_i/N_i)^2$.

In a similar manner it can be shown that

$$\sigma^2 \equiv m_2 - m_1{}^2 \doteq d_n N^n \qquad (3\text{-}1\text{-}23)$$

for small S_i/N_i.

The output signal-to-noise ratio as defined by Eq. (3-1-17) is thus given by

$$S_0/N_0 = K_n(S_i/N_i)^2 \qquad (3\text{-}1\text{-}24)$$

with K_n a constant depending on the particular detector type used. The constant K_n can be written explicitly as

$$K_n = \frac{\Gamma^2(n/2)}{4[\Gamma(n+1) - \Gamma^2(n/2)]} \qquad (3\text{-}1\text{-}25)$$

$\Gamma(x)$ is the usual gamma function, expressible for integral values of x in terms of factorial x.

3-2. Spectral Analysis of Envelope Detectors

We now consider the envelope-detection process in more detail. We assume it to consist of a nonlinear device followed by an ideal low-pass filter. For simplicity's sake the nonlinear device will be considered to

[1] G. N. Watson, "Theory of Bessel Functions," The Macmillan Company, New York, 1944; Middleton, *op. cit.*

be quadratic with output $y = v^2$. The variable v is again the output voltage of the i-f strip.[1]

Various approaches are possible in finding the spectrum of y when v contains both signal and noise components. The direct approach of expanding y in a Fourier series was utilized by Rice for both the square-law and half-wave linear detectors.[2] This direct technique is particularly appropriate where the i-f noise spectrum is of the rectangular bandpass form and provides results that are easily interpreted in that case.

For other types of noise spectrum and other detectors, the method becomes somewhat cumbersome, and the correlation-function technique is more readily utilized. Here the correlation function of the output variable y is found in terms of the nonlinear characteristic and the input correlation function, and from this the output spectral density found. We shall consider both techniques very briefly.

Fourier (Direct) Approach: Unmodulated Carrier. At the i-f output we have as previously, assuming an unmodulated carrier at first,

$$v(t) = A \cos \omega_0 t + n(t) \qquad (3\text{-}2\text{-}1)$$

The square-law device has as its output

$$y = v^2 = \underbrace{A^2 \cos^2 \omega_0 t}_{s \times s} + \underbrace{2nA \cos \omega_0 t}_{s \times n} + \underbrace{n^2(t)}_{n \times n} \qquad (3\text{-}2\text{-}2)$$

(Strictly speaking we should write $y = bv^2$, b a constant. Since we shall again take ratios to find S_0/N_0, we can assume $b = 1$.)

Note that the three types of terms, $n \times n$, $s \times n$, and $s \times s$, again appear explicitly. We shall consider these one at a time, finding the spectrum due to each and then superimposing to get the complete output spectrum.

The signal term consists of the dc quantity $A^2/2$ and the term $A^2/2 \cos 2\omega_0 t$ at frequency $2f_0$. The $s \times n$ term consists of all noise frequency components beating with the carrier and gives rise to sum-and-difference frequency terms. It is apparent that sum frequencies will be centered about $2f_0$ cps, while the difference frequencies will be low-pass frequencies extending from 0 to B cps. (The i-f bandwidth is assumed to be $2B$ cps.)

The $n \times n$ terms will contain a low-frequency contribution extending from 0 to $2B$ cps (the latter due to noise components at opposite ends of the i-f spectrum beating with each other), and a high-frequency contribution also centered about $2f_0$.

---

[1] Other nonlinear devices such as the half-wave linear detector, the general nth-law device, etc. are considered in Middleton, *op. cit.*, and Davenport and Root, *op. cit.*

[2] S. O. Rice, Mathematical Analysis of Random Noise, *Bell System Tech. J.*, vol. 24, pp. 96–157, January, 1945.

The total dc contribution is easily found by averaging Eq. (3-2-2) over y:

$$\langle y \rangle = \frac{A^2}{2} + \langle n^2 \rangle = \frac{A^2}{2} + N \tag{3-2-3}$$

(Recall that $\langle n \rangle = 0$, $\langle n^2 \rangle = N$.)

To find the spectral contributions from the $n \times n$ and $s \times n$ terms, assume the noise is band-limited white noise of spectral density n_0 with bandwidth $2B$ cps centered at the i-f frequency f_0, (Fig. 3-2-1).

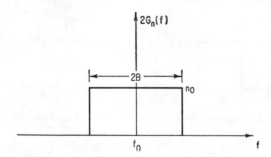

FIG. 3-2-1. One-sided spectral density of i-f noise.

The $s \times n$ contribution to the spectrum of y is found quite simply by considering the appropriate term in Eq. (3-2-2):

$$y_{s \times n} = 2nA \cos \omega_0 t \tag{3-2-4}$$

Writing $n(t)$ in the narrowband form

$$n(t) = x(t) \cos \omega_0 t - y(t) \sin \omega_0 t \tag{3-2-5}$$

$$y_{s \times n} = xA + \underbrace{xA \cos 2\omega_0 t - yA \sin 2\omega_0 t}_{\text{high-frequency terms}} \tag{3-2-6}$$

Consider the low-frequency contribution xA. This will just have the spectral form of the in-phase noise term $x(t)$ multiplied by A^2. As shown in Chap. 1 and again in Eq. (3-1-2) the two-sided spectral density of x, $G_x(f)$, is found by shifting the noise spectral density $G_n(f)$ down to dc. In particular, for the noise spectral density symmetrical about f_0, (implying a symmetrical filter transfer function), as is the case assumed here,

$$G_x(f) = 2G_n(f + f_0) \tag{3-2-7}$$

(see Fig. 3-2-2).

The low-frequency contribution to the two-sided spectral density of the $s \times n$ term is thus

$$G_{s \times n}(f) \bigg|_{\text{low}} = \begin{cases} A^2 G_x(f) = n_0 A^2 & -B < f < B \\ 0 & \text{elsewhere} \end{cases} \tag{3-2-8}$$

in this special case of band-limited white noise. The low-frequency one-sided spectral density (defined over positive frequencies only) is

$$2G_{s \times n}(f) \Big|_{low} = 2n_0 A^2 \qquad 0 < f < B \qquad (3\text{-}2\text{-}9)$$

Both spectral densities are shown in Fig. 3-2-3. As a check, the area under either curve is $2n_0 B A^2 = A^2 N$, while $A^2 \langle x^2 \rangle = A^2 N$ also.

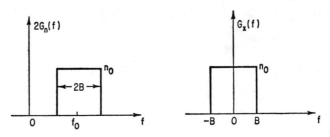

Fig. 3-2-2. Spectral density of total noise and in-phase component.

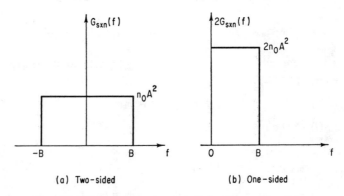

Fig. 3-2-3. Low-frequency spectral densities, $s \times n$ term.

Similarly, the one-sided $s \times n$ spectral-density term centered at frequency $2f_0$ is given by

$$2G_{s \times n}(f) \Big|_{high} = n_0 A^2 \qquad 2f_0 - B < f < 2f_0 + B \qquad (3\text{-}2\text{-}10)$$

extending $\pm B$ cps about $2f_0$.

The total one-sided $s \times n$ spectral-density term is sketched in Fig. 3-2-4.

Now consider the $n \times n$ contribution. This is given by

$$y_{n \times n} = n^2(t) \qquad (3\text{-}2\text{-}11)$$

For the rectangular bandpass i-f filter assumed we note that the output $n \times n$ spectrum will be triangular. Consider the Fourier-series representation of $n(t)$ given by Eq. (1-4-1).   We write this in the form

$$n(t) = \sum_l c_l \cos(\omega_l t + \theta_l) \qquad (3\text{-}2\text{-}12)$$

where $c_l^2/2 \equiv 2G_n(f_l)\,\Delta f$, $\omega_l = 2\pi l\,\Delta f$, and θ_l is random, as in Chap. 1. As in Fig. 1-2-1 the noise spectrum can then be represented by its line-spectrum equivalent.   This is also shown in Fig. 3-2-5.

The spectrum of $n^2(t)$ will be the result of each of the terms in Eq. (3-2-12) or in Fig. 3-2-5 beating with each other; it will give rise to difference frequencies extending from 0 to $2B$ cps and to sum frequencies

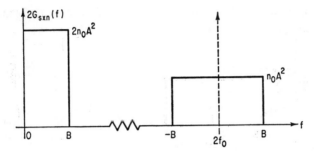

Fig. 3-2-4. One-sided spectral density, $s \times n$ term.

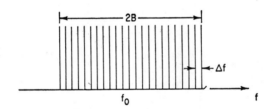

Fig. 3-2-5. Line-spectrum model of noise.

extending from $2f_0 - 2B$ to $2f_0 + 2B$.   The contributions to the lowest frequency Δf cps [aside from dc which we have already considered in Eq. (3-2-3)] arise from all adjacent noise-frequency terms beating with one another.   The total contributions at higher frequencies become smaller since they arise from noise components in Fig. 3-2-5 spaced further apart, and there are correspondingly fewer of these.   In particular, the highest low-frequency spectral term is at $2B$ cps, and, in the model of Fig. 3-2-5, is caused by the two outermost components beating with one another.   This accounts for the triangular-spectrum mentioned.[1]

The $n \times n$ spectrum thus has the triangular form of Fig. 3-2-6.   To

[1] The mathematical proof that the spectrum of $n^2(t)$ is triangular if $n(t)$ has a rectangular spectrum is simple but is delayed until the discussion of correlation functions in a later paragraph.

find the analytical expression for $G_{n \times n}(f)$ it suffices to find the power contribution at $f = \Delta f$. Squaring Eq. (3-2-12) and expanding, the contribution to $f = \Delta f$ comes from terms of the form

$$2c_l c_{l+1} \cos(\omega_l t + \theta_l) \cos(\omega_l t + 2\pi \Delta f + \theta_{l+1})$$

These give rise to power at the difference frequency Δf and the sum frequency $2f_l + \Delta f$.

Retaining the difference-frequency term only at this point (the high-frequency term can be handled similarly), this will be given by

$$c_l c_{l+1} \cos(2\pi \Delta f t + \phi_l)$$

with ϕ_l a new random variable. The *total* contribution at frequency Δf,

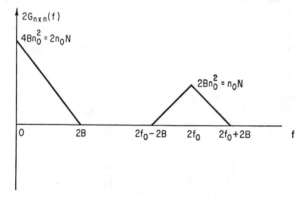

FIG. 3-2-6. One-sided $n \times n$ spectrum, quadratic detector (d-c is excluded).

found by summing over all values of l, is given by

$$y_{n \times n} \Big|_{\Delta f} = n^2(t) \Big|_{\Delta f} = \sum_l c_l c_{l+1} \cos(2\pi \Delta f t + \phi_l) \qquad (3\text{-}2\text{-}13)$$

Since the ϕ_l are *random*, the ensemble mean-squared value of $y_{n \times n}$ at Δf, or the total power at this frequency, is given by the sum of the individual power contributions. Letting $c_{l+1} \doteq c_l$, (this is exactly true in the limit as $\Delta f \to 0$).

$$\left\langle y_{n \times n}^2 \Big|_{\Delta f} \right\rangle = \sum_l \frac{c_l^4}{2} \qquad (3\text{-}2\text{-}14)$$

For the rectangular filter assumed, $c_l^2/2 = n_0 \Delta f$, and there are $2B/\Delta f$ terms in the sum. Then

$$\left\langle y_{n \times n}^2 \Big|_{\Delta f} \right\rangle = 4Bn_0^2 \Delta f \qquad (3\text{-}2\text{-}15)$$

The spectral density at $f = \Delta f$ is just $\langle y_{n \times n}^2 \rangle / \Delta f$, or

$$2G_{n \times n}(\Delta f) = 4Bn_0^2 = 2Nn_0 \qquad (3\text{-}2\text{-}16)$$

In the limit, as $\Delta f \to 0$, this gives the intercept shown in Fig. 3-2-6. (Note again that this excludes the dc contribution calculated previously.) The total video $n \times n$ noise out to $2B$ cps is $2Nn_0B = N^2$. The high-frequency contributions are found in a similar manner.

We now combine all spectral contributions to get the *total* one-sided output spectrum $2G_0(f)$ for the square-law detector, with band-limited white noise plus an unmodulated carrier assumed at the input. This is shown in Fig. 3-2-7.

Note that the relative size of the $s \times n$ and $n \times n$ contributions depend on the ratio A^2/N, as expected. If negative low frequencies were included and a two-sided low-frequency spectrum defined, it would be identical with the high-frequency spectrum shown.

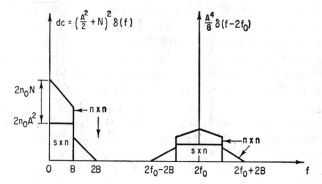

FIG. 3-2-7. $2G_0(f)$: total one-sided spectrum at output of square-law detector; band-limited white noise + carrier at input.

As a check on these results we can calculate the output signal-to-noise ratio S_0/N_0 and compare with the result of Sec. 3-1. Thus consider the *total low-frequency power* from 0 to $2B$ cps.

$$P_0 = \underbrace{\left(\frac{A^2}{2} + N\right)^2}_{dc} + \underbrace{N^2}_{n \times n} + \underbrace{NA^2}_{s \times n} \qquad (3\text{-}2\text{-}17)$$

This includes both signal and noise components. The signal output, if noise were absent, would be $S_0 = A^4/4$. (The signal in this case is just the unmodulated carrier of amplitude A, which appears as dc in this case. In the previous section we had $S_0 = A^4$. But there the quantity r^2 or the quadratic *envelope* detector output was considered. Here we have been considering $y = v^2$, with $v = r \cos \omega_0 t$, as the detector output. The low-frequency output is then $y = r^2/2$, accounting for the factor-of-4 difference in the *power* outputs. Since this factor appears in both the signal and noise terms, the S_0/N_0 ratios will be the same in the two cases.)   The mean noise power at the output is thus

$$N_0 = P_0 - A^4/4 = NA^2 + N^2 + N^2 + NA^2 = 2N^2 + 2NA^2 \quad (3\text{-}2\text{-}18)$$

(Compare with Eq. 3-1-15.)

The output signal-to-noise is thus

$$\frac{S_0}{N_0} = \frac{A^4/4}{2N^2 + 2NA^2} = \frac{(S_i/N_i)^2}{2(1 + 2S_i/N_i)} \quad (3\text{-}2\text{-}19)$$

as in Eq. (3-1-16).

This result obtained using spectral considerations thus checks the result obtained previously using the probability distribution.   Note however that this requires integrating out to $2B$ cps.   In the AM case the signal will occupy a bandwidth of B cps only, so that using the usual low-pass filter cutting off at B cps *decreases* the noise somewhat and *increases* S_0/N_0 from the value found above.   In particular, the $n \times n$ noise term is reduced from N^2 to $0.75N^2$.

With a modulating signal introduced the dc components can also be eliminated and S_0/N_0 (as redefined) improved further.

Sinusoidal Modulating Signal.[1]   The direct approach of evaluating the output spectrum and output signal-to-noise ratio can be applied readily to sinusoidal modulating signals.   Consider the voltage at the i-f amplifier output to consist an amplitude-modulated carrier plus noise:

$$v(t) = A[1 + mf(t)] \cos \omega_0 t + n(t) \quad (3\text{-}2\text{-}20)$$

$f(t)$ represents the modulating intelligence ($|f(t)| \leq 1$), and m the modulation index.   (We shall specialize to sinusoidal modulating signal shortly.)

At the output of the quadratic detector we then have

$$y = v^2 = \underbrace{n^2(t) + 2nA \cos \omega_0 t + A^2 \cos^2 \omega_0 t}_{\text{previous terms}}$$

$$+ \underbrace{2n(t)mf(t)A \cos \omega_0 t}_{\text{additional } s \times n \text{ term}} + \underbrace{2mf(t)A^2 \cos^2 \omega_0 t}_{\substack{\text{output signal term} \\ + \text{ higher-frequency terms}}} \quad (3\text{-}2\text{-}21)$$

$$+ \underbrace{m^2f^2A^2 \cos^2 \omega_0 t}_{\text{distortion and high-frequency terms}}$$

Assume low modulation index so that the distortion term is small.   (This could be included as an additional "noise" term if so desired.)   Then the effect of the modulating signal is to introduce the additional noise

---

[1] See Lawson and Uhlenbeck, *op. cit.*, chaps. 7 and 13, for an alternative treatment using correlation functions.   They obtain results for both the linear and quadratic detectors.

term
$$2n(t)mf(t)A \cos \omega_0 t$$
and the new *signal* term
$$mA^2 f(t)$$
(disregarding the additional signal term centered about $2f_0$).

In evaluating S_0/N_0 we shall now ignore the dc terms, previously considered to contain the output "intelligence." These are assumed to be filtered out of the output. (The unmodulated-carrier case considered previously was essentially an example of an on-off carrier system.)

To be specific now in further calculations, assume $f(t)$ is a sine wave at the highest modulating frequency B cps:

$$f(t) = \sin 2\pi Bt \qquad (3\text{-}2\text{-}22)$$

The i-f spectrum thus consists of the two sideband frequencies $f_0 \pm B$, the carrier at f_0, and band-limited white noise of spectral density n_0. (See Fig. 3-2-8. Note that in the figure the noise power spectrum is shown, while the signal frequencies appear in volts.)

Because of the symmetry in the signal sidebands and noise spectrum, the rms output noise due to each of the two sideband terms beating with the i-f noise will be the same. Each sideband term gives rise to a low-frequency rectangular noise spectrum extend-

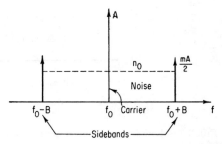

FIG. 3-2-8. I-F spectrum, sinusoidal modulating signal (noise in volts^2/cps, signal in volts).

ing from 0 to $2B$ cps. To derive the magnitude of this spectrum quantitatively we again use the Fourier-series representation of the noise:

$$n(t) = \sum_l c_l \cos (\omega_l t + \theta_l) \qquad (3\text{-}2\text{-}23)$$

$$\frac{c_l^2}{2} \equiv 2G_n(f_l) \, \Delta f = n_0 \, \Delta f$$

over the range $f_0 \pm B$ in this case. The instantaneous $s \times n$ component of the output y is, from Eq. (3-2-21),

$$y_{s \times n} = 2n(t)mA \sin 2\pi Bt \cos \omega_0 t$$
$$= mA[\sin (\omega_0 + 2\pi B)t - \sin (\omega_0 - 2\pi B)t]n(t) \qquad (3\text{-}2\text{-}24)$$

Consider the lower signal-sideband frequency mixing with a particular noise frequency f_l. This gives rise to an output noise component at the difference frequency $(f_l - f_0 + B)$ of amplitude $mAc_l/2$ and mean-squared value

$$\frac{m^2 A^2 c_l^2}{4} = \frac{m^2 A^2 2G_n(f_l) \, \Delta f}{2} = \frac{m^2 A^2 n_0 \, \Delta f}{2}$$

in the rectangular i-f spectrum case. The spectral density due to this term is thus $m^2A^2n_0/2$ and is shown in Fig. 3-2-9. The upper sideband term contributes the same noise in this case and is also shown in the figure. The total low-frequency spectral density is of course the sum of the two. The total additional noise introduced over the range 0–2B cps is thus $2Bn_0m^2A^2 = m^2A^2N$.

Assume at first that *all* low-frequency noise terms from 0 to 2B cps (excluding the dc contributions) appear at the output. Then the total output noise power is

$$N_0 = m^2A^2N + A^2N + N^2 = (1 + m^2)A^2N + N^2 \quad (3\text{-}2\text{-}25)$$

The first term is the $s \times n$ term due to the modulating signal beating with

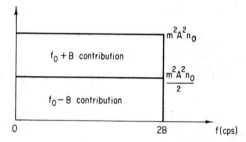

FIG. 3-2-9. Low-frequency noise spectrum due to mixing of sinusoidal modulation and i-f noise.

the noise, the second term, as previously, results from the carrier beating with the noise, and the third term is again the $n \times n$ term.

Note that if $m^2 \ll 1$ (low modulation index) the sideband-noise power term is negligible compared with the carrier-noise term, and the output noise is essentially the same as for the unmodulated-carrier case.

To be somewhat more realistic assume all frequency components above B cps are suppressed. The output noise is again reduced somewhat and becomes

$$N_0 = 0.75N^2 + A^2N + 0.5m^2A^2N \doteq 0.75N^2 + A^2N \quad m^2 \ll 1 \quad (3\text{-}2\text{-}26)$$

The output-signal power at frequency B is, from the signal term in Eq. (3-2-21),

$$S_0 = \frac{m^2A^4}{2} \quad (3\text{-}2\text{-}27)$$

The output signal-to-noise ratio is then the ratio of Eqs. (3-2-27) to (3-2-26). The comparison of the output and input signal-to-noise ratios is somewhat ambiguous here since we can use for the input ratio either the carrier-to-noise ratio $A^2/2N$ or the signal-to-noise ratio $m^2A^2/2N$.

Either comparison results in the same type of S_0/N_0 versus S_i/N_i behavior described previously. For large S_i/N_i the output is linearly proportional to the input, for small S_i/N_i there is a quadratic dependence. In either case the suppression effect results from the *carrier* amplitude A sinking below the rms input noise $\sqrt{N}$. So it is the *carrier*-to-noise ratio that is crucial in determining the output S/N characteristics. The input signal amplitude is, however, directly proportional to A.

Note that the output S/N ratio has no explicit dependence on bandwidth as will be shown to be the case with FM in Sec. 3-4. In wideband PCM and FM systems the output S/N can be improved by widening the transmission bandwidths. Widening the AM bandwidth leads to additional noise, however, and the possibility of interference from adjacent channels. The bandwidth is thus chosen as large as necessary to accommodate the signals transmitted and *no larger*.[1]

3-3. Correlation-function Method of Determining Power Spectrum[2]

We shall demonstrate the correlation-function method of obtaining output spectra by considering noise $n(t)$ only applied to a quadratic detector. The output is then $n^2(t)$ and corresponds to the $n \times n$ term considered in previous sections. Further details, and generalizations to more complicated situations, can be found in the references cited. We shall use the correlation-function technique further in discussing the spectrum of FM noise in the sections following.

The correlation-function method of finding the power spectrum is based on the fact that the autocorrelation function $R(\tau)$ and spectral density $G(f)$ of a stationary random process constitute a Fourier-transform pair (Sec. 1-1). In particular, by calculating the autocorrelation function $R_{n^2}(\tau)$ of the noise at the quadratic detector output we can then proceed to find the spectral density $G_{0_{n \times n}}(f)$.

The desired autocorrelation function is defined as the ensemble average

$$R_{n^2}(\tau) \equiv \langle n^2(t) n^2(t + \tau) \rangle \qquad (3\text{-}3\text{-}1)$$

The ensemble average indicated can be formally written as

$$\langle n_1{}^2 n_2{}^2 \rangle = \int_{-\infty}^{\infty} \int_{-\infty}^{\infty} n_1{}^2 n_2{}^2 p(n_1, n_2)\, dn_1\, dn_2 \qquad (3\text{-}3\text{-}2)$$

with $\qquad n_1 \equiv n(t) \qquad$ and $\qquad n_2 \equiv n(t + \tau)$

and $p(n_1, n_2)$ the bivariate Gaussian distribution discussed in Chap. 1. The integration of Eq. (3-3-2), although not difficult, is however, rather

[1] See Davenport and Root, *op. cit.*, p. 265, for a signal-to-noise analysis of the double-sideband, suppressed-carrier system.

[2] Davenport and Root, *op. cit.*, chap. 12; Lawson and Uhlenbeck, *op. cit.*, chap. 7; Rice, *op. cit.*; Middleton, *op. cit.*

tedious.   Instead it is much simpler to find the desired ensemble average by appropriate differentiation of the characteristic function.[1]

The characteristic function $G_{12}(z_1,z_2)$ of two variables z_1 and z_2 is defined as the ensemble average $\langle [e^{i(z_1 n_1 + z_2 n_2)}] \rangle$.

$$G_{12}(z_1,z_2) \equiv \langle [e^{i(z_1 n_1 + z_2 n_2)}] \rangle \tag{3-3-3}$$

$$= \int_{-\infty}^{\infty} \int_{-\infty}^{\infty} e^{i(z_1 n_1 + z_2 n_2)} p(n_1,n_2) \, dn_1 dn_2$$

The definition can be extended to any number of variables so that the characteristic function (c.f.) also can be considered the complex conjugate of the Fourier transform of the multivariate distribution.   For the multivariate Gaussian distribution the c.f. takes on the Gaussian form also. In particular, for the bivariate distribution with zero average value of the variable $(m_{10} = \langle n_1 \rangle = \langle n_2 \rangle = 0)$

$$G_{12}(z_1,z_2) = e^{-\frac{1}{2} \sum_{s=1}^{2} \sum_{r=1}^{2} \mu_{rs} z_r z_s} \tag{3-3-4}$$

The μ_{rs} constants are the central moments given by

$$\left\{ \begin{aligned} \mu_{11} &\equiv \langle (n_1 - m_{10})^2 \rangle = \langle n_1^2 \rangle = N \\ \mu_{22} &\equiv \langle n_2^2 \rangle = N \\ \mu_{12} &\equiv \langle n_1 n_2 \rangle = R_n(\tau) = \mu_{21} \end{aligned} \right\} \tag{3-3-5}$$

The quantity $R_n(\tau)$ is the autocorrelation function of the input noise $n(t)$.

The various moments of n_1 and n_2 can be found by appropriate differentiation of $G_{12}(z_1,z_2)$.   This is apparent from Eq. (3-3-3).   Thus, differentiating Eq. (3-3-3) twice with respect to z_1 and twice with respect to z_2 and then setting $z_1 = z_2 = 0$,

$$\frac{\partial^4 G_{12}}{\partial z_1^2 \partial z_2^2} \bigg|_{z_1,z_2=0} = \int_{-\infty}^{\infty} \int_{-\infty}^{\infty} n_1^2 n_2^2 p(n_1,n_2) \, dn_1 \, dn_2 = \langle n_1^2 n_2^2 \rangle \tag{3-3-6}$$

Other moments may be found similarly.   From Eq. (3-3-4),

$$\frac{\partial^4 G_{12}}{\partial z_1^2 \partial z_2^2} \bigg|_{z_1,z_2=0} = \mu_{11}\mu_{22} + 2\mu_{12}\mu_{21} \tag{3-3-7}$$

Using Eq. (3-3-5), we get finally

$$\langle n_1^2 n_2^2 \rangle = N^2 + 2R_n^2(\tau) \tag{3-3-8}$$

The first term N^2 is just the dc contribution to the output spectrum. ($\langle y \rangle = \langle n^2 \rangle = N$ is the dc *voltage* at the output of the quadratic detector, and $\langle y \rangle^2 = N^2$ is the dc power contribution.)   It gives rise to the delta function $N^2 \delta(f)$ in the output power spectrum.

The continuous spectral density is obtained from the second term

[1] Schwartz, *op. cit.*; Davenport and Root, *op. cit.*; A. Papoulis, "Probability Random Variables, and Stochastic Processes," McGraw-Hill Book Company, New York, 1965.

$2R_n{}^2(\tau)$. Thus the two-sided spectral density $G_{0n\times n}(f)$ is given by

$$G_{0_{n\times n}}(f) = \int_{-\infty}^{\infty} R_{n^2}(\tau)e^{-j\omega\tau}\,d\tau$$

$$= 2\int_{-\infty}^{\infty} R_{n^2}(\tau)e^{-j\omega\tau}\,d\tau + N^2\,\delta(f) \qquad (3\text{-}3\text{-}9)$$

But recall that

$$R_n(\tau) = \int_{-\infty}^{\infty} G_n(f)e^{j\omega\tau}\,df \qquad (3\text{-}3\text{-}10)$$

with $G_n(f)$ the two-sided spectral density of the noise at the detector input (the i-f spectrum).

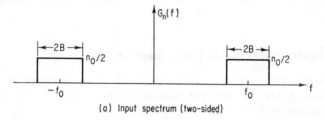

(a) Input spectrum (two-sided)

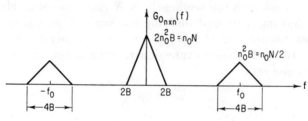

(b) Output spectrum (two sided)

FIG. 3-3-1. Noise spectrum at quadratic detector output obtained by convolution (excluding d-c term).

It is then readily established that the spectral density at the *quadratic detector output* (excluding dc) is given by the following convolution-type integral:[1]

$$G_{0_{n\times n}}(f) = 2\int_{-\infty}^{\infty} G_n(f')G_n(f - f')\,df' \qquad (3\text{-}3\text{-}11)$$

[1] Consider two functions $f_1(t)$ and $f_2(t)$ with respective Fourier transforms $F_1(\omega)$ and $F_2(\omega)$. Then, if $F(\omega) = F_1F_2$, the convolution integral gives

$$f(t) = \int_{-\infty}^{\infty} f_1(\tau)f_2(t - \tau)\,d\tau$$

with $f(t)$ the inverse Fourier transform of $F(\omega)$. In particular, let $F_1 = F_2$; that is, $F = F_1{}^2$. Then

$$f(t) = \int_{-\infty}^{\infty} f_1(\tau)f_1(t - \tau)\,d\tau$$

Now substitute $R_n(\tau)$ for $F_1(\omega)$ and $G_n(f)$ for $f_1(t)$. Equation (3-3-11) follows immediately. In particular, if $f_1(t)$ is a rectangular pulse, $f(t)$ will be a triangle. This is the proof of the statement in a previous paragraph that rectangular spectrum noise convolved with itself gives triangular spectrum noise.

The $n \times n$ component of the noise spectrum at the quadratic detector output (excluding the dc term) is thus simply obtained by convolving the input spectral density with itself. For the case of band-limited input white noise with *two-sided* spectral density $G_n(f) = n_0/2$ over the ranges $f_0 \pm B$ and $-f_0 \pm B$, as assumed here, this gives the characteristic triangular spectrum found previously. Both the input and output spectral densities are shown in Fig. 3-3-1. The output spectral density shown agrees of course with the $n \times n$ component of the one-sided spectral density shown in Figs. 3-2-6 and 3-2-7.

We shall use the correlation-function technique further in the sections that follow.

3-4. Frequency-modulation Noise Analysis

Frequency modulation is an example of an analogue-type wideband modulation system in which the increased bandwidth provides substantial improvements in S/N.

We shall consider in this section the S/N properties of an idealized FM receiver, drawing upon and unifying the work of several investigators. The first case considered, that of high carrier-to-noise ratio, will lead quite simply to the well-known expression relating output S_0/N_0 ratio and carrier-to-noise ratio

$$\frac{S_0}{N_0} = 3\beta^2 \frac{S_c}{N_c} \tag{3-4-1}$$

The ratio S_c/N_c represents the carrier-to-noise ratio of an equivalent AM system with the same carrier amplitude and noise spectral density. β is the modulation index. The transmission bandwidth is directly proportional to β for large values so that the output S_0/N_0, *as compared with an equivalent AM system*, increases with the square of the bandwidth.

We shall also consider threshold effects in FM, leading to the conclusion that Eq. (3-4-1) is only valid for $S_c/N \gtrsim 10$, with S_c/N the actual FM carrier-to-noise ratio at the i-f output. For carrier-to-noise ratios less than 10 db, the noise at the output of an FM receiver increases very sharply, changing in the order of 30 db for a 10 db decrease in S_c/N. For still further decreases in S_c/N the output signal itself begins to be suppressed by the noise. (This is equivalent to "capture" of the system by noise.)

A typical FM signal can be written in the form

$$A \cos \alpha = A \cos [\omega_0 t + \phi(t)] = A \cos [\omega_0 t + b \int s(t) \, dt] \tag{3-4-2}$$

Here ω_0 is the unmodulated carrier frequency, $s(t)$ the modulating signal or intelligence, and b a proportionality factor.

The instantaneous frequency ω_i is defined as

$$\omega_i \equiv \frac{d\alpha}{dt} = \omega_0 + bs(t) \tag{3-4-3}$$

The maximum swing of ω_i about ω_0, $|bs(t)|$, is called the frequency deviation.

As a specific example, let

$$bs(t) = \Delta\omega \cos \omega_m t \tag{3-4-4}$$

This is the usual example of a sinusoidal modulating signal. Then $\Delta\omega$ is the frequency deviation (in radians/sec), and

$$\omega_i = \omega_0 + \Delta\omega \cos \omega_m t \tag{3-4-5}$$

The FM signal in this case takes on the form

$$A \cos \alpha = A \cos (\omega_0 t + \beta \sin \omega_m t) \tag{3-4-6}$$

with the modulation index β given by

$$\beta \equiv \frac{\Delta\omega}{\omega_m} \tag{3-4-7}$$

For wideband FM, with its associated noise-improvement properties, $\beta > \pi/2$ radians. As β is made large ($\beta \gg \pi/2$), the i-f bandwidth $2B$ cps approaches the well-known value[1]

$$2B \doteq 2\beta f_m = 2\Delta f \qquad \beta \gg \frac{\pi}{2} \tag{3-4-8}$$

Equations (3-4-1) and (3-4-8) indicate both the S_0/N_0 improvement possible and the corresponding bandwidth increase necessary for FM.

Noise Analysis, Geometric Arguments.[2] Consider narrowband noise $n(t)$ added to the FM signal. The noise, measured at the i-f output, can be written as previously in the form

$$\begin{aligned} n(t) &= x(t) \cos \omega_0 t - y(t) \sin \omega_0 t \\ &= r(t) \cos (\omega_0 t + \theta) \end{aligned} \tag{3-4-9}$$

With x and y independent Gaussian variables, $r(t)$ is Rayleigh-distributed and θ uniformly distributed over 2π radians (Sec. 1-4). The FM signal

---

[1] H. S. Black, "Modulation Theory," chaps. 3 and 12, D. Van Nostrand Company, Inc., Princeton, N.J., 1953. See also Schwartz, *op. cit.*, chaps. 3 and 6. A common rule-of-thumb figure for the bandwidth valid for all β is $2B = 2(\beta + 1)f_m$. Bandwidth considerations for a noiselike modulating signal are considered in Sec. 3-10.

[2] N. M. Blachman, The Demodulation of a Frequency-Modulated Carrier and Random Noise by an FM Receiver, *Cruft Laboratory Report*, no. 31, March, 1948, Harvard University, Cambridge, Mass. Much of the reasoning in this paragraph is also due to Dr. D. T. Hess of the Polytechnic Institute of Brooklyn.

plus noise at the i-f output thus becomes

$$v(t) = A \cos [\omega_0 t + b\int s(t) \, dt] + r(t) \cos (\omega_0 t + \theta) \qquad (3\text{-}4\text{-}10)$$
$$= G \cos (\omega_0 t + \phi)$$

Here $\phi(t)$ is the time-varying phase angle and G the amplitude of the composite sinusoid representing signal plus noise.

We define a balanced ideal FM detector to be one which provides as its output $d\phi/dt$ (Fig. 3-4-1a). For the case of signal alone, this of course reproduces $bs(t)$ as desired. The presence of noise produces random variations in this output. We shall show shortly that the average value of $d\phi/dt$ (taken in an ensemble sense) is a suppressed version of $bs(t)$, while mean-squared variations about the desired output constitute the output noise. In practice, a limiter and balanced discriminator (Fig. 3-4-1b), followed by a low-pass filter, provide the desired FM output.

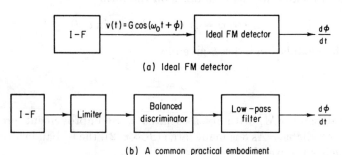

(a) Ideal FM detector

(b) A common practical embodiment

FIG. 3-4-1. FM detection.

The desired phase angle ϕ can be found rather easily by a geometric construction involving rotating phasors. Thus, letting $D(t) \equiv b\int s(t) \, dt$,

$$v(t) = \text{Re} \{e^{j\omega_0 t}[Ae^{jD} + r(t)e^{j\theta}]\} = \text{Re} \{e^{j\omega_0 t}[Ge^{j\phi(t)}]\} \qquad (3\text{-}4\text{-}11)[1]$$

The phasor construction of $Ge^{j\phi}$ is shown in Fig. 3-4-2. Another representation, useful in finding $\phi(t)$ directly, is shown in Fig. 3-4-3. In the latter representation, the phasors move with respect to $\omega_0 + \dot{D}$ as a rotating reference. From Fig. 3-4-3 we have directly

$$\phi = D + \tan^{-1} \frac{r \sin (\theta - D)}{A + r \cos (\theta - D)} \qquad (3\text{-}4\text{-}12)$$

For $r = 0$, ϕ reduces to D and $\dot{\phi}$ to $\dot{D} = bs(t)$ as desired.

[1] The ideal limiter in the FM detector Fig. 3-4-1b provides an output with constant amplitude G_0. The differentiation performed by the discriminator then produces $d\phi/dt$ at the output, independent of the time rate of change of G. Practical nonideal limiters introduce additional complications. The effect of nonideal limiting on the signal and noise characteristics of FM receivers is considered by D. Middleton, "Introduction to Statistical Communication Theory," chap. 15, McGraw-Hill Book Company, New York, 1960.

An ideal FM detector with perfect limiting is assumed in all of the analysis to follow.

The effect of the noise is apparent from either of the two phasor representations. For large carrier-to-noise ($A \gg \sqrt{N}$ or $A \gg r$ in an instantaneous sense) note that variations in r and θ produce small perturbations about the varied angle D. The symmetry of the picture and the uniform distribution of θ indicate that the ensemble average of ϕ will be just D in this case. Similar geometric arguments about the rate of change of the phasors also can be made, as we shall demonstrate analytically in a later paragraph. The perturbations give rise to a nonzero mean-squared variation about D and $\dot{D}$, however, and this will give rise to the noise at the output.

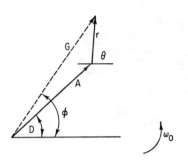

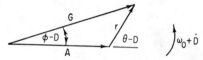

FIG. 3-4-2. Phasor representation of signal plus noise.   FIG. 3-4-3. An alternative phasor representation.

These mean-squared perturbations about $\dot{D}$ become particularly significant when $r \approx A/3$ or so. As $(\theta - D)$ moves through π radians the rate of change of $(\phi - D)$ in Fig. 3-4-3 becomes quite large and contributes significantly to the mean-squared noise at the output. The abrupt increase in $\dot{\phi} - \dot{D}$ as r approaches $A/3$ is shown in the curves of Fig. 3-4-4.[1] It is this abrupt increase that gives rise to the threshold effect in FM. Output-noise calculations made by various investigators, and to be reviewed in a later paragraph, indicate the FM threshold occurs rather sharply at a carrier-to-noise ratio of 10 db. This agrees quite closely with the intuitive picture presented here.

Now consider the case where the noise increases to the order of the carrier or greater. Note from either Fig. 3-4-2 or Fig. 3-4-3 that for $r > A$, the noise "captures" the signal and the average value of ϕ (in an ensemble sense) abruptly plunges to zero. This leads to the signal-suppression characteristic noted previously. For we have $\langle \phi \rangle = \langle D \rangle$ when $r < A$ and $\langle \phi \rangle = 0$ when $r > A$.

Similarly, a more detailed argument shows that $\langle \dot{\phi} \rangle = \langle \dot{D} \rangle = bs(t)$ when $r < A$ and $\langle \dot{\phi} \rangle = 0$ when $r > A$. Since the noise envelope $r(t)$ is Rayleigh-distributed we can show quite easily that the probability that $r < A$ is $1 - e^{-A^2/2N} = 1 - e^{-S_c/N}$. We would thus expect the average value of the *signal* output in an ensemble sense to be

$$\langle \dot{D} \rangle = bs(t)(1 - e^{-S_c/N}) \tag{3-4-13}$$

[1] These curves are similar to those plotted by L. B. Arguimbau and R. D. Stuart, "Frequency Modulation," Methuen and Co., Ltd., London, 1956, in considering the case of an FM signal plus interfering carrier.

This signal-suppression effect will be obtained in a more rigorous fashion in a later paragraph.

Noise Analysis, High Carrier-to-Noise Case.   Note from Eq. (3-4-12) and also from Fig. 3-4-3 that the effect of variations in the random-noise phase angle θ appears referred to the signal term D.   Since θ is uniformly distributed in an ensemble sense, covering the range 0 to 2π radians, it is

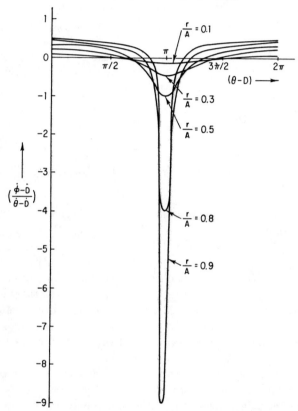

FIG. 3-4-4. Instantaneous noise output, ideal FM detector.

tempting to assume that the quantity $\theta - D$ will also be uniformly distributed over 2π radians, in an *ensemble* sense.   The noise output, due to mean-square perturbations of ϕ about D, will thus be independent of the signal and depend only on the carrier and noise characteristics.   In finding the *noise* at the FM detector output we could therefore consider the simpler case of an unmodulated carrier plus narrowband noise. Rice[1] has shown that for high carrier-to-noise ratio this assumption is very nearly valid.   For carrier-to-noise ratios below the threshold value

[1] S. O. Rice, "Noise in FM Receivers," chap. 25, pp. 375–424, in "Proceedings, Symposium on Time Series Analysis," M. Rosenblatt, (ed.), John Wiley & Sons, Inc., New York, 1963.

of 10 db, the modulating signal affects the noise output. In this paragraph, with high carrier-to-noise ratio to be assumed, we shall neglect the modulating signal. For this case

$$v(t) = (A + x) \cos \omega_0 t - y \sin \omega_0 t$$
$$= G \cos (\omega_0 t + \phi) \tag{3-4-14}$$

Then
$$\phi = \tan^{-1} \frac{y}{x + A} \tag{3-4-15}$$

This is also apparent from Eq. (3-4-12) and Fig. 3-4-3, for $y = r \sin \theta$ and $x = r \cos \theta$.

The discriminator output is given by

$$\dot{\phi} = \frac{(x + A)\dot{y} - y\dot{x}}{y^2 + (x + A)^2} \tag{3-4-16}$$

For large carrier-to-noise ratio this reduces quite simply to

$$\dot{\phi} \doteq \frac{1}{A} \dot{y} \qquad A \gg \sqrt{N} \tag{3-4-17}$$

The output for large carrier-to-noise ratio is thus proportional to the rate of change of the out-of-phase noise term $y(t)$.

Just as in the AM analysis we cannot simply find the mean-squared value of $\dot{\phi}$. This includes high-frequency components that would not be passed by the low-pass filter in the video portion of the FM receiver. The mean-squared output depends on the *spectral distribution of* $\dot{\phi}$. For the case of large signal-to-noise ratio the spectral density is easily found. Recalling that differentiation of a function with respect to time corresponds to passing that function through a linear filter with transfer function $H(\omega) = j\omega$ and that the spectral density at the output is given by $G_0(f) = |H(\omega)|^2 G_i(f)$ the spectral density of the derivative of a random function is just ω^2 times the spectral density of the function.[1]

[1] Alternatively, we may note that the autocorrelation functions for $n_0(t)$ and $n(t)$, with $n_0(t) = dn/dt$, are related as follows:

$$\langle n_0(t_1)n_0(t_2) \rangle = \left\langle \frac{dn}{dt}\bigg|_{t_1} \frac{dn}{dt}\bigg|_{t_2} \right\rangle = \frac{d}{dt_1}\frac{d}{dt_2} \langle n(t_1)n(t_2) \rangle, \tag{3-4-18a}$$

upon interchanging the order of differentiation and ensemble-averaging.

But
$$R_n(t_1 - t_2) = \langle n(t_1)n(t_2) \rangle = R_n(\tau) \tag{3-4-18b}$$

Also
$$\frac{d}{dt_1}\frac{d}{dt_2} R_n(t_1 - t_2) = -\frac{d^2}{d\tau^2} R_n(\tau) \tag{3-4-18c}$$

Therefore
$$R_0(\tau) = -\frac{d^2}{d\tau^2} R_n(\tau) \tag{3-4-18d}$$

is the desired relation.

But we also have
$$R_n(\tau) = \int_{-\infty}^{\infty} G_n(f)e^{j\omega\tau} \, df \tag{3-4-18e}$$

then
$$-\frac{d^2 R_n(\tau)}{d\tau^2} = \int_{-\infty}^{\infty} \omega^2 G_n(f)^{j\omega\tau} \, df \tag{3-4-18f}$$

upon differentiating under the integral sign.

It is then apparent that
$$G_0(f) = \omega^2 G_n(f) \tag{3-4-18g}$$

Thus
$$G_{\dot{y}}(f) = \omega^2 G_y(f)$$
$$= \omega^2[G_n(f - f_0) + G_n(f + f_0)] \qquad (3\text{-}4\text{-}18)$$

from Eq. (3-1-2). (See Fig. 3-4-5 for $G_y(f)$ in the symmetrical-bandpass case).

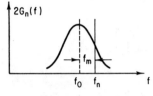 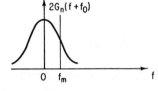

(a) Total noise spectral density   (b) Spectral density of y(t) and x(t)

FIG. 3-4-5. Spectral density of noise and its in-phase and quadrature components (symmetrical filter).

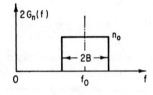 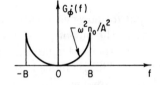

(a) Spectrum of I-F noise   (b) Spectrum at output of FM detector

FIG. 3-4-6. FM noise spectrum (rectangular input) $(A \gg \sqrt{N})$.

The two-sided spectral density of $\dot{\phi}(t)$ for the high carrier-to-noise case is then, from Eq. (3-4-17),

$$G_{\dot{\phi}}(f) = \frac{\omega^2}{A^2}[G_n(f - f_0) + G_n(f + f_0)] \qquad A \gg \sqrt{N} \quad (3\text{-}4\text{-}19)$$

In particular, for the symmetrical-bandpass case, with

$$G_n(f - f_0) = G_n(f + f_0) \qquad (3\text{-}4\text{-}20)$$

$$G_{\dot{\phi}}(f) = \frac{2\omega^2}{A^2} G_n(f + f_0) \qquad A \gg \sqrt{N} \qquad (3\text{-}4\text{-}21)$$

Two examples are of interest:
1. Rectangular i-f spectrum (Fig. 3-4-6)

Then
$$G_{\dot{\phi}}(f) = \frac{\omega^2 n_0}{A^2} \qquad -B < f < B \qquad (3\text{-}4\text{-}22)$$

This can be put in normalized form by recalling that $N = 2n_0B$ is the total i-f noise ($2B$ is the i-f bandwidth) and $S_c = A^2/2$ the mean-squared carrier voltage. Then

$$G_{\dot{\phi}}(f) = \frac{\pi^2}{B}\left(\frac{N}{S_c}\right)f^2 \qquad -B < f < B \qquad (3\text{-}4\text{-}23)$$

The quantity S_c/N represents the i-f carrier-to-noise ratio.

2. Gaussian i-f spectrum (Fig. 3-4-7)

Here we assume

$$2G_n(f) = \frac{Ne^{-(f-f_0)^2/2\sigma^2}}{\sqrt{2\pi\sigma^2}} \tag{3-4-24}$$

The parameter 2σ is one measure of the i-f bandwidth and can be readily shown to be $1.7B$, with $2B$ the usual 3-db bandwidth. N again represents the mean noise power at the i-f output.

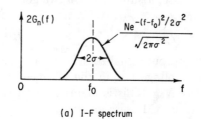

(a) I-F spectrum

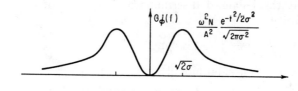

(b) Spectrum at detector output

Fig. 3-4-7. FM noise spectrum (Gaussian i-f spectrum) $(A \gg \sqrt{N})$.

The two-sided noise spectrum at the FM detector output is then

$$G_\phi(f) = \frac{\omega^2}{A^2}\frac{Ne^{-f^2/2\sigma^2}}{\sqrt{2\pi\sigma^2}} \tag{3-4-25}$$

and is readily shown to have a peak at $f = \sqrt{2}\sigma \equiv 1.2B$. In normalized form,

$$G_\phi(f) = \frac{2\pi^2}{\sqrt{2\pi\sigma^2}}\left(\frac{N}{S_c}\right)f^2e^{-f^2/2\sigma^2} = \frac{0.94\pi^2}{B}\left(\frac{N}{S_c}\right)f^2e^{-f^2/1.4B^2} \tag{3-4-26}$$

Note that for $f \ll B$, the quadratic term dominates, giving the same dependence as in the rectangular i-f case.

Assuming a video bandwidth of f_m cps we can readily calculate the mean noise power at the low-pass filter output. (The video bandwidth is normally chosen just large enough to accommodate the desired modulating signal while keeping the output noise as small as possible. For wideband FM $f_m \ll B$. It is this reduction in video or signal bandwidth as compared to the transmission bandwidth that provides the S/N gain of FM. Additional S/N improvement is possible using preemphasis and deemphasis techniques. See Black, *op. cit*, and Schwartz, *op. cit.*, for detailed discussions of these techniques.)

The total noise power out, assuming an ideal low-pass filter, is

$$N_0 = \int_{-f_m}^{f_m} G_\phi(f)\, df \tag{3-4-27}$$

For the rectangular i-f case N_0 becomes

$$N_0 = \frac{2\pi^2}{B}\left(\frac{N}{S_c}\right)\int_0^{f_m} f^2\, df = \frac{2}{3}\frac{\pi^2}{B}\left(\frac{N}{S_c}\right)f_m{}^3 \tag{3-4-28}$$

For the Gaussian i-f case, assuming $f \ll \sigma$, we get

$$N_0 = \frac{2}{3}\frac{\pi^2}{\sqrt{2\pi^2\sigma^2}}\left(\frac{N}{S_c}\right)f_m{}^3 = \frac{2}{3}(0.94)\frac{\pi^2}{B}\left(\frac{N}{S_c}\right)f_m{}^3 \tag{3-4-29}$$

We now define the output signal-to-noise ratio S_0/N_0 as the ratio of the mean-squared signal voltage out in the absence of noise to the mean-squared noise voltage N_0. This is identical with the approach used in the previous sections on AM noise analysis.

From Eq. (3-4-2), or from Eq. (3-4-12) with the noise set equal to zero, the signal at the balanced discriminator output is of course just the desired quantity

$$\frac{d\phi}{dt} = bs(t) \tag{3-4-30}$$

For the case of a sinusoidal modulating signal

$$\frac{d\phi}{dt} = \Delta\omega \cos \omega_m t \tag{3-4-31}$$

as in Eq. (3-4-4) or Eq. (3-4-5). The mean-squared signal output is thus

$$S_0 = \frac{\Delta\omega^2}{2} \tag{3-4-32}$$

(As previously, the detector constant is taken as 1.) The output signal-to-noise ratio, for high *carrier-to-noise ratio* and rectangular i-f spectrum, is thus

$$\frac{S_0}{N_0} = 3\beta^2 \frac{S_c}{N}\left(\frac{B}{f_m}\right) \qquad S_c/N \gg 1 \tag{3-4-33}$$

This equation relates S_0/N_0 to the carrier-to-noise ratio S_c/N. To pinpoint the specific dependence on transmission bandwidth we note that $N = 2n_0 B$. Defining $N_c \equiv 2n_0 f_m$ as the equivalent AM i-f noise, we also have

$$\frac{S_0}{N_0} = 3\beta^2 \frac{S_c}{N_c} \qquad \frac{S_c}{N} \gg 1 \tag{3-4-34}$$

as in Eq. (3-4-1).

With the modulating frequency f_m and mean carrier power S_c fixed, the output signal-to-noise is proportional to the square of β or to the square of the frequency deviation Δf. For large β, as assumed here, the transmission bandwidth $2B \doteq 2\Delta f$, so that S_0/N_0 is equally proportional to the square of the transmission bandwidth. In effect, the FM technique of processing the signal requires much larger bandwidths than an equivalent AM system but results in a significant improvement in S_0/N_0 ratio.

3-5. FM Noise Output, Carrier Absent

We now consider the other extreme of very small carrier-to-noise ratio. Here, with the carrier small or absent, we shall find the output-noise *magnitudes larger* than for the case of high carrier-to-noise ratio. This is just the reverse of the AM case where, as noted previously, the presence of an unmodulated carrier increases the noise output.

This large increase in FM output noise with reduction of the carrier level is consistent with the phasor representation of Figs. 3-4-2 and 3-4-3. Note that the perturbation due to noise in the angle ϕ of the figures, and the corresponding discriminator output $\dot{\phi}$, are quite small for the case of high carrier-to-noise ratio ($A \gg \sqrt{N}$, or $A \gg r$ in an instantaneous sense). As the carrier amplitude A decreases below r, however, the angle ϕ is "captured" by the noise and takes on all possible values from 0 to 2π. Its derivative $\dot{\phi}$ will also be expected to increase very greatly above the high carrier-to-noise case and will in fact depend on the transmission bandwidth $2B$ and the video bandwidth f_m.

The analysis performed by various investigators bears this out. In this section we shall simply present the results as obtained independently by S. O. Rice,[1] M. C. Wang,[2] and D. Middleton.[3] The analysis technique used is a correlation-function procedure, similar to that described previously, in which the noise spectrum at the discriminator output is found by first finding the correlation function of the noise at that point. All three references contain results for various carrier-to-noise ratios from zero to high values. The analysis becomes quite cumbersome, however, so we shall restrict ourselves here to outlining the case of 0 carrier only. We shall then reproduce the curves obtained for various values of S_c/N by all three investigators. In a later section we shall summarize a different method of obtaining the noise spectrum at the output of an FM discriminator, as developed by F. L. H. M. Stumpers.[4] Stumpers' technique

[1] S. O. Rice, Statistical Properties of a Sine Wave Plus Random Noise, *Bell System Tech. J.*, vol. 27, secs. 7 and 8, pp. 138–151, January, 1948.

[2] J. L. Lawson and G. E. Uhlenbeck, "Threshold Signals," McGraw-Hill Book Company, New York, 1950, chap. 13.

[3] D. Middleton, "An Introduction to Statistical Communication Theory," chap. 15, McGraw-Hill Book Company, New York, 1960. This book contains references to, and reproduces much of, Middleton's work on FM first published in 1948–1949. Middleton considers the effect of imperfect limiting, mistuned carrier, and various other factors of interest in FM noise. The book contains extensive references in this and related areas.

[4] F. L. H. M. Stumpers, "Theory of Frequency-Modulation Noise," *Proc. IRE*, vol. 36, pp. 1081–1092, September, 1948.

utilizes a zerocrossing procedure. We shall also summarize Rice's interesting work analyzing FM noise phenomena in terms of "clicks" in a later section.[1]

These results for the noise spectrum at the output of an FM detector have been verified experimentally[2] and are shown in Fig. 3-5-1.

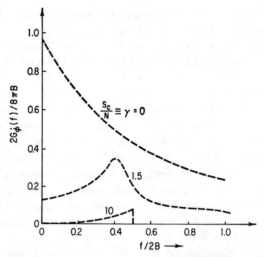

FIG. 3-5-1. Output noise spectrum, FM discriminator, rectangular i-f spectrum (ideal limiting assumed). (*Reproduced, with change in notation, from J. L. Lawson and G. E. Uhlenbeck, "Threshold Signals," Figs. 13.2, 13.3, and 13.4.*)

For the noise-only case ($A = 0$) we have at the i-f output

$$v(t) = n(t) = x(t) \cos \omega_0 t - y(t) \sin \omega_0 t = r(t) \cos (\omega_0 t + \theta) \quad (3\text{-}5\text{-}1)$$

with
$$\theta = \tan^{-1} \frac{y}{x} \quad (3\text{-}5\text{-}2)$$

a uniformly distributed random variable.

Then the voltage at the balanced discriminator output (again assuming perfect limiting and taking the detector constant to be 1) is

$$\frac{d\phi}{dt} = \frac{d\theta}{dt} = \frac{\dot{y}x - y\dot{x}}{x^2 + y^2} \quad (3\text{-}5\text{-}3)$$

from Eq. (3-5-2), or from Eq. (3-4-16) with $A = 0$.)

[1] S. O. Rice, "Noise in FM Receivers," chap. 25, pp. 375–424, in "Proceedings Symposium of Time Series Analysis," M. Rosenblatt (ed.), John Wiley & Sons, Inc., New York, 1963.

[2] Harrison W. Fuller, Signals and Noise in a Frequency Modulation Receiver, *Cruft Laboratory Technical Report* 243, Harvard University, February, 1957. Also J. T. Frankle, Frequency Modulation Noise, Report No. PIBMRI-1041-62, Electrical Engineering Dept., Polytechnic Institute of Brooklyn, August, 1962. Fuller, utilizing a low-frequency receiver expressly built for the experiments, verified the theoretical results for various degrees of limiting, offtuned carrier, various types of filter characteristics, etc. Frankle used a commercial FM receiver in performing his experiments.

To find the spectrum at the discriminator output it is first necessary to calculate the correlation function

$$R_\theta(\tau) \equiv \langle \dot{\theta}(t)\dot{\theta}(t+\tau) \rangle = \langle \dot{\theta}_1 \dot{\theta}_2 \rangle = \left\langle \left[\frac{\dot{y}_1 x_1 - y_1 \dot{x}_1}{x_1^2 + y_1^2} \right] \left[\frac{\dot{y}_2 x_2 - y_2 \dot{x}_2}{x_2^2 + y_2^2} \right] \right\rangle$$

$$(3\text{-}5\text{-}4)$$

where the subscript 1 refers to time t, the subscript 2 to time $(t + \tau)$ (that is, $y_1 \equiv y(t)$, $y_2 \equiv y(t + \tau)$, etc.)   The direct evaluation of $R_{\dot{\theta}}(\tau)$ in terms of the eight-fold integral

$$R_{\dot{\theta}}(\tau) = \int \cdots \int \dot{\theta}_1 \dot{\theta}_2 p(x_1, y_1, x_2, y_2, \dot{x}_1, \dot{y}_1, \dot{x}_2, \dot{y}_2) \, dx_1, \ldots, dy_2 \quad (3\text{-}5\text{-}5)$$

turns out to be impossibly difficult.   Instead, characteristic functions can be used, as they were in Sec. 3-3.   One procedure, utilized in the references mentioned, is to replace the eighth-order probability distribution by its Fourier-integral representation in terms of the characteristic function. The following multidimensional version of Parseval's theorem leads to the same results in simpler fashion:[1]

$$\int_{-\infty}^{\infty} \cdots \int_{-\infty}^{\infty} f(x_1, x_2, \ldots, x_m) g(x_1, x_2, \ldots, x_m) \, dx_1 \cdots dx_m = \left(\frac{1}{2\pi} \right)^m$$

$$\int_{-\infty}^{\infty} \cdots \int_{-\infty}^{\infty} F(z_1, z_2, \ldots, z_m) G^*(z_1, z_2, \ldots, z_m) \, dz_1 \cdots dz_m \quad (3\text{-}5\text{-}6)$$

Here F and G are Fourier transforms of f and g respectively, and the asterisk represents complex conjugate.

In particular, given an ensemble average $f(x_1, x_2, \ldots, x_m)$ defined as

$$\langle f(x_1, \ldots, x_m) \rangle = \int_{-\infty}^{\infty} f(x_1, \ldots, x_m) p(x, \ldots, x_m) \, dx_1 \cdots dx_m$$

$$(3\text{-}5\text{-}7)$$

then the average is also given by

$$\langle f(x_1, \cdots, x_m) \rangle = \left(\frac{1}{2\pi} \right)^m \int_{-\infty}^{\infty} \cdots \int_{-\infty}^{\infty} F(z_1, z_2, \cdots, z_m)$$

$$G(z_1, \cdots, z_m) \, dz_1 \cdots dz_m \quad (3\text{-}5\text{-}8)$$

Here F is the Fourier transform of f, and G is just the characteristic function (c.f.) of $p(x_1, \cdots, x_m)$.   In this problem f is just $\dot{\theta}_1 \dot{\theta}_2$ written, as in Eq. (3-5-4), in terms of x_1, x_2, y_1, etc.   The evaluation of $R_{\dot{\theta}}(\tau)$ using Eq. (3-5-8) is straightforward but tedious.   The resultant expres-

---

[1] The procedure has been utilized extensively by Bennett, Rice, Middleton, and others in calculating the autocorrelation functions and power spectrum at the output of nonlinear devices (see Davenport and Root, *op. cit.*, chap. 13, for an extensive discussion and bibliography).   Its application to FM noise analysis was suggested by Dr. Donald T. Hess of The Polytechnic Institute of Brooklyn.

sion for $R_{\dot{\theta}}(\tau)$ takes the surprisingly simple form

$$R_{\dot{\theta}}(\tau) = \frac{1}{2}\left(\frac{\ddot{\rho}}{\rho} - \frac{\dot{\rho}^2}{\rho^2}\right) \log\,(1 - \rho^2) \qquad (3\text{-}5\text{-}9)[1]$$

with $\rho \equiv R_x(\tau)/N$, the normalized correlation function of either the in-phase noise term $x(t)$ or the quadrature term $y(t)$. The correlation function at the discriminator output thus appears in terms of the low-frequency equivalent correlation function at the i-f output. (The derivation of Eq. (3-5-9) assumes $G_n(f)$ symmetrical about the carrier frequency f_0).

Note that for $\tau \to 0$, $R_{\dot{\theta}}(\tau) \to \infty$. This implies that the *total* mean-squared noise at the discriminator output becomes infinite if no video filtering is used. This corresponds to the fact that x and y may sometimes approach zero simultaneously, giving rise to infinite $d\theta/dt$, as apparent from Eq. (3-5-3). In practice, of course, filtering is always used so that the mean-squared value of θ is finite.

Although the output noise spectrum $G_{\dot{\theta}}(f)$ can be expressed readily as the Fourier transform of $R_{\dot{\theta}}(\tau)$, the actual integration using Eq. (3-5-9) only can be carried out numerically and depends on the particular form of the i-f noise spectrum. Rice, "Statistical Properties of a Sine Wave Plus Random Noise," plots $G_{\dot{\theta}}(f)$ versus frequency f for the Gaussian i-f spectrum case [Eq. (3-4-24)] in his Fig. 8, p. 41. The analogous curve for the rectangular i-f spectrum case is given by Lawson and Uhlenbeck, *op. cit.*, in their Fig. 13-2, p. 373. The two curves don't differ very much, as might be expected. Similar curves for both cases appear in Figs. 1 and 6 of Stumpers, *op. cit.* His results were obtained using the zero-crossing technique to be described later.

Fig. 3-5-1 is a reproduction of the curve for the rectangular i-f spectrum case put in terms of our notation. Also included, for reference's sake, are the analogous curves for input carrier-to-noise ratio $S_c/N = 1.5$ and 10. The enormously large increase in output noise as the carrier-to-noise ratio drops below $S_c/N = 10$ is apparent from these curves.

As an example assume the audio bandwidth $f_m \ll B$, with $2B$ the i-f bandwidth. Then the output noise N_0 for the case of zero carrier is essentially the zero-frequency ordinate times f_m. Thus

$$N_0 \doteq 8\pi B(0.955)f_m \qquad S_c = 0 \qquad \text{and} \qquad f_m \ll B \qquad (3\text{-}5\text{-}10)$$

From Eq. (3-4-28), the output noise for the large carrier-to-noise case is

$$N_0 = \frac{(\omega_m)^2 f_m}{6B}\left(\frac{N}{S_c}\right) \qquad \frac{S_c}{N} \gg 1 \qquad (3\text{-}5\text{-}11)$$

The condition $f_m \ll B$ corresponds of course to the usual wideband FM case with the modulation index $\beta = \Delta f/f_m \gg 1$.

---

[1] See Lawson and Uhlenbeck, *op. cit.*, p. 373, for details of some of the integration involved.

The ratio of the output noise powers in these two cases (no carrier/large carrier) is then

$$\frac{N_0 \big|_{S_c/N=0}}{N_0 \big|_{S_c/N\gg1}} = \frac{12}{\pi}(0.955)\left(\frac{B}{f_m}\right)^2 \frac{S_c}{N} \tag{3-5-12}$$

$$\doteq 3\beta^2 \frac{S_c}{N}$$

with
$$\beta = \frac{\Delta f}{f_m} \doteq \frac{B}{f_m}$$

With $S_c/N = 10$, as an example, the ratio of the noise power is $30\beta^2$. For $\beta = 10$ this is 3,000 or 34 db. For $\beta = 4$ this is 480 or 27 db. As a rough figure, then, the output-noise power increases 30 db when the carrier-to-noise ratio drops from 10 to 0.

Actually most of the increase in the noise comes as the S_c/N decreases from 10 to about 1 (0 db). This is apparent from the curve for $S_c/N = 1.5$ in Fig. 3-5-1. This is then the threshold effect in FM. For $S_c/N \geq 10$ the simplified approach of the last paragraph is valid, and, as is apparent from Eq. (3-5-11), the output-noise power varies inversely with S_c/N. It is only for $S_c/N < 10$ db that the output-noise power increases much more rapidly. This is in agreement with the qualitative picture based on the phasor plot that was discussed previously.

The curve for $S_c/N = 1.5$ in Fig. 3-5-1 was obtained by an analysis similar to the one just outlined here for the zero carrier ($S_c/N = 0$) case. Reference may be made to Lawson and Uhlenbeck, op. cit., pp. 374–380, for details of the analysis with an i-f rectangular spectrum assumed. The corresponding analysis for a Gaussian i-f spectrum is outlined by Rice op. cit., pp. 39–43. Middleton, op. cit., has in addition detailed calculations and curves indicating the effect of nonideal limiting. (As noted previously, Stumpers, op. cit., has handled both i-f spectrum cases, obtaining identical results but using a different procedure. This will be outlined in a later section.)

The total output-noise power can of course be found by integrating the output-noise-spectrum curves over the assumed video bandwidth. This has been carried out by Stumpers for both the rectangular and Gaussian i-f spectrum characteristics, assuming an ideal rectangular video filter. The resultant curves for the rectangular-spectrum case are reproduced in Fig. 3-5-2.

Note the abrupt increase in output noise as the carrier-to-noise ratio drops below the threshold value of 10 db. The threshold is particularly marked for small ratios of video to i-f bandwidth and is almost independent of bandwidth ratios. As an example, for $B/f_m = 10$ (the total i-f bandwidth is $2B$), N_0 increases by a factor of about 30 db as S_c/N decreases 10 db, from 10 to 0 db. For S_c/N less than 0 db the output noise levels off at an almost constant value. This is of course in agreement with the statements made previously. The marked increase in noise as S_c/N drops below 10 db disappears only when $B/f_m = 1$, corresponding to the narrowband FM case. This threshold effect, and curves close to those in Fig. 3-5-2, will be obtained in a much more intuitive way later using Rice's "noise clicks" approach.

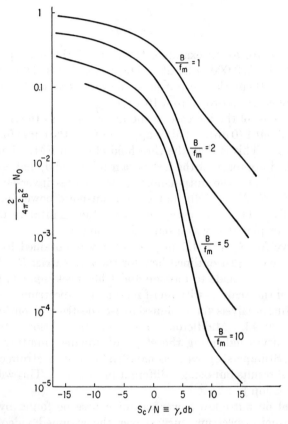

FIG. 3-5-2. Output noise power, FM discriminator, rectangular i-f spectrum, (ideal limiting assumed). (*Adapted, with change in notation, from F. L. H. M. Stumpers, Proc. IRE, vol. 36, no. 9, September, 1948, Figs. 2 and 3*).

3-6. Second Threshold in FM: Decrease in Output Signal

It was indicated previously, again on the basis of qualitative reasoning and the phasor diagram, that signal suppression takes place as the carrier-to-noise ratio drops below 0 db. On the basis of the phasor diagram of Fig. 3-4-2, the noise "takes over" the signal when it instantaneously exceeds the carrier level. Since the noise is Rayleigh-distributed we can calculate the probability of such an occurrence and come to the conclusion that the average signal is reduced by the factor $1 - e^{-S_c/N}$. Since this factor begins to play a significant role only when $S_c/N \leq 1$, we may say that a second threshold appears at the $S_c/N = 0$ db. point.

The first threshold, discussed in the previous section, then corresponds to $S_c/N = 10$ db and is caused by the output *noise* increasing precipitously below that point. The output *signal* remains very nearly unchanged, however. As S_c/N drops below 0 db, the signal begins to decrease while the noise levels off to a fixed value. This is the second threshold. We shall derive this signal suppression effect in this section for deterministic modulating signals.[1]

To do this we go back to Eq. (3-4-12) for the instantaneous phase angle ϕ of an arbitrarily modulated sinewave carrier plus slowly varying Gaussian noise. This is given by

$$\phi = D + \tan^{-1} \frac{r \sin (\theta - D)}{A + r \cos (\theta - D)} \qquad (3\text{-}6\text{-}1)$$

Here $D \equiv b\int s(t)\, dt$ represents the integral of the signal, θ is the instantaneous noise phase angle, r the instantaneous noise amplitude, and A the carrier amplitude.

Assuming ideal limiting again, the discriminator output is $d\phi/dt \equiv \dot{\phi}$, given by

$$\dot{\phi} = \dot{D} + \frac{rA \cos (\theta - D)(\dot{\theta} - \dot{D}) + A\dot{r} \sin (\theta - D) + r^2(\dot{\theta} - \dot{D})}{r^2 + A^2 + 2rA \cos (\theta - D)}$$

$$(3\text{-}6\text{-}2)$$

We now define the signal output in a statistical sense to be the ensemble average of $\dot{\phi}$. We shall use the symbol Ω to represent the instantaneous noise output $\dot{\phi} - \dot{D}$. Then

$$\langle \dot{\phi} \rangle = \dot{D} + \langle \Omega \rangle \qquad (3\text{-}6\text{-}3)$$

The symbol $\langle \rangle$ is used to represent the ensemble average with respect to the noise. The ensemble average $\langle \Omega \rangle$ is the statistical average of the noise term in Eq. (3-6-2) and is given by

$$\langle \Omega \rangle = \int\int\int\int \Omega p(r,\dot{r},\theta,\dot{\theta})\, dr\, d\dot{r}\, d\theta\, d\dot{\theta} \qquad (3\text{-}6\text{-}4)$$

The problem here is thus to find the four-dimensional probability distribution $p(r,\dot{r},\theta,\dot{\theta})$ and integrate as indicated. We proceed formally by first finding the joint probability distribution $p(x,y,\dot{x},\dot{y})$ and transforming variables.

---

[1] The approach used is similar to that of Blachman, *op. cit.* The details are due to Dr. Donald T. Hess of The Polytechnic Institute of Brooklyn. An identical result obtained in a different manner appears in Middleton, *op. cit.*, and in Rice, "Noise in FM Receivers." In addition, the signal-suppression effect for the *special case* of *sinusoidal modulating* signal has been obtained by S. O. Rice (1948), *op. cit.*, Wang in Lawson and Uhlenbeck, *op. cit.*, and Stumpers, *op. cit.*

To simplify matters we now assume the i-f noise spectral density $G_n(f)$ to be symmetrical about the center of the passband. This is the same assumption noted in the previous section as necessary to simplify the analysis there. Under this assumption the variables x, y, $\dot{x}$, and $\dot{y}$ are all *independent* Gaussian variables and the joint probability distribution is easily written down. For it can be shown that,

$$\langle x\dot{y}\rangle = \int_0^\infty 2(\omega - \omega_0)G_n(f)\,df = 0 = \langle y\dot{x}\rangle \qquad (3\text{-}6\text{-}5)$$

if $G_n(f)$ is symmetrical about ω_0. Similarly, $\langle x\dot{x}\rangle = \langle y\dot{y}\rangle = 0$ and $\langle xy\rangle = 0$.

Also,

$$\langle \dot{y}^2\rangle = \langle \dot{x}^2\rangle = (2\pi)^2 \int_0^\infty 2(f - f_0)^2 G_n(f)\,df \equiv V \qquad (3\text{-}6\text{-}6)^{[1]}$$

The fourfold Gaussian distribution, under the assumption of symmetric i-f spectrum, is thus the product of four Gaussian distributions and is given by

$$p(x,y,\dot{x},\dot{y}) = \frac{e^{-(x^2+y^2)/2N}}{2\pi N}\,\frac{e^{-(\dot{x}^2+\dot{y}^2)/2V}}{2\pi V} \qquad (3\text{-}6\text{-}7)$$

To transform to r, $\dot{r}$, θ, $\dot{\theta}$ coordinates we use the transformation equations

$$\left.\begin{array}{cc} x^2 + y^2 = r^2 & \theta = \tan^{-1}\dfrac{y}{x} \\[2pt] x = r\cos\theta & y = r\sin\theta \\[2pt] \dot{x} = -r\sin\theta\,\dot{\theta} + \dot{r}\cos\theta \\[2pt] \dot{y} = r\cos\theta\,\dot{\theta} + \dot{r}\sin\theta \\[2pt] \dot{x}^2 + \dot{y}^2 = r^2\dot{\theta}^2 + \dot{r}^2 \end{array}\right\} \qquad (3\text{-}6\text{-}8)$$

Writing, as in Chap. 1,

$$p(r,\theta,\dot{r},\dot{\theta})\,dr\,d\theta\,d\dot{r}\,d\dot{\theta} = p(x,y,\dot{x},\dot{y})\,dx\,dy\,d\dot{x}\,d\dot{y} \qquad (3\text{-}6\text{-}9)$$

with the Jacobian of the transformation given by r^2,

$$(dx\,dy\,d\dot{x}\,d\dot{y} = r^2 dr\,d\theta\,d\dot{r}\,d\dot{\theta}) \quad .$$

we get finally,

$$p(r,\theta,\dot{r},\dot{\theta}) = \frac{1}{2\pi}\,\frac{e^{-\dot{r}^2/2V}}{\sqrt{2\pi V}}\,\frac{r^2 e^{-\left(\frac{r^2}{2N}+\frac{r^2\dot{\theta}^2}{2V}\right)}}{\sqrt{2\pi V}\,N} \qquad (3\text{-}6\text{-}10)$$

Note that θ and $\dot{r}$ are independent variables ($\dot{r}$ is Gaussian-distributed), while r and $\dot{\theta}$ are correlated.

Using this rather cumbersome-looking equation in Eq. (3-6-4) and integrating first with respect to $\dot{r}$ and then θ, the equation simplifies

[1] Equations (3-6-5) and (3-6-6) are obtained by generalizing Eq. (3-4-18d) and then applying Eqs. (1-7-22) and (1-7-23).

considerably and gives

$$\langle \Omega \rangle = \langle \dot{\phi} \rangle - \dot{D} = -\frac{\dot{D}}{2\pi} \int_0^\infty \int_{-\pi}^\pi \frac{r/A \cos (\theta - D) \, d\theta}{1 + (r/A)^2 + 2r/A \cos (\theta - D)} \frac{r \, dr}{N} e^{-r^2/2N} \quad (3\text{-}6\text{-}11)$$

We now integrate with respect to θ. Note that the integrand is just the amplitude of the noise-plus-carrier resultant phasor in the phasor diagram of Fig. 3-4-3. As is apparent from the phasor diagram, and as noted previously, this resultant phasor changes markedly as r becomes greater than A. This is borne out by the integration with respect to θ:

$$\text{integral} = \begin{cases} 2\pi & \dfrac{r}{A} > 1 \\[2mm] 0 & \dfrac{r}{A} < 1 \end{cases}$$

This is just the capture effect alluded to previously: for $r > A$ the noise "captures" the signal, and the signal output is reduced to zero.

The resultant ensemble average of Ω is then given by

$$\langle \Omega \rangle = \langle \dot{\phi} \rangle - \dot{D} = -\dot{D} \int_A^\infty \frac{r \, dr}{N} e^{-r^2/2N} \quad (3\text{-}6\text{-}12)$$

and

$$\langle \dot{\phi} \rangle = \dot{D}(1 - e^{-S_c/N}) \quad (3\text{-}6\text{-}13)$$

with $S_c \equiv A^2/2$.

The average value of the discriminator output, *defined* as the signal term, thus appears reduced because of noise capture whenever the noise instantaneously exceeds the carrier. Note that this signal-suppression effect becomes significant in the vicinity of $S_c/N = 1$. We now define output signal power as

$$S_0 \equiv \langle \dot{\phi} \rangle^2 = \dot{D}^2(1 - e^{-S_c/N})^2 \quad (3\text{-}6\text{-}14)[1]$$

For $S_c/N \ll 1$,

$$S_0 \doteq \dot{D}^2 \left(\frac{S_c}{N}\right)^2 \quad (3\text{-}6\text{-}15)$$

Since the output noise N_0 approaches a constant value for $S_c/N \ll 1$, $S_0/N_0 \propto (S_c/N)^2$. This is the same asymptotic behavior as noted previously in the case of envelope detection.

We can sum up these results again by stating that for wideband FM ($\beta > \pi/2$, $f_m \ll B$) two thresholds appear at the FM detector output. The first, characterized by a sharp increase in the output noise, occurs as the carrier-to-noise S_c/N drops below 10 db. As S_c/N decreases below 0 db, the output noise levels off at a large constant value, but the

[1] $\dot{D}^2$ can be further averaged in time to obtain the normal time-averaged signal power.

output signal is now suppressed. In the 10-db interval from $S_c/N = 10$ to 1, output noise increases roughly by 30 db. A typical S/N curve for wideband FM showing the two thresholds is sketched in Fig. 3-6-1.

For narrowband FM only the second, signal-suppression, threshold appears. These results assume perfect limiting at all levels of carrier and noise.

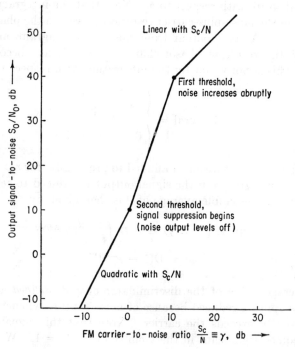

FIG. 3-6-1. Typical S/N curve for wideband FM, showing two thresholds.

3-7. Zero-crossing Analysis[1]

As noted previously the theory of FM noise has been developed by Stumpers using a zero-crossing approach. It is instructive to outline his procedure, since it is another method of obtaining the spectral density of the noise at the FM detector output.

Stumpers' technique implicitly assumes ideal limiting with essentially an infinite bandwidth limiter. The FM detector is then assumed to be a device whose output is a measure of the average number of zero crossings per second. For a narrowband i-f filter (bandwidth $2B \ll f_0$, the carrier frequency), it is easily shown that the detector output is the instantaneous frequency $d\phi/dt$ of previous paragraphs.

[1] F. L. H. M. Stumpers, Theory of Frequency-Modulation Noise, *Proc. IRE*, vol. 36, pp. 1081–1092, September, 1958.

To demonstrate this consider the time intervals shown in Fig. 3-7-1
The time interval τ is chosen such that

$$\frac{1}{f_0} \ll \tau \ll \frac{1}{2B} \tag{3-7-1}$$

Then τ is large enough to enable us to count many zeros in the interval,
but it is small enough so that the average number of zeros does not change
appreciably. (Recall that significant voltage changes occur only over

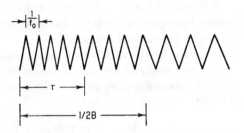

FIG. 3-7-1. Time intervals in zero-crossing analysis.

an interval the order of $1/2B$.) The instantaneous radian frequency, or
discriminator output, is then defined as

$$\omega_i \equiv \frac{\pi}{\tau} \times \text{number of zeros in } \tau \text{ sec}$$
$$= \frac{2\pi}{\tau} \times \text{number of positive zero crossings in } \tau \text{ sec} \tag{3-7-2}$$

Now assume the time function at the i-f output is the phase- or frequency-modulated carrier

$$v(t) = A \cos [\omega_0 t + \phi(t)] \tag{3-7-3}$$

Assume this has consecutive zeros at times t_1 and t_2. Then $v(t)$ changes
π radians in this interval, or

$$\omega_0(t_1 - t_2) + \phi(t_1) - \phi(t_2) = \pi \tag{3-7-4}$$

But $\phi(t)$ is assumed varying slowly over this interval $(\tau \ll 1/2B)$. Then

$$\phi(t_1) - \phi(t_2) \doteq (t_1 - t_2)\dot{\phi}(t_1) \tag{3-7-5}$$

or

$$(t_1 - t_2) \doteq \frac{\pi}{\omega_0 + \dot{\phi}(t_1)} \tag{3-7-6}$$

This is by hypothesis the time between successive zeros. In τ sec
$(\tau \gg t_1 - t_2)$ there will be $\tau/(t_1 - t_2)$ zeros. The instantaneous frequency
is therefore given, from Eqs. (3-7-2) and (3-7-6), by

$$\omega_i = \frac{\pi}{\tau}\left(\frac{\tau}{t_1 - t_2}\right) = \omega_0 + \dot{\phi}(t) \tag{3-7-7}$$

in agreement with the definition of instantaneous frequency noted
previously.

Since we have shown, following Stumpers' procedure, that a zero-counting technique results in the same instantaneous frequency or FM detector output defined previously, it now remains to set up a method of counting the zero crossings of the time function $v(t)$, consisting of signal plus noise, that appears at the i-f output. Stumpers utilizes an ingenious representation of the average number of zero crossings of $v(t)$ in the time interval τ. This number varies slowly with time about the carrier frequency ω_0. In the case of an unmodulated carrier plus noise the time variation about ω_0 is due to the noise. Expanding this in a Fourier series we can find, following Stumpers' approach, the spectrum of the output-noise perturbation about the desired output.

Stumpers' representation of the number of zero crossings in τ sec as a function of $v(t)$ is obtained using an impulse-function counting technique. Assume at first that $v(t)$ has one zero crossing in the τ-sec interval. Then from the definition of the impulse function

$$\int \delta(v)\, dv = \int \delta(v) \frac{dv}{dt}\, dt = \int_{t_0-\tau/2}^{t_0+\tau/2} \delta(v)\dot{v}\, dt = 1 \qquad (3\text{-}7\text{-}8)$$

The impulse function provides a count of 1 here.

Now assume several zeros appear in this interval. Equation (3-7-8) as it stands no longer provides a correct count of the number of zeros because $\dot{v}$ changes sign from one zero to the next. Consider instead the integral

$$\int_{t_0-\tau/2}^{t_0+\tau/2} \delta(v)\dot{v}u(\dot{v})\, dt = n \qquad (3\text{-}7\text{-}9)$$

which is the number of positive zero crossings in τ sec. Multiplying by the unit-step function $u(\dot{v})$ ensures that only positive values of $\dot{v}$ contribute to the integral. The integral has a value of 1 in the interval of any positive zero crossing, so that over the range τ sec long it measures the total number of zero crossings.

From Eq. (3-7-2), then,

$$\omega_i(t_0) = \frac{2\pi}{\tau} \int_{t_0-\tau/2}^{t_0+\tau/2} \delta(v)\dot{v}u(\dot{v})\, dt \qquad (3\text{-}7\text{-}10)$$

We now have an expression for ω_i in terms of the arbitrary quantity $v(t)$.

The instantaneous frequency ω_i will vary slowly with time about the carrier frequency ω_0. An expansion of ω_i in a Fourier series will therefore give a dc contribution of ω_0 plus low-frequency terms ($f < B \ll f_0$) that represent the spectrum at the FM detector output. Using an arbitrary interval T sec long as the base period of the Fourier expansion ($T \gg \tau$),

$$\left.\begin{aligned} \omega_i(t) &= \frac{1}{T} \sum_{m=-\infty}^{\infty} c_m e^{j\omega_m t} \\ c_m &= \int_0^T \omega_i(t)e^{-j\omega_m t}\, dt \end{aligned}\right\} \qquad \omega_m \equiv 2\pi m/T \qquad (3\text{-}7\text{-}11)$$

The Fourier coefficient c_m can be evaluated by using Eq. (3-7-10). The *low-frequency* coefficients (those of interest in this case) can be obtained in simpler form, however, by use of the following artifice due to Stumpers: Break the T-sec interval up into τ-sec intervals,

$$c_m = \int_0^\tau \omega_i(t)e^{-j\omega_m t}\, dt + \int_\tau^{2\tau} + \int_{2\tau}^{3\tau} + \cdots + \int_{T-\tau}^{T} \quad (3\text{-}7\text{-}12)$$
$$= d_0 + d_1 + d_2 + \cdots$$

with
$$d_j \equiv \int_{j\tau}^{(j+1)\tau} \omega_i(t)e^{-j\omega_m t}\, dt \quad (3\text{-}7\text{-}13)$$

Then the Fourier coefficient c_m or spectral component at frequency ω_m is obtained by superposing the subcoefficients d_0, d_1, etc. Consider a typical coefficient d_j. This is the contribution to the spectrum due to the count of zero crossings in the time interval $j\tau \equiv x$ to $(j+1)\tau \equiv x + \tau$.

FIG. 3-7-2. Output of counting integral.

Consider the counting integral Eq. (3-7-9). As it sweeps through the τ-sec interval beginning at time x it generates the series of unit steps shown in Fig. 3-7-2. Over the τ-sec interval it produces essentially a pulse of amplitude n and width τ. The *low-frequency* spectrum of this narrow pulse $(\tau \ll T/m)$ is just

$$n\tau e^{-j\omega_m(x+\tau/2)}$$

the area of the pulse times the phase-shift term due to the time delay.[1] The coefficient d_j is just $2\pi/\tau$ times this, or

$$d_j = \frac{2\pi}{\tau}\, n\tau e^{-j\omega_m(x+\tau/2)} \quad (3\text{-}7\text{-}14)$$

This also can be obtained simply from Eq. (3-7-13) by noting that by hypothesis $\omega_i(t)$ is essentially constant and equal to $2\pi n/\tau$ over a τ-sec interval. Then

$$d_j \doteq \frac{2\pi n}{\tau} \int_x^{x+\tau} e^{-j\omega_m t}\, dt$$
$$= 2\pi n \left(\frac{\sin \omega_m\tau/2}{\omega_m\tau/2}\right) e^{-j\omega_m(x+\tau/2)} \quad (3\text{-}7\text{-}15)$$

after integration. But with $\omega_m\tau/2 \ll \pi/2$, the low-frequency assumption, we again obtain Eq. (3-7-14).

[1] Schwartz, *op. cit.*, chap. 2.

Replacing the parameter n in Eq. (3-7-14) by its representation in terms of the counting integral, Eq. (3-7-9),

$$d_j = 2\pi e^{-j\omega_m(x+\tau/2)} \int_x^{x+\tau} \delta(v)\dot{v}u(\dot{v})\, dt$$
$$\doteq 2\pi \int_x^{x+\tau} \delta(v)\dot{v}u(\dot{v})e^{-j\omega_m t}\, dt \qquad (3\text{-}7\text{-}16)$$

since the exponential term is essentially constant over the τ-sec interval under the low-frequency assumption ($\omega_m \tau \ll \pi/2$).

Reintroducing this low-frequency approximation to d_j in Eq. (3-7-12) and again integrating over the complete T-sec interval,

$$c_m = 2\pi \int_0^T \delta(v)\dot{v}u(\dot{v})e^{-j\omega_m t}\, dt \qquad (3\text{-}7\text{-}17)$$

Note from a comparison of Eqs. (3-7-11) and (3-7-17) that we have essentially replaced $\omega_i(t)$ by $2\pi\delta(v)\dot{v}u(\dot{v})$. The time function $\omega_i(t)$, in terms of its positive zero-crossing representation, appears as a series of pulses. The quantity $\delta(v)\dot{v}u(\dot{v})$ represents the same series of *impulses*. The *low-frequency* spectrum of both is the same and is what accounts intuitively for the conversion of one equation to the other.

The low-frequency Fourier-series expansion of $\omega_i(t)$ can thus be written

$$\left.\begin{aligned} \omega_i(t) &= \frac{1}{T}\sum_m c_m e^{j\omega_m t} \\ c_m &= 2\pi \int_0^T \delta(v)\dot{v}u(\dot{v})e^{-j\omega_m t}\, dt \end{aligned}\right\} \qquad (3\text{-}7\text{-}18)$$

$$\omega_m \equiv \frac{2\pi m}{T} \ll \frac{\pi}{\tau}$$

Although Eq. (3-7-18) shows the dependence of c_m on the input time function $v(t)$ (as measured at the i-f output), it is not useful for calculations because v and $\dot{v}$ appear in functional form as arguments of the impulse and step functions, respectively. The explicit dependence of c_m on $v(t)$ can be obtained, following Stumpers, by representing $\delta(v)$ and $\dot{v}u(\dot{v})$ in terms of their Fourier transforms. (There is a question of convergence here, however, so that one must then be careful in using these formulations). Thus,

$$\delta(v) = \frac{1}{2\pi} \int_{-\infty-jc}^{\infty-jc} e^{ju_1 v}\, du_1 \qquad (3\text{-}7\text{-}19)$$

is the usual Fourier-integral representation of the impulse function and

$$\dot{v}u(\dot{v}) = -\frac{1}{2\pi} \int_{-\infty-jc}^{\infty-jc} \frac{e^{ju_2 \dot{v}}}{u_2{}^2}\, du_2 \qquad (3\text{-}7\text{-}20)$$

the Fourier representation of a *ramp*.

(Recall that the Laplace transform of $tu(t)$ is $1/s^2$. We then write the *Fourier* transform of $tu(t)$ as $1/(jx)^2 = -1/x^2$. Convergence of the inverse integral, as in Eq. (3-7-20), is then ensured by choosing c properly.)

With these representations for $\delta(v)$ and $\dot{v}u(\dot{v})$, the coefficient c_m becomes

$$c_m = -\frac{1}{2\pi} \int_0^T e^{-j\omega_m t} \, dt \int_{-\infty}^{\infty} du_1 \int_{-\infty}^{\infty} du_2 u_2^{-2} e^{j(u_1 v + u_2 \dot{v})} \quad (3\text{-}7\text{-}21)$$

This expresses the low-frequency spectral component of $\omega_i(t)$, the discriminator output, in terms of $v(t)$, the i-f output. The power at frequency $\omega_m = 2\pi m/T$ is then $2c_m c_m^*/T^2$ and the *power density*, or *spectral density*, for a random function $v(t)$ is the limit, as $T \to \infty$, of $\langle 2|c_m|^2 \rangle/T$ (see Chap. 1).

Although Eq. (3-7-21) appears quite formidable and leads to rather cumbersome series expansions when evaluated for various time functions $v(t)$ of interest, Stumpers has used this technique to obtain the low-frequency discriminator-noise output spectral density for unmodulated carrier plus noise at the i-f output and sinusoidally modulated carrier plus noise. His results, for the two cases of rectangular and Gaussian i-f filters, check the results obtained independently by other investigators using the correlation-function technique described in the previous section. We shall not reproduce Stumpers' detailed calculations here, but simply indicate the method of attack used for random functions.

Thus, assume as does Stumpers, that $v(t)$ is given by signal plus noise

$$v(t) = A \cos \omega_0 t + n(t) \quad (3\text{-}7\text{-}22)$$

with the noise $n(t)$ representable by the Fourier-series model

$$n(t) = \sum_{M=1}^{M} [a_n \cos \omega_n t + b_n \sin \omega_n t) \quad (3\text{-}7\text{-}23)$$

The $2M$ Fourier coefficients a_n and b_n are assumed Gaussian-distributed and independent.

The Fourier coefficient c_m and corresponding power $2|c_m|^2/T^2$ at frequency f_m are first found by substituting Eq. (3-7-22) into Eq. (3-7-21). The ensemble average power is then found by writing

$$\left\langle \frac{2|c_m|^2}{T^2} \right\rangle - 2 \int\int \cdots \int da_1 \cdots da_m db_1$$

$$\cdots db_M p(a_1 \cdots b_M) \frac{|c_m|^2}{T^2} \quad (3\text{-}7\text{-}23)$$

with $p(a_1 \cdots b_M)$ the probability density of the $2M$ independent Gaussian variables.

3-8. A Heuristic Approach to FM Threshold Analysis— Rice's "Clicks" Analysis

The calculation of noise effects in FM detection using the techniques of the foregoing sections is quite tedious and frequently quite difficult mathematically. Physical insight into the phenomena taking place, particularly those leading to the first FM threshold in which the noise begins to increase precipitously, tends to become obscured in the mathematical manipulations. Extensions to different types of FM receivers, specifically to such feedback devices as the phase-locked loop and FM demodulators with feedback, are also extremely difficult.

It is therefore of considerable practical interest to consider an alternative approach to FM noise analysis which is suggested specifically by experimental measurements. This is Rice's analysis, leading to the FM noise threshold, in terms of the expected number of "clicks" per second at the output of an FM receiver. It is found experimentally that as the input noise begins to increase, individual clicks are heard at the receiver output. As the carrier-to-noise ratio continues to decrease, the number of clicks rapidly increases and the clicks merge into a crackling sound. It is at this point that the FM threshold is found to appear experimentally. We shall summarize Rice's analysis of this phenomenon,[1] comparing the noise spectral density curves and S/N curves with those obtained using the techniques of previous sections. In Sec. 3-9 we shall consider briefly an extension to FM demodulators with feedback.

Unmodulated Carrier. For simplicity's sake assume an unmodulated carrier. (Rice extends this to the case of modulation by both deterministic and random modulating signals.) Then, as previously, the carrier plus noise can be written

$$v(t) = A \cos \omega_0 t + n(t)$$
$$= G \cos (\omega_0 t + \phi) \tag{3-8-1}$$

Here
$$n(t) = x \cos \omega_0 t - y \sin \omega_0 t \tag{3-8-2}$$

and
$$\phi(t) = \tan^{-1} \frac{y}{x + A}$$

$$\doteq \frac{y}{A} \tag{3-8-3}$$

$$\gamma = A^2/2N \gg 1$$

With $y(t)$ a Gaussian variable $\phi(t)$ is very nearly Gaussian also in the high carrier-to-noise ($\gamma \gg 1$) case. The relations between ϕ, A, x, and y are shown in phasor form in Fig. 3-8-1. As y and x fluctuate randomly the angle ϕ will fluctuate correspondingly. Occasionally the angle ϕ

[1] S. O. Rice, "Noise in FM Receivers," chap. 25, pp. 395–424, in "Proceedings Symposium of Time Series Analysis," M. Rosenblatt (ed.), John Wiley & Sons, Inc., New York, 1963.

will change by $\pm 2\pi$ radians.   Examples are shown in Fig. 3-8-2.   The discriminator output, defined to be $d\phi/dt = \dot{\phi}(t)$, will then have pulses of area $\pm 2\pi$ superimposed on the (usually) Gaussian nature of the time fluctuations.   These pulses are shown directly below the corresponding variations of $\phi(t)$ in Fig. 3-8-2.   These pulses, passed through the lowpass filter of the FM discriminator, will produce the series of random clicks heard in practice. (The output pulses will of course be broad-ened considerably over the input pulses of Fig. 3-8-2.)

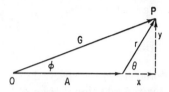

FIG. 3-8-1. Phasor diagram— unmodulated carrier plus noise.

It is apparent from the phasor diagram of Fig. 3-8-1 that the conditions for a posi-tive click to occur can be phrased in either of the following equivalent ways:

$$\pi < \theta < \pi + \Delta\theta, \, \dot{\theta} > 0 \qquad r > A$$
$$0 < y < \Delta y, \, \dot{y} < 0 \qquad x < -A$$

Either of these two equivalent statements will ensure that ϕ changes by $+2\pi$ radians.   Similarly, if θ happens to be in the range $-\pi$ to $-\pi - \Delta\theta$, with $\dot{\theta} < 0$, and $r > A$, ϕ will change by -2π radians and a

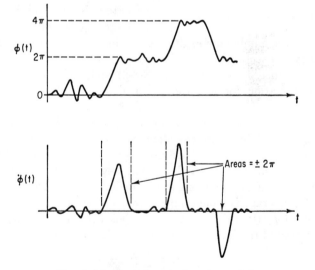

FIG. 3-8-2. Typical variation of ψ and $\dot{\phi}$.

negative click will occur.   The average number of clicks per unit time should depend on the i-f bandwidth, as will be verified in the analysis to follow.   As the carrier-to-noise ratio $\gamma \equiv A^2/2N$ decreases, the number of clicks per second should increase.   The threshold will then be said to occur when this number begins to get appreciably large.

Following Rice we now make the assumption that the total noise spectrum at the discriminator output (the spectrum of $\dot{\phi}$) will be the sum of the spectrum in the high carrier-to-noise case [see Sec. 3-4; this is the spectrum of the Gaussian component of $\dot{\phi}(t)$] plus that due to the noise clicks. Thus, assuming a symmetrical i-f filter to simplify the analysis, we postulate that

$$G_{\dot{\phi}}(f) = G_1(f) + G_2(f) \tag{3-8-4}$$

with

$$G_1(f) = 2\frac{\omega^2}{A^2} G_n(f + f_o) \tag{3-8-5}$$

and $G_n(f)$ the spectral density of the noise at the discriminator input. It is the additional term $G_2(f)$ assumed due to the clicks that will give rise to the threshold effect. We shall show that to a good approximation

$$G_2(f) = 4\pi^2(N_+ + N) = 8\pi^2 N_+ \tag{3-8-6}$$

with N_+ the average number of positive-going clicks per second and N_- the average number of negative-going clicks. For an unmodulated carrier $N_+ = N_-$.

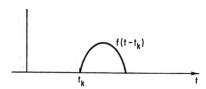

FIG. 3-8-3. Pulse at time t_k.

As noted by Rice, and as has also been verified experimentally, the rather simple form of Eq. (3-8-4) leads to noise spectral-density curves that agree quite well with those found using the more cumbersome, although perhaps more rigorous, approaches of the previous sections.

We now proceed to obtain Eq. (3-8-6) and, following that, a rather simple formulation for N_+, the average number of positive clicks per second.

Assume that the individual pulses of Fig. 3-8-2, of area $\pm 2\pi$, are spaced far enough apart to be independent of one another, and are therefore representable as Poisson-distributed shot-noise pulses.[1] Consider a sequence of positive pulses only. (The negative-pulse case is identical and the results of that analysis will be included at the end.) We assume that on the average N_+ such pulses occur per second. The sum of these gives rise to $\dot{\phi}_2^+(t)$, the positive-noise click component of $\dot{\phi}(t)$. Calling a pulse initiated randomly at time t_k, $f(t - t_k)$ (Fig. 3-8-3),

$$\dot{\phi}_2^+(t) = \sum_k f(t - t_k) \tag{3-8-7}$$

where

$$\int f(t - t_k)\, dt = 2\pi$$

It is apparent that $\dot{\phi}_2^+(t)$ may be visualized as the response of a linear

[1] Papoulis, "Probability, Random Variables, and Stochastic Processes," op. cit., pp. 287, 288; pp. 357–360; chap. 16. See also Davenport and Root, op. cit., pp. 119–123; S. O. Rice, Mathematical Analysis of Random Noise, Bell System Tech. J., vol. 23, 1944, articles 1.2 and 1.3.

filter with impulse response $f(t)$ to a Poisson-distributed sequence of impulses occurring randomly at time t_k, with N_+ the average number of such impulses per second. Calling this sequence of impulses $z(t)$,

$$z(t) = \sum_k \delta(t - t_k)$$

It is readily shown that the expected value of $z(t)$ is just N_+, while its spectral density $G_z(f)$ consists of this dc contribution plus a white-noise contribution equal to N_+:

$$\langle z \rangle = N_+$$
$$G_z(f) = (N_+)^2 \delta(f) + N_+ \tag{3-8-8}[1]$$

But we noted that $\dot{\phi}_2^+(t)$ can be represented as the convolution of $z(t)$ with $f(t)$:

$$\dot{\phi}_2^+(t) = \int_{-\infty}^{\infty} z(\tau) f(t - \tau)\, d\tau \tag{3-8-9}$$

Hence the ensemble average of $\dot{\phi}_2^+(t)$ is just

$$\langle \dot{\phi}_2^+ \rangle = \langle z \rangle \int_{-\infty}^{\infty} f(t - \tau)\, d\tau = 2\pi \langle z \rangle = 2\pi N_+ \tag{3-8-10}$$

Its spectral density is also given by

$$G_2^+(f) = (N_+)^2 F^2(0) \delta(f) + N_+ |F(\omega)|^2 \tag{3-8-11}$$

with $F(\omega)$ the Fourier Transform of $f(t)$.

Repeating for the negative-going clicks it is apparent that we get the same result except for a sign change in the average value:

$$\langle \dot{\phi}_2^- \rangle = -2\pi N_-$$

The overall ensemble average of $\dot{\phi}_2(t)$ (the random sequence of both positive and negative clicks) is then

$$\langle \dot{\phi}_2 \rangle = 2\pi(N_+ - N_-) = 0 \tag{3-8-12}$$

for the case of an unmodulated carrier, where we would expect $N_+ = N_-$. Similarly, the spectral density of the overall click sequence $\dot{\phi}_2(t)$ is given by

$$G_2(f) = |F(\omega)|^2 (N_+ + N_-) = 2N_+ |F(\omega)|^2 \tag{3-8-13}$$

if the positive and negative clicks have the same shape and the same average number. (Note that the dc contribution has cancelled out in calculating the spectrum of the overall sequence, under the assumption $N_+ = N_-$.)

We now make the further assumption that all the pulses may be approximated as delta functions of weight 2π. Since their width is on the average $\ll 1/f_m$, with f_m the video bandwidth, this is a valid assumption. (The clicks then are assumed to have a flat or white noise spectrum.

---

[1] Papoulis, *ibid.*, p. 358. [His λ is the same as our N^+ and his $2\pi\delta(\omega)$ is the same as our $\delta(f)$.]

This is valid providing the bandwidth f_m of the low-pass filter following the discriminator is $\ll$ the spectral width of the noise clicks, which is just the statement made concerning the width of the pulses compared with $1/f_m$.) This is equivalent to stating $f(t - t_k) \doteq 2\pi\delta(t - t_k)$, $|F(\omega)|^2 \doteq (2\pi)^2$, and

$$G_2(f) \doteq 4\pi^2(N_+ + N_-)$$
$$= 8\pi^2 N_+ \tag{3-8-14}$$

in the case of symmetrical positive and negative pulses. The total two-sided spectrum $G_{\dot\phi}(f)$, under the assumption that we simply add the click spectrum to $G_1(f)$, the high carrier-to-noise spectrum of $\dot\phi(t)$, is then

$$G_{\dot\phi}(f) \doteq 2\frac{\omega^2}{A^2} G_n(f + f_0) + 8\pi^2 \dot N_+ \tag{3-8-15}$$

Note that this introduces a nonzero value for $G_{\dot\phi}(0)$, as is found in the exact analyses of Rice, Wang, Stumpers, and Middleton referenced in the previous sections. In particular, we shall find good agreement between the spectrum $G_{\dot\phi}(f)$ of Eq. (3-8-15) and curves of the spectrum sketched previously even for the carrier-to-noise γ as low as 1.5.

To complete the picture here we need a quantitative expression for N_+, the average number of positive-going clicks per second. To do this we use the conditions for a click to occur noted previously. Thus, consider an arbitrary interval t_1 to $t_1 + \Delta t$, with Δt small enough so that the chance of a positive pulse being initiated is much less than one. For the shot-noise process assumed previously, we have $N_+ \Delta t$ as the probability of a positive click occurring. But this must be just the chance that at time t_1 the following three conditions are simultaneously satisfied:

$$\pi < \theta < \pi + \Delta\theta \qquad \dot\theta > 0 \qquad r > A$$

This gives

$$N_+ \Delta t = \int_A^\infty \int_\pi^{\pi+\Delta\theta} \int_0^\infty p(r,\theta,\dot\theta) \, dr \, d\theta \, d\dot\theta$$
$$= \frac{1}{2\pi} \int_A^\infty \int_0^\infty \Delta\theta \, p(r,\dot\theta) \, dr \, d\dot\theta \tag{3-8-16}$$

since $p(\theta)$ is uniformly distributed over the range 0 to 2π. Dividing through by Δt, taking the limit as $\Delta t \to 0$ with $\Delta\theta/\Delta t \to \dot\theta$, we get as the average number of clicks per second in the interval t_1 to $t_1 + \Delta t$,

$$N_+ = \frac{1}{2\pi} \int_A^\infty \int_0^\infty \dot\theta p(r,\dot\theta) \, dr \, d\dot\theta \tag{3-8-17}$$

(Note that this is just the average of $\dot\theta$ over all positive values, with $r > A$.)

Under the assumption of an unmodulated carrier, N_+ is the same over *any* interval and so represents the average number of clicks per second over the entire range. (We have of course invoked the ergodic hypothesis, equating ensemble and time averages.   This is not possible in general for the case of a modulated carrier, the average number of clicks changing from time to time because of the modulation.)

The joint distribution $p(r,\theta)$ for r and θ was found in Sec. 3-6 (see Eq. 3-6-10).   As written there,

$$p(r,\theta) = r^2 \exp - \frac{\dfrac{r^2}{2N} + \dfrac{r^2\theta^2}{2V}}{\sqrt{2\pi V}\, N} \tag{3-8-18}$$

with $N = \int_{-\infty}^{\infty} G_n(f)\, df$, the mean noise power, and

$$V = (2\pi)^2 \int_0^{\infty} (f - f_0)^2 2G_n(f)\, df \tag{3-8-19}$$

Inserting Eq. (3-8-18) into Eq. (3-8-17), integrating first with respect to θ and then r, we find

$$N_+ = \frac{1}{2\pi} \sqrt{\frac{V}{N}} \frac{1}{2} \operatorname{erfc} \sqrt{\gamma} \qquad \gamma \equiv A^2/2N \tag{3-8-20},$$

with $\operatorname{erfc} x = 1 - \operatorname{erf} x$ the complementary error function introduced in Chap. 1.

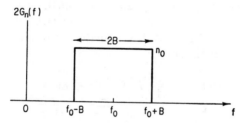

Fig. 3-8-4. One-sided spectral density, rectangular bandpass filter.

For large γ, $\operatorname{erfc} \sqrt{\gamma} \sim e^{-\gamma}/\sqrt{\pi\gamma}$, so that N_+, and hence the zero intercept of the noise spectrum $G_\phi(0)$, decreases as $e^{-\gamma}$.   This is in agreement with the exact analyses carried out by the investigators referenced previously.   In addition $1/2\pi \sqrt{V/N}$ is effectively the rms bandwidth about the carrier frequency f_0 [see Eq. (3-8-19] and is one measure of the spectral occupancy of the original FM signal. N_+ is thus proportional to the receiver bandwidth before detection, as to be expected.   In particular, for a receiver with the rectangular frequency characteristic of Fig. 3-8-4,

$$V = \frac{(2\pi)^2 n_0 (2B)^3}{12}$$

$$N = 2n_0 B$$

and

$$\frac{1}{2\pi} \sqrt{\frac{V}{N}} = \frac{2B}{\sqrt{12}} = \frac{B}{\sqrt{3}}$$

The rms bandwidth is thus $1/\sqrt{3}$ times the rectangular bandwidth B, and

$$N_+ = \frac{B}{2\sqrt{3}} \operatorname{erfc} \sqrt{\gamma}$$

Similar results are obtained for other filter shapes.

Equation (3-8-20) for N_+ can be obtained in an even simpler way by using the second of the two equivalent conditions under which a positive pulse is formed: This is the chance that at time t, the quadrature noise term y in Fig. 3-8-1 is in the vicinity of zero, while $dy/dt < 0$, and $x < -A$. Then,

$$N_+ \Delta t = \int_{-A}^{-\infty} \int_0^{\Delta y} \int_0^{-\infty} p(x,y,\dot{y})\, dx\, dy\, d\dot{y} \tag{3-8-21}$$

But, as noted in earlier sections, x, y, $\dot{y}$ are independent Gaussian variables with zero average value and variances given respectively by N, N, and V. Letting $y = 0$, dividing through by Δt and taking the limit as $\Delta t \to 0$, as previously, we find

$$N_+ = \int_{-A}^{-\infty} \int_0^{-\infty} \dot{y} p(x,0,\dot{y})\, dx\, d\dot{y} \tag{3-8-22}$$

Here $p(x,0,\dot{y}) = p(x)p(y)|_0\, p(\dot{y})$. Inserting the appropriate Gaussian functions and integrating, Eq. (3-8-20) is obtained.

In summary we now have Rice's result for the two-sided noise spectral density at the output of an FM discriminator with unmodulated carrier plus Gaussian noise at the input:

$$G_\phi(f) = 2\, \underbrace{\frac{\omega^2}{A^2}\, G_n(f + f_o)}_{G_1(f)} + \underbrace{8\pi^2 N_+}_{G_2(f)} \tag{3-8-15}$$

with

$$N_+ = \frac{1}{2\pi}\sqrt{\frac{V}{N}}\frac{1}{2} \operatorname{erfc} \sqrt{\gamma} \tag{3-8-20}$$

$1/2\pi \sqrt{V/N}$ the rms bandwidth just prior to the discriminator, and γ the carrier-to-noise ratio at that point.

As an example, $2G_\phi(f)$ (the one-sided spectral density) is plotted in Fig. 3-8-5 for the rectangular i-f filter and input noise spectral density of Fig. 3-8-4. A value of γ of 1.5 has been assumed. Also superimposed is the $\gamma = 1.5$ curve of Fig. 3-5-1, reproduced from Lawson and Uhlenbeck, op. cit., and based on the analysis described in Sec. 3-5. For the special case of a rectangular i-f filter,

$$\frac{2G_\phi(f)}{8\pi B} = \frac{\pi}{\gamma}\left(\frac{f}{2B}\right)^2 + \frac{2\pi}{\sqrt{12}} \operatorname{erfc} \sqrt{\gamma} \tag{3-8-23}$$

Note that although the exact and approximate spectra differ substantially in this case of carrier-to-noise ratio $= 1.5$, there are some marked similarities: The values at the origin are, respectively, 0.15 and 0.12 for the approximate and exact cases, the click approach thus providing a nonzero value close to the exact one; they both rise at roughly the same rate, the exact one peaking at $f = 0.4B$, the approximate case at $f = 0.5B$; their values beyond the peak are roughly the same.   For larger values of γ the agreement improves markedly.[1]

Further comparison between the exact and approximate analysis can be made on the basis of total noise out.   Thus assuming an ideal rectangular filter following the discriminator and cutting off at f_m cps, we find

$$N_0 = 2 \int_0^{f_m} G_\phi(f)\, df = \frac{2}{3} \frac{\pi^2}{B} \frac{f_m{}^3}{\gamma} + 16\pi^2 N_+ f_m \qquad (3\text{-}8\text{-}24)$$

for the click approximation.   This is sketched in normalized form in Fig.

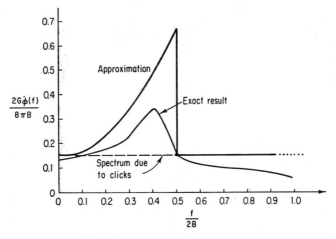

FIG. 3-8-5. Output noise spectrum, FM discriminator, exact and approximate case using "clicks" approach ($\gamma = 1.5$).

3-8-6 for the particular cases of $B/f_m = 10$ and $B/f_m = 5$ for comparison with the exact results as reproduced from Stumpers, *op. cit.*   (See also Fig. 3-5-2.)   Note the close correspondence between the two sets of curves.   Note especially the appearance of the noise threshold in the vicinity of $\gamma = 8$–10 db.   Above these values of carrier-to-noise ratio the number of clicks per second is small enough to be negligible and the Gaussian-type output noise dominates, leading to the usual high S/N FM performance.   Below these carrier-to-noise values the intensity of the clicks increases markedly, dominating the noise at the discriminator output and resulting in a sharp increase in output noise.

Similar curves can be drawn for the output S/N as a function of the carrier-to-noise ratio γ.   Assuming, as in previous sections, that the signal out is the signal measured in the absence of noise, while the noise out is

[1] Rice, *op. cit.*

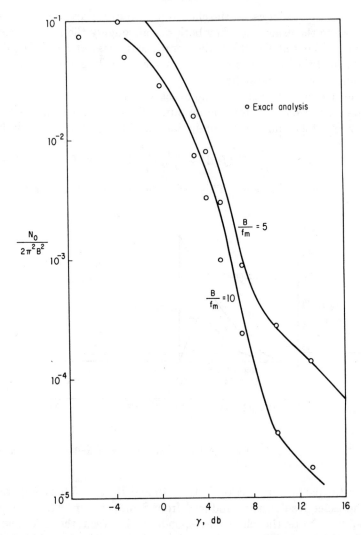

FIG. 3-8-6. Normalized output noise; exact and approximate cases (unmodulated carrier).

just N_0 above, evaluated for an unmodulated carrier, we get

$$\frac{S_0}{N_0} = \frac{3\beta^2\gamma(B/f_m)}{1 + 24B\gamma N_+/f_m^2} \tag{3-8-25}$$

In particular, for the rectangular i-f case,

$$\frac{S_0}{N_0} = \frac{3\beta^2\gamma(B/f_m)}{1 + 4\sqrt{3}\,\gamma(B/f_m)^2\,\text{erfc}\,\sqrt{\gamma}} \tag{3-8-25a}$$

For large modulation index ($\beta \gg 1$), the i-f bandwidth $2B \doteq 2\beta f_m$, so that the equation can be further rewritten in terms of β.   If the common rule-of-thumb bandwidth relation $2B \doteq 2(\beta + 1)f_m$ is utilized, the extension to smaller values of β is possible.[1]

A sketch of S_0/N_0 versus γ is shown in Fig. 3-8-7.   Also included are experimentally determined points for comparison.[2]

Rice has extended these results to include the effect of a modulating signal.   The reader is referred to his paper, cited at the beginning of this

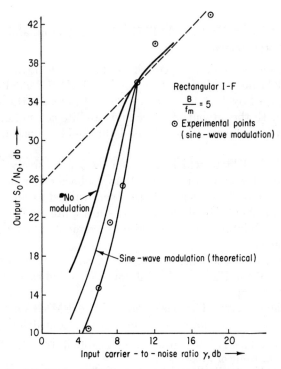

FIG. 3-8-7. Output S_0/N_0 for FM discriminator using "clicks" analysis.   (*From S. O. Rice, "Proceedings Symposium of Time Series Analysis," M. Rosenblatt (ed.), chap. 25, John Wiley & Sons, Inc., New York, 1963.   Experimental points due to Dr. D. Schilling.*)

section, for details of the analysis and curves obtained from it.   He has considered the case of both deterministic and random signals.   In particular, for sine-wave modulation, the average number of clicks per second increases appreciably over the unmodulated case.   The general trend of the S_0/N_0 curve is similar to that for the unmodulated case, however, the noise threshold occurring over roughly the same range of γ.   The enhanced

[1] See Sec. 3-10 for discussion of FM bandwidths.
[2] These were measured by Dr. D. Schilling and Mr. J. Billig of The Polytechnic Institute of Brooklyn.

increase of the expected number of clicks per second below the threshold causes the output S_0/N_0 to fall more sharply just below the threshold level in the modulation case.   The S_0/N_0 curve for sine-wave modulation is also plotted in Fig. 3-8-7.

Note that the curves of Fig. 3-8-7, showing output S_0/N_0 versus input carrier-to-noise ratio γ, stop short of the second threshold due to signal suppression.   As noted in an earlier section this second threshold occurs roughly in the vicinity of $\gamma = 0$ db.

3-9. Threshold Extension in FM : FMFB Demodulators and Phase-locked Loops[1]

Various schemes have been suggested for decreasing the noise threshold in FM.   An FM demodulator with feedback (FMFB demodulator) was originally proposed by J. G. Chaffee in 1939.[2]   Interest in this system has been revived with the advent of space and satellite communication, and experiments with Project Echo indicated threshold reduction of 7 db is quite feasible.[3]

The phase-locked loop, which has been used extensively in tracking applications and for maintaining the desired phase coherence of locally generated signals at a receiver, has also been utilized as an FM demodulator.[4]   Its threshold-reduction properties are quite similar to those of the FMFB demodulator[5] and threshold improvement of as much as 10 db has been obtained.[6]

We shall utilize Rice's "clicks" analysis in this section to discuss the S/N properties of the FMFB demodulator, and to indicate extensions to the phase-locked loop.[7]

FMFB Demodulator.   The basic form of the FMFB demodulator is shown in Fig. 3-9-1.   A noise-free situation is assumed for simplicity's

---

[1] The approach utilized in this section is due primarily to Dr. Donald Schilling of The Polytechnic Institute of Brooklyn.

[2] J. G. Chaffee, The Application of Negative Feedback to Frequency-modulation systems, *Bell System Tech. J.*, vol. 18, pp. 403–437, July, 1939.

[3] L. H. Enloe, Decreasing the Threshold in FM by Frequency Feedback, *Proc. IRE*, vol. 50, pp. 23–29, January, 1962.   Also, C. L. Ruthroff, Project Echo: FM Demodulators with Negative Feedback, *Bell System Tech. J.*, vol. 40, pp. 1149–1157, July, 1961.

[4] D. T. Hess, Theory and Design of FM Receivers, Report no. PIBMRI-1026-62, Electrical Engineering Dept., Polytechnic Institute of Brooklyn, May, 1962.

[5] J. A. Develet, A Threshold Criterion for Phase-Lock Demodulation, *Proc. IRE*, vol. 51, pp. 349–356, February, 1963.

[6] D. L. Schilling and J. Billig, A Comparison of the Threshold Performance of the Frequency Demodulator Using Feedback and the Phase-Locked Loop, Report no. PIBMRI-1207-64, Electrical Engineering Department, Polytechnic Institute of Brooklyn, February, 1964.   See also On the Threshold Extension Capability of PLL and the FDMFB, *Proc. IEEE*, vol. 52, p. 621, May, 1964.

[7] See Schilling and Billig, *op. cit.*, for a much more extensive treatment.

sake. The phase- or frequency-modulated carrier $A \cos (\omega_0 t + D)$ is multiplied by the output $C \cos [(\omega_0 - \omega_1)t + k\phi_1]$ of the voltage-controlled oscillator (VCO) shown. The frequency of the VCO is assumed proportional to the FMFB demodulator output $\dot{\phi}_1(t)$. Filter H_1, centered at f_1 cps, passes only the difference frequency term at the multiplier output, and this is detected by a standard FM discriminator. The combination H_1, discriminator, and low-pass filter following thus perform the same functions as the FM receiver analyzed in previous sections. The one crucial distinction is that the frequency-feedback operation effectively reduces the frequency deviation and hence the required bandwidth of H_1. It is this fact that results in the threshold extension. The FM signal at point (2) *inside* the loop behaves essentially as a *narrowband* FM signal.

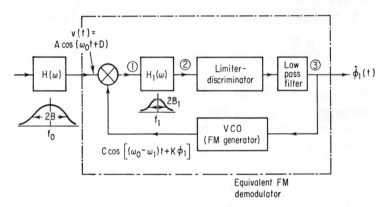

FIG. 3-9-1. FMFB demodulator.

In analyzing this FMFB demodulator we ignore the transient "locking" conditions. We assume steady-state behavior, with the VCO following the input carrier voltage $v(t)$ precisely.

From Fig. 3-9-1 the voltages at the various points indicated are written as follows:

$$\text{At (1)} \quad v_1 = AC \cos (\omega_0 t + D) \cos [(\omega_0 - \omega_1)t + k\phi_1] \qquad (3\text{-}9\text{-}1)$$

$$\text{(2)} \quad v_2 = \frac{AC}{2} \cos [\omega_1 t + D - k\phi_1] \qquad (3\text{-}9\text{-}2)$$

$$\text{(3)} \quad v_3 = \dot{D} - k\dot{\phi}_1 = \dot{\phi}_1 \qquad (3\text{-}9\text{-}3)$$

Hence
$$\dot{\phi}_1 = \frac{\dot{D}}{1 + k} \qquad (3\text{-}9\text{-}4)$$

and the output $\dot{\phi}_1$ is exactly the desired FM signal $\dot{D}$ reduced by the feedback factor $(1 + k)$. The phase term $D - k\phi_1$ in Eq. (3-9-2) is thus $\phi_1 = D/(1 + k)$, and the bandwidth required of $H_1(\omega)$ is $1/(1 + k)$ of the bandwidth of $H(\omega)$ (subject, however, to the restriction that it cannot be less than that required to pass the signal v_2).

As an example, assume $\dot{D} = \Delta\omega \cos \omega_m t$ (sinusoidal modulating signal). Then $D = \beta \sin \omega_m t$, with the modulation index $\beta = \Delta\omega/\omega_m$, and $\phi_1 = [\beta/(1 + k)] \sin \omega_m t$ and $\dot{\phi}_1 = [\Delta\omega/(1 + k)] \cos \omega_m t$. The effective modulation index and frequency deviation inside the loop are thus reduced by the feedback factor. The mean-squared output signal is $\frac{1}{2}(\Delta\omega)^2/(1 + k)^2$.

Now consider the case of an unmodulated carrier plus noise. (We shall consider this case only, just as in previous sections. The extension to the case of a modulated carrier can be made straightforwardly by using Rice's "clicks" analysis for a modulated carrier.) The voltage at the input to the FMFB demodulator can be written in the usual narrowband form

$$v(t) = (A + x) \cos \omega_0 t - y \sin \omega_0 t \tag{3-9-5}$$

After multiplication by the VCO output, $C \cos [(\omega_0 - \omega_1)t + k\phi_1]$, and filtering by $H_1(\omega)$, the voltage v_2 at point (2) in Fig. 3-9-1 becomes

$$\begin{aligned} 2v_2 &= (A + x_1)C \cos (\omega_1 t - k\phi_1) - y_1 C \sin (\omega_1 t - k\phi_1) \\ &= RC \cos (\omega_1 t + \theta_1 - k\phi_1) \end{aligned} \tag{3-9-6}$$

with
$$\theta_1 = \tan^{-1} \frac{y_1}{x_1 + A}$$

In writing this expression we have made use of the fact that the bandwidth f_m of the low-pass filter at the discriminator output is much less than the bandwidth B of the noise terms x and y. The random variables ϕ_1 and x, y can thus be assumed uncorrelated:

$$\langle \phi_1 x \rangle = \langle \phi_1 y \rangle = 0 \qquad f_m \ll B \tag{3-9-7}$$

The variables $x_1(t)$ and $y_1(t)$ are the noise terms passed through filter $H_1(\omega)$ of bandwidth $2B_1$. Hence,

$$N_1 = \langle x_1{}^2 \rangle = \langle y_1{}^2 \rangle = N \frac{B_1}{B} \tag{3-9-8}$$

with $2B$ the bandwidth of the original noise and N its mean-squared value. (If $B_1 \ll B$, $\langle xx_1 \rangle = \langle yy_1 \rangle \doteq 0$.) Assuming rectangular bandpass filters throughout and ignoring gain constants (both signal and noise are multiplied by the same constants), the one-sided spectral density of $x_1(t)$ and $y_1(t)$ is the same as that of the original $x(t)$ and $y(t)$:

$$\left. \begin{aligned} 2G_x(f) = 2G_y(f) &= \begin{cases} 2n_0 & 0 < f < B \\ 0 & \text{elsewhere} \end{cases} \\ 2G_{x_1}(f) = 2G_{y_1}(f) &= \begin{cases} 2n_0 & 0 < f < B_1 \\ 0 & \text{elsewhere} \end{cases} \end{aligned} \right\} \tag{3-9-9}$$

Since the discriminator output $\dot{\phi}_1$ is by definition the time derivative of the phase factor in Eq. (3-9-6) we have

$$\phi_1 = \frac{\theta_1}{1 + k} = \frac{1}{1 + k} \tan^{-1} \frac{y_1}{x_1 + A} \tag{3-9-10}$$

In the case of high carrier-to-noise ratio $A^2 \gg N_1$, we can then write, as in Sec. 3-4,

$$\dot{\phi}_1 \doteq \frac{1}{1+k} \frac{\dot{y}_1}{A} \qquad A^2 \gg N_1 \qquad (3\text{-}9\text{-}11)$$

The mean-squared output noise at the output of the low-pass filter following the discriminator is thus, as in Sec. 3-4,

$$N_0 = \frac{2}{3} \frac{\pi^2}{B} f_m{}^3 \frac{1}{\gamma(1+k)^2} \qquad (3\text{-}9\text{-}12)$$

with $\gamma = A^2/2N = A^2/4n_0 B$ again the carrier-to-noise at the FMFB demodulator input. [This assumes rectangular filters. See Eq. (3-4-28).] Note that the mean-squared output noise appears reduced by the same factor $(1+k)^2$, as does the signal in the noise-free case. *There is thus no change in the output S/N due to feedback.* For example, for a sine-wave modulating signal, with the mean-squared output given, as noted above, by $S_0 = \frac{1}{2}(\Delta\omega)^2/(1+k)^2$, we have, just as in the usual FM case,

$$\frac{S_0}{N_0} = 3\beta^2 \gamma \frac{B}{f_m} \qquad A^2 \gg N_1 = \frac{B_1}{B} \qquad (3\text{-}9\text{-}13)$$

Here $\beta = \Delta f/f_m$ is the modulation index, $\gamma = A^2/2N$, and f_m is the bandwidth of the output low-pass filter.

The FMFB demodulator gives no additional S/N improvement above that provided by the common FM discriminator. However, note from the condition on the validity of Eq. (3-9-13) that the range of input carrier-to-noise ratios over which the FM S/N improvement is obtained has apparently been extended by the ratio of bandwidths B/B_1. Thus Eq. (3-9-13) is valid for $A^2 \gg N_1 = NB_1/B$. We would thus expect the FM threshold to be reduced by the ratio B/B_1 of the bandwidths. A more detailed analysis to follow using the "clicks" approach will bear this out. (The threshold now occurs approximately at the point where $\gamma_1 = \gamma B/B_1$ is 10 db, with a corresponding reduction in terms of the input carrier-to-noise ratio γ).

The ratio of bandwidths and threshold improvement possible depends on both the modulation index and the feedback factor k. As noted earlier, the effect of the feedback is to reduce the modulation index by the factor $(1+k)$. Using as the required FM bandwidth the rule-of-thumb expression $B \doteq (\beta + 1)f_m$ (for $\beta \gg 1$ this gives $B = \beta f_m = \Delta f$ and for $\beta \ll 1$, the narrowband FM case, $B \doteq f_m$), we have

$$\frac{B_1}{B} \doteq \frac{\beta/(1+k) + 1}{\beta + 1} \qquad (3\text{-}9\text{-}14)$$

For $k \gg 1$, $B_1/B \doteq 1/(\beta + 1)$. This corresponds to the case where the effective modulation index $\beta/(1 + k)$ is so low because of the large feed-back factor that $H_1(\omega)$ need only have the minimum bandwidth f_m nec-essary to pass the modulating signal.   If $\beta = 5$, we get a threshold reduc-tion of $\doteq 7$ db.   If $\beta = 10$, the reduction is 10 db.

For smaller values of feedback factor the improvement is of course less. In particular, with $k = 1$, the improvement expected is from 2 to 3 db. Experimental verification of these results has been obtained.[1]   (See Fig. 3-9-2.)

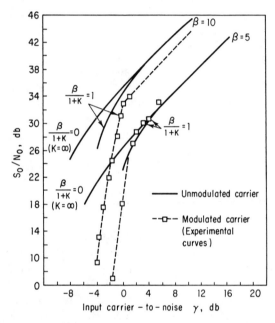

FIG. 3-9-2. FMFB demodulator characteristic.   *(From D. Schilling and J. Billig, On the Threshold Extension Capability of the PLL and the FMFB, Proc. IEEE, vol. 52, p. 621, May, 1964, Fig. 2.)*

The threshold effect in the FMFB demodulator can be analyzed more precisely and a quantitative expression for the output-input S/N char-acteristic obtained by use of the Rice "clicks" analysis.   This is done quite simply by noting that the feedback reduces the instantaneous signal and noise terms by the same factor $(1 + k)$.   In the previous section a click was assumed to occur whenever the phase angle ϕ at the input to the discriminator changed by 2π radians.   This gave rise to impulses in $\dot\phi$ of area 2π.   Here the corresponding angle is ϕ_1 (Fig. 3-9-1) and a click will be assumed to occur when ϕ_1 changes by $2\pi/(1 + k)$ radians. $\dot\phi_1(t)$ will then consist of an impulse of area $2\pi/(1 + k)$.   This impulse passing through the low-pass filter gives rise to the click.   Equa-

---

[1] Schilling and Billig, *op. cit.*

tion (3-8-14) for the spectrum of the clicks is then modified to read

$$G_2(f) \doteq \frac{8\pi^2}{(1+k)^2} N_+ \tag{3-9-15}$$

with
$$N_+ = \frac{1}{4\pi} \sqrt{\frac{V_1}{N_1}} \, \mathrm{erfc} \sqrt{\gamma_1} \tag{3-9-16}$$

the average number of clicks per second. Here V_1, N_1, and γ_1 depend on the properties of the noise at point (2) in the FMFB demodulator. In particular, for $H_1(\omega)$ a rectangular bandpass filter of bandwidth $2B_1$,

$$N_+ = \frac{B_1}{\sqrt{12}} \, \mathrm{erfc} \sqrt{\gamma_1} \qquad \gamma_1 = \frac{B\gamma}{B_1} \tag{3-9-17}$$

Proceeding as in the previous section the total noise power at the output of the low-pass filter following the discriminator is the sum of the Gaussian background-noise power (the noise in the high carrier-to-noise case) and the noise power due to the clicks. This gives

$$N_0 = \frac{2}{3} \frac{\pi^2}{B} \frac{f_m^3}{(1+k)^2 \gamma} + \frac{16\pi^2}{(1+k)^2} N_+ f_m \tag{3-9-18}$$

[Compare with Eq. (3-8-24).]   Again assuming a sinusoidal FM modulating signal of amplitude $\Delta\omega$ the output power due to signal alone is $S_0 = \frac{1}{2}[\Delta\omega/(1+k)]^2$, and the output S/N becomes

$$\frac{S_0}{N_0} = \frac{3\beta^2 \gamma \dfrac{B}{f_m}}{1 + 4\sqrt{3}\, \dfrac{BB_1\gamma}{f_m^2} \, \mathrm{erfc} \sqrt{\gamma_1}} \tag{3-9-19}$$

[Compare with Eq. (3-8-25a).]   Here $f_m \leq B_1 \leq B$, $\gamma_1 = (B/B_1)\gamma$, and $\gamma \equiv A^2/2N$ is the carrier-to-noise ratio at the input to the FMFB demodulator.   (Note again that γ_1 is the corresponding ratio at the discriminator input.)

The feedback factor $1 + k$ can be made explicit by writing, as previously, $B \doteq (\beta + 1)f_m$, $B_1 \doteq [\beta/(1+k) + 1]f_m$. The "best" possible case corresponds to the one for which $k \gg 1$ and $B_1 \doteq f_m$. The normal FM discriminator result is of course obtained by setting $B_1 = B$ and $\gamma_1 = \gamma$. To a good approximation, since $\mathrm{erfc}\sqrt{\gamma} \sim e^{-\gamma}$ for $\gamma \gg 1$, the erfc term dominates and changes in threshold correspond to changes in $\mathrm{erfc}\sqrt{\gamma_1}$, or, more specifically to B/B_1, as noted earlier.

The effect of modulation also can be taken into account, as noted previously, with the help of Rice's results for this case.[1]   As in the case of the normal FM discriminator the modulating signal is found to have negligible effect on the threshold location.

[1] See D. Schilling and J. Billig, op. cit.

Equation (3-9-19) has been plotted in Fig. 3-9-2. Also superimposed are experimental points obtained for the case of sinusoidal modulation with $\beta = 5$ and 10.[1] (The displacement of the $\beta = 10$ curve from the theoretical curve is attributed to difficulty in measuring the output noise level, which was quite low because of the feedback.) The measurements were made with $\beta/(1 + k) = 1$, so that the threshold improvement predicted by Eq. (3-9-14) is $2/(1 + \beta)$, or 7.4 db in the case of $\beta = 10$ and 4.8 db in the case of $\beta = 5$. Recalling that the normal FM threshold occurs at roughly 10 db (see Fig. 3-8-7), we would expect the thresholds here to appear at 2.5 db and 5 db for $\beta = 10$ and 5, respectively. Note that the theoretical curves do begin to deviate from the high carrier-to-noise straight line at roughly these values. Theoretical curves are also drawn for the limiting case of infinite feedback, with the additional threshold extension possible indicated.

The theoretical curves are subject to substantial error below the threshold and so should be interpreted carefully below that point. As noted in the previous section the "clicks" analysis becomes somewhat inaccurate in that region, while signal-suppression effects, which ultimately tend to a second threshold, have been ignored. The theoretical curves shown are also for the unmodulated case. Note, as mentioned in the previous section, and as shown by the experimental points, that the effect of modulation is to produce a sharper drop below the threshold.

Phase-locked Loop as an FM Demodulator. The basic configuration for the phase-locked loop as an FM demodulator is shown in Fig. 3-9-3. The second harmonic suppressor shown is not actually necessary for FM demodulation to take place,[2] but its presence simplifies the discussion considerably. (In practice there will always be a certain amount of high-frequency filtering, and the effects can be lumped in there.) An amplifier of gain $-G$ would perform the function of sign-changing indicated. Note that the voltage-controlled oscillator provides an output at frequency f_0, the carrier frequency, in this case. (Compare with the FMFB demodulator in Fig. 3-9-1). We also assume the VCO output to be $C \sin (\omega_0 t + k\phi_1)$ rather than $C \cos [(\omega_0 - \omega_1)t + k\phi_1]$ as in the FMFB case. This corresponds to steady-state operation, with the phase-locked loop essentially "locked in" to the incoming carrier, and we again ignore the dynamics of locking in the presence of both signal and noise.[3]

To demonstrate the FM demodulation property of the loop, we simply perform the multiplication indicated and get at the output, after sup-

[1] *Ibid.*

[2] Hess, *op. cit.*, p. 72.

[3] D. L. Schilling and M. Schwartz, The Response of an Automatic Phase Control system to FM Signals and Noise, *IRE Intern. Conv. Rec.*, part 8, pp. 111–121, 1962. Also D. L. Schilling, The Response of an APC System to FM Signals in Noise, *Proc. IEEE*, vol. 51, pp. 1306–1316, October, 1963.

pressing the second harmonic of the carrier,

$$\dot{\phi}_1 = -\frac{ACG}{2} \sin{(k\phi_1 - D)} \tag{3-9-20}$$

Assuming $k\phi_1 - D \ll \pi/2$ (this is close to the condition of lock and gives the usual linearized version of the phase-locked loop), we get the linearized differential equation of the system:

$$\dot{\phi}_1 + \omega_a\phi_1 = \frac{ACG}{2} D \qquad k\phi_1 - D \ll \frac{\pi}{2} \tag{3-9-21}$$

Here $\omega_a \equiv \frac{ACGk}{2}$ is the closed-loop equivalent bandwidth of the linearized model of the circuit.

With time constant $1/\omega_a$, it is apparent that $\phi_1(t) \to D(t)/k$, *providing* $D(t)$ *varies slowly enough so that it is effectively constant in the time*

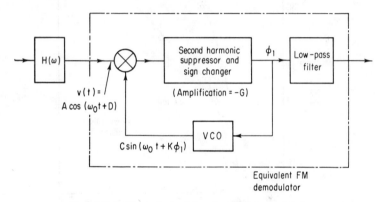

Fig. 3-9-3. Phase-locked loop as FM demodulator.

$1/\omega_a$. With $D(t)$ or the FM signal $\dot{D}(t)$ band-limited to ω_m radians/sec, this implies $\omega_a \gg \omega_m$. Under this condition the device does function as an FM demodulator, since the output is $\dot{\phi}_1(t) = (1/k)\dot{D}(t)$. (Note how similar this is to the FMFB case.) Actually, this condition is already implied in the condition leading to Eq. (3-9-21). For with the assumption that $k\phi_1 - D \ll \pi/2$, we have

$$k\phi_1 - D \doteq \frac{-2}{ACG}\dot{\phi}_1 \doteq \frac{1}{\omega_a}\dot{D}(t) \ll \frac{\pi}{2} \tag{3-9-22}$$

Assuming for simplicity's sake that the modulating signal is sinusoidal, we have $D(t) = \beta \sin{\omega_m t}$, and

$$\frac{\omega_m\beta}{\omega_a} \cos{\omega_m t} \ll \frac{\pi}{2}$$

This is of course satisfied if

$$\frac{\omega_m}{\omega_a} \ll \frac{\pi}{2\beta} \tag{3-9-23}$$

For the wideband FM case in which we would normally consider using the phase-locked loop as an FM discriminator, $\beta > \pi/2$ and we thus have

$$\dot{\phi}_1(t) \doteq \frac{1}{k}\dot{D}(t) \qquad \frac{\omega_m}{\omega_a} \ll \frac{\pi}{2\beta} < 1 \qquad (3\text{-}9\text{-}24)[1]$$

It is interesting to note that the phase-locked loop demodulates an FM signal under the condition indicated without the use of an FM discriminator in the usual sense of the word! The necessary differentiation of a phase term is accomplished by the inverse operation of phase modulation

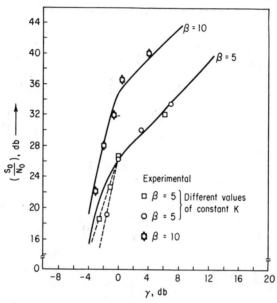

FIG. 3-9-4. Phase-locked loop characteristics. (*From D. Schilling and J. Billig, On the Threshold Extension Capability of the PLL and the FMFB, Proc. IRE, vol. 52, p. 621, May, 1964, Fig. 4.*)

of the VCO in the feedback path, using the integral of the output voltage $\dot{\phi}_1$.

If noise is now added to the signal at the input to the phase-locked loop, and the carrier-to-noise ratio is "high enough," the device behaves just like the normal FM detector or FMFB demodulator, providing the same S/N improvement, or noise suppression at the output.

The threshold value of carrier-to-noise ratio below which the S/N improvement rapidly deteriorates, is found to be substantially below that of the normal FM detector, however. The phase-locked loop and the FMFB demodulator both provide threshold improvement. Experimental

---

[1] Hess, *op. cit.*, chap. 3, pp. 73–78, includes much more detailed design information. See also Enloe, *op. cit.*

points of S_0/N_0 versus the carrier-to-noise ratio γ are shown in Fig. 3-9-4.[1] A sinusoidal modulating signal was used in the experiments. The two sets of curves for $\beta = 5$ correspond to two different values of k. Note that the threshold occurs at $\gamma \doteq 0$ db. For these values of β the phase-locked loop provides 10 db of threshold improvement.

3-10. FM Spectrum Analysis, Noiselike Modulating Signal[2]

It was noted in Sec. 3-4 that the rule-of-thumb value for the bandwidth of an FM signal is commonly given as

$$2B \doteq 2(\beta + 1)f_m \qquad (3\text{-}10\text{-}1)$$

This is based on sinusoidal-modulating-signal analysis, with f_m the modulating frequency and β the modulation index given by

$$\beta = \frac{\Delta f}{f_m} \qquad (3\text{-}10\text{-}2)$$

Δf is, for sinusoidal signals, the maximum instantaneous frequency excursion away from the carrier frequency and represents the amplitude of the sinusoidal modulating signal.

In particular, for $\beta \gg 1$, or wideband FM,

$$2B \to 2\Delta f \qquad (3\text{-}10\text{-}1a)$$

and for $\beta \ll 1$, or narrowband FM,

$$2B \to 2f_m \qquad (3\text{-}10\text{-}1b)$$

The wideband FM result is also obtained for various other kinds of deterministic modulating signals.[3] The narrowband case is obtained very simply for *any* modulating signal $s(t)$ band-limited to f_m cps by trigonometric expansion of the expression for the FM signal in Eq. (3-4-2).

It is of interest to consider an extension of these results to a noiselike modulating signal as a more realistic representation of the complex modulating signals encountered in FDM or multichannel common-carrier FM systems. (See Chap. 5.) Specifically, we assume an FM signal centered at carrier frequency f_0 and given by

$$v(t) = A \cos [\omega_0 t + \phi(t)] \qquad (3\text{-}10\text{-}3)$$

[1] Schilling and Billig, *op. cit.*

[2] The approach here follows that of Dr. D. T. Hess, Theory and Design of FM Receivers, Report No. PIBMRI-1026-62, Electrical Engineering Dept., Polytechnic Institute of Brooklyn, May, 1962, sec. 1.1. See also, D. Middleton, "Introduction to Statistical Communication Theory," chap. 14, for extensions and references to the literature.

[3] See, e.g., H. S. Black, "Modulation Theory," *op. cit.*, and S. Goldman, "Frequency Analysis, Modulation, and Noise," McGraw-Hill Book Company, New York, 1948. D. Middleton, "Introduction to Statistical Communication Theory," *op. cit.*, considers both deterministic and random-type signals.

The phase-modulation term $\phi(t)$ is assumed to be stationary Gaussian noise of zero mean value and spectral density $G_\phi(f)$. The output of an FM discriminator is then $d\phi/dt \equiv \dot\phi(t)$, with spectral density

$$G_{\dot\phi}(f) = \omega^2 G_\phi(f)$$

The mean-squared phase variation is then

$$\langle \phi^2 \rangle = \int_{-\infty}^{\infty} G_\phi(f)\, df = R_\phi(0) \tag{3-10-4}$$

with $R_\phi(\tau)$ the correlation function of $\phi(t)$. The mean-squared output of the FM discriminator, or the mean-squared signal output in this case, is given by

$$(\Delta\omega)^2 \equiv \int_{-\infty}^{\infty} G_{\dot\phi}(f)\, df = \int_{-\infty}^{\infty} \omega^2 G_\phi(f)\, df = R_{\dot\phi}(0) \tag{3-10-5}$$

The rms frequency deviation $\Delta\omega$, defined here in a statistical sense, is comparable to the maximum frequency deviation $\Delta\omega$ defined previously for sinusoidal signals.

We shall find shortly that the value of the mean-squared phase fluctuation $\langle \phi^2 \rangle = R_\phi(0)$ determines whether the FM signal $v(t)$ is to be narrow or wideband. Thus, $R_\phi(0) \ll 1$ will be the condition for narrowband FM and $R_\phi(0) \gg 1$ the condition for wideband FM. Alternatively, to relate this analysis more closely to that of the usual sinusoidal analysis, we can define a modulation index β and show that narrowband FM corresponds to $\beta \ll 1$, wideband FM to $\beta \gg 1$.

In particular we define β as the ratio of the rms frequency deviation $\Delta f = \Delta\omega/2\pi$ to the rms bandwidth $B_{\dot\phi}$ of $\dot\phi(t)$, the FM discriminator output. Thus, assuming $\phi(t)$ and $\dot\phi(t)$ are baseband signals, we have as the mean-squared bandwidth of $\dot\phi$,

$$(B_{\dot\phi})^2 = \frac{\displaystyle\int_{-\infty}^{\infty} f^2 G_{\dot\phi}(f)\, df}{\displaystyle\int_{-\infty}^{\infty} G_{\dot\phi}(f)\, df} \tag{3-10-6}$$

(Note that this is the same sort of definition that arose in the "clicks" analysis of Sec. 3-8. The rms equivalent bandwidth in cps there was $1/2\pi \sqrt{V/N}$). We then define the modulation index β as

$$\beta \equiv \frac{\Delta f}{B_{\dot\phi}} \tag{3-10-7}$$

This index, defined in terms of rms frequencies, is to be compared with the modulation index for sinusoidal modulating signals, defined as the ratio of the maximum frequency deviation Δf to the modulation frequency f_m.

We can relate the β defined here to $R_\phi(0)$ by also defining the rms bandwidth B_ϕ of the phase-modulation signal $\phi(t)$:

$$(B_\phi)^2 = \frac{\int_{-\infty}^{\infty} f^2 G_\phi(f)\, df}{\int_{-\infty}^{\infty} G_\phi(f)\, df}$$

$$= \frac{(\Delta f)^2}{R_\phi(0)} \tag{3-10-8}$$

Since $G_{\dot\phi}(f) = \omega^2 G_\phi(f)$, we can rewrite Eq. (3-10-6) in terms of $G_\phi(f)$. Then, taking the ratio of bandwidths squared, we get

$$\left(\frac{B_\phi}{B_{\dot\phi}}\right)^2 = \frac{\left[\int_{-\infty}^{\infty} f^2 G_\phi(f)\, df\right]^2}{\left[\int_{-\infty}^{\infty} f^4 G_\phi(f)\, df\right]\left[\int_{-\infty}^{\infty} G_\phi(f)\, df\right]} \tag{3-10-9}$$

We would expect this ratio to be <1, since differentiation serves to increase the bandwidth of a signal. This is readily verified here by utilizing the Schwarz inequality

$$\left[\int_{-\infty}^{\infty} a(x)b(x)\, dx\right]^2 \le \int_{-\infty}^{\infty} a^2(x)\, dx \int_{-\infty}^{\infty} b^2(x)\, dx \tag{3-10-10}$$

Denoting $f^2\sqrt{G_\phi(f)}$ by $a(f)$ and $\sqrt{G_\phi(f)}$ by $b(f)$, we note that Eq. (3-10-9) is in exactly the form of Eq. (3-10-10) and we get $(B_\phi/B_{\dot\phi}) \le 1$. (Actually the equality here is only valid if $G_\phi(f)$ is an impulse at frequency B_ϕ.)

But, from Eq. (3-10-8), we have

$$R_\phi(0) = \left(\frac{\Delta f}{B_\phi}\right)^2 = \left(\frac{\Delta f}{B_{\dot\phi}}\right)^2 \left(\frac{B_{\dot\phi}}{B_\phi}\right)^2$$

$$= \beta^2 \left(\frac{B_{\dot\phi}}{B_\phi}\right)^2 > \beta^2 \tag{3-10-11}$$

We shall show that the actual condition for narrowband FM is $R_\phi(0) \ll 1$. Then $\beta^2 \ll 1$ is an equivalent condition. The condition for wideband FM will turn out to be $\beta^2 \gg 1$. Then it is apparent that $R_\phi(0) \gg 1$ is an equivalent condition.

For the case of narrowband FM we shall find the one-sided spectrum of $v(t)$ to be given by

$$2G_v(f) = \frac{A^2}{2} e^{-R_\phi(0)}[\delta(f - f_0) + G_\phi(f - f_0)] \tag{3-10-12}$$

As expected, this consists of a carrier term at frequency f_0 plus the original modulating spectrum shifted up symmetrically about frequency f_0. The overall bandwidth is therefore just twice the modulation bandwidth. A typical example is shown in Fig. 3-10-1b.

[Note that we are actually dealing with the spectrum of a phase-modulated carrier. If $\phi(t)$ is band-limited to f_m cps, however, so that

$G_\phi(f)$ is restricted to the range $-f_m < f < f_m$, $G_{\dot\phi}(f) = \omega^2 G_\phi(f)$ will also occupy the same range and we can talk of the spectrum of an FM or PM carrier interchangeably.]

For wideband FM we shall obtain the rather startling result that the spectrum of $G_v(f)$ is *Gaussian-shaped*, independent of $G_\phi(f)$ or the shape of the modulating signal $\phi(t)$! The only stipulation here is that $\phi(t)$ be a

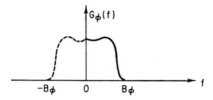

(a) Spectrum of phase-modulating signal

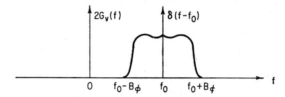

(b) Narrowband case $(R_\phi \ll 1)$: one-sided spectrum of modulated carrier

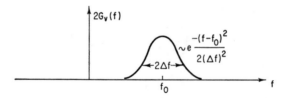

(c) Wideband case $(R_\phi \gg 1)$: one-sided spectrum of modulated carrier

FIG. 3-10-1. Spectrum of noise-modulated carrier.

stationary Gaussian random variable with $\beta^2 \gg 1$ and therefore with variance $R_\phi(0) \gg 1$. In particular, we shall find the one-sided spectrum of $v(t)$ given by

$$2G_v(f) = \frac{A^2}{2} \frac{e^{-(f-f_0)^2/2(\Delta f)^2}}{\sqrt{2\pi(\Delta f)^2}} \qquad \beta \gg 1 \qquad (3\text{-}10\text{-}13)$$

with $\Delta f = \dfrac{\Delta\omega}{2\pi}$ the rms frequency deviation (in cps) about f_0 as defined in Eq. (3-10-5). Δf also represents the rms signal (in cps) at the discriminator output, as noted previously. This spectrum is sketched in Fig. 3-10-1c. Note that $2\Delta f$ as defined is then a measure of the FM (or PM) transmission bandwidth, just as in the case of sinusoidal and other deterministic modulating signals. (Because of the Gaussian shape of the spectrum, substantially all of the signal energy is concentrated within $\pm 3 \Delta f$ of the carrier frequency.) As in the sinusoidal case an increase in the intensity of the modulating signal requires a corresponding increase in transmission bandwidth, the baseband signal bandwidth (B_ϕ or B_ϕ) remaining fixed.

To obtain the spectrum $G_v(f)$ of the modulated carrier $v(t)$ we first find the correlation function $R_v(\tau)$ and then take its Fourier transform. Under the two limiting conditions, $R_\phi \geq \beta^2 \gg 1$ and $\beta^2 < R_\phi(0) \ll 1$, we shall show we obtain Eqs. (3-10-13) and (3-10-12), respectively.

Thus, letting

$$v(t) = A \cos (\omega_0 t + \phi) = \text{Re } [A e^{j(\omega_0 t + \phi)}]$$
$$= \text{Re } [V_t e^{j\omega_0 t}] \qquad (3\text{-}10\text{-}14)$$

with V_t the complex phasor indicated, we have

$$R_v(\tau) \equiv \langle v(t) v(t + \tau) \rangle = \text{Re } [\langle V_t V_{t+\tau}^* \rangle]$$
$$= \frac{A^2}{2} \text{ Re } [e^{-j\omega_0 \tau} \langle e^{j\phi(t)} e^{-j\phi(t+\tau)} \rangle] \qquad (3\text{-}10\text{-}15)$$

The problem then is to find the average indicated. (Note that for $\tau = 0$, $R_v(0) = A^2/2$, and the average power of $v(t)$ is constant independent of modulating signal. This is of course well known in FM theory.)

Recalling that $\phi(t)$ has been assumed Gaussian, it is apparent that the indicated ensemble average is just the joint (two-dimensional) characteristic function of

$$\phi_1 \equiv \phi(t) \qquad \text{and} \qquad \phi_2 \equiv \phi(t + \tau)$$

[See, e.g., Eq. (3-3-3).] Thus,

$$\langle e^{j(z_1 \phi_1 + z_2 \phi_2)} \rangle \equiv G_{12}(z_1, z_2)$$
$$= \int_{-\infty}^{\infty} \int_{-\infty}^{\infty} e^{j(z_1 \phi_1 + z_2 \phi_2)} p(\phi_1, \phi_2) \, d\phi \, d\phi_2$$
$$= e^{-\frac{1}{2}[\mu_{11} z_1^2 + \mu_{22} z_2^2 + 2\mu_{12} z_1 z_2]} \qquad (3\text{-}10\text{-}16)$$

For the Gaussian process,

$$\langle e^{j\phi_1} e^{-j\phi_2} \rangle = G_{12}(1, -1) = e^{-[R_\phi(0) - R_\phi(\tau)]} \qquad (3\text{-}10\text{-}17)$$

Here we have made use of the fact that the central moments are given by $\mu_{11} = \mu_{22} = \langle \phi^2 \rangle = R_\phi(0)$, $\mu_{12} = R_\phi(\tau)$.

From Eq. (3-10-15) then,

$$R_v(\tau) = \frac{A^2}{2} \cos \omega_0 \tau e^{-[R_\phi(0) - R_\phi(\tau)]} \qquad (3\text{-}10\text{-}18)[1]$$

---

[1] D. Middleton, "Introduction to Statistical Communication Theory," pp. 604ff.

The spectral density of $v(t)$ is then

$$G_v(f) = \int_{-\infty}^{\infty} R_v(\tau) e^{-j\omega\tau} \, d\tau = \frac{A^2}{2} \int_{-\infty}^{\infty} \cos \omega_0\tau e^{-[R_\phi(0)-R_\phi(\tau)]} e^{-j\omega\tau} \, d\tau$$

$$(3\text{-}10\text{-}19)$$

Writing $\cos \omega_0\tau$ as the sum of two exponentials and combining terms, we also get

$$G_v(f) = \tfrac{1}{2}G_L(f - f_0) + \tfrac{1}{2}G_L(f + f_0) \qquad (3\text{-}10\text{-}20)$$

where the equivalent low-frequency spectrum $G_L(f)$ of $v(t)$ is given by

$$G_L(f) = \frac{A^2}{2} \int_{-\infty}^{\infty} e^{j\omega\tau} e^{-[R_\phi(0)-R_\phi(\tau)]} \, d\tau \qquad (3\text{-}10\text{-}21)$$

It is much simpler algebraically to deal with $G_L(f)$.

We now consider limiting cases. First, assume $R_\phi(0) \ll 1$. Then $|R_\phi(\tau)| \leq R_\phi(0) \ll 1$. Expanding the exponential in an infinite series we have

$$G_L(f) = \frac{A^2}{2} e^{-R_\phi(0)} \int_{-\infty}^{\infty} e^{j\omega\tau} e^{R_\phi(\tau)} \, d\tau$$

$$= \frac{A^2}{2} e^{-R_\phi(0)} \int_{-\infty}^{\infty} e^{j\omega\tau}[1 + R_\phi(\tau) + \cdots] \, d\tau \qquad (3\text{-}10\text{-}22)$$

Retaining just the first two terms in the series, $(|R_\phi(\tau)| \ll 1)$ and recalling that $\delta(f) = 2\pi\delta(\omega) = \int_{-\infty}^{\infty} e^{j\omega\tau} \, d\tau$, we get finally,

$$G_L(f) \doteq \frac{A^2}{2} e^{-R_\phi(0)}[\delta(f) + G_\phi(f)] \qquad R_\phi(0) \ll 1 \qquad (3\text{-}10\text{-}23)$$

This is of course the result noted previously and also agrees with the more general relation that the spectrum of a narrowband FM signal is identical with that of the original modulating signal shifted up symmetrically about the carrier frequency. Note that as $R_\phi(0)$ decreases, the carrier energy increases while the sideband energy [proportional to $G_\phi(f)$] decreases correspondingly. The *total* energy in the FM signal, of course, remains unchanged.

The wideband FM case can also be obtained readily from Eq. (3-10-21) by expanding the correlation function $R_\phi(\tau)$ in its Taylor series. Thus, recalling that R_ϕ is an even function of τ,

$$R_\phi(\tau) = R_\phi(0) + \frac{\ddot{R}_\phi(0)}{2!} \tau^2 + \frac{\overset{IV}{R}_\phi(0)}{4!} \tau^4 + \cdots \qquad (3\text{-}10\text{-}24)$$

Noting that $d^2R_\phi(\tau)/d\tau^2 = \ddot{R}_\phi(\tau) = -R_{\dot{\phi}}(\tau)$ [see Eq. 3-4-18d], so that

$\overset{IV}{R}_\phi(0) = -R_\phi(0) = -(\Delta\omega)^2$, while

$$\overset{IV}{R}_\phi(0) = -\ddot{R}_\phi(0) = \int_{-\infty}^{\infty} \omega^2 G_\phi(f)\, df$$
$$= (2\pi B_\phi\, \Delta\omega)^2 \qquad (3\text{-}10\text{-}25)$$

from Eq. (3-10-6), we get

$$R_\phi(0) - R_\phi(\tau) = \frac{(\Delta\omega)^2}{2}\tau^2 - \frac{(2\pi B_\phi\, \Delta\omega)^2}{4!}\tau^4 + \cdots \qquad (3\text{-}10\text{-}26)$$

Substituting into Eq. (3-10-21), and making the change of variables $x = \Delta\omega\tau$, we get

$$G_L(f) = \frac{A^2}{2\,\Delta\omega} \int_{-\infty}^{\infty} e^{j\omega x/\Delta\omega} e^{-x^2/2} e^{\left[\frac{x^4}{4!}\left(\frac{1}{\beta}\right)^2 + \cdots\right]} dx \qquad (3\text{-}10\text{-}27)$$

with $\beta \equiv (\Delta f/B_\phi)$ the modulation index described previously. It is thus apparent that as $\beta \to \infty$ the bracketed term goes to zero and $G_L(f)$ approaches the Gaussian form,

$$G_L(f) \to \frac{A^2}{2}\sqrt{\frac{2\pi}{(\Delta\omega)^2}}\, e^{-\omega^2/2(\Delta\omega)^2} = \frac{A^2}{2}\frac{e^{-f^2/2(\Delta f)^2}}{\sqrt{2\pi(\Delta f)^2}} \qquad \beta \to \infty \qquad (3\text{-}10\text{-}28)$$

The spectrum of $G_v(f)$ thus approaches the Gaussian shape, independent of $G_\phi(f)$, for the modulation index β very large.

A more precise condition for this case of wideband FM can be found by expanding the bracketed exponent in Eq. (3-10-27) in the power series

$$1 + \frac{x^4}{4!}\left(\frac{1}{\beta}\right)^2 + \cdots$$

We then have

$$G_L(f) = G_{LL}(f) + G_E(f) \qquad (3\text{-}10\text{-}29)$$

with $G_{LL}(f)$ the Gaussian-shaped spectrum and $G_E(f)$ an error term incorporating all terms beyond the first in the power-series expansion. An upper bound for $G_E(f)$ can be shown to be given by[1]

$$G_E(f) \le \frac{G_{LL}(0)}{8}\frac{1}{\beta^2} \qquad (3\text{-}10\text{-}30)$$

This thus represents the error between $G_v(f)$ and its Gaussian form in the wideband case. As an example, if the baseband modulating signal $G_\phi(f)$ is band-limited to f_m cps [then $G_\phi(f) = \omega^2 G_\phi(f)$ is band-limited to f_m also], it is apparent that $B_\phi \le f_m$. The bound on $G_E(f)$ can then be written

$$G_E(f) < \frac{G_{LL}(0)}{8}\left(\frac{f_m}{\Delta f}\right)^2 \qquad (3\text{-}10\text{-}31)$$

[1] Hess, *op. cit.*

For commercial FM the frequency deviation Δf is specified to be 75 kc and the frequency f_m is 15 kc.   Then $G_E(f) < \dfrac{1}{200} G_{LL}(0)$.   It is apparent that the FM signal is for all practical purposes wideband in this case. For $\beta \geq 5$, then, the Gaussian spectrum, assuming a noiselike modulating signal, is a good approximation to the transmission spectrum.

PART II

William R. Bennett

CHAPTER 4

AMPLITUDE MODULATION AND RELATED
CW SYSTEMS

The previous chapters have summarized a general mathematical formulation of the theory of communication in the presence of noise. The sophisticated analysis contained therein has sufficient capability to yield significant results for a great variety of complicated situations. In the next three chapters we shall explore important areas in the field of communication techniques for which simpler analysis is usually adequate. The systems to be described transmit signals under conditions of low distortion and noise. The relation between channel output and input is substantially linear and the principle of superposition is applicable.[1] Hence, a basic description in terms of the response to a single-frequency signal component can be used as a basis for constructing a response to more general signal waves. Nonlinear effects can be evaluated with sufficient accuracy from the response to a few sinusoidal components— one if only harmonic production is of interest and two or three if intermodulation effects are important.

The input to the systems under consideration consists of a *baseband* signal which represents the original information and which must be delivered in nearly intact form at the destination. The word *baseband* is used as a generic term to include, for example, the audio signal produced by a microphone in the case of speech or music, the video signal derived from a television camera, and the pulse train representing a data source. Since the channel itself typically makes use of frequency ranges entirely different from those important in the baseband, we require techniques for frequency translation at the transmitter and receiver. The translations are accomplished by modulation processes in which a source of oscillations in an appropriate frequency range is made to furnish a carrier for the baseband signal information and by demodulation processes in which the baseband signal is recovered from the modulated carrier wave.

We distinguish between modulation of a sustained source of oscillations

---

[1] This statement remains true even in the case of frequency-modulation and pulse-modulation systems, where the relation between the waveform actually transmitted and the original signal is highly nonlinear.

and modulation of an intermittent source. The former we call *cont'nuous wave*, abbreviated as CW. An unmodulated CW source typically delivers a sinusoidal wave of nearly constant amplitude and frequency. An intermittent source delivers pulses, which may or may not be oscillatory.

The unmodulated output of a CW source is characterized by three parameters:

1. The *amplitude*, which is the maximum instantaneous magnitude.
2. The *frequency*, which is the number of oscillations per second.
3. The *phase*, which designates the point of the oscillatory cycle reached at a specified reference time.

It appears then that there are three ways in which the CW source can be modulated, and it is natural to call these three ways *amplitude modulation* (AM), *frequency modulation* (FM), and *phase modulation* (PM). We find, however, that the latter two methods are closely related. In general, a change in frequency results in a change of phase and vice versa. If we write the sine wave in the form $A \sin (2\pi f t + \theta) = A \sin (\omega t + \theta)$, we note that the frequency f and the phase θ both help to define an angle $2\pi f t + \theta$. Therefore, it is appropriate to use the more general term *angle modulation* to include both FM and PM. We accordingly divide CW modulation systems into two classes:

1. Those based on amplitude modulation.
2. Those based on angle modulation.

4-1. Structure of an AM Wave

A simple way to construct an amplitude-modulated wave is to multiply a sine wave by the sum of a signal wave and a constant. The result of such a multiplication is an expression of form:

$$E(t) = a[s_o + s(t)] \cos (\omega_c t + \theta) \tag{4-1-1}$$

In this equation $s(t)$ represents the signal wave and s_o is an added positive bias sufficiently large to prevent the sum $s_o + s(t)$ from ever becoming negative. The amplitude of the wave is the positive-valued quantity $a[s_o + s(t)]$. It consists of a constant term plus a term proportional to the signal.

Assume that the signal wave can be resolved into sinusoidal components and consider a representative component of form $Q \cos qt$. The resulting AM wave with only this component of signal present becomes:

$$
\begin{aligned}
E(t) &= a(s_o + Q \cos qt) \cos (\omega_c t + \theta) \\
&= a s_o \cos (\omega_c t + \theta) + \frac{aQ}{2} \cos [(\omega_c + q)t + \theta] \\
&\qquad\qquad + \frac{aQ}{2} \cos [(\omega_c - q)t + \theta] \quad (4\text{-}1\text{-}2)
\end{aligned}
$$

Other sinusoidal components of the signal will lead to corresponding added terms like the last two terms shown in Eq. (4-1-2). We call ω_c the carrier frequency and q the typical signal frequency. Both are expressed in radians per second. Equation (4-1-2) contains an unmodulated carrier-frequency term, an upper side-frequency component with frequency equal to the sum of the carrier and signal frequencies, and a lower side-frequency component with frequency equal to the difference between the carrier and signal frequencies. Presence of more than one signal component leads to a band of upper side frequencies called the upper sideband and a band of lower side frequencies called the lower sideband.[1]

Resolution of physically interesting signals into sinusoidal components presents no practical difficulties. Periodic waves can be so resolved by

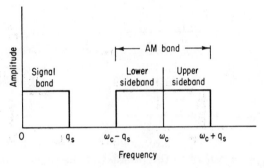

Fig. 4-1-1. Relation of signal and sidebands in amplitude modulation.

Fourier-series expansion. Aperiodic waves can be expressed as Fourier integrals, at least over a finite time of interest. In both cases the range of frequencies required to represent the waves with sufficient accuracy is finite. We can thus speak of a highest signal frequency q_s. In an AM wave q_s is represented by the highest upper sideband frequency $\omega_c + q_s$ and the lowest lower sideband frequency $\omega_c - q_s$. Other signal frequencies produce sideband components between these two. Graphic representation of the signal and the AM wave is shown in Fig. 4-1-1. On the signal-frequency scale a rectangle indicates a range of frequencies from 0 to q_s. On the frequency scale representing the components of the AM wave, corresponding rectangles extend from ω_c to $\omega_c + q_s$ for the upper sideband, and from $\omega_c - q_s$ to ω_c for the lower sideband. In the general case the components would not all have the same amplitude, and the rectangles would be replaced by curves showing relative sizes. One significant fact deducible from the figure is that the carrier frequency ω_c should not be less than the highest signal frequency q_s. For if ω_c is

[1] R. V. L. Hartley, Relations of Carrier and Sidebands in Radio Transmission, *Bell System Tech. J.*, vol. 2, pp. 90–112, April, 1923.

less than q_s, the situation of Fig. 4-1-2 arises. Here some of the lower sideband frequencies are negative, and since physical systems cannot distinguish between negative and positive frequencies, the negative values in effect fold back and superimpose on the corresponding positive frequencies. This phenomenon, called *sideband foldover* or *overlap*, leads to distortion because it is not possible to separate the spurious foldover components from the legitimate ones.

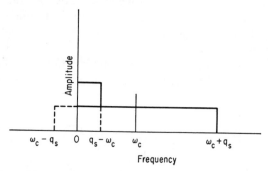

Fɪɢ. 4-1-2. Sideband foldover caused by a too-low carrier frequency.

4-2. Amplitude Modulators

An ideal amplitude modulator follows a pure product law. That is, its output is proportional to the product of the signal and carrier waves. Physical devices can at best only approximate a product law.

Curvature Modulators. One example is a device having a nonlinear relation between output and input—a so-called *curvature modulator*. If the departure from nonlinearity can be approximated by a square-law term, the response to the sum of signal and carrier waves will contain a term proportional to their product. There will also be terms proportional to the square of the signal and to the square of the carrier. From the trigonometric formula $\cos^2 x = (1 + \cos 2x)/2$, we see that second harmonics of signal and carrier frequencies appear. Furthermore, if the signal contains components with different frequencies, the square of the signal will contain components having sums and differences of these frequencies.

The extraneous components distort the AM wave. If they fall outside the frequency range of the sidebands produced by the signal itself, they can be removed by filtering. If they fall within the desired sidebands, the only hope is that they can be made negligibly small in amplitude. One way of helping the situation is to keep the input signal small compared with the carrier. Products in which signal components are multiplied by each other are then small compared with products of signal and carrier. Another method of reducing the effect of unwanted modulation terms is the use of balanced curvature modulators.   If two devices have identical square-law responses, we apply the sum of carrier and signal to one and the difference between carrier and signal to the other; that is, we reverse the polarity of the signal in the input to the second device, and we then take the difference between the outputs.   Since

$$[A \cos \omega_c t + s(t)]^2 - [A \cos \omega_c t - s(t)]^2 = 4As(t) \cos \omega_c t \quad \text{(4-2-1)}$$

the resulting output obeys a pure product law.   In practical devices the two curvatures cannot be matched exactly and a finite but relatively small amount of distortion persists.   Note that the pure product law by itself does not give pure AM because the signal wave can change sign.

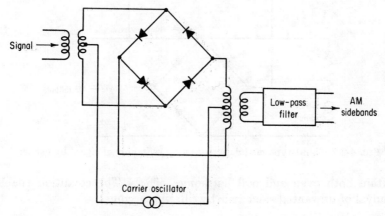

Fig. 4-2-1. Ring-modulator circuit for multiplication of signal and carrier.

This difficulty can be remedied either by adding a sufficiently large constant bias to the signal or by adding a sufficiently large amount of unmodulated carrier to the output of the modulator.

Switch-type Modulators.   Some of the difficulties associated with curvature modulators are avoided in the so-called *switch-type modulator*. One form often called a *ring modulator*, shown in Fig. 4-2-1, acts essentially like a reversing switch driven by the source of carrier frequency. The polarity of the modulating wave is thus switched at the carrier-frequency rate.   This is equivalent to multiplying the wave by $+1$ during one half of the carrier cycle and by -1 during the other half.   Such a switching function can be represented by a Fourier series as follows:

$$g(t) = \frac{4}{\pi} \cos \omega_c t - \frac{4}{3\pi} \cos 3\omega_c t + \frac{4}{5\pi} \cos 5\omega_c t - \cdots \quad \text{(4-2-2)}$$

When we multiply this switching function by a signal, the first term of the series gives the desired product law.   The remaining terms indicate sidebands on the third, fifth, and higher odd harmonics of the carrier frequency. The unwanted sidebands can be removed by filtering if the lowest sideband frequency associated with the third harmonic exceeds the highest upper sideband frequency on the carrier itself. That is, we require

$$3\omega_c - q_s > \omega_c + q_s \qquad \text{from which} \qquad q_s < \omega_c \qquad (4\text{-}2\text{-}3)$$

This result is dependent on symmetry of the switching function $g(t)$. If the positive and negative lobes of the carrier wave do not switch equally, the Fourier-series representation of the switching function will

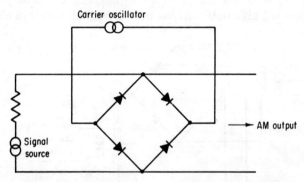

Fig. 4-2-2. Shunt-type modulator for on-off switching of signal by carrier.

contain both even and odd harmonics of ω_c. The condition enabling removal of unwanted sidebands by filtering becomes

$$2\omega_c - q_s > \omega_c + q_s \qquad \text{or} \qquad q_s < \frac{\omega_c}{2} \qquad (4\text{-}2\text{-}4)$$

The switch-type modulator can also be of the on-off form shown in Fig. 4-2-2. Here the signal is multiplied by $+1$ when the carrier wave is positive and by zero when the carrier wave is negative. The corresponding switching function is represented by the following Fourier series:

$$g_o(t) = \frac{1}{2} + \frac{2}{\pi} \cos \omega_c t - \frac{2}{3\pi} \cos 3\omega_c t + \frac{2}{5\pi} \cos 5\omega_c t - \cdots \qquad (4\text{-}2\text{-}5)$$

When this series is multiplied by the signal, a component proportional to the signal itself results from the initial constant term of the series. To prevent this component from overlapping the lower sideband on the carrier, we must have $q_s < \omega_c/2$. This is the same requirement found above for the nonsymmetrical reversing switch. Note that this is also the same as the Nyquist sampling procedure discussed in Chap. 2.

Actual modulators depart from the ideal properties we have assumed in explaining their principles of operation. We shall defer a discussion of more realistic models suitable for evaluation of actual performance until we have completed a description of idealized demodulating as well as modulating methods. In general, the same circuits function as either demodulators or modulators and the same analytical procedures apply to both uses. Also the methods applicable to pure AM systems are readily extended to related systems in which portions of the AM signal are suppressed at the transmitter. The more complete treatment is accordingly given in Sec. 4-5 following the sections on amplitude detectors and on systems derived from AM.

4-3. Amplitude Detectors

The detection of an amplitude-modulated wave can be accomplished with very simple circuits. The one most commonly used is the envelope detector, in which a reverse bias is built up on a rectifying element by the charge on a capacitor shunted by a high resistance. A linear or a square-law rectifier without bias can also be used. From the theoretical standpoint the best amplitude detector is the synchronous, coherent, or homodyne variety, which multiplies the received AM wave by a sine wave having the frequency and phase of the transmitted carrier.

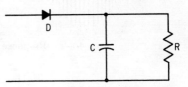

FIG. 4-3-1. Envelope detector.

Envelope Detectors. Figure 4-3-1 shows a standard envelope detector consisting of a diode D in series with a parallel combination of the resistor R and capacitor C. When the applied voltage is in the conducting direction of D, the capacitor charges quickly to the peak values. When the applied voltage is negative, the resistance of D becomes high and the capacitor can only discharge slowly through its shunt resistor. With proper choice of time constants, the voltage across R remains near the positive peaks of the applied wave and is a fair replica of the original AM signal, as shown in Fig. 4-3-2.

To analyze the circuit mathematically,[1-3] we assume that the carrier and sideband frequencies are high compared with the signal frequencies. We assume, also, that the impedance of the capacitor is very high at the signal frequencies and negligibly small at the sideband frequencies. Under these circumstances the signal components flow through R and the

---

[1] H. A. Wheeler, Design Formulas for Diode Detectors, *Proc. IRE*, vol. 26, pp. 745–759, June, 1938.

[2] H. J. Reich, "Theory and Applications of Electron Tubes," McGraw-Hill Book Company, Inc., New York, 1944.

[3] W. R. Bennett, The Biased Ideal Rectifier, *Bell System Tech. J.*, vol. 26, pp. 139–169, January, 1947.

sideband components flow through C. Let I represent the current through R. The bias voltage on the rectifier is equal to IR. Assume that the diode D is an ideal linear rectifier in which the current is kV when the applied voltage V is positive, and equal to zero when the applied voltage is negative.

If the voltage across an ideal linear rectifier is of form $A \cos x - B$, where $x = \omega_c t + \theta$, the current $G(x)$ is equal to $k(A \cos x - B)$ when

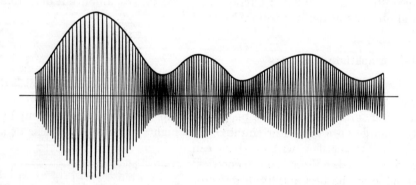

Fig. 4-3-2.   Response of envelope detector to AM wave.

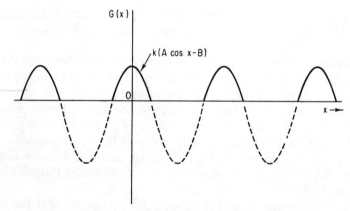

Fig. 4-3-3. Response of biased linear rectifier to sine wave.

$\cos x$ exceeds B/A. Otherwise the current is zero.   A graphic representation of $G(x)$ is shown by the full-line positive segments in Fig. 4-3-3.   The function can be expressed in a Fourier series:

$$G(x) = \frac{a_0}{2} + \sum_{m=1}^{\infty} a_m \cos mx \qquad (4\text{-}3\text{-}1)$$

where

$$a_m = \frac{2}{\pi} \int_0^{\arccos (B/A)} k(A \cos x - B) \cos mx \, dx \qquad (4\text{-}3\text{-}2)$$

In particular

$$\frac{a_0}{2} = \frac{k}{\pi} \int_0^{\arccos (B/A)} (A \cos x - B) \, dx$$

$$= \frac{k}{\pi} \left[(A^2 - B^2)^{1/2} - B \arccos \frac{B}{A} \right] \qquad (4\text{-}3\text{-}3)$$

The above equations hold provided A and B are positive with B less than A. Subject to these restrictions A and B can vary with time. In our problem we set A equal to $s_o + s(t)$. Assuming the value of this expression is never negative, we can now calculate the response to an AM wave.

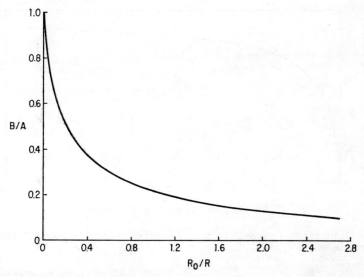

FIG. 4-3-4. Response of envelope detector versus ratio of forward diode resistance to load resistance.

The only term in the Fourier-series expansion of the current which produces a voltage across R is the constant $a_0/2$. Hence the bias B can be set equal to $a_0 R/2$. That is,

$$B = \frac{kR}{\pi} \left[(A^2 - B^2)^{1/2} - B \arccos \frac{B}{A} \right] \qquad (4\text{-}3\text{-}4)$$

Let R_0 represent the forward resistance of the diode. Then $k = 1/R_0$ and Eq. (4-3-4) can be rewritten as:

$$\frac{\pi R_0}{R} = [(B/A)^{-2} - 1]^{1/2} - \arccos \frac{B}{A} \qquad (4\text{-}3\text{-}5)$$

From Eq. (4-3-5) we have calculated $\pi R_0/R$ as a function of B/A. We then used the resulting data to plot B/A as a function of R_0/R in Fig. 4-3-4 and as a function of R/R_0 in Fig. 4-3-5. The curve shows that B/A, the ratio of output voltage to envelope, approaches unity as the ratio of forward diode resistance to discharge resistance approaches zero. In the limit reached by a perfect switching diode, the voltage output B is equal to the envelope $s_o + s(t)$. The signal $s(t)$ is thus recovered with an additive d-c bias s_o necessary to prevent the envelope A from reversing its sign.

Rectifiers. An unbiased rectifier can be used as an amplitude detector. A half-wave linear rectifier, for example, gives a response proportional to applied voltage when the voltage is positive and gives zero response to negative voltages. The response to an AM wave can be represented by

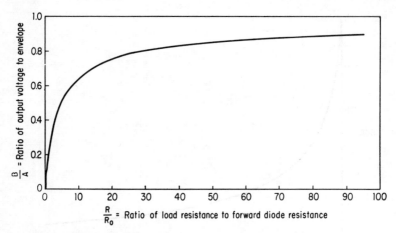

FIG. 4-3-5. Response of envelope detector versus ratio of load resistance to forward diode resistance.

the function $G(x)$ of Eqs. (4-3-1) and (4-3-2) with the bias B set equal to zero. The result is

$$G(x) = \frac{kA}{\pi} + \frac{kA}{2} \cos x - \frac{2kA}{\pi} \sum_{m=1}^{\infty} \frac{(-)^m}{4m^2 - 1} \cos 2mx \qquad (4\text{-}3\text{-}6)$$

If $x = \omega_c t + \theta$ and $A = s_o + s(t)$, the first term of the series contains the undistorted signal. The other terms represent the modulated carrier and its even harmonics. The signal can be selected from the other terms by filtering if the carrier frequency is sufficiently high relative to the signal band. Specifically, if the signal contains a component $Q \cos qt$, the term $A \cos x$ contains a corresponding lower sideband component proportional to $Q \cos (\omega_c - q)t$. In order for a filter to pass the signal component and suppress the lower sideband component, we must have $\omega_c - q > q$, which implies that $\omega_c > 2q$. That is, the carrier frequency must exceed twice the highest signal frequency in order for the half-wave rectifier to separate the signal from the modulated carrier.

A less stringent requirement holds for the full-wave linear rectifier such as shown in Fig. 4-3-6.   Here the zero response to negative applied voltage is replaced by the same response function as for the positive voltage, except that the sign is reversed.   The complete specification is:

$$G(x) = \begin{cases} kA \cos x & \cos x > 0 \\ -kA \cos x & \cos x < 0 \end{cases} \quad (4\text{-}3\text{-}7)$$

In the Fourier-series expansion of this function, the coefficient a_1 vanishes and the other terms in Eq. (4-3-6) are doubled.   The new expression is

$$G(x) = \frac{2kA}{\pi} - \frac{4kA}{\pi} \sum_{m=1}^{\infty} \frac{(-)^m}{4m^2 - 1} \cos 2mx \quad (4\text{-}3\text{-}8)$$

Since the modulated carrier is now absent, the nearest sideband which can interfere with the signal is the lower sideband on the second harmonic of the carrier.   The condition under which filtering can successfully isolate the signal is $2\omega_c - q > q$, which implies that $\omega_c > q$.   Thus the full-wave

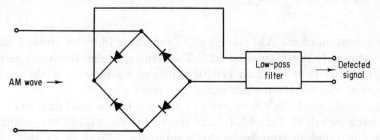

AM wave →

Low-pass filter

Detected signal

FIG. 4-3-6. Full-wave rectifier used as AM detector.

rectifier is theoretically satisfactory when the carrier frequency exceeds the highest signal frequency.   This is one-half as great a value as is required for the half-wave rectifier.

We note that the full-wave rectifier recovers a signal component which is $2k/\pi$ times that recovered by an ideal envelope detector.   We also note that an analysis similar to the above can be performed when the rectifier does not have a linear response in its conducting range.   The recovered signal term will be found to contain distortion due to the nonlinearity.

Synchronous Detection.   In synchronous, coherent, or homodyne detection, the received AM wave is multiplied by an unmodulated carrier wave coincident in frequency and phase with the carrier wave accompanying the received AM signal.   Thus if the AM wave is given by Eq. (4-1-1), synchronous detection would be accomplished by multiplying $E(t)$ by $P \cos (\omega_c t + \theta)$.   The product can be written as

$$PE(t) \cos (\omega_c t + \theta) = aP[s_o + s(t)] \cos^2 (\omega_c t + \theta)$$

$$= \frac{aP}{2}[s_o + s(t)] + \frac{aP}{2}[s_o + s(t)] \cos 2(\omega_c t + \theta) \quad (4\text{-}3\text{-}9)$$

The first term represents the recovered signal. The second term represents the second harmonic of the carrier, amplitude modulated by the signal. The signal can be separated by filtering if the carrier frequency is greater than the highest signal frequency. Synchronous detection requires availability of the carrier wave at the receiver. The carrier can be obtained from the incoming AM signal by a narrow bandpass filter centered at the carrier frequency.

The multiplication can be performed by switch-type modulators such as previously described. In the circuit of Fig. 4-2-1, for example, the carrier and the AM wave would be applied to conjugate ports of the diode bridge. By making the carrier amplitude large compared with the AM wave, we obtain the switching function $g(t)$ of Eq. (4-2-2) except that a carrier phase angle is now inserted to match the carrier of Eq. (4-1-1). The resulting expression is:

$$g(t) = \frac{4}{\pi} \cos (\omega_c t + \theta) - \frac{4}{3\pi} \cos 3(\omega_c t + \theta) + \frac{4}{5\pi} \cos 5(\omega_c t + \theta) - \cdots$$

$$(4\text{-}3\text{-}10)$$

Multiplication of the AM wave by the switching function yields a wave proportional to the original signal. The terms of higher frequency resulting from the multiplication can be removed by filtering if the carrier frequency exceeds the highest signal frequency.

An on-off switch such as shown in Fig. 4-2-2 can be used instead of the reversing switch of Fig. 4-2-1. As shown by Eq. (4-2-5) the resulting switching function contains a d-c component. Presence of this term causes a modulated carrier component to appear in the output along with the signal. In order to separate the signal from the modulated carrier, we must now make the carrier frequency at least twice as great as the highest signal frequency.

4-4. Systems Derived from AM

We observe that the upper and lower sidebands of an AM signal contain the same information in duplicate. Also, the carrier itself does not contain any information, except as a key for restoring the signal to its proper frequency range. To obtain more efficient use of bandwidth and power, various modifications of AM have been devised which reduce the transmitted wave more nearly to the essential ingredients. We now consider a number of these modifications.

Double-sideband Suppressed Carrier (DSBSC). A saving in transmitted power can be obtained either by not sending the carrier at all or by sending only a small amount of carrier. The result is not strictly an AM wave and cannot be detected by an envelope detector. It is the type of wave generated by a product modulator in which no bias is added to the signal. An example is given by Eq. (4-2-1) for the output of balanced curvature modulators. If the signal changes sign, the amplitude, which is to be taken as positive, does not correctly represent the signal. Detection of a DSBSC wave requires multiplication by the carrier, which can be obtained by selecting and amplifying a small amount of transmitted carrier. Even if the carrier is completely missing from the transmitted wave, it is possible to generate it from the two sidebands.

One way of obtaining the carrier is to pass the DSBSC wave through a square-law device. The output contains terms proportional to the products of input components. In particular the product of an upper side-frequency component $Q \cos (\omega_c + q)t$ and the corresponding lower side-frequency component $Q \cos (\omega_c - q)t$ can be resolved as follows:

$$Q^2 \cos (\omega_c + q)t \cos (\omega_c - q)t = \frac{Q^2}{2} \cos 2\omega_c t + \frac{Q^2}{2} \cos 2qt \quad (4\text{-}4\text{-}1)$$

Each pair of corresponding upper and lower sideband terms thus produces a component of frequency equal to $2\omega_c$, which is twice the carrier frequency. A bandpass filter centered at $2\omega_c$ will select the resultant of such components, and if the band is sufficiently narrow, a pure sine wave of twice the carrier frequency will be obtained. This wave can be passed through a 2:1 frequency step-down circuit to obtain the carrier wave itself. There are two possible carrier phases 180° apart which are obtainable in this way. If the polarity of the recovered signal is immaterial, either phase is satisfactory for detecting the DSBSC wave.

Another method, proposed by Costas,[1] recovers the carrier from the two sidebands by the circuit shown in Fig. 4-4-1. A local oscillator adjusted to nearly the right frequency serves as carrier to two homodyne detectors. A 90° phase shifter is inserted in the carrier lead to one of the detectors. Low-pass filters in the detector outputs select the low-frequency detected components. Multiplying a typical pair of DSBSC input terms $Q \cos (\omega_c + q)t + Q \cos (\omega_c - q)t$ by the carrier wave $A \cos (\omega t + \theta)$ and rejecting the high-frequency terms in the product lead to the following expression for the output of one postdetection filter

$$v_1(t) = AQ \cos qt \cos [(\omega - \omega_c)t + \theta] \quad (4\text{-}4\text{-}2)$$

The output of the other low-pass filter is obtained by replacing $\cos (\omega t + \theta)$ by $\sin (\omega t + \theta)$. It is

$$v_2(t) = AQ \cos qt \sin [(\omega - \omega_c)t + \theta] \quad (4\text{-}4\text{-}3)$$

The filtered product of the two low-pass filter responses is

$$V(t) = \frac{A^2 Q^2}{4} \sin [2(\omega - \omega_c)t + 2\theta] \quad (4\text{-}4\text{-}4)$$

[1] J. P. Costas, Synchronous Communication, *Proc. IRE*, vol. 44, pp. 1713–1718, December, 1956.

A tuning control governed by $V(t)$ is provided for the oscillator. The tuning approaches equilibrium as $V(t)$ approaches zero, which means that ω approaches ω_c and θ approaches zero. The output of the local oscillator thus not only approaches the absent carrier frequency ω_c but acquires the right phase. The output of Costas's circuit is identified in Fig. 4-4-1. Equation (4-4-2) shows that the output of the low-pass filter on the left side of Fig. 4-4-1 approaches the correct detected signal. The output of the low-pass filter on the right, Eq. (4-4-3), approaches zero.

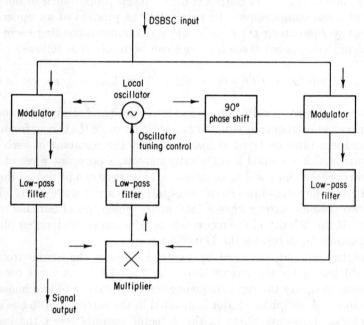

FIG. 4-4-1. Schematic diagram of Costas's receiver for DSBSC wave. (*From J. P. Costas, Proc. IRE, vol. 44, December, 1956, p. 1714.*)

To demonstrate the importance of supplying the demodulating carrier in the right phase, we consider the problem of detecting DSBSC components with a carrier of arbitrary phase. Specifically we multiply the sum of the sideband components $Q \cos (\omega_c + q)t$ and $Q \cos (\omega_c - q)t$ by the carrier wave $2P \cos (\omega_c t + \theta)$, where θ can be any angle. We find

$$[Q \cos (\omega_c + q)t + Q \cos (\omega_c - q)t] \, 2P \cos (\omega_c t + \theta)$$
$$= 2PQ \cos \theta \cos qt + 2PQ \cos qt \cos (2\omega_c t + \theta) \quad (4\text{-}4\text{-}5)$$

The second term of the final expression represents sidebands on the second harmonic of the carrier and can be eliminated by filtering. The first term is the recovered signal. Its magnitude is seen to be proportional to $\cos \theta$, where θ is the difference between the phase angle of the actual demodulating carrier and the correct phase angle. The effect of wrong carrier phase, therefore, is a diminution of recovered signal in accordance with a cosine law.   When the phase error reaches 90° the factor cos θ becomes zero and no signal is recovered.

Quadrature-carrier Two-channel Multiplex.   The fact that the recovered signal in a homodyne carrier system vanishes when the error in the local carrier phase is 90° shows that it is possible to transmit and receive two independent DSBSC waves in the same carrier band.   The modulating carriers for the two channels have the same frequencies but differ in phase by exactly 90°.   Failure to supply the correct carrier phases for demodulation at the receiver not only results in loss of signal within each channel but also leads to interference between the channels.   We note also that equality of amplitude must be maintained for corresponding upper and lower sideband components to prevent interchannel interference.   The

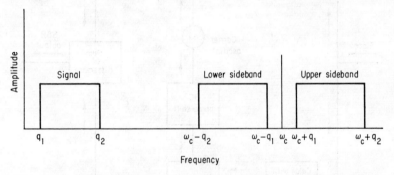

FIG. 4-4-2. Sideband produced by signal with low-frequency energy gap.

quadrature-carrier method compensates for the waste of bandwidth in double-sideband systems by inserting a second independent channel. Thus, although we transmit two sidebands for each signal, we cancel the redundancy in effect by sending two independent sets of sidebands within the same frequency allocation.

Single Sideband (SSB).   Since the signal information is duplicated in the upper and lower sidebands, either sideband by itself is sufficient for signal recovery with the aid of a demodulating carrier.   The carrier can be transmitted at low level along with one sideband, or it can be generated at the receiving terminal by a sufficiently stable oscillator.   Suppression of one sideband at the transmitter is commonly done by filtering.   Since filters require a transition band between low and high loss, complete removal of one sideband without impairment of the other may be difficult. The problem is simplified if the signal does not contain important components at low frequencies.   As shown in Fig. 4-4-2, absence of signal energy at low frequencies results in a frequency separation between the upper and lower sidebands.   Voice signals furnish an example in which there is such a low-frequency gap.   In television signals on the other hand the energy does not fall off at the low frequencies, and the upper and lower sidebands, therefore, meet at the carrier frequency.

As an alternative to filtering, a balanced modulation scheme such as previously explained in Chap. 1 and illustrated by the block diagram of Fig. 4-4-3, can be used to isolate one sideband for transmission. Two balanced modulators are provided with carriers at the same frequency but 90° apart in phase. The signal inputs to the two modulators are also made to differ from each other in phase by 90°. It can be shown that a network with a constant 90° phase shift and constant amplitude over a

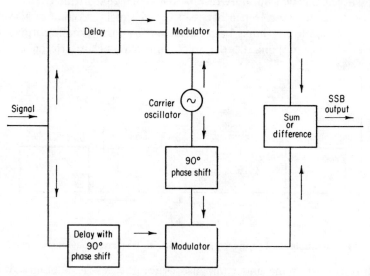

FIG. 4-4-3. Production of single sideband by balanced modulators and phase shift.

band of frequencies is physically unrealizable. The desired difference of 90° between signal phases is accomplished by inserting phase-shifting networks in both signal input paths. The two networks should have parallel linear phase-versus-frequency curves 90° apart over the signal band. Their amplitude-versus-frequency curves should be equal and constant over the same band. The two output waves are then Hilbert transforms of each other, as defined in Chap. 1. Ideally if the signal input to one modulator is $\cos qt$ and the carrier wave is $2 \cos \omega_c t$, the signal input to the other modulator is $\sin qt$ and the carrier is $2 \sin \omega_c t$. The sideband components generated by the first modulator can then be represented by

$$V_1(t) = 2 \cos qt \cos \omega_c t = \cos (p - q)t + \cos (p + q)t \quad (4\text{-}4\text{-}6)$$

The corresponding output of the second modulator is

$$V_2(t) = 2 \sin qt \sin \omega_c t = \cos (p - q)t - \cos (p + q)t \quad (4\text{-}4\text{-}7)$$

If these two outputs are added, the upper sideband terms cancel and the lower sideband components reinforce each other. If the difference between the two outputs is taken, the lower sideband components cancel and only the upper sideband is transmitted.

A third method of generating a single-sideband wave has been suggested by Weaver.[1] The method is applicable to signals with finite energy gap near zero frequency. Assume the signal band extends from ω_1 to $\omega_1 + 2\omega_0$, where $2\omega_0$ is the bandwidth. Let ω_m represent the center frequency of the band, that is,

$$\omega_m = \omega_1 + \omega_0 \qquad (4\text{-}4\text{-}8)$$

The signal first modulates quadrature carriers at frequency ω_m in balanced modulators. A representative signal component $Q \cos qt$ thus produces the wave $Q \cos (\omega_m + q)t + Q \cos (\omega_m - q)t$ from one modulator and the wave $Q \sin (\omega_m + q)t + Q \sin (\omega_m - q)t$ from the other modulator. A low-pass filter with cutoff at ω_0 is inserted in the output of each modulator. We note that

$$\omega_1 < q < \omega_1 + 2\omega_0 \qquad (4\text{-}4\text{-}9)$$

Hence substituting the value of ω_1 from Eq. (4-4-8)

$$\omega_m - \omega_0 < q < \omega_m + \omega_0 \qquad (4\text{-}4\text{-}10)$$

Therefore $\qquad \omega_m - q < \omega_0 \qquad$ and $\qquad q - \omega_m < \omega_0 \qquad (4\text{-}4\text{-}11)$

Also since $\qquad\qquad\qquad \omega_m > \omega_0$

$$q + \omega_m > \omega_0 \qquad (4\text{-}4\text{-}12)$$

From these results, which are shown graphically in Fig. 4-4-4, we see that the low-pass filters pass the components of frequency $\omega_m - q$ and suppress the components of frequency $\omega_m + q$.

The next step is to apply the low-pass filter outputs as signals to balanced modulators with quadrature carriers at ω_c, the center of the desired single-sideband range. It is then found that the sum of the two modulator outputs is an upper sideband on carrier frequency $\omega_c - \omega_m$. The difference is a lower sideband on carrier frequency $\omega_c + \omega_m$.

The advantage of this method is that the critical filtering necessary to isolate a sideband is done at cutoff frequency equal to half the bandwidth instead of at a cutoff equal to at least the bandwidth as in the conventional filter method. The percentage bandwidth available for building up loss in the filter is thus made at least twice as great. A disadvantage is that sideband suppression is obtained partly by balance, which is difficult to make as effective as direct filtering.

A single-sideband wave should be detected by homodyne means. If the homodyne carrier does not have the correct frequency and phase, the

[1] D. K. Weaver, Jr., A Third Method of Generation and Detection of Single-Sideband Signals, *Proc. IRE*, vol. 44, pp. 1703–1705, December, 1956.

recovered signal waveform will be distorted. Some types of signals such as speech tolerate this form of distortion up to several cycles of frequency error. The effect of wrong carrier phase has previously been derived in

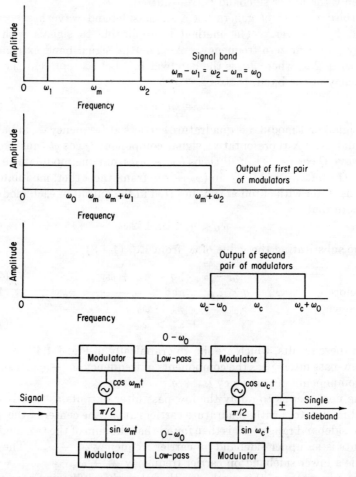

Fig. 4-4-4. Weaver's method of generating a single sideband. (*From D. K. Weaver, Jr., Proc. IRE, vol. 44, December, 1956, p. 1704.*)

Chap. 1. As shown there the detected signal with phase error θ becomes

$$s_d(t) = s(t) \cos \theta + \hat{s}(t) \sin \theta \qquad (4\text{-}4\text{-}13)$$

The effect of the phase error is thus to introduce a component proportional to the Hilbert transform of the signal. In particular if the phase error is 90°, the detected wave is the Hilbert transform instead of the original signal.

The effect of phase error on waveform can be studied by examining the Hilbert transform of typical signals. A basic signal wave important in television and data transmission is the rectangle of height h and duration T shown in Fig. 4-4-5. Its Fourier-integral representation can be written as

$$s(t) = \frac{h}{\pi} \int_0^\infty \frac{\sin \omega t - \sin \omega(t - T)}{\omega} \, d\omega \qquad (4\text{-}4\text{-}14)$$

The Hilbert transform is calculated by retarding the phase of the sinusoidal terms by 90° giving

$$\hat{s}(t) = -\frac{h}{\pi} \int_0^\infty \frac{\cos \omega t - \cos \omega(t - T)}{\omega} \, d\omega$$

$$= -\frac{h}{\pi} \log \left| \frac{t - T}{t} \right| \qquad (4\text{-}4\text{-}15)$$

As shown in Fig. 4-4-5, the Hilbert transform becomes infinite at the

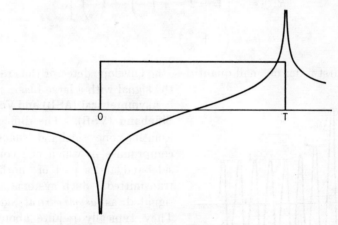

FIG. 4-4-5. Rectangular signal and its Hilbert transform.

beginning and end of the pulse. In a physical system, the peaks would be finite but still very high. Such peaks are called "horns" by television engineers and the fill-in before and after the pulse is called "smear." These effects would be found if a single-sideband signal were detected by demodulating with a carrier with phase error approaching 90°. They would also be found if we applied the SSB wave to an envelope detector, as we shall now show.

Making use of the expression for an SSB wave given in Eq. (1-6-1), we write

$$s(t) \cos \omega_c t - \hat{s}(t) \sin \omega_c t = R(t) \cos [\omega_c t + \theta(t)] \qquad (4\text{-}4\text{-}16)$$

where
$$R(t) = [s^2(t) + \hat{s}^2(t)]^{1/2} \qquad (4\text{-}4\text{-}17)$$

and
$$\theta(t) = \arctan \frac{\hat{s}(t)}{s(t)} \qquad (4\text{-}4\text{-}18)$$

The envelope $R(t)$ is the square root of the sum of squares of the signal and its Hilbert transform.   Figure 4-4-6 shows the appearance of the SSB wave for the previous example of a signal step.   The envelope is distorted by horns and smear.   Even if an envelope detector is not used, the linear transmission path must be capable of delivering the horns without overloading.

An envelope detector can be made effective for an SSB signal by adding a large amount of unmodulated in-phase carrier.   The wave $[s_o + s(t)] \cos \omega_c t - \hat{s}(t) \sin \omega_c t$ has envelope

$$R(t) = \{[s_o + s(t)]^2 + \hat{s}^2(t)\}^{1/2} \qquad (4\text{-}4\text{-}19)$$

If s_o is large compared with the peak values of $s(t)$ and $\hat{s}(t)$, we can expand $R(t)$ by the binomial theorem and neglect higher order terms in s/s_o and $\hat{s}/s_o$, thus

$$R(t) = s_o \left[1 + 2\frac{s}{s_o} + \left(\frac{s}{s_o}\right)^2 + \left(\frac{\hat{s}}{s_o}\right)^2 \right]^{1/2}$$
$$\approx s_o \left(1 + \frac{s}{s_o} \right) = s_o + s \qquad (4\text{-}4\text{-}20)$$

To the first order of small quantities, the envelope detector thus recovers the signal with a large bias.

Asymmetrical (ASB) and Vestigial Sideband (VSB).   The difficulty of isolating one sideband suggests a compromise in which one complete sideband and a part of another are transmitted.   Such systems are designated as *asymmetrical sideband.* They typically require about 1.25 times the bandwidth of one sideband instead of the factor of 2 used in double-sideband systems.   Detection is accomplished by the homodyne-carrier method.   The lowest frequencies in the band are sent by double sideband and the highest frequencies by single sideband.   This

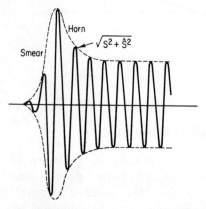

FIG. 4-4-6. Envelope of SSB wave resulting from signal step.

means that the low signal frequencies are doubled in amplitude relative to the high-frequency components in the detector output.   The gain-versus-frequency of the complete system shows a 6-db drop in the transition region from full double-sideband transmission to complete suppression of one sideband.   An equalizer with a complementary gain-versus-frequency characteristic can be inserted to restore uniform response over the signal band.

A special type of asymmetry which does not require equalization is called *vestigial sideband.* This method, originally suggested by H. Nyquist,[1] reduces transmission of the wanted sideband components to compensate for the contributions of the incompletely suppressed components from the other sideband. This is accomplished by passing the double-sideband wave through a network having a gain-versus-frequency curve such as shown in Fig. 4-4-7. The relative transmittance of this network is one-half at the carrier frequency and has odd symmetry about this point. It has the property that the sum of the transmittances at any two frequencies equally displaced above and below the carrier is unity. The sum of the detected contributions of the upper and lower sidebands is, therefore, the

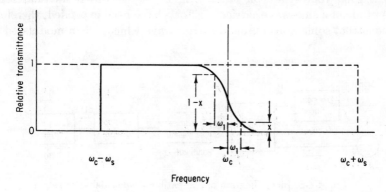

FIG. 4-4-7. Vestigial-sideband filter characteristic.

same as would be obtained from a complete sideband. In mathematical terms, if the transmittance at frequency ω is represented by $Y(\omega)$, the transmittance of a vestigial-sideband filter must satisfy

$$Y(\omega_c - \omega) + Y(\omega_c + \omega) = 2Y(\omega_c) \qquad (4\text{-}4\text{-}21)$$

for all values of ω in the signal band.

In commercial television broadcasting an asymmetrical-sideband signal is radiated with the transition region occurring between signal frequencies of 0.75 and 1.25 Mc. The shape of the transition region is not rigidly controlled at the transmitter. Complementary equalization at the receivers is not attempted. Instead a vestigial-sideband filter is inserted in each receiver. The performance is the same as vestigial sideband except for some wasted power and bandwidth in the unused part of the asymmetrical sideband.

Compatible Single Sideband. Pure amplitude-modulation systems are wasteful of bandwidth because the two sidebands contain duplicate information and are wasteful of power because the unmodulated carrier component carries no information. They have the advantage, however,

[1] H. Nyquist, Certain Topics in Telegraph Transmission Theory, *Trans. AIEE*, vol. 47, pp. 617–644, April, 1928.

that a simple detector is sufficient. All that is needed at the receiver is recovery of the envelope. Single-sideband systems are more efficient in conservation of both bandwidth and power, but they require a more complicated receiver in order to provide the necessary demodulating carrier. Radio broadcasting is an example in which amplitude modulation prevails primarily because the large ratio of number of receivers to number of transmitters makes simplicity of the receiver a decisive factor.

More widespread adoption of single sideband would take place if a simple compatible receiver which could detect either SSB or AM were available. We have seen that the envelope of an SSB wave is in general not a good representation of an original signal which modulates the amplitude of a sine-wave carrier. Efforts have been expended, therefore, to construct some nonsinusoidal carrier wave which, when modulated by

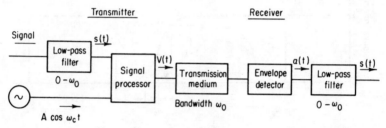

FIG. 4-4-8. Block diagram of compatible single-sideband system.

a signal, meets the simultaneous requirements of single-sideband frequency occupancy and envelope linearly related to signal. Various approximate solutions of this problem have been found in terms of a carrier wave with signal-dependent phase. Before discussing these methods we shall describe an exact mathematical solution[1] valid for a certain idealized class of signals.

Consider the block diagram of Fig. 4-4-8. At the transmitter an original signal $s(t)$ band-limited to frequencies less than ω_0, which is in turn less than ω_c, and a sinusoidal carrier wave $A \cos \omega_c t$ are applied as inputs to a signal processor from which emerges the single-sideband wave

$$V(t) = x(t) \cos \omega_c t - \hat{x}(t) \sin \omega_c t$$
$$= \alpha(t) \cos [\omega_c t + \beta(t)] \tag{4-4-22}$$

The bandwidth occupied by $V(t)$ is to be made equal to ω_0. At the receiver an envelope detector delivers the wave $\alpha(t)$ which is in general not band-limited. A low-pass filter cutting off at ω_0 selects the part of the envelope in the band of the original signal. The system becomes compatible if the output of the low-pass filter is equal to the original signal $s(t)$. From the

[1] B. F. Logan and M. R. Schroeder, A Solution to the Problem of Compatible Single-Sideband Transmission, *IRE Trans. Inform. Theory*, vol. IT-8, pp. 252–259, September, 1962.

analysis given by Logan and Schroeder, this requirement is fulfilled if the signal processor performs the following operations:

1. Determines a positive-valued function $\alpha^2(t)$ band-limited to ω_0 such that its square root applied to a low-pass filter cutting off at ω_0 generates the signal wave $s(t)$. The solution of this problem can be obtained, for example, by the method of Landau and Miranker.[1,2] Since the envelope $\alpha(t)$ is inherently positive, the signal $s(t)$ must include a sufficiently large positive constant to prevent admission of negative envelope values in the solution. If the d-c signal bias is of no interest in the receiver output, the input and output signals can differ by a constant.

2. Generates the Hilbert transform of log $\alpha(t)$.

3. Phase modulates the carrier oscillator with the output of step 2.

4. Modulates the amplitude of the wave obtained in step 3 by the signal.

While the procedures just described are mathematically correct they are not recommended for actual systems. Band-limited functions and Hilbert transforms require a description over the entire time domain and can only be approximated in terms of finite time intervals. The iterative nature of the computations makes a realization in real time difficult.

A method closely related to the theoretical one just described is that of Powers.[3] In the strict sense the Powers method is not compatible since it requires a square-law detector. The signal represented by the square of the envelope instead of by the envelope itself. Since the square of the envelope is band-limited, the first step in the procedure just described becomes unnecessary. Signals which assume both positive and negative values must have a sufficient positive bias added to prevent any changes of sign.

The compatible single-sideband systems which have been seriously proposed are based on approximations for specialized types of signals. One approach is to secure compatibility for a single sinusoidal signal component. Since the envelope of a wave is derived by nonlinear operations, the compatibility suffers when more signal components are added. In a method suggested by van Kessel, Stumpers, and Uyen[4] the carrier and one sideband are selected from an AM wave, passed through a squarer, and then applied to a bandpass filter centered at the second harmonic of the carrier frequency. For a single-frequency signal the output of the

[1] H. J. Landau and W. L. Miranker, The Recovery of Distorted Band-Limited Signals, *J. Math. Anal. Appl.*, vol. 2, pp. 97–104, February, 1961.

[2] H. J. Landau, On the Recovery of a Band-Limited Signal After Instantaneous Companding and Subsequent Band-Limiting, *Bell System Tech. J.*, vol. 39, pp. 351–364, March, 1960.

[3] K. H. Powers, The Compatibility Problem in Single-Sideband Transmission, *Proc. IRE*, vol. 48, pp. 1431–1435, August, 1960.

[4] T. J. van Kessel, F. L. H. M. Stumpers, and J. M. A. Uyen, A Method for Obtaining Compatible Single-Sideband Modulation, *Proc. IRE*, vol. 50, p. 1998, September, 1962.

squarer is of form

$$V_1(t) = A^2[\cos \omega_c t + k \cos (\omega_c + q)t]^2$$

$$= \frac{A^2}{2} [1 + \cos 2\omega_c t + 2k \cos (2\omega_c + q)t + 2k \cos qt$$

$$+ k^2 + k^2 \cos 2(\omega_c + q)t] \quad (4\text{-}4\text{-}23)$$

The output of the bandpass filter is

$$V_2(t) = \frac{A^2}{2} [\cos 2\omega_c t + 2k \cos (2\omega_c + q)t + k^2 \cos 2(\omega_c + q)t]$$

$$= \frac{A^2}{2} R(t) \cos [2\omega_c t + \theta(t)] \qquad (4\text{-}4\text{-}24)$$

The envelope function $R(t)$ is defined by

$$R(t) = [(1 + 2k \cos qt + k^2 \cos 2qt)^2 + (2k \sin qt + k^2 \sin 2qt)^2]^{\frac{1}{2}}$$
$$= 1 + k^2 + 2k \cos qt \qquad (4\text{-}4\text{-}25)$$

The envelope thus consists of a d-c term plus the undistorted signal. If, however, the signal consists of two sinusoidal terms $k_1 \cos q_1 t$ and $k_2 \cos q_2 t$, the envelope is found to be

$$R(t) = 1 + k_1^2 + k_2^2 + 2k_1 \cos q_1 t + 2k_2 \cos q_2 t + 2k_1 k_2 \cos (q_1 - q_2)t$$
$$(4\text{-}4\text{-}26)$$

This envelope is distorted by the presence of the beat-frequency term $\cos (q_1 - q_2)t$.

The theoretical difficulties involved in an ideal compatible single-sideband system become less formidable for certain specialized kinds of signals such as the waves representing speech and music. Speech waves in particular have a rugged structure which permits considerable non-linear processing without intolerable loss of quality. Speech waves can be regarded as a band of frequencies modulated both in amplitude and frequency at rates which are slow compared with the bandwidth. To obtain a speech signal with nonnegative values, we do not have to add a positive bias which is at all times equal to the absolute value of the most negative peak. Instead we can use a slowly varying bias which follows the speech peaks and is small when the speech oscillations are small. The slowly varying biasing wave does not add appreciably to the bandwidth of the signal. We thereby obtain a positive-valued signal suitable for transmission by the Powers single-sideband method. The bias can be removed from the signal output at the receiver since it can be determined from the envelope of the speech wave. The quality of such a system must be judged subjectively since it is the effect on the human ear which determines whether or not the recovered signal is acceptable.

Empirical attempts to obtain freedom from SSB envelope distortion for a more general class of signals than simple sine waves have commonly been aimed at deriving the appropriate carrier phase variation by clipping a wave containing the original carrier and SSB waves with various relative amounts of each. The resulting phase-modulated carrier is then amplitude modulated by the signal. In general, such a process generates a band of modulation products of width considerably greater than one sideband. For certain kinds of signals such as music and speech, however, it has been found possible to concentrate the most important products within the range of one sideband and thereby to achieve a subjectively acceptable envelope representation of the signal with SSB economy of bandwidth. Analysis of such a system must take into account the frequency content and amplitude range of the signal.

After experimenting with a number of simpler single-sideband systems of moderate compatibility, L. R. Kahn[1] evolved the SSB method shown in Fig. 4-4-9, which is claimed to perform well in radio broadcasting. The particular technique used is designated as "1 PM + 0.5 PM," which means that a phase-modulated carrier is derived by clipping the sum of two waves, each of which contains the original carrier and one sideband but with different proportions. At full load on the transmitter, one of the two waves contains carrier and sideband in equal strength, while in the other the sideband amplitude is half that of the carrier. The effect of the signal on the resultant carrier phase is most prominent at full load and is removed rapidly as the signal level decreases. The control as a function of signal level is obtained by passing the sideband inputs through separate expander circuits which provide increased gain when the signal is at maximum strength. An important advantage is taken of the distribution of energy versus frequency in speech and music signals. Such signals characteristically exhibit considerably greater energy density in the low-frequency part of the band than at the higher frequencies. The weak high-frequency components produce sideband contributions which are small relative to the transmitted carrier amplitude, and hence can be recovered by single-sideband envelope detection without objectionable distortion. The stronger low-frequency signal components produce a plurality of sidebands, but with Kahn's processing they are principally on one side of the carrier frequency and within a band of width no greater than that of the total signal.

It is to be noted that a common characteristic of the compatible SSB systems we have described is the presence of a fairly significant component at the carrier frequency. Performance of the systems should therefore be compared with that attainable by simple SSB with transmitted carrier and envelope detection.

[1] L. R. Kahn, Compatible Single Sideband, *Proc. IRE*, vol. 49, pp. 1503–1527, October, 1961.

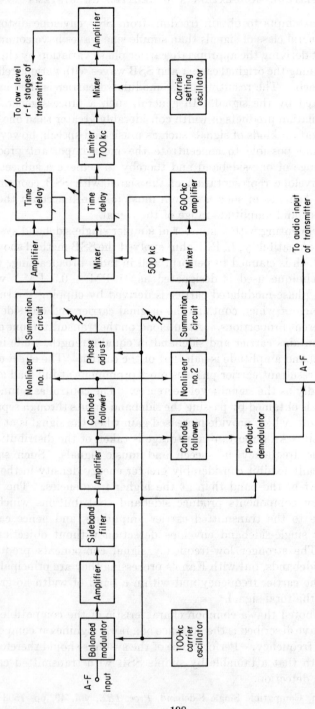

Fig. 4-4-9. Block diagram of CSSB system using 1 PM and 0.5 PM technique. (*From L. R. Kahn, Proc. IRE, vol. 49, October, 1961, p. 1518.*)

198

4-5. Analysis of Modulating and Demodulating Circuits[1-7]

Actual modulators and demodulators are constructed from nonlinear elements which cannot be accurately described in terms of simple power-law responses or by idealized cutoff characteristics. For purpose of quantitative design a description in terms of response to a carrier wave which spans the operating range is convenient. The signal input to a modulator or the sideband input to a demodulator is preferably kept small in amplitude relative to the carrier. The relations between signal and sideband components are then expressible in terms of small perturbations of the response to carrier alone. For sufficiently small excursions of signal and sideband, the perturbations are linear even though the large-scale carrier response is highly nonlinear.

Nonlinear Resistors. Consider a nonlinear element in which the voltage V is related to the current I by

$$V = F(I) \tag{4-5-1}$$

Then if $I = P \cos pt + Q \cos qt$ with $Q \ll P$, the voltage can be written to a first approximation as

$$V \approx F(P \cos pt) + F'(P \cos pt)Q \cos qt \tag{4-5-2}$$

We next expand $F'(P \cos pt)$ in a Fourier series as follows:

$$F'(P \cos pt) = R_0 + 2 \sum_{n=1}^{\infty} R_n \cos npt \tag{4-5-3}$$

where $$R_n = \frac{1}{2\pi} \int_{-\pi}^{\pi} F'(P \cos x) \cos nx \, dx \tag{4-5-4}$$

The function $F'(P \cos pt)$ can be regarded as a time-varying differential resistance[8] encountered by the signal current $Q \cos qt$. The modulating

[1] E. Peterson and L. W. Hussey, Equivalent Modulator Circuits, *Bell System Tech. J.*, vol. 18, pp. 32–48, January, 1939.

[2] R. S. Caruthers, Copper Oxide Modulators in Carrier Telephone Systems, *Bell System Tech. J.*, vol. 18, pp. 315–337, April, 1939.

[3] S. Kruse, "Theory of Rectifier Modulators," Thesis for Doctorate, K. Tekniska Högskolan, May 26, 1939. Copyright by Telefonaktiebolaget, L. M. Ericsson, Stockholm.

[4] L. C. Peterson and F. B. Llewellyn, The Performance and Measurement of Mixers in Terms of Linear-Network Theory, *Proc. IRE*, vol. 33, pp. 458–476, July, 1945.

[5] S. Duinker, "General Properties of Frequency-Converting Networks," Thesis, Technical University of Delft, June, 1957.

[6] V. Belevitch, "Théorie des Circuits Non-Linéaires en Régime Alternatif (Redresseurs, Modulators, Oscillateurs)," Gauthier-Villars, Paris, 1959.

[7] W. R. Bennett, Amplification in Nonlinear Reactive Networks, *IRE Trans. Circuit Theory*, vol. CT-7, pp. 440–446, December, 1960.

[8] E. Peterson and L. W. Hussey, Equivalent Modulator Circuits, *Bell System Tech. J.*, vol. 18, pp. 32–48, January, 1939.

properties of the nonlinear element are fully described by the Fourier coefficients $R_0, R_1, \ldots$, which are dependent only on the element and the carrier wave.

In general, a single-frequency component of signal generates an infinite number of modulation products since there can be side frequencies on each harmonic of the carrier. Even though the relations are linear the solution for a specific circuit is complicated because the number of equations to be satisfied is infinite. Efficient design minimizes the power consumption resulting from unwanted modulation products. The circuit modifications necessary to bring about this result also tend to reduce the number of important equations and to make the solution manageable.

As an illustrative example consider the circuit shown in Fig. 4-5-1, in which a single nonlinear element is used in a single-sideband modulator

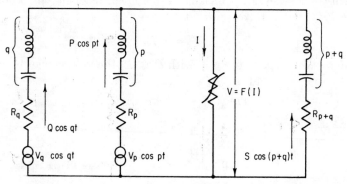

FIG. 4-5-1. Single-sideband modulator with high impedance outside the band.

with high impedance outside the band. The carrier and signal sources as well as the sideband output branch are all in parallel with the nonlinear element. Series-resonant circuits in each of the three external branches make the impedances of the signal source, carrier source, and sideband load, respectively, equal to resistances R_q, R_p, and R_{p+q} at the frequencies q, p, and $p + q$, respectively, and high away from these frequencies. In the absence of signal, the current is sinusoidal at the carrier frequency since harmonic currents cannot flow through the resonant circuits. The voltage V is determined by

$$V = F(I) = F(P \cos pt)$$

$$= A_0 + 2 \sum_{n=1}^{\infty} A_n \cos npt \qquad (4\text{-}5\text{-}5)$$

where
$$A_n = \frac{1}{2\pi} \int_{-\pi}^{\pi} F(P \cos x) \cos nx \, dx \qquad (4\text{-}5\text{-}6)$$

The component of voltage at the carrier frequency across the nonlinear element must be equal to the carrier generator voltage minus the voltage drop across R_p. Hence

$$2A_1 = V_p - PR_p \tag{4-5-7}$$

When this equation is combined with the previous one, we obtain

$$PR_p + \frac{1}{\pi} \int_{-\pi}^{\pi} F(P \cos x) \cos x \, dx = V_p \tag{4-5-8}$$

This equation defines V_p as a function of P and hence can be used inversely to obtain P as a function of V_p. The values of the differential resistance coefficients R_n can then be computed from Eq. (4-5-4).

We next consider the case of a small superimposed signal. The added currents consist of a component $Q \cos qt$ in the signal branch and a component $S \cos (p + q)t$ in the sideband load. The sum of these two components flows through the nonlinear element and produces a voltage equal to the product of current and the differential resistance given by Eq.

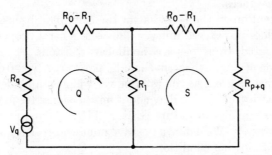

FIG. 4-5-2. Equivalent linear circuit for single-sideband modulator of Fig. 4-5-1.

(4-5-3). The perturbation in the voltage across the nonlinear element is thus given by

$$v = [Q \cos qt + S \cos (p + q)t][R_0 + 2 \sum_{n=1}^{\infty} R_n \cos npt]$$

$$= (QR_0 + SR_1) \cos qt + (QR_1 + SR_0) \cos (p + q)t + \cdots \tag{4-5-9}$$

The terms not shown in the equation have frequencies other than q and $p + q$. The sum of the voltage drops around the mesh containing the signal source and nonlinear element must vanish for the signal-frequency components, and likewise the sum of the voltage drops around the mesh containing the sideband load and nonlinear element must vanish for the sideband components. These conditions lead to the following pair of equations.

$$Q(R_0 + R_q) + SR_1 = V_q \tag{4-5-10}$$
$$QR_1 + S(R_0 + R_{p+q}) = 0$$

We recognize that this pair of equations would be obtained for the two-mesh linear circuit of Fig. 4-5-2. We can, therefore, make use of the known properties of such a circuit. In particular the condition for maximum power transferred from signal to sideband is obtained by matching the terminal resistances to the iterative resistance of the network, thus

$$R_q = R_{p+q} = (R_0{}^2 - R_1{}^2)^{1/2} \qquad (4\text{-}5\text{-}11)$$

The conversion power gain is

$$G_c = R_1{}^2 [R_0 + (R_0{}^2 - R_1{}^2)^{1/2}]^{-2} \qquad (4\text{-}5\text{-}12)$$

The maximum value of gain is unity, which is obtained when $R_1 = R_0$. This result is approached when the differential resistance is a sharply peaked pulse repeated at the carrier rate. The optimum terminating impedances approach zero as the maximum gain is approached, and hence unity conversion gain cannot actually be attained. Physically the highest gain is approached by switching the nonlinear element from a very low to a very high differential resistance throughout a relatively small part of the carrier cycle and working between very low signal source and sideband load resistances.

We call attention to the fact that in the examples discussed, the conversion gain does not exceed unity. This is a general property of modulators constructed from passive nonlinear resistors. It is in fact a corollary of the stronger theorem that the power received from the signal source is at least as great as the total power which can be delivered to all components with frequencies dependent on the signal frequencies. This theorem was originally proved by G. R. Stibitz.[1] The following proof is due to C. H. Page.[2] We define a positive nonlinear resistor as an element satisfying the following conditions:

1. The current is a single-valued time-invariant function of the voltage.
2. Current and voltage increments never have opposite signs.
3. The current is zero when the voltage is zero.

The carrier and signal frequencies are assumed unrelated.

We resolve the total voltage v across the nonlinear resistor into two parts: v_1, containing all components with frequencies dependent on the carrier frequencies only; and v_2, containing all other components. That is, v_1 contains the carrier and its harmonics or, if there is more than one carrier frequency, v_1 includes all cross products between the carriers as well as the carriers themselves and their harmonics. If there is a d-c term it is included in v_1. The other part v_2 contains the signal frequencies, their harmonics and cross products, and all cross products of signal frequencies with carrier frequencies. Then the total current i is given by

$$i = F(v) = F(v_1 + v_2) \qquad (4\text{-}5\text{-}13)$$

where $F(v)$ satisfies the conditions defining a positive nonlinear resistor.

[1] G. R. Stibitz, General Modulation with Nonlinear Resistances, Unpublished Bell Telephone Laboratories Technical Memorandum, April 6, 1932.

[2] C. H. Page, Frequency Conversion with Positive Nonlinear Resistors, *J. Res. Natl. Bur. Std. (U.S.)*, vol. 56, pp. 179–182, April, 1956.

Consider the current component

$$i_1 = F(v_1) \tag{4-5-14}$$

which is a uniquely defined function of v_1 containing no frequencies related to those present in the signal. It follows that i_1 and v_2 share no frequencies in common and hence that the product $v_2 i_1$ is a sum of sinusoidal terms. Therefore

$$\text{av } (v_2 i_1) = 0 \tag{4-5-15}$$

The average power absorbed by the resistor at frequencies related to the signal is

$$
\begin{aligned}
w_q &= \text{av } (v_2 i) \\
&= \text{av } [v_2(i - i_1) + v_2 i_1] \\
&= \text{av } \{v_2[F(v_1 + v_2) - F(v_1)]\} + av \ (v_2 i_1) \tag{4-5-16}
\end{aligned}
$$

In the first term it follows from the definition of a positive nonlinear resistor that if v_2 is positive, $F(v_1 + v_2)$ exceeds $F(v_1)$; if v_2 is negative, $F(v_1 + v_2)$ is less than $F(v_1)$. The product of v_2 and $F(v_1 + v_2) - F(v_1)$ is positive in both cases. Since we have already proved that av $(v_2 i_1)$ is zero, it follows that

$$w_q \geq 0 \tag{4-5-17}$$

For individual components of v_2 at the various frequencies, a positive value of average absorbed power means that an external generator at that frequency is supplying a net amount of positive average power, while a negative value means that net power is delivered to a load at that frequency. Equation (4-5-17) states that the algebraic sum of all net power components cannot be negative and hence that the amount of power available for all loads related to the signal is limited to that supplied by generators related to the signal. The conversion gain cannot exceed unity even if all the available power from the signal source is concentrated in one sideband. No power can be transferred from carrier sources to signal-dependent products. In this respect the positive nonlinear resistor differs from the negative nonlinear resistor and the nonlinear reactor, which can transfer power from carrier supply to sideband output and thus give conversion gains greater than unity.

Nonlinear Reactors. Two idealized types of nonlinear reactors are the nonlinear capacitor, in which the voltage v is expressed by a single-valued nonlinear functional relationship in terms of the charge q, i.e., $v = F(q)$, and the nonlinear inductor, in which the current i is expressed by a single-valued relationship in terms of the flux linkages, i.e., $i = F(\phi)$. In the case of the nonlinear capacitor, the current i is given by $i = dq/dt$, while in the case of the nonlinear inductor, the voltage v is given by $v = d\phi/dt$. Since the relations for the inductor can be obtained from those of the capacitor by replacement of v by i, q by ϕ, and i by v, analytical results for one type can readily be extended to the other type.

To show that an ideal nonlinear reactor cannot dissipate power, we let W represent the instantaneous value of power in a nonlinear capacitor and calculate

$$\text{av } W = \text{av } (vi) = \text{av } \left(v \frac{dq}{dt} \right)$$

$$= \lim_{T \to \infty} \frac{1}{T} \int_{t_1}^{t_1+T} v \frac{dq}{dt} \, dt$$

$$= \lim_{T \to \infty} \frac{1}{T} \int_{q(t_1)}^{q(t_1+T)} F(q) \, dq \qquad (4\text{-}5\text{-}18)$$

Since $F(q)$ is single valued, the area accumulated in the integration process cancels whenever the curve is retraced, and the value of the integral cannot exceed the area under the curve swept out by the maximum monotonic variation in q. For finite impressed waves the area under one traversal is finite, and division by indefinitely large T gives the limiting value zero for the average power. Over a long time the nonlinear reactor returns as much power to the external circuit as it absorbs from it. Hysteresis would destroy this property and is excluded from our definition of the reactor. Freedom from dissipation removes a possible contribution of thermal noise in a modulator and is, therefore, a valuable property when low noise figures are of great importance.

Assume a nonlinear capacitor connected to an external network with a finite number of internal sinusoidal voltage or current generators having a finite number of independent base frequencies $\omega_1, \omega_2, \ldots, \omega_N$. Then in the steady state the voltage v and charge q in the capacitor can be represented by:

$$v = \sum_{m_1} \cdots \sum_{m_N} [A_{m_1 \cdots m_N} \cos (m_1\omega_1 + m_2\omega_2 + \cdots + m_N\omega_N)t$$

$$+ B_{m_1 \cdots m_N} \sin (m_1\omega_1 + m_2\omega_2 + \cdots + m_N\omega_N)t] \qquad (4\text{-}5\text{-}19)$$

$$q = \sum_{m_1} \cdots \sum_{m_N} [C_{m_1 \cdots m_N} \cos (m_1\omega_1 + m_2\omega_2 + \cdots + m_N\omega_N)t$$

$$+ D_{m_1 \cdots m_N} \sin (m_1\omega_1 + m_2\omega_2 + \cdots + m_N\omega_N)t] \qquad (4\text{-}5\text{-}20)$$

In the multiple summations the value of m_1 takes on all positive integer values and zero, while all other indices are summed from $-\infty$ to ∞. The single-valued functional relationship $v = F(q)$ can be used to define a more general function[1] of N independent variables $x_1, x_2, \ldots, x_N$, of which v and q form the special case when

$$x_1 = \omega_1 t \qquad x_2 = \omega_2 t \qquad \cdots \qquad x_N = \omega_N t \qquad (4\text{-}5\text{-}21)$$

If the C's and D's in Eq. (4-5-20) are given, the corresponding set of A's and B's in Eq. (4-5-19) can be computed by the formula for N-tuple Fourier-series expansion. The calculation is done entirely in terms of

[1] W. R. Bennett, New Results in the Calculation of Modulation Products, *Bell System Tech. J.*, vol. 12, pp. 228–243, April, 1933.

the variables $x_1, x_2, \ldots, x_N$ and the function $v = F(q)$. The results do not depend on the choice of $\omega_1, \omega_2, \ldots, \omega_N$ for the special case. By suitable adjustment of the source generators and terminating circuit elements we can adjust the C and D coefficients at will. The A and B coefficients then become determined and are independent of the ω values.

The current $i = dq/dt$ can be found by differentiating Eq. (4-5-20) with respect to time. Each coefficient of i is, therefore, a linear function of the base frequencies. Our previously derived result that the average total power absorbed by a reactor is zero can be used to obtain an important relation between power supplied to and delivered from the reactor at specific frequencies. An expression for the average total power can be formulated by integrating the product vi over a time interval T, dividing by T, and taking the limit as T goes to infinity. Since in this process we multiply coefficients independent of the base frequencies by coefficients which are linear functions of the base frequencies, it follows that the product vi is a linear function of the base frequencies. Hence we can write for the instantaneous power:

$$W = \sum_{n=1}^{N} W_n \omega_n \qquad (4\text{-}5\text{-}22)$$

where W_n does not depend on the choice of ω_n's.

The value of the W_n's can be determined by a method due to Page.[1] Let $W_{m_1 \cdots m_N}$ represent the instantaneous power absorbed by the component of frequency $m_1\omega_1 + \cdots + m_N\omega_N$. Then since the total power is the sum of the power in all components,

$$W = \sum_{m_1 \cdots m_N} W_{m_1 \cdots m_N} = \sum_{m_1 \cdots m_N} \frac{W_{m_1 \cdots m_N} \displaystyle\sum_{n=1}^{N} m_n \omega_n}{m_1\omega_1 + \cdots + m_N\omega_N}$$

$$= \sum_{n=1}^{N} \omega_n \sum_{m_1 \cdots m_N} \frac{m_n W_{m_1 \cdots m_N}}{m_1\omega_1 + \cdots + m_N\omega_N} \qquad (4\text{-}5\text{-}23)$$

By comparison of Eqs. (4-5-22) and (4-5-23):

$$W_n = \sum_{m_1 \cdots m_N} \frac{m_n W_{m_1 \cdots m_N}}{m_1\omega_1 + \cdots + m_N\omega_N} \qquad (4\text{-}5\text{-}24)$$

The average value of W over a time increasing without limit has been previously shown to be zero for a nonlinear reactor. From Eq. (4-5-22) then

$$\text{av } W = \sum_{n=1}^{N} \omega_n \text{ av } W_n = 0 \qquad (4\text{-}5\text{-}25)$$

---

[1] C. H. Page, Frequency Conversion with Nonlinear Reactance, *J. Res. Natl. Bur. Std. (U.S.)*, vol. 58, pp. 227–236, May, 1957.

A linear function of N independent variables cannot vanish for all choices of the variables unless each coefficient individually vanishes. Therefore, av $W_n = 0$ and from Eq. (4-5-24), for all choices of n,

$$\sum_{m_1 \cdots m_N} \frac{m_n \text{ av } W_{m_1 \cdots m_N}}{m_1 \omega_1 + \cdots + m_N \omega_N} = 0 \qquad (4\text{-}5\text{-}26)$$

Equation (4-5-26) is the generalized form of the Manley-Rowe[1] relations, which apply to the special case of $N = 2$:

$$\sum_{m_1=0}^{\infty} \sum_{m_2=-\infty}^{\infty} \frac{m_1 \text{ av } W_{m_1 m_2}}{m_1 \omega_1 + m_2 \omega_2} = 0$$

$$\sum_{m_2=0}^{\infty} \sum_{m_1=-\infty}^{\infty} \frac{m_2 \text{ av } W_{m_1 m_2}}{m_1 \omega_1 + m_2 \omega_2} = 0 \qquad (4\text{-}5\text{-}27)$$

It can be shown from these relations that it is possible to deliver more

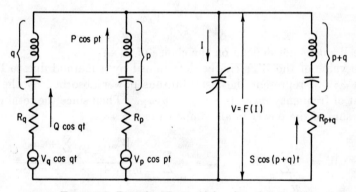

Fig. 4-5-3. Reactive single-sideband modulator.

power to a sideband product than is furnished by the signal generator. An analogous set of relations for nonlinear resistors has been given by Pantell.[2]

As an illustration consider the circuit of Fig. 4-5-3, which is obtained from Fig. 4-5-1 by replacing the nonlinear resistor by a nonlinear capacitor. Since the current is zero except at the frequencies ω_1, ω_2, and $\omega_1 + \omega_2$, the average power absorbed by the capacitor must be zero except at these frequencies. The only terms which are significant in Eq. (4-5-27) are $m_1 = 1$, $n_1 = 0$; $m_1 = 0$, $n_1 = 1$; and $m_1 = n_1 = 1$.

[1] J. M. Manley and H. E. Rowe, Some General Properties of Nonlinear Elements, Part I, General Energy Relations, *Proc. IRE*, vol. 44, pp. 904–913, July, 1956.

[2] R. H. Pantell, General Power Relationships for Positive and Negative Nonlinear Resistive Elements, *Proc. IRE*, vol. 46, pp. 1910–1913, December, 1958.

The equations reduce to the following form, in which the notation is simplified by letting the W's represent average values of power:

$$\frac{W_{10}}{\omega_1} + \frac{W_{11}}{\omega_1 + \omega_2} = 0$$
$$\frac{W_{01}}{\omega_2} + \frac{W_{11}}{\omega_1 + \omega_2} = 0$$

(4-5-28)

This pair of equations can also be written in the form

$$W_{11} = -\frac{\omega_1 + \omega_2}{\omega_1} W_{10} = -\frac{\omega_1 + \omega_2}{\omega_2} W_{01}$$

(4-5-29)

The interpretation is that power supplied to the reactor at frequency ω_1 results in $(\omega_1 + \omega_2)/\omega_1$ times as much power delivered to the sideband load. Likewise power supplied to the reactor at frequency ω_2 results in $(\omega_1 + \omega_2)/\omega_2$ times as much power delivered to the sideband load. If ω_1 represents the carrier frequency and ω_2 the signal frequency and ω_1 is much larger than ω_2, the ratio $(\omega_1 + \omega_2)/\omega_2$ is large compared with unity, and a large conversion gain from signal to sideband can be obtained. This result is not restricted to the small-signal case but holds for all signal and carrier amplitudes. For linear conversion gain it is desirable to make the signal amplitude small relative to that of the carrier.

If the load circuit is tuned to the lower side frequency instead of the upper sideband, the term $m_1 = n_1 = 1$ is replaced by one in which $m_1 = 1$, $n_1 = -1$. Equation (4-5-29) then becomes

$$W_{1,-1} = -\frac{\omega_1 - \omega_2}{\omega_1} W_{10} = \frac{\omega_1 - \omega_2}{\omega_2} W_{01}$$

(4-5-30)

The significance of the opposite signs is that if the carrier source supplies power, then both the sideband and signal circuits absorb power. Potential instability thus exists, and under certain conditions the system can oscillate at the signal and side frequencies with power supplied only at the carrier terminals. Under other conditions the power supplied to the signal circuit can be used to make up for losses there, and a negative-resistance amplifier to the signal is thereby obtained. It is to be noted that this requires provision of a load circuit for the lower side frequency even though this frequency does not actually appear at the carrier or signal terminals. The mechanism may be thought of as including a remodulation of $\omega_1 - \omega_2$ with ω_1 to regenerate the product

$$\omega_1 - (\omega_1 - \omega_2) = \omega_2$$

The carrier frequency is called the "pump frequency" and the lower side frequency the "idler frequency."

4-6. Effect of Distortion in Transmitting Medium

In the path from transmitter to receiver, the AM wave is exposed to a variety of effects which may distort the recovered signal. In linear time-invariant systems the signal waveform can be distorted by unequal treatment of component frequencies. Nonlinear systems distort the wave by generating new frequencies not present in the original wave as well as by upsetting the relations between the original components. The transmitting medium may also contain sources of interference and noise which cause extraneous components to be received with the wanted signal.

Distortion in Time-invariant Linear Media. The response of a linear medium is conveniently described in terms of the response to individual sine waves with frequencies in the range of interest. In a linear time-invariant system the response to a sine wave is a sine wave of the same frequency with amplitude proportional to the amplitude of the applied wave and a shift in phase from that of the applied wave. Both the factor of proportionality and the amount of phase shift vary in general with the frequency. Two functions of frequency are thus required for a complete description, namely, the amplitude-versus-frequency function and the phase-versus-frequency function. Quantitatively if the application of $V \cos \omega t$ produces the response $Y(\omega) V \cos [\omega t - \phi(\omega)]$, $Y(\omega)$ is the amplitude-versus-frequency function and $\phi(\omega)$ is the phase-versus-frequency function. The response of a system to any impressed wave can be easily calculated from these two functions if the wave can be expressed as the sum of sinusoidal components. The linearity of the system enables one to equate the response to the sum of the individual responses.

Thus if the applied wave can be expressed as

$$V(t) = \sum_n V_n \cos (\omega_n t + \theta_n) \tag{4-6-1}$$

the response $I(t)$ is given by

$$I(t) = \sum_n Y(\omega_n) V_n \cos [\omega_n t + \theta_n - \phi(\omega_n)] \tag{4-6-2}$$

Distortionless transmission is obtained if the value of $Y(\omega_n)$ is constant for all the values of ω_n and the values of $\phi(\omega_n)$ fall on a straight line with intercept zero or a multiple of $\pm \pi$. To verify this, substitute $Y(\omega_n) = k$ and $\phi(\omega_n) = \tau \omega_n + m\pi$ in the equation for $I(t)$. The result is

$$I(t) = \sum_n k V_n \cos [\omega_n t + \theta_n - \tau \omega_n - m\pi]$$

$$= k \cos m\pi \sum_n V_n \cos [\omega_n(t - \tau) + \theta_n] \tag{4-6-3}$$

$$= k(-)^m V(t - \tau)$$

The response is, therefore, proportional to the applied wave delayed by time τ. The polarity is reversed if the phase intercept is an odd multiple of $\pm\pi$. The amount of delay τ is equal to the slope of the straight line representing phase versus frequency.

An AM wave modulated by a sum of sinusoidal components can be represented by

$$V(t) = A \cos \omega_c t + \sum_n Q_n \cos \left[(\omega_c + q_n)t + \theta_n\right]$$
$$+ \sum_n Q_n \cos \left[(\omega_c - q_n)t - \theta_n\right] \quad (4\text{-}6\text{-}4)$$

The first summation represents the upper sideband, in which the carrier frequency ω_c is added to the frequency of each signal component. The second summation represents the lower sideband, in which the components have frequencies equal to the difference between the carrier frequency and the original frequencies. The response of the system $I(t)$ to the AM wave is found by multiplying each term by the value of the amplitude-frequency function $Y(\omega)$ at the frequency of the term and inserting a phase shift equal to the value of the phase function $\phi(\omega)$ at the frequency of the term. That is,

$$I(t) = Y(\omega_c)A \cos \left[\omega_c t - \phi(\omega_c)\right]$$
$$+ \sum_n Y(\omega_c + q_n)Q_n \cos \left[(\omega_c + q_n)t + \theta_n - \phi(\omega_c + q_n)\right]$$
$$+ \sum_n Y(\omega_c - q_n)Q_n \cos \left[(\omega_c - q_n)t - \theta_n - \phi(\omega_c - q_n)\right] \quad (4\text{-}6\text{-}5)$$

A simple description of the effect of the transmission characteristic on the recovered AM signal can be given when a synchronous detector is used. For this case we multiply the expression for $I(t)$ by $2 \cos(\omega_c t - \alpha)$, express the products of cosines as cosines of sums and differences, and retain only the difference terms. The following expression is thus obtained for the detected wave:

$$D(t) = Y(\omega_c)A \cos \left[\alpha - \phi(\omega_c)\right]$$
$$+ \sum_n Y(\omega_c + q_n)Q_n \cos \left[q_n t + \theta_n + \alpha - \phi(\omega_c + q_n)\right]$$
$$+ \sum_n Y(\omega_c - q_n)Q_n \cos \left[q_n t + \theta_n - \alpha + \phi(\omega_c - q_n)\right] \quad (4\text{-}6\text{-}6)$$

The first term is a d-c component, often of no interest. The two summations represent the contributions of the upper and lower sidebands to the recovered signal. The two contributions at each signal differ in general with respect to both amplitude and phase. The sum can be found by the standard methods of complex algebra. We introduce a complex transmittance function:

$$Y_D(q) = Y(\omega_c + q)e^{j[\alpha - \phi(\omega_c + q)]} + Y(\omega_c - q)e^{j[\phi(\omega_c - q) - \alpha]} \quad (4\text{-}6\text{-}7)$$

The detected response to an original signal component $Q \cos (qt + \theta)$ is then

$$D_q(t) = |Y_D(q)| Q \cos [qt + \theta + phY_D(q)] \qquad (4\text{-}6\text{-}8)$$

The convenient value of α, the homodyne carrier phase, is $\phi(\omega_c)$. If the phase-versus-frequency function is linear, it can be written in the form

$$\phi(\omega) = \phi(\omega_c) + (\omega - \omega_c)\tau \qquad (4\text{-}6\text{-}9)$$

Then if $\alpha = \phi(\omega_c)$, we obtain

$$Y_D(q) = [Y(\omega_c + q) + Y(\omega_c - q)]e^{-jq\tau} \qquad (4\text{-}6\text{-}10)$$

Therefore, in the case of linear phase, a synchronous detector with phase equal to that of the transmitted carrier gives an equivalent transmission characteristic obtained by adding the amplitude factors at the upper and lower sideband frequencies and delaying the wave by the slope of the phase function.

The d-c component of $D(t)$ contributed by the first term of Eq. (4-6-6) arises from the transmitted carrier and disappears in a DSBSC system. Note that even when no carrier is transmitted it is important for the homodyne carrier to have the phase which the carrier would have had if it were transmitted. In other words the demodulating carrier should have the phase of the carrier on which the sidebands are modulated.

When envelope detection or linear rectification is used, the recovered signal cannot be represented so simply. These detection processes are nonlinear and distort the signal if the transmission path does not preserve the shape of the envelope. The distortion can be reduced by adding a relatively large amount of unmodulated carrier, which as pointed out before causes the envelope detector to approach the same performance as homodyne detection.

The results we have derived from signal waves which can be resolved into discrete sinusoidal components can be readily extended to signal waves expressible as Fourier integrals. If we replace Eq. (4-6-1) by

$$V(t) = \int_0^\infty U(\omega) \cos [\omega t + \theta(\omega)] \, d\omega \qquad (4\text{-}6\text{-}11)$$

the response $I(t)$ becomes

$$I(t) = \int_0^\infty Y(\omega) U(\omega) \cos [\omega t + \theta(\omega) - \phi(\omega)] \, d\omega \qquad (4\text{-}6\text{-}12)$$

The remainder of the analysis can be carried through in a manner similar to that for the case of discrete components. The summations are replaced by integrals throughout.

Nonlinear Distortion. A small amount of memory-free nonlinearity can be effectively represented by a power series. For example, the response $I(t)$ can be described approximately in many important cases by the equation

$$I(t) = a_1 V(t) + a_2 V^2(t) + a_3 V^3(t) + \cdots \qquad (4\text{-}6\text{-}13)$$

If we substitute Eq. (4-6-4) for $V(t)$, we obtain an equation showing the effect of this sort of nonlinearity on an AM wave. It is seen that new frequencies are generated, some lying within and some without the original AM band. The components with frequencies outside the band can be excluded by filtering, but those that fall within the band are thenceforward indistinguishable from legitimate signal components. It becomes important, therefore, to determine the position of new frequencies relative to the original AM band. The width of the sidebands relative to the carrier frequency is all-important here. In the so-called narrowband case in which the sideband width is small compared with the carrier frequency, the distortion terms arising from the square-law part of Eq. (4-6-13) are either far above or far below the AM band. The reason for this is that the new frequencies are either sums or differences of pairs of the original frequencies. The sums cluster around twice the carrier frequency and the differences fall near zero frequency. The cube-law term of the expression, on the other hand, contains components with frequencies equal to the sum of two original frequencies minus another original frequency. Such frequencies fall within or near the original band.

In the wideband AM case, which is characterized by sidebands of width comparable with the carrier frequency, the square-law distortion products can overlap the frequency range of the AM wave. Such overlap sometimes becomes a problem in wire-line carrier systems, in which the carrier frequency may be placed only slightly higher than the highest baseband frequency. The resulting distortion is called the Kendall effect, after B. W. Kendall, who predicted its existence. Note that after the overlap has occurred the extraneous components are accepted by the receiver as bona fide signal components. Their presence can be more offensive than linear distortion of the baseband since they may depend on the carrier frequency, which is in general not related to the baseband component frequencies.

Even when new components are not introduced by the nonlinearity, distortion can occur in the response to components already present. For example, the cube of a single-frequency term can be expressed as the sum of fundamental and third-harmonic components as follows:

$$(Q \cos \omega t)^3 = \frac{3Q^3}{4} \cos \omega t + \frac{Q^3}{4} \cos 3\omega t \qquad (4\text{-}6\text{-}14)$$

Therefore, a term $a_3 (Q \cos \omega t)^3$ contributes a term of fundamental frequency ω to the output. Depending on the sign of the coefficient a_3, it may add or subtract to the term of frequency ω arising from the linear part of the response. The result is an increase or decrease in gain when the signal amplitude is increased. By cubing the sum of two sine waves, we can show that the gain at one frequency is affected by the presence of the other.   The result is commonly a reduction in gain at one frequency when the amplitude of the component of the other frequency is increased. The name *crowding effect* is applied to this phenomenon.   An increase or decrease in gain at one frequency when the amplitude of the component at that frequency is increased is called *expansion* or *compression*, respectively.

Interference and Noise.   The effect of a single-frequency interfering wave can be readily calculated for the case of synchronous detection. If the carrier frequency is ω_c and the interfering component is of form $B_n \cos \omega_n t$, a synchronous detector delivers a corresponding output component proportional to $B_n \cos (\omega_n - \omega_c)t$.   The constant of proportionality is the same as that for conversion of a sideband component to the signal band.   The interference must be accepted by the signal-output circuit if the difference frequency $\omega_n - \omega_c$ falls within the signal band.

When an envelope detector is used the effect of a single-frequency interfering wave is more complicated.   Consider the general AM wave described by Eq. (4-1-1).   If a wave $B_n \cos (\omega_n t + \theta_n)$ is added, we obtain the resultant wave

$$E(t) = a[s_o + s(t)] \cos (\omega_c t + \theta) + B_n \cos (\omega_n t + \theta_n)$$
$$= R(t) \cos [\omega_c t + \phi(t)] \qquad (4\text{-}6\text{-}15)$$

where $R^2(t) = a^2[s_o + s(t)]^2 + 2aB_n[s_o + s(t)] \cos [(\omega_n - \omega_c)t$
$$+ \theta_n - \theta] + B_n{}^2 \quad (4\text{-}6\text{-}16)$$

The envelope is seen to be a nonlinear function of the signal and the interference.   The output of the envelope detector therefore contains harmonics of the frequency difference between interference and carrier as well as cross products between the signal and the difference frequency. When the unmodulated-carrier term has large amplitude relative to the other terms, the envelope approaches a linear function of signal and interference.   The result is then similar to synchronous detection.

As previously illustrated in Eq. (1-2-21), a Gaussian noise wave can be approximated by the sum of a large number of closely spaced single-frequency components with random phase.   The amplitudes are adjusted to fit the spectral density.   Thus, if the spectral density function $G(f)$ multiplied by df gives the mean-square value of the noise voltage in a band of width df centered at f, we can simulate the noise by sine-wave voltage components of amplitude $[2G(f) \Delta f]^{1/2}$ spaced Δf cps apart in frequency.   The mean-square value of each elementary sine wave is $G(f) \Delta f$, and this is the mean-square value in a frequency interval Δf. The width of the interval Δf must be taken small enough not to influence results obtained from the model.

The response of a homodyne detector to an AM wave with added random noise can be calculated by summing the contributions of the elementary components. The elementary noise received in a narrow band centered at frequency f at the detector output is produced by original noise components in the upper sideband at frequency $f_c + f$ and from the lower sideband at frequency $f_c - f$. The noise waves in the upper and lower sideband intervals are, in general, independent of each other. Hence the two contributions add as power; that is, the mean-square amplitudes add directly. If the sideband-to-signal conversion factor is unity, the spectral density of the detected noise is $G(f_c + f) + G(f_c - f)$. If each of the sidebands representing the signal has average power W_s and the homodyne carrier has the correct phase, the signal contributions from the two sidebands add in phase to give mean total power $4W_s$. In the case of white noise, i.e., noise with constant spectral density, the mean detected noise power from the two sidebands is twice that from one. Therefore, use of two sidebands doubles the signal-to-noise power ratio as compared with one sideband but does so at the expense of transmitting twice as much sideband power. Double- and single-sideband systems are thus equivalent in signal-to-noise ratio for fixed average transmitted power. Double-sideband, however, suffers the disadvantages of requiring twice as much bandwidth and for the case of a sinusoidal signal $\sqrt{2}$ times as much peak-to-peak voltage variation as single-sideband. Pure AM suffers from the additional handicap of transmitting power in the unmodulated carrier, which contributes nothing to signal-to-noise ratio.

Compandors. In transmission of speech and music, the effects of noise and interference must be evaluated subjectively. It is found that the most stringent requirements on suppression of extraneous sounds apply when the wanted signal is weak. Loud sounds tend to mask the noise, and therefore it becomes permissible for the noise to increase when the signal level increases. Advantage of this property is taken in the art of companding, which consists of compressing the range of signal power at the transmitter with a complementary expansion at the receiver.[1] For weak signals the transmitted power is made large enough to secure a satisfactory margin over noise. As the signal power is increased the gain of the transmitter is reduced to prevent overload. At the receiver a complementary increase of gain with signal power restores the original range.

Compandors are of two types, the syllabic and the instantaneous. In the syllabic compandors the gain varies with the envelope of the signal. The envelope varies slowly relative to the important frequencies in the signal band and, therefore, the compressed signal occupies practically the same bandwidth as the original. In an instantaneous compandor the gain varies with the instantaneous value of the signal. The resulting compressed wave contains harmonics and intermodulation products of

[1] R. C. Mathes and S. B. Wright, The Compandor—An Aid Against Static in Radio Telephony, *Bell System Tech. J.*, vol. 13, pp. 315–332, July, 1934.

the signal components and occupies a bandwidth much greater than that of the original signal. If the transmitted band is restricted to the original signal bandwidth, the compression and expansion are no longer complementary and serious distortion of the signal occurs. Syllabic compandors[1,2] have accordingly been the type chosen for CW transmission. We shall see in Sec. 6-1 that the bandwidth penalty can be avoided when instantaneous companding is used in pulse-transmission systems. The disadvantage of syllabic companding is that an envelope detector and low-pass filter are required in the gain-control circuits.

In order to avoid signal distortion from syllabic companding, the signal wave itself must be restricted to a nearly linear portion of a compressor or expander characteristic. That is, the nonlinear elements which perform the actual compression or expansion in the signal path are biased to an operating point dependent on the signal envelope. The excursions of the signal about the operating point are confined to a substantially linear segment of the general nonlinear characteristic.

In an instantaneous compandor the signal values must be subjected to the full nonlinear treatment provided by the compressing and expanding circuits. Sizable harmonics and cross products of the signal components are generated at the compressor. The complementary expander cannot restore the original signal if the channel fails to deliver the harmonics and cross products in undistorted form to the receiver. Since the harmonics and cross products spill over into a considerably wider band of frequencies than the original signal occupies, instantaneous compandors are not viewed with favor in CW systems. It is to be noted that a single-frequency representation of the signal does not suffice for an analysis of instantaneous companding. A signal band could be so placed on the frequency scale that all harmonics fall outside the band. Reception of the single-frequency component at the receiver would then be sufficient to restore the original sine wave at the proper relative amplitude. But if components of two different frequencies exist in the signal band, the compressed wave contains cross products both within and without the band. These products are not removed from the recovered signal unless all products reach the receiver.

It is of theoretical interest to point out that the excess bandwidth charged to instantaneous CW companding is a fault of the particular method of restoration which we have described rather than an inherent consequence of indispensable information in the wider band. The possibility of an instantaneous compandor operating without distortion over a channel having the same bandwidth as the original signal can be demon-

[1] A. C. Norwine, Devices for Controlling Amplitude Characteristics of Telephone Signals, *Bell System Tech. J.*, vol. 17, pp. 539–554, October, 1938.

[2] W. R. Bennett and S. Doba, Vario-Losser Circuits, *Elec. Eng., Trans. Sec.*, vol. 60, pp. 17–22, January, 1941.

strated mathematically by a theorem due to Arne Beurling. The theorem can be stated as follows:

Theorem. Given that a signal wave which is band-limited to the frequency range from $-W$ to W is applied as input to a device. The device is characterized by a uniquely defined output value for each input value such that a positive increment in one implies a positive increment in the other. The output of the device is transmitted through a linear channel with unit response throughout the band from $-W$ to W and zero response to frequencies outside this band. It follows that the original signal wave is uniquely determined by the wave received from the channel.

Proof. Let $g(t)$ represent the signal wave, and let the output voltage v_2 of the device be represented in terms of the input voltage v_1 by

$$v_2 = F(v_1) \tag{4-6-17}$$

Then by hypothesis

$$g(t) = \frac{1}{2\pi} \int_{-W}^{W} G(\omega) e^{j\omega t} \, d\omega \tag{4-6-18}$$

and

$$F(v_1 + v) > F(v_1) \qquad v > 0 \tag{4-6-19}$$

Let

$$h(t) = F[g(t)] = \frac{1}{2\pi} \int_{-\infty}^{\infty} H(\omega) e^{j\omega t} \, d\omega \tag{4-6-20}$$

Then the wave received from the band-limited channel is

$$h_0(t) = \frac{1}{2\pi} \int_{-W}^{W} H(\omega) e^{j\omega t} \, d\omega \tag{4-6-21}$$

Assume that the theorem is false and that there are two distinct functions $g_1(t)$ and $g_2(t)$ which when substituted for $g(t)$ give the same function $h_0(t)$. Let the Fourier transforms of $g_1(t)$ and $g_2(t)$ be $G_1(\omega)$ and $G_2(\omega)$, respectively, and the corresponding responses of the device be $h_1(t)$ and $h_2(t)$. Since $h_0(t)$ is the same for both functions, the Fourier transforms $H_1(\omega)$ and $H_2(\omega)$ of $h_1(t)$ and $h_2(t)$, respectively, are equal when ω lies between $-W$ and W.

By Parseval's theorem

$$\int_{-\infty}^{\infty} [g_1(t) - g_2(t)][h_1(t) - h_2(t)] \, dt$$
$$= \frac{1}{2\pi} \int_{-\infty}^{\infty} [G_1(\omega) - G_2(\omega)][H_1^*(\omega) - H_2^*(\omega)] \, d\omega \tag{4-6-22}$$

Since $G_1(\omega)$ and $G_2(\omega)$ vanish when $|\omega| > W$, and $H_1^*(\omega) = H_2^*(\omega)$ when $|\omega| < W$, the integral on the right is equal to zero. Furthermore, since $h_1(t) > h_2(t)$ if $g_1(t) > g_2(t)$, and $h_1(t) < h_2(t)$ if $g_1(t) < g_2(t)$, the integrand on the left is never negative. Hence the only way in which the integral on the left can vanish as required is for the integrand itself to be identically zero. It follows that $g_1(t) = g_2(t)$, and therefore that there cannot be two distinct functions leading to the same $h_0(t)$.

As is characteristic of existence proofs obtained by a *reductio ad absurdum* argument, no method of finding the desired function is exhibited. The theorem merely shows that if any function can be found which under the assumed conditions leads to the observed $h_0(t)$, that function must be the original signal wave. An iterative solution based on Picard's method of successive approximations has been demonstrated by Landau and Miranker.[1] Their solution was carried out on a large-scale computer and cannot be claimed to be practical in real time with terminal apparatus of reasonable complexity.

4-7. Multiplexing of AM Channels

By choosing properly spaced carrier frequencies, it is possible to send and receive a number of AM signals independently over one medium. The carrier frequencies must be separated far enough from each other to prevent appreciable sideband overlap. Design of such a system, called a frequency-division multiplex (FDM), would be greatly simplified if signal bands could be precisely defined and if wave filters could be provided with infinite loss outside their passbands. Real signals do not have their energies confined to a definite finite range of frequencies but are characterized rather by a gradual diminishing of importance with frequency measured from the central part of the band. Real filters likewise must have a finite range of frequencies in the transition from low loss to high loss.

Linear Interference. It becomes necessary in the design of an FDM system to evaluate the distortion of the received signal in one channel caused by attenuating the components with frequencies at the edge of the band and also to evaluate the interference caused by accepting energy from components originating in other channels. A diagram of an FDM system for AM channels is shown in Fig. 4-7-1. Each channel input typically has its own low-pass filter restricting the signal band applied to the modulator. Following each modulator there is a sending bandpass filter restricting the frequency range of the transmitted sidebands. The outputs of the sending filters are combined as a composite input to the transmission line. The combining is commonly done by connecting the filter outputs in parallel to form a common input to the line.

At the receiving end, the line delivers the composite signal wave to a bank of bandpass filters with input terminals in parallel. The outputs of these filters are connected separately to the individual channel demodulators. Each channel demodulator is followed by a low-pass filter which restricts the demodulated output to the signal band. The channel low-pass and sending bandpass filters at the transmitter are to a certain

[1] H. J. Landau and W. L. Miranker, The Recovery of Distorted Band-Limited Signals, *J. Math. Anal. Appl.*, vol. 2, pp. 97–104, February, 1961.

extent interchangeable in function, since both limit the frequency occupancy of the channel signal on the line. Likewise, the receiving bandpass and channel low-pass filters at the receiver perform similar functions in limiting the frequency range accepted by the channel from the line.

It is in fact possible with modulators and demodulators of sufficient precision to make a DSBSC-FDM system[1] operate satisfactorily without any channel bandpass filters. The transmitting low-pass filters can perform adequately to restrict the sideband widths of the channels to prevent overlapping with neighbors, and the receiving channel low-pass filters remove the demodulated sidebands from the neighboring channels.

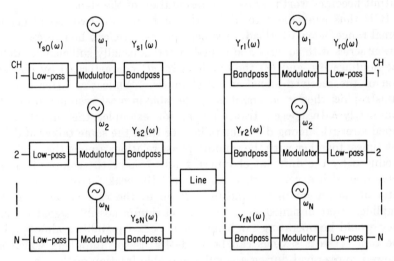

Fig. 4-7-1. FDM system for AM channels.

Even in this case, however, channel bandpass filters would usually be provided to remove imperfectly balanced products from the modulators.

In an AM-FDM system with envelope detection, receiving channel bandpass filters are necessary to select the envelope of the wanted channel. In a single-sideband system (SSB-FDM) the channel bandpass filters are vital to both the sending and receiving ends. At the sending end the filter suppresses one sideband, and at the receiver the filter prevents the channel demodulator from superimposing detected signals from adjacent channel sidebands. We can perform a quantitative analysis of the FDM system by tracing the course of a single-frequency component from signal source to signal sink. Since the operations are linear, the calculation is straightforward and need not be described in detail here.

Nonlinear Interference. We have previously discussed nonlinear distortion within an AM channel. When AM channels are multiplexed

[1] B. W. Kendall, Multiplex Signaling, U.S. Patent 1,459,709, June 19, 1923.

by frequency division on a common medium, nonlinearity in the medium generates interchannel interference as well as distortion within the channels. One of the principal sources of nonlinearity is the multi-channel repeater, which in long-haul transmission is inserted into the line to amplify the composite FDM signal wave. Design of stable multi-channel amplifiers is facilitated by the use of negative feedback, which reduces the amount of nonlinearity for small signals. In such amplifiers the response at low signal inputs can be approximately described as nearly linear with small square-law and cube-law departures. As the signal input is increased, a rather sharp break occurs beyond which the amplifier output becomes worthless as a representation of the signal.

It is thus convenient to divide the problem into two parts: (1) the signal range below overload, in which the response can be expressed as a power series with square- and cube-law terms usually sufficient to define the nonlinearity, and (2) the overload range, characterized by obliteration of the received signal in all channels. While the latter event is catastrophic when it occurs, it is not feasible in most systems to avoid it completely. In speech transmission, for example, the variations in signal strength among different talkers or from the same talker at different times, together with the random-phase relations among the sidebands produced by the different channels, tend to make the composite FDM wave one with a very high peak factor. By peak factor we mean the ratio of maximum instantaneous voltage to the rms voltage. If the amplifiers were designed to handle the maximum possible signal voltage, they would be operating far below their peak capabilities almost all of the time. Great savings can be made by use of amplifiers which are allowed to overload during a small acceptable fraction of the time.

The importance of taking full advantage of the multiplex load factor in speech transmission is illustrated by the following example:[1] In a 1,000-channel SSB-FDM speech-transmission system permitting overload during 0.1 per cent of the busiest hour, it is possible to overload the entire system by inserting full-load test tones in six of the channels while leaving the 994 other channels idle.

The effect of brief multichannel overload intervals is an occasional "click" or "bat" heard in all channels. Experimental tests have shown how frequently these can occur without being objectionable.[2] Table 4-7-1 shows how the power which a multichannel amplifier should deliver increases with the number of speech channels. The power for a single channel is taken as a reference.

[1] C. B. Feldman and W. R. Bennett, Bandwidth and Transmission Performance, *Bell System Tech. J.*, vol. 28, pp. 490–595, July, 1949.

[2] B. D. Holbrook and J. T. Dixon, Load Rating Theory for Multichannel Amplifiers, *Bell System Tech. J.*, vol. 18, pp. 624–644, October, 1939.

TABLE 4-7-1. NONSIMULTANEOUS MULTIPLEX LOAD ADVANTAGE

Number of channels	Required relative power capacity, db
1	0
10	6
100	9
500	13
1000	16

Note that if the amplifier were made capable of handling simultaneous in-phase peaks from 1,000 channels, the increment in power over one channel would be 60 db instead of 16 as shown.

Below overload the nonlinear distortion causes cross-modulation products which appear as noise in the channels occupying frequency bands in

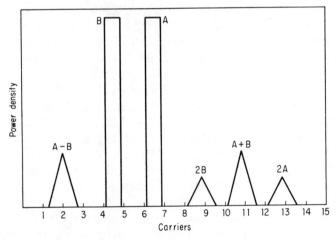

FIG. 4-7-2. Spectra of second-order modulation products from two FDM channels. (*From W. R. Bennett, BSTJ, vol. 19, October, 1940, p. 595.*)

which the products fall. To estimate the noise arising from modulation products falling within a specified channel requires a count of the numbers of the various types of products to which that channel is exposed and an evaluation of the disturbing effect of each type of product. Square-law products can be classified as sums, differences, and second harmonics. These products are often designated as $A + B$, $A - B$, and $2A$ types. An $A + B$ product, as shown in Fig. 4-7-2, consists of all the components which can be formed by pairing each component of channel A with each component of channel B, multiplying their amplitudes, and adding their frequencies. An $A + B$ product extends in frequency from the sum of the lowest frequencies in A and B to the sum of the highest frequencies. If A and B have equal bandwidth, the $A + B$ product extends over twice as great a bandwidth as either one.   An $A - B$ product contains all the possible difference frequencies of the components of channels A and B. The frequency band of an $A - B$ product extends from the difference between the lowest frequency of A and the highest frequency of B to the difference between the highest frequency of A and the lowest frequency of B.   The bandwidth is twice that of either A or B.   A $2A$ product consists of all the sum frequencies which can be formed from the components within one channel.   It is an $A + B$ product in which A and B represent the same channel, and its bandwidth is twice that of A.   We should also mention that there are $A - B$ products in which A and B represent the same channel.   These are composed of all the possible difference frequencies which can be formed from the components of a channel. Their range of frequencies extends from zero to the bandwidth of the channel.

Cube-law modulation products can be classified into the types $3A$, $2A + B$, $2A - B$, $A - 2B$, $A + B + C$, $A + B - C$, and $A - B - C$. The designations imply that the frequency of the modulation product is not negative.   For example, if ω_A, ω_B, and ω_C are frequencies of components in channels A, B, and C, respectively, $\omega_A - \omega_B - \omega_C$ is the frequency of an $A - B - C$ product if $\omega_A > \omega_B + \omega_C$.   If $\omega_B + \omega_C > \omega_A$, the symbols A, B, and C would be interchanged to identify the product properly as an $A + B - C$ type.   Note that a $2A \pm B$ product is a special case of an $A + B \pm C$ type in which two of the channels are the same.   It can be thought of as formed by first taking all possible sums of frequencies in channel A and then combining these sum frequencies with the frequencies present in channel B.   Likewise a $3A$ product is a special case of an $A + B + C$ type in which the A, B, and C channels are the same.   It is in general necessary to treat these special cases differently because the dependence among some of the contributing terms imparts a different character to the modulation product.

In multiplex systems with a small number of channels, it may indeed be necessary to describe carefully each of all the possible types and the frequency ranges in which they fall.   As the number of channels in the system is made larger, the number of products of some types increases so much more rapidly than that of others that only a few predominant types need to be considered.   The predominant types in the case of cube law are those originating from three independent channels and in the case of square law from two independent channels.

We note that if all channels of the multiplex system have the same bandwidth, then as shown in Fig. 4-7-3, each cube-law modulation product spreads over three channel bands.   In the case of speech transmission, the concentration of important components in a part of the channel range results in an unequal interfering effect in the several channels over which a given modulation product is distributed. For practical purposes we can assume that one channel bears the brunt of the interference from any one product. The amount of interference from a particular type of product must be determined experimentally.

To determine the amount of interference falling in a particular channel we need to know the number of cross-modulation products of each type which fall in the channel, the interfering effect which each type produces per unit power in the product, the relation between the power in the product and the power in the channels which produced that product, and finally the distribution of power in the channels. A census of the number and types of modulation products falling in specified channels of an FDM system is given in Table 4-7-2.

The relation between the product power and originating channel power can be deduced for the square- and cube-law cases by squaring and cubing

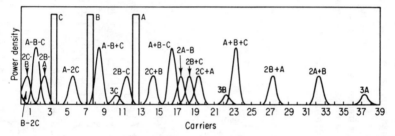

Fig. 4-7-3. Spectra of third-order modulation products from three FDM channels. (*From W. R. Bennett, BSTJ, vol. 19, October, 1940, p. 596.*)

expressions for the composite FDM signal. Actually while we have developed our treatment so far for square and cube laws, the method applies equally well to second- and third-order modulation of any kind in which products can be superimposed. In an actual system the relations between product and channel powers is conveniently determined by making two- and three-tone modulation measurements. For example, consider an SSB-FDM system with carriers placed at harmonics of 4 kc. We wish to evaluate the product of $A + B - C$ type falling at 800 kc when the originating channels have carriers at 600, 300, and 100 kc. If complete multiplexing and demultiplexing were available, we would simply supply 1-kc signals to the 600-, 300-, and 100-kc channels and measure the resulting 1-kc signal received in the 800-kc channel. To measure on the high-frequency medium without using the channel terminals, we insert the appropriate three side frequencies at the sending end of the line and measure the product frequency at the receiving end.

It is often desirable to have a more convenient procedure for evaluating a large multiplex system than the elaborate synthesis we have described

TABLE 4-7-2. NUMBER OF PRODUCTS FALLING IN kTH CHANNEL OF MULTICHANNEL CARRIER SYSTEM WITH HARMONIC CARRIER FREQUENCIES n_1p, $(n_1 + 1)p$, . . . , $(n_1 + N - 1)p$*

n_1p = lowest carrier frequency

$n_2p = (n_1 + N - 1)p$ = highest carrier frequency

kp = carr. freq. associated with mod. product

N = number of channels

$I(x)$ = "largest integer $\leq x$"

No. of products is 0 outside ranges indicated

NUMBER OF PRODUCTS

Type	Second Order
2A	$1, \ n_1 \leq \dfrac{k}{2} \leq n_2 \text{ if } \dfrac{k}{2} \text{ is an integer}$
A + B	$\begin{cases} I\left(\dfrac{k+1}{2}\right) - n_1, \ 2n_1 - 1 \leq k \leq n_1 + n_2 \\[2mm] n_2 - I\left(\dfrac{k}{2}\right), \ n_1 + n_2 \leq k \leq 2n_2 \end{cases}$
A − B	$N - k, \ 0 < k < N$

Third Order

Type	Third Order
3A	$1, \ n_1 \leq \dfrac{k}{3} \leq n_2 \text{ if } \dfrac{k}{3} \text{ is an integer}$
2A + B	$\begin{cases} I\left(\dfrac{k - n_1}{2}\right) - I\left(\dfrac{k}{3}\right) + I\left(\dfrac{k-1}{3}\right) - n_1 + 1, \ 3n_1 \leq k \leq 2n_1 + n_2 \\[2mm] I\left(\dfrac{k - n_1}{2}\right) - I\left(\dfrac{k}{3}\right) + I\left(\dfrac{k-1}{3}\right) - I\left(\dfrac{k - n_2 + 1}{2}\right) + 1, \ 2n_1 + n_2 \leq k \leq n_1 + 2n_2 \\[2mm] n_2 - I\left(\dfrac{k}{3}\right) + I\left(\dfrac{k-1}{3}\right) - I\left(\dfrac{k - n_2 + 1}{2}\right) + 1, \ n_1 + 2n_2 \leq k \leq 3n_2 \end{cases}$
2A − B	$\begin{cases} I\left(\dfrac{n_2 + k}{2}\right) - n_1 + 1, \ 2n_1 - n_2 \leq k \leq n_1 - 1, \ k \geq 0 \\[2mm] I\left(\dfrac{n_2 - k}{2}\right) - I\left(\dfrac{n_1 + k + 1}{2}\right), \ n_1 \leq k \leq n_2 \\[2mm] n_2 + 1 - I\left(\dfrac{n_1 + k + 1}{2}\right), \ n_2 + 1 \leq k \leq 2n_2 - n_1 \end{cases}$

TABLE 4-7-2. NUMBER OF PRODUCTS FALLING IN kTH CHANNEL OF MULTICHANNEL CARRIER SYSTEM WITH HARMONIC CARRIER FREQUENCIES $n_1 p$, $(n_1 + 1)p$, ..., $(n_1 + N - 1)p$* (Continued)

$A - 2B$ .... $I\left(\dfrac{n_2 - k}{2}\right) - n_1 + 1$, $\quad 0 < k \le n_2 - 2n_1$, $\ n_2 \ge 2n_1$

$A + B + C$ ....

$$I\left(\frac{k - 3n_1 + 3}{6}\right) + I\left[\frac{(k - 3n_1 - 1)^2}{12}\right], \quad 3n_1 + 3 \le k \le 2n_1 + n_2 + 1$$

$$(N - 1)\left[k - 2n_1 + 1 - \frac{N}{2}\right] + I\left(\frac{3n_2 - k + 3}{6}\right) + I\left[\frac{(3n_2 - k - 1)^2}{12}\right] - I\left[\frac{(k - 3n_1)^2}{4}\right]$$

$$-\frac{1}{2}I\left(\frac{k - 3n_1 + 2}{3}\right)I\left(\frac{k + 3n_1 + 5}{3}\right) - \frac{1}{2}I\left(\frac{3n_2 - k}{3}\right)I\left(\frac{3n_2 + k + 5}{3}\right),$$
$$2n_1 + n_2 + 2 \le k \le n_1 + 2n_2 - 2$$

$$I\left(\frac{3n_2 - k + 3}{6}\right) + I\left[\frac{(3n_2 - k - 1)^2}{12}\right], \quad n_1 + 2n_2 - 1 \le k \le 3n_2 - 3$$

$A + B - C$ ....

$$I\left(\frac{N - n_1 + k}{2}\right)I\left(\frac{N - n_1 + k + 1}{2}\right), \quad 2n_1 - n_2 + 1 \le k \le n_1 - 1$$

$$I\left(\frac{k - n_1}{2}\right)I\left(\frac{N - n_1 - 1}{2}\right) + (k - n_1)(n_2 - k) + I\left(\frac{n_2 - k}{2}\right)I\left(\frac{n_2 - k - 1}{2}\right), \quad n_1 \le k \le n_2$$

Note: Number of products included in which k-channel signal is one fund. component $= \begin{cases} k - n_1, & n_1 \le k \le n_1 + \dfrac{N - 1}{2} \\[2mm] n_2 - k, & n_1 + \dfrac{N - 1}{2} < k \le n_2 \end{cases}$

$A - B - C$ ....

$$\left[n_2 - I\left(\frac{k + n_1}{2}\right)\right]\left[I\left(\frac{k + n_1}{2}\right) - k + N\right], \quad n_2 < k \le 2n_2 - n_1 - 1$$

$$I\left(\frac{N - k - n_1 - 1}{2}\right)I\left(\frac{N - k - n_1 - 1}{2}\right), \quad 0 < k \le n_2 - 2n_1 - 1, \ n_2 \ge 2n_1 + 1$$

Note: Number of products included in which k-channel signal is one fund. component $= \begin{cases} N - 2k - 1, & n_1 \le k \le \dfrac{n_2}{3} \\[2mm] N - 2k, & \dfrac{n_2 + 1}{3} \le k \le \dfrac{N}{2} \end{cases}$

*W. R. Bennett, Cross-Modulation in Multichannel Amplifiers, *Bell System Tech. J.*, vol. 19, pp. 587–610, October, 1940.

in terms of individual channel signals. One method of accomplishing this uses a wideband noise wave to simulate the composite multiplex signal. To obtain an idle channel in which to measure distortion, we remove from the noise wave the energy in the band of frequencies reserved for that channel, as shown in Fig. 4-7-4. The energy received in that

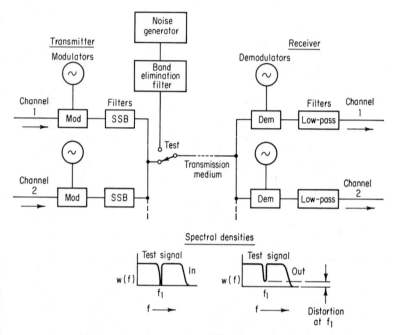

FIG. 4-7-4. Testing of multichannel FDM system by noise loading.

channel after transmission of the slotted noise band over the multiplex system is a measure of interchannel interference.

For a complete description of the many factors entering into the design of an FDM system, the reader is referred to the Bell System papers on the L3 Coaxial System.[1-6]

[1] C. H. Elmendorf, R. D. Ehrbar, R. H. Klie, and A. J. Grossman, The L3 Coaxial System, System Design, *Bell System Tech. J.*, vol. 32, pp. 781–832, July, 1953.

[2] R. W. Ketchledge and T. R. Finch, *ibid.*, Equalization and Regulation, pp. 833–878.

[3] L. H. Morris, G. H. Lovell, and F. R. Dickinson, *ibid.*, Amplifiers, pp. 879–914.

[4] J. W. Rieke and R. S. Graham, *ibid.*, Television Terminals, pp. 915–942.

[5] H. F. Dodge, B. J. Kinsburg, and M. K. Kruger, *ibid.*, Quality Control Requirements, pp. 943–967.

[6] R. F. Garrett, T. L. Tuffnell, and R. A. Waddell, *ibid.*, Application of Quality Control Requirements in the Manufacture of Components, pp. 969–1005.

CHAPTER 5

ANGLE MODULATION IN CW SYSTEMS

An angle-modulated CW wave can be written in the form

$$E(t) = A \cos \phi(t) \qquad (5\text{-}0\text{-}1)$$

where A is a constant, which we shall call the amplitude, and $\phi(t)$ is the phase. If $\phi(t)$ increases linearly with time, that is, if

$$\phi(t) = pt + \theta \qquad (5\text{-}0\text{-}2)$$

with p and θ constant, there is no modulation, for we then have a wave of constant amplitude, constant frequency, and constant phase epoch.

5-1. Phase Modulation

Phase modulation (PM) is the special kind of angle modulation in which

$$\phi(t) = pt + \theta_0 + ks(t) \qquad (5\text{-}1\text{-}1)$$

where $s(t)$ is the modulating signal. That is, in phase modulation the phase varies linearly with the signal. If the signal is sinusoidal, say

$$s(t) = Q \cos (qt + \theta_s) \qquad (5\text{-}1\text{-}2)$$

the expression for the phase-modulated wave is

$$E(t) = A \cos [pt + \theta_0 + kQ \cos (qt + \theta_s)] \qquad (5\text{-}1\text{-}3)$$

The term kQ here is called the "phase deviation."

5-2. Frequency Modulation

Frequency is usually defined as the number of vibrations per second; in this sense it requires an interval of time including a number of complete oscillations to be meaningful. However, we can extend the definition to give meaning to *instantaneous frequency*, by noting that the average frequency (av f) over an interval of time Δt is given by the relation

$$\text{av } f = \frac{\Delta\phi/2\pi}{\Delta t} \qquad (5\text{-}2\text{-}1)$$

That is, the total change in phase $\Delta\phi$ radians over the interval is divided by 2π to give the total number of complete oscillations, and when the latter number is divided by Δt, we have the average number of "cycles" per second. To express the average frequency in radians per second, we multiply by 2π, thus

$$\text{av } \omega = 2\pi \text{ av } f = \frac{\Delta\phi}{\Delta t} \tag{5-2-2}$$

From these relations it seems natural to define the instantaneous frequency ω_i as

$$\omega_i = \lim_{\Delta t \to 0} \frac{\Delta\phi}{\Delta t} = \frac{d\phi}{dt} \text{ radians/sec} \tag{5-2-3}$$

(This is a definition, not a theorem.)

Then
$$\phi = \int \omega_i \, dt \tag{5-2-4}$$

A frequency-modulated (FM) wave is then defined as one in which the instantaneous frequency varies linearly with the signal.

If
$$\omega_i = ks(t) \tag{5-2-5}$$
then
$$\phi(t) = k \int s(t) \, dt \tag{5-2-6}$$

and the standard expression for an FM wave is

$$E(t) = A \cos \left[pt + \theta_0 + k \int_{t_0}^{t} s(t) \, dt \right] \tag{5-2-7}$$

The lower limit t_0 on the integral may be taken arbitrarily and only serves to fix the phase angle θ_0. If the signal is sinusoidal, the standard expression becomes

$$E(t) = A \cos \left[pt + \theta_0 + \frac{kQ}{q} \sin (qt + \theta_s) \right] \tag{5-2-8}$$

The corresponding instantaneous frequency is

$$\omega_i = p + kQ \cos (qt + \theta_s) \tag{5-2-9}$$

Here kQ is called the *frequency deviation* and the ratio kQ/q the modulation index.[1]

Comparing Eq. (5-2-8) for sinusoidal FM with the corresponding Eq. (5-1-3) for sinusoidal PM, we note that they differ only in that the phase deviation is independent of the signal frequency in the PM case and is inversely proportional to the signal frequency in the FM case. Now if the signal frequency q is constant, there is no way of demonstrating a

---

[1] In Chap. 3 the unmodulated carrier frequency p and the signal frequency q were designated by ω_0 and ω_m, respectively. The frequency deviation was there called $\Delta\omega$, and the modulation index β. The notation introduced here is parallel to that used in the treatment of AM in Chap. 4.

dependence or independence. We conclude that we cannot distinguish between sinusoidal FM and sinusoidal PM from measurements at a single frequency. It is only by examining the behavior of the wave over a range of signal frequencies that we can observe a difference between FM and PM. This can be done either by making measurements on several sinusoidal modulating waves of different frequencies separately or by using a composite test signal containing components of several different frequencies. In the general case the modulation may be neither FM nor PM but one in which the phase deviation varies in some other way with the signal frequency.

5-3. Spectral Resolution for Sinusoidal Angle Modulation[1]

We note that in both PM and FM a single-frequency modulating signal leads to a wave of form

$$E(t) = A \cos [pt + \theta_0 + x \sin (qt + \alpha)] \qquad (5\text{-}3\text{-}1)$$

In the PM case we reduce Eq. (5-1-3) to this form by setting $x = kQ$ and $\alpha = \theta_s + \pi/2$. In the FM case we reduce Eq. (5-2-9) to the form of Eq. (5-3-1) by setting $x = kQ/q$ and $\alpha = \theta_s$. The phase angles θ_0 and α are seen to be of trivial significance. We can carry through our analysis here without them and reintroduce them later if we wish by adding a term θ_0 to pt wherever pt occurs and a term α to qt wherever qt occurs. A sufficiently general formula for resolution of the case in which the signal is sinusoidal can be obtained from the well-known expansion in terms of Bessel functions:

$$\cos (pt + x \sin qt) = \sum_{n=-\infty}^{\infty} J_n(x) \cos (p + nq)t \qquad (5\text{-}3\text{-}2)$$

$$\sin (pt + x \sin qt) = \sum_{n=-\infty}^{\infty} J_n(x) \sin (p + nq)t \qquad (5\text{-}3\text{-}3)$$

These equations enable the sinusoidally modulated FM wave to be expressed as the sum of a carrier component and an infinite number of upper and lower side-frequency terms corresponding to the signal frequency and its harmonics.

It is instructive to study the Bessel functions with argument x fixed and order n variable, since this is the situation we encounter as we go along the frequency scale and examine the successive side-frequency component amplitudes in turn. Figure 5-3-1 shows such a plot. The significant property to note is that the magnitude of $J_n(x)$ falls off rapidly for values

---

[1] See Sec. 3-10 for the spectral analysis of angle-modulated signals modulated by a Gaussian random modulating signal.

of $n > x$. We may say then that the principal components of the spectrum are contained between $p - xq$ and $p + xq$. But this is also the extent of variation of the instantaneous frequency. We conclude then that the spectrum is localized approximately in the region traversed by the instantaneous frequency.

A caution must be observed here in the case in which the range of excursion of the instantaneous frequency is less than the signal frequency q. For such a case, an adequate representation of the wave requires at least

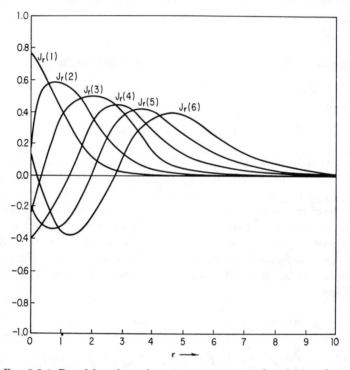

FIG. 5-3-1. Bessel functions of constant argument and variable order.

the frequency range $p - q$ to $p + q$, since a smaller range would restrict the output to the steady unmodulated sine wave of frequency p. In other words even though the amplitude associated with the nearest pair of side-frequency components is small in this case, these components are essential to preserve the modulation. To avoid error in this respect, the rule is usually stated in the following form: Transmission of an FM wave requires the band traversed by the instantaneous frequency plus the width of the signal band added at both the top and bottom. That is, if Δf is the frequency deviation in cps and B is the baseband width in cps, the r-f band required extends from $p/(2\pi) - \Delta f - B$ to $p/(2\pi) + \Delta f + B$ and has total width $2(\Delta f + B)$ cps.

5-4. Transmission through Linear Networks

Resolution of an angle-modulated wave into discrete sinusoidal components makes the well-developed transmission theory of linear networks available for FM and PM. Thus if we apply the wave, Eq. (5-3-2), to a network with transmittance $y(\omega)e^{-j\theta(\omega)}$, where $y(\omega)$ and $\theta(\omega)$ are real functions of frequency, we operate on each component of the wave with the appropriate amplitude factor and phase shift. The response is, therefore,

$$I(t) = A \sum_{n=-\infty}^{\infty} J_n(x)y(p+nq) \cos[(p+nq)t - \theta(p+nq)]$$

$$= A \sum_{n=-\infty}^{\infty} J_n(x)y(p+nq)\{\cos pt \cos[nqt - \theta(p+nq)]$$

$$- \sin pt \sin[nqt - \theta(p+nq)]\}$$

$$= A_1 \cos pt - A_2 \sin pt \tag{5-4-1}$$

where

$$A_1 = A \sum_{n=-\infty}^{\infty} J_n(x)y(p+nq) \cos[nqt - \theta(p+nq)] \tag{5-4-2}$$

$$A_2 = A \sum_{n=-\infty}^{\infty} J_n(x)y(p+nq) \sin[nqt - \theta(p+nq)] \tag{5-4-3}$$

Then by a useful trigonometric identity

$$I(t) = (A_1{}^2 + A_2{}^2)^{1/2} \cos\left(pt + \arctan\frac{A_2}{A_1}\right) \tag{5-4-4}$$

We thus obtain an amplitude and phase function resulting from the transmission through the network.

The instantaneous frequency is now

$$\omega_i = p + \frac{d}{dt}\arctan\frac{A_2}{A_1} = p + \frac{A_1 A_2' - A_2 A_1'}{A_1{}^2 + A_2{}^2} \tag{5-4-5}$$

where the prime means the derivative with respect to t.

The solution is thus formally complete but is too involved for non-machine calculation if more than a few components must be taken into account. There is an alternative approach to the problem which avoids the spectral resolution. This is the so-called "quasistationary" method which postulates that the steady-state solution evaluated at the instantaneous frequency is a good first approximation and that the approximation can be improved in a systematic manner. The method requires considerable caution in its application because divergent series are the typical outcome and estimation of the error at a particular stage of the calculation is difficult.

The quasistationary method is most useful when the transmission characteristics vary in a simple manner in the frequency range traversed by the instantaneous frequency. As an example of a simple manner, we consider the case in which the transfer admittance can be expanded in a power series about the midfrequency with only a few terms sufficient to give an accurate representation. This may be the case, for example, when a cascade of tuned circuits is used to limit the band or when one side of a resonance curve is used as a "slope circuit" in a frequency detector.

Assume that the complex transfer admittance $Y(\omega)$ can be expanded in a Taylor's series about $\omega = \omega_0$ with $Y'(\omega_0) = dY(\omega_0)/d(j\omega_0)$, etc.

$$Y(\omega) = Y(\omega_0) + \frac{Y'(\omega_0)}{1!} j(\omega - \omega_0) + \frac{Y''(\omega_0)}{2!} j^2(\omega - \omega_0)^2 + \cdots \quad (5\text{-}4\text{-}6)$$

Assume the applied angle-modulated wave to be the real part of

$$E(t) = A e^{j[\omega_0 t + \mu(t)]} \quad (5\text{-}4\text{-}7)$$

where $\mu(t)$ is the modulating signal. By the principle of superposition, the response to $E(t)$ can be calculated by summing the responses of the separate terms of the series. The first term is a constant and the response it provides is found by direct multiplication of applied voltage by this constant. The second term consists of constants except for the term $j\omega$. To obtain the response $j\omega$ produces, we visualize momentarily the representation of $E(t)$ as a Fourier integral of form

$$E(t) = \int_{-\infty}^{\infty} S(\omega)e^{j\omega t} \, d\omega \quad (5\text{-}4\text{-}8)$$

We know that the response of a network with transfer admittance $Y(\omega)$ to $E(t)$ is obtained by multiplying the integrand by $Y(\omega)$ and integrating. Hence the response to a transfer admittance $j\omega$ is

$$I_1(t) = \int_{-\infty}^{\infty} j\omega S(\omega)e^{j\omega t} \, d\omega \quad (5\text{-}4\text{-}9)$$

But this is also seen to be equal to $dE(t)/dt$, and we conclude, therefore, that a $j\omega$ term by itself differentiates the time function. Similarly a term in $(j\omega)^2$ differentiates the applied time function twice, and a term $(j\omega)^n$ differentiates n times. Hence the response of $Y(\omega)$ can be written

$$I(t) = \left[Y(\omega_0) + \frac{Y'(\omega_0)}{1!} \left(\frac{d}{dt} - j\omega_0 \right) \right.$$
$$\left. + \frac{Y''(\omega_0)}{2!} \left(\frac{d}{dt} - j\omega_0 \right)^2 + \cdots \right] A e^{j[\omega_0 t + \mu(t)]} \quad (5\text{-}4\text{-}10)$$

Here it is understood that a symbol such as $(d/dt - j\omega_0)^n$ means that the operation $d/dt - j\omega_0$ is performed n times in succession. We note that

$$\left(\frac{d}{dt} - j\omega_0\right) e^{j[\omega_0 t + \mu(t)]} = [j\omega_0 + j\mu'(t) - j\omega_0]e^{j[\omega_0 t + \mu(t)]}$$

$$= j\mu'(t)e^{j[\omega_0 t + \mu(t)]} \quad (5\text{-}4\text{-}11)$$

$$\left(\frac{d}{dt} - j\omega_0\right)^2 e^{j[\omega_0 t + \mu(t)]} = \left(\frac{d}{dt} - j\omega_0\right) j\mu'(t)e^{j[\omega_0 t + \mu(t)]}$$

$$= \{j\mu''(t) - [\mu'(t)]^2\}e^{j[\omega_0 t + \mu(t)]} \quad (5\text{-}4\text{-}12)$$

Thus neglecting terms of higher order than the second, we obtain

$$I(t) = A e^{j[\omega_0 t + \mu(t)]} \left\{ Y(\omega_0) + Y'(\omega_0)j\mu'(t) \right.$$

$$\left. + \frac{Y''(\omega_0)}{2} [j\mu''(t) - [\mu'(t)]^2] \right\} \quad (5\text{-}4\text{-}13)$$

To interpret this result, we notice that the instantaneous frequency is $\omega_0 + \mu'(t)$ and that the steady-state response of the network at the instantaneous frequency is

$$Y[\omega_0 + \mu'(t)] = Y(\omega_0) + Y'(\omega_0)j\mu'(t) - \frac{Y''(\omega_0)}{2} [\mu'(t)]^2 + \cdots \quad (5\text{-}4\text{-}14)$$

Comparing with Eq. (5-4-13) we see that to this degree of approximation

$$I(t) = A e^{j[\omega_0 t + \mu(t)]} \{ Y[\omega_0 + \mu'(t)] + \frac{Y''(\omega_0)}{2} j\mu''(t) \} \quad (5\text{-}4\text{-}15)$$

It appears from Eq. (5-4-15) that the transmittance at the instantaneous frequency may be a good approximate solution if the second and higher derivatives of the transmittance with respect to frequency and of the modulating signal with respect to time are small.

We illustrate by considering the case of a "slope circuit." The object here is to obtain a linear variation of absolute value of transmittance with frequency over the important components of the FM wave. If such a curve could be obtained, say of the form

$$|Y(\omega)| = a + b(\omega - \omega_0) \quad (5\text{-}4\text{-}16)$$

and if the term in $Y''\mu''$ in Eq. (5-4-15) could be ignored, the response would be

$$I(t) = A e^{j[\omega_0 t + \mu(t)]}[a + b\mu'(t)]e^{j\theta(t)} \quad (5\text{-}4\text{-}17)$$

where $\theta(t)$ is the phase angle of $Y[\omega_0 + \mu'(t)]$. We write Eq. (5-4-17) as

$$I(t) = A[a + b\mu'(t)]e^{j[\omega_0 t + \mu(t) + \theta(t)]} \quad (5\text{-}4\text{-}18)$$

Since the applied wave is the real part of $E(t)$, the received current is the real part of $I(t)$, or

$$\text{Re } I(t) = A[a + b\mu'(t)] \cos [\omega_0 t + \mu(t) + \theta(t)] \qquad (5\text{-}4\text{-}19)$$

This wave applied to an envelope detector yields the response $a + b\mu'(t)$ and thus enables the recovery of a term proportional to $\mu'(t)$, the instantaneous frequency.

The published literature[1-5] on the quasistationary method of analyzing the response of a network to an FM wave is extensive. Some of it is controversial insofar as the accuracy of various approximations is concerned. We only point out here that the solution embodied in Eqs. (5-4-6) to (5-4-15) depends upon how well the finite number of terms used in Eq. (5-4-6) represents $Y(\omega)$ in the range of frequencies throughout which $S(\omega)$ in Eq. (5-4-8) has appreciable magnitude. Since an exact finite representation of $Y(\omega)$ by power series is, in general, not possible, and since $E(t)$ is, in general, not band-limited, a nonzero error in the solution is to be expected. Estimation of the amount of error is tantamount to solving the very difficult problem of calculating the error in the time-domain representation of a function when the error in the frequency-domain representation is given.

5-5. The FM Interference Problem

Signal-to-interference and signal-to-noise ratios are conveniently expressed in terms of ratios of signal power at full load to disturbing power in the absence of signal. Presence of signal exerts a masking effect on interference and noise, thereby leading to a less severe requirement. Evaluation of the disturbance in the case of no modulating signal thus usually gives the most important information. Since the effect of noise has been previously discussed in Sec. 3-5, we concentrate attention here on single-frequency interference.

We consider the case of a sine wave $P \cos pt$ disturbed in phase and frequency by another sine wave $Q \cos qt$ with $Q < P$. To calculate the

[1] J. R. Carson and T. C. Fry, Variable Frequency Electric Circuit Theory with Application to the Theory of Frequency Modulation, *Bell System Tech. J.*, vol. 16, pp. 513–540, October, 1937.

[2] B. van der Pol, The Fundamental Principles of Frequency Modulation, *J. Inst. Elec. Engrs. (London)*, vol. 93, part III, pp. 153–158, May, 1946.

[3] F. L. H. M. Stumpers, Distortion of Frequency Modulated Signals in Electrical Networks, *Commun. News*, vol. 9, pp. 82–92, April, 1948.

[4] E. J. Baghdady (ed.), "Lectures on Communication System Theory," McGraw-Hill Book Company, New York, 1961.

[5] H. E. Rowe, "Signals and Noise in Communication Systems," D. Van Nostrand Company, Inc., Princeton, N.J., 1965.

phase and frequency error resulting we seek a representation

$$P \cos pt + Q \cos qt = A(t) \cos \phi(t) \tag{5-5-1}$$

$A(t)$ and $\phi(t)$ are found as follows

$$P \cos pt + Q \cos qt = \text{Re} \, (Pe^{jpt} + Qe^{jqt})$$
$$= \text{Re} \left\{ Pe^{jpt} \left[1 + \frac{Q}{P} e^{j(q-p)t} \right] \right\} \tag{5-5-2}$$

Let
$$\frac{Q}{P} = \alpha \qquad \alpha < 1 \tag{5-5-3}$$

Then
$$1 + \frac{Q}{P} e^{j(q-p)t} = 1 + \alpha \cos (q - p)t + j\alpha \sin (q - p)t$$
$$= B(t)e^{j\beta(t)} \tag{5-5-4}$$

where
$$B^2(t) = [1 + \alpha \cos (q - p)t]^2 + [\alpha \sin (q - p)t]^2$$
$$= 1 + 2\alpha \cos (q - p)t + \alpha^2 \tag{5-5-5}$$

and
$$\beta(t) = \arctan \frac{\alpha \sin (q - p)t}{1 + \alpha \cos (q - p)t} \tag{5-5-6}$$

Then
$$P \cos pt + Q \cos qt = \text{Re} \, \{PB(t)e^{j[pt+\beta(t)]}\}$$
$$= PB(t) \cos [pt + \beta(t)] \tag{5-5-7}$$

Then from comparison of Eq. (5-5-7) with Eq. (5-5-1)

$$A(t) = P[1 + \alpha^2 + 2\alpha \cos (q - p)t]^{1/2} \tag{5-5-8}$$
$$\phi(t) = pt + \beta(t) \tag{5-5-9}$$

An ideal phase detector is insensitive to variations in $A(t)$ and delivers an output proportional to $\phi(t)$. Likewise an ideal frequency detector delivers an output proportional to $\phi'(t)$, i.e.,

$$\phi'(t) = p + \frac{d}{dt} \arctan \frac{\alpha \sin (q - p)t}{1 + \alpha \cos (q - p)t}$$
$$= p + \alpha(q - p) \frac{\cos (q - p)t + \alpha}{1 + 2\alpha \cos (q - p)t + \alpha^2} \tag{5-5-10}$$

The frequency error produced by the presence of the interfering component $Q \cos qt$ is the term added to p in Eq. (5-5-10), namely

$$\omega_e = \alpha(q - p) \frac{\cos (q - p)t + \alpha}{1 + \alpha^2 + 2\alpha \cos (q - p)t} \tag{5-5-11}$$

The error varies periodically in time with the period of the beat frequency between q and p. It is instructive to resolve the error into harmonic components by the Fourier-series expansion

$$\omega_e = (q - p) \sum_{n=1}^{\infty} (-)^{n+1} \left(\frac{Q}{P} \right)^n \cos n(q - p)t \tag{5-5-12}$$

The following properties of the frequency error are thus exhibited:

1. There is no constant (or d-c) component, and the lowest frequency represented is $q - p$. This means that if the beat frequency is above the baseband, the error can be completely removed by a low-pass filter following the frequency detector.

2. The error is proportional to the difference frequency $q - p$ and approaches zero as the two frequencies approach coincidence.

3. When Q/P is nearly equal to unity, the series converges slowly and many harmonics are required to transmit the error term accurately. This means that wideband circuits are necessary in the frequency detector up to the point at which the frequency is actually detected. If the band is narrowed before the frequency is actually detected, the waveform of the output becomes distorted and a d-c term may appear. The necessity for a wideband frequency detector becomes more urgent if relatively strong interference is to be suppressed.

4. While a d-c term (in the error) would not in itself be harmful in an audio receiver, we must remember that we have evaluated a static interference case. As soon as any signal modulation is impressed on either the wanted or interfering tone, the d-c component changes to a time-varying component capable of disturbing the signal band.

Resolution of the phase error ϕ_e is obtained by integrating Eq. (5-5-12).

$$\phi_e = \int \omega_e \, dt = \sum_{n=1}^{\infty} \frac{(-)^{n+1}}{n} \left(\frac{Q}{P}\right)^n \sin n(q - p)t \qquad (5\text{-}5\text{-}13)$$

The magnitude of the phase error is independent of the difference frequency.

5-6. Compound CW Modulation Systems

For various reasons it is sometimes found advantageous to use more than one kind of modulation in processing a signal for transmission. Thus an amplitude-modulated signal on one carrier frequency may be used to frequency-modulate another carrier. The term *subcarrier* is often used to designate the first carrier used in this process. We adopt here a notation in which the abbreviations of the modulation methods are listed in the order used and separated by hyphens. Thus an AM-FM system is one in which the signal amplitude-modulates a subcarrier frequency and the resulting wave frequency-modulates a carrier frequency in the range of the transmission medium. Two such systems of considerable importance are (1) SSB-FM, in which the SSB wave comprises a number of channels in frequency-division multiplex, and (2) FM-FM.

SSB-FM. We define an SSB-FM system as one in which a group of single-sideband channels occupying mutually exclusive frequency ranges is transmitted by FM. We have shown previously that a nonlinear response to a group of SSB channels causes interchannel interference. When the group is transmitted by FM, interchannel interference results from a nonlinear relation between the instantaneous frequency of the response of the medium and the instantaneous frequency of the input. In many cases the principal contributor to nonlinearity in frequency is a nonlinear phase-frequency characteristic in the medium. A case of practical interest is that in which the phase distortion can be expressed by square-law and cube-law phase-frequency terms. It is assumed that the amplitude-frequency function does not depart appreciably from a constant over the transmission band. The linear component of the phase-frequency curve can be ignored because it merely causes a transmission delay with no distortion of waveform.

Assume that the phase-frequency relationship is described by

$$\theta = b_2(\omega - \omega_0)^2 + b_3(\omega - \omega_0)^3 \qquad (5\text{-}6\text{-}1)$$

Represent the composite SSB wave by a set of sine waves, one for each channel. The signal wave can then be written as

$$E_s = \sum_n Q_n \cos q_n t \qquad (5\text{-}6\text{-}2)$$

The frequency q_n is chosen to fall in the frequency range of the nth channel. The SSB-FM output wave from the transmitter can be written

$$E_1 = A \cos \left(\omega_0 t + \lambda \int \sum_n Q_n \cos q_n t \, dt \right) \qquad (5\text{-}6\text{-}3)$$

In the quasi-steady-state approximation, the response of the medium is found by inserting the phase shift obtained by treating the instantaneous frequency as if it were steady state. The resulting expression for the output of the medium is

$$E_2 = A \cos \left[\omega_0 t + \lambda \int \sum_n Q_n \cos q_n t \, dt - b_2 \left(\lambda \sum_n Q_n \cos q_n t \right)^2 \right.$$
$$\left. - b_3 \left(\lambda \sum_n Q_n \cos q_n t \right)^3 \right] \qquad (5\text{-}6\text{-}4)$$

The instantanteous frequency deviation of the response is given by

$$\omega - \omega_0 = \lambda \sum_n Q_n \cos q_n t - b_2 \frac{d}{dt} \left(\lambda \sum_n Q_n \cos q_n t \right)^2$$
$$- b_3 \frac{d}{dt} \left(\lambda \sum_n Q_n \cos q_n t \right)^3 \qquad (5\text{-}6\text{-}5)$$

The squared and cubed terms are like those that appear because of amplitude nonlinearity in an SSB system. The difference is that these terms are now differentiated with respect to time. Differentiation of a sine wave with respect to time multiplies the amplitude by the angular frequency. Considering the interference received within any channel from the square- and cube-law terms, we note that it consists of sine waves of the frequency of that channel. Hence we can obtain the solution of the interchannel interference problem in the SSB-FM case from that of the SSB case by inserting the channel frequency as a multiplying factor on all products received within a channel. For this reason the high-frequency channels suffer more from interchannel modulation than the low-frequency channels. The high-frequency channels also tend to suffer more interference from external noise because of the quadratic spectral density function holding for the noise in an FM detector output.

The relative deterioration of high-frequency channels can be prevented by tapering the levels of the SSB channels. To compensate for noise and interference voltages varying with the channel frequency, the sideband voltage should be made proportional to the channel frequency. Our equation for E_1 then becomes of form

$$E_1 = A \cos \left(\omega_0 t + \lambda \int \sum_n Q_n q_n \cos q_n t \, dt \right)$$

$$= A \cos \left(\omega_0 t + \lambda \sum_n Q_n \sin q_n t \right) \qquad (5\text{-}6\text{-}6)$$

This represents a phase-modulated wave and could be designated as SSB-PM. Since in practice frequency modulators and frequency detectors are more easily provided than phase modulators and phase detectors, an SSB-PM system would be constructed by adding the appropriate signal preemphasis and postemphasis to an SSB-FM system. The interchannel interference problem in the SSB-PM case with phase distortion is similar to that of the SSB system with nonlinear amplifiers. Note that memory-free nonlinear amplification does not distort an FM wave because the information is contained entirely in the axis crossings.

In radio transmission the phase distortion may be caused by presence of echoes in the received signal. The effect of a single echo can be analyzed by calculating the instantaneous frequency of the resultant wave formed by the main wave and a small delayed version of itself. The type of phase distortion so produced cannot be adequately approximated by square- and cube-law variation with frequency. By an easy generalization of the analysis used in going from Eq. (5-5-1) to Eq. (5-5-12), it can be shown[1] that the instantaneous frequency of the wave $P \cos \theta + Q \cos \phi$,

---

[1] C. B. Feldman and W. R. Bennett, Bandwidth and Transmission Performance, Appendix II, *Bell System Tech. J.*, vol. 28, pp. 490–595, July, 1949.

where P and Q are constants and θ and ϕ vary with time, is given by

$$\Omega = \theta' + (\theta' - \phi') \sum_{m=1}^{\infty} \left(-\frac{Q}{P}\right)^m \cos m(\theta - \phi) \qquad Q < P \quad (5\text{-}6\text{-}7)$$

For the case of an SSB-FM wave and its echo we write

$$\theta = \omega_0 t + \sum_{n=1}^{N} x_n \sin q_n t \tag{5-6-8}$$

$$\phi = \omega_0(t - \tau) + \sum_{n=1}^{N} x_n \sin q_n(t - \tau) \tag{5-6-9}$$

If the echo amplitude is small compared with the main wave, $Q/P = r$ is small compared with unity, and we need retain only the linear term in r in the expression for instantaneous frequency. This approximation leads to a resolution of the error in instantaneous frequency caused by the echo into a series of modulation products with typical amplitude A_ν of the product at frequency $\nu = m_1 q_1 + m_2 q_2 + \cdots + m_N q_N$ given by:

$$A_\nu = 2r\nu J_{m_1}\left(2x_1 \sin \frac{q_1\tau}{2}\right) J_{m_2}\left(2x_2 \sin \frac{q_2\tau}{2}\right) \cdots$$

$$J_{m_N}\left(2x_N \sin \frac{q_N\tau}{2}\right) \begin{Bmatrix} \sin \omega_0\tau, \; m_1 + m_2 + \cdots + m_N \text{ even} \\ \cos \omega_0\tau, \; m_1 + m_2 + \cdots + m_N \text{ odd} \end{Bmatrix} \tag{5-6-10}$$

The ratio of product amplitude to the mth fundamental amplitude is found by dividing by $q_m x_m$. The special case in which the modulation product is a harmonic of a single frequency has been treated by Meyers.[1] Having determined the coefficient of the modulation products resulting from echoes, we can use Table 4-7-2 to obtain the total number of products of each type falling in any channel.

Experimental testing of SSB-FDM transmission is conveniently carried out by applying a random-noise test signal with the energy removed from one channel band as previously described for AM systems. An analytical evaluation of the effect of a small echo on the random-noise test signal has been published by Bennett, Curtis, and Rice.[2]

FM-FM. To a first approximation an FM signal is affected by phase distortion in the same way an AM signal is affected by a nonlinear output-input response. This oversimplified description tempts one to assign considerable virtue to an FM-FM system. The argument is that a non-linear phase characteristic in a medium causes a nonlinear output-input relation between the detected and applied FM signals. If the detected

[1] S. T. Meyers, Nonlinearity in Frequency-Modulation Radio Systems Due to Multipath Propagation, *Proc. IRE*, vol. 34, pp. 256–265, May, 1946.

[2] W. R. Bennett, H. E. Curtis, and S. O. Rice, Interchannel Interference in FM and PM Systems Under Noise Loading Conditions, *Bell System Tech. J.*, vol. 34, pp. 601–636, May, 1955.

FM signal itself represents another FM signal, a second frequency-detection process suffers only from a nonlinearity to which FM is immune. If the quasistationary method of calculating FM response were rigorously correct, we could indeed show that FM-FM gives very good results over a medium with phase distortion.   In practical cases, however, a near-vanishing of the distortion in the quasistationary approximation to the response calls for careful scrutiny of the neglected terms.   It is important to note that the modulating signal for the second FM step is nonsinusoidal even when the original signal is a sine wave.   The simplification associated with sinusoidal signals therefore does not apply.   Advantages hoped for in the double FM method on the basis of intuitive reasoning have not materialized in real applications.

CHAPTER 6

PULSE MODULATION

Pulse modulation differs from CW modulation in that the signal is transmitted intermittently rather than continuously. In order for pulse modulation to be successful, the signal must be of such character that it can be reconstructed from samples. This is not really a radical departure from CW techniques. If we examine the waveform emitted from an AM transmitter, we find that not all of the values of a signal wave are represented. At the nulls of the carrier wave there is no signal information. In the neighborhood of the nulls, there can be only scant information about the signal. The mathematical analysis shows, however, that a complete signal wave can be delivered by the receiver. If we modulate the heights of detached rectangles instead of sine-wave lobes, we would intuitively expect that the receiver could bridge the gaps in the signal just as well. We have previously touched on this idea when we showed that amplitude modulation could be performed by switching a signal on and off at the carrier rate. The mathematical theorem describing conditions under which a signal can be reproduced from its samples is called the sampling theorem and has been previously discussed in Sec. 2-6. The sampling theorem justifies the soundness of pulse-amplitude modulation (PAM), which is basic to all pulse modulation systems.

6-1. Pulse Amplitude Modulation (PAM)

Pulse amplitude modulation consists of the generation of a train of pulses with heights proportional to samples of a signal wave. We can approach a mathematical description of a PAM wave by multiplying a signal wave by a sequence of regularly spaced rectangular pulses of equal height and duration. If the duration is made to approach zero while maintaining constant pulse area, the product approaches a train of samples of the signal wave.

Application of Sampling Theorem. Consider the train of rectangular pulses shown in Fig. 6-1-1. The pulses have height h and width b. The spacing between centers is T. The origin of time is taken at the center of one of the pulses. Let $y(t)$ represent the ordinates of the pulse train as a function of time t. The function $y(t)$ is equal to h for values of t in the range from $-b/2$ to $b/2$. It is zero throughout the remainder of the interval from $-T/2$ to $T/2$. The function repeats itself periodically at ordinates T apart. It is representable by a Fourier series thus

$$y(t) = \frac{a_0}{2} + \sum_{n=1}^{\infty} a_n \cos \frac{2n\pi t}{T} \qquad (6\text{-}1\text{-}1)$$

$$a_n = \frac{2}{T} \int_{-T/2}^{T/2} y(t) \cos \frac{2n\pi t}{T} \, dt = \frac{2h}{n\pi} \sin \frac{n\pi b}{T} \qquad (6\text{-}1\text{-}2)$$

That is, if $T = 1/f_r$

$$y(t) = hbf_r + 2h \sum_{n=1}^{\infty} \frac{\sin n\pi b f_r}{n\pi} \cos 2n\pi f_r t \qquad (6\text{-}1\text{-}3)$$

If $s(t)$ represents the signal wave, the PAM wave is equal to $s(t)y(t)$.

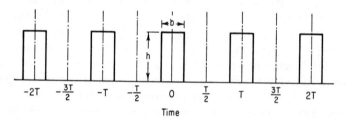

-2T $-\frac{3T}{2}$ -T $-\frac{T}{2}$ 0 $\frac{T}{2}$ T $\frac{3T}{2}$ 2T

Time

Fig. 6-1-1. Train of rectangular pulses.

The significance can be more readily appreciated by considering a single-frequency component of $s(t)$.

Let

$$s(t) = Q \cos 2\pi f_s t \qquad (6\text{-}1\text{-}4)$$

Then $s(t)y(t) = hbf_r Q \cos 2\pi f_s t + hQ \sum_{n=1}^{\infty} \frac{\sin n\pi b f_r}{n\pi}$

$$[\cos 2\pi(nf_r + f_s)t + \cos 2\pi(nf_r - f_s)t] \qquad (6\text{-}1\text{-}5)$$

The first term represents the signal component itself. The remaining terms represent upper and lower side-frequency components on each harmonic of the sampling frequency f_r. If $f_r - f_s > f_s$, that is, if $f_r > 2f_s$, a low-pass filter with cutoff frequency at $f_r/2$ separates the undistorted signal from the PAM wave train. It is clear that a similar conclusion holds when the signal is made up of a sum of sinusoidal components having individual frequencies less than $f_r/2$.

We have thus demonstrated conditions under which a signal can be reconstructed from chopped segments. The signal must be band-limited with its highest frequency less than half the chopping rate. The duration of the segments affects only the amplitude and not the waveform of the recovered signal. If we let the width of the pulses go to zero and the heights go to infinity in such a way that the area hb is unity, we obtain the idealized sampled output

$$s(t)y(t) = f_r Q \left\{ \cos 2\pi f_s t + \sum_{n=1}^{\infty} [\cos 2\pi (nf_r + f_s)t \right.$$
$$\left. + \cos 2\pi (nf_r - f_s)t] \right\} \quad (6\text{-}1\text{-}6)$$

Here all the side-frequency components have the same amplitude. The series does not actually converge, and it is to be understood that the coefficient of the nth-order terms in Eq. (6-1-5) must be retained at harmonic frequencies comparable with the reciprocal of the pulse duration. Equation (6-1-6) can be made to represent the PAM wave over the frequency range of practical interest.

Modulation theory thus shows how a wave containing no components of frequency greater than f_s can be constructed from samples taken at a rate greater than $2f_s$. The corresponding mathematical theorem was first proved by E. T. Whittaker[1] in 1915. Whittaker's work was based on functions which had been used since the days of Newton and Lagrange to interpolate between a given set of points. He studied the particular case in which the values of a function $f(x)$ were given for equally spaced values of x. He recognized that there could be no unique function of x which would assume the given values, since to any one such function we could add any other function which vanished at the given values of x. Whittaker defined the equally valid interpolatory functions for a specified set of points as *cotabular*. From all the possible cotabular functions he sought one which would have sufficient distinction to merit the name of cardinal function of the cotabular set. He first showed how cotabular functions with singularities could be replaced by other cotabular functions without the singularities. He then studied the Fourier transforms of the nonsingular cotabular functions and showed in the general case how to replace any such cotabular function by one with Fourier transform equal to zero for all frequencies with absolute value exceeding twice the sampling rate. The function $f(x)$ which he thus discovered and defined as the cardinal function was

$$f(x) = \sum_{n=-\infty}^{\infty} \frac{f(a + rw) \sin [\pi(x - a - rw)/w]}{\pi(x - a - rw)/w} \quad (6\text{-}1\text{-}7)$$

Whittaker observed that in order to construct this expression for $f(x)$ we do not need to know anything about $f(x)$ except its values $f(a), f(a + w)$, $f(a - w)$, etc., at the tabulated values of the argument. These values are common to the whole set of cotabular functions. It follows that we

[1] E. T. Whittaker, On the Functions Which Are Represented by the Expansions of the Interpolation Theory, *Proc. Roy. Soc. Edinburgh*, vol. 35, pp. 181–194, 1915.

arrive at the same function expressed by Eq. (6-1-7) no matter which member of the cotabular set we replace by one giving the same samples at reduced bandwidth.   Out of all the possible functions which have the given sample values, Whittaker's cardinal function is the only one which is band-limited to frequencies less than the reciprocal of $2w$.   The communications engineer of the present day would recognize the coefficient of $f(a + rw)$ as proportional to the impulse response of an ideal low-pass filter cutting off at $1/(2w)$.   Since each term of the series is band-limited, the sum of the series must also be limited to the same band.   We know, therefore, that $f(x)$ as defined by the series is band-limited to frequencies less than the reciprocal of $2w$.   The same samples could be produced by waves with wider frequency content, but the operation performed by the series finds an equivalent low-frequency function as far as the samples are concerned.

Bandwidth, Pulse Shaping, and Multiplexing.   Both modulation theory and sampling theory demonstrate the validity of transmitting continuously varying signals by means of isolated instantaneous samples. The sampled values could be transmitted as weighted impulses of very short duration, but this would require a very wide band of frequencies. A realistic description of a PAM system can be formulated in terms of a standard pulse $g(t)$ which the system is capable of transmitting.   The PAM signal consists of a train of such pulses with individual multiplying factors corresponding to the signal samples.   A signal $s(t)$ is represented by a PAM wave

$$E(t) = \sum_{n=-\infty}^{\infty} s(nT)g(t - nT) \qquad (6\text{-}1\text{-}8)$$

If the standard pulses are sufficiently isolated from each other, the signal can be recovered from the PAM wavetrain by measuring each pulse height separately and using the measured heights as weighting factors for impulses applied to an ideal low-pass filter.

The principal advantage offered by PAM is a conservation of time. By making the standard pulse duration small compared with the interval between samples we can clear some of the time interval between samples for use by other independent signal sources on a shared-time basis.   We thereby realize a time-division multiplex system[1] for joint utilization of a transmission medium by distinct channels.   The symbolic representation of a multichannel PAM system is shown in Fig. 6-1-2 in terms of synchronized commutators which perform the sampling operations.   The bandwidth required for transmission is fixed by that necessary to transmit the standard pulse.   The fidelity with which the pulse must be reproduced depends on the allowable intersymbol interference caused by the overlapping in time of successive pulses.   Intersymbol interference is

[1] W. R. Bennett, Time-Division Multiplex Systems, *Bell System Tech. J.*, vol. 20, pp. 199–221, April, 1941.

particularly objectionable in the case of a multiplex analog transmission system, where adjacent pulses represent samples of signals in different channels.

It was shown by Nyquist[1] that complete suppression of intersymbol interference between independent samples can be attained in an ideal bandwidth equal to half the reciprocal of the interval between pulses from adjacent channels. His solution employed as standard pulse the response of an ideal low-pass filter to an impulse. If the cutoff of the low-pass filter is W, the standard pulse of unit height is

$$g(t) = \frac{\sin 2\pi W t}{2\pi W t} \tag{6-1-9}$$

The wave $g(t)$ reaches a peak value of unity at $t = 0$ and vanishes at all

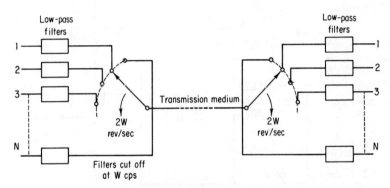

FIG. 6-1-2. Time-division-multiplex system.

instants of time separated from $t = 0$ by multiples of the reciprocal of $2W$. If we sample at any multiple of $1/(2W)$ we obtain the value of one channel sample undisturbed by any other sample value. Let the number of channels in the PAM system be N and the bandwidth of each channel be W_0. The sampling theorem requires $2W_0$ samples per second for each channel and hence a total of $2NW_0$ samples per second for N channels. The interval between adjacent samples on the line is, therefore, $1/(2NW_0)$. The bandwidth required on the line is accordingly NW_0 or, the bandwidth of one channel multiplied by the number of channels. Since an ideal filter is difficult to approximate physically, a practical PAM system typically requires a wider band than NW_0.

A PAM system can be realized with fairly simple transmitting and receiving terminals but imposes a difficult requirement on the amplitude- and phase-frequency characteristics of the line. These properties are attractive for time-division switching systems in which the common

[1] H. Nyquist, Certain Topics in Telegraph Transmission Theory, *Trans. AIEE*, vol. 47, pp. 617–644, April, 1928.

medium is of short electrical length.   For transmission over long distances, PAM would be more likely used only as an initial step from which conversion to some other form of pulse modulation can be made.

One difficulty in PAM systems used for time-division switching is that the short samples do not deliver very much average signal power to the individual receiving channels.   The difficulty can be remedied by the use of a *sample-and-hold circuit,* as shown in Fig. 6-1-3.   An electronic switch, actuated by a short control pulse, allows a capacitor to charge quickly to the instantaneous signal voltage.   The charge is held on the capacitor until the next sample is taken.   The held voltage forms the input to an emitter follower which delivers the sample values in the form of rectangular waves filling the entire interval between successive channel samples.   The

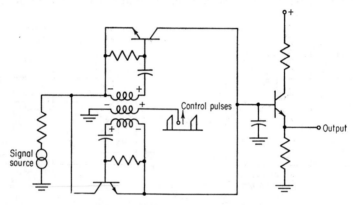

FIG. 6-1-3. Sample-and-hold circuit.

term *boxcar circuit* has also been applied to this scheme because the sampled values are joined on the time scale like boxcars on a train.   The result is a very considerable increase in signal power received by the channel. Offsetting this advantage there is a small loss of high-frequency response in the signal band.

We can analyze the effect of holding the samples by considering Eq. (6-1-5) for a PAM wave obtained by sampling a sinusoidal signal wave. The low-frequency part of the pulse train consists of the signal wave multiplied by the area of the pulse and by the sampling frequency.   It will be recalled that this equation was derived for the case in which finite segments of the signal are delivered to the line and represents instantaneous samples only in the limiting case in which the pulse width b approaches zero.   Assuming that b is small compared with the sampling interval, we can regard the PAM wave as a train of impulses weighted by the signal samples.   To convert such a wave to a train of held samples, we need only pass it through a network whose response to a rectangular pulse of infinitesimal width b is another rectangular pulse of the same height but finite width $1/f_r$. The transmittance function of such a network is the ratio of the Fourier transform of a rectangular pulse of height h and width $1/f_r$ to the Fourier transform of an impulse with weight hb. That is,

$$
\begin{aligned}
Y(\omega) &= \frac{1}{b} \int_0^{1/f_r} e^{-j2\pi ft}\, dt \\
&= \frac{e^{-j\pi f/f_r}}{\pi bf} \sin \frac{\pi f}{f_r}
\end{aligned}
\tag{6-1-10}
$$

Each term in Eq. (6-1-5) is operated on by the transmittance function at the frequency of the term. The exponential part of $Y(\omega)$ corresponds to a time delay of one-half the sampling interval. The remaining part represents an amplitude factor which is equal to $1/(f_r b)$ at $f = 0$. This is the factor by which the pulse width has been multiplied in the holding process. Hence, at low signal frequencies an amplification equal to the ratio of final to initial pulse widths is obtained. The amplification decreases with signal frequency. At $f = f_r/2$ the amplification is lower than at $f = 0$ by a factor of $2/\pi$, which is equivalent to a reduction of 3.9 db. This is the highest signal frequency permitted by the sampling theorem. The falloff in gain with signal frequency is called *aperture effect*, after the similar effect observed in television from scanning with an aperture of finite size. The aperture effect can be compensated by a linear equalizing network in the signal path.

In some cases the sample-and-hold circuit is regarded as objectionable because it requires electronic gear in the receiving branch of each channel. A compromise result can be obtained when the input circuit to the channel receiver terminates in a shunt capacitor. If the time constants can be so adjusted that the capacitor charges quickly when it is connected to the line and discharges slowly during the remainder of the interval between samples, an effect somewhat like holding is obtained. A better result is obtained with a resonant transfer switch, which includes a small inductor in series with the switch. The value of inductance is chosen so that in combination with the shunt terminating capacitors of the sending and receiving channel circuits, a sinusoidal oscillation occurs in which the charge on the sending capacitor is completely transferred to the receiving capacitor during the switch closure.[1] A high value of peak current on the line is required for the transfer, but this is a property of the common medium which does not have to be duplicated in the individual channels.

Signal-to-noise Ratio. To analyze the performance of PAM in the presence of noise, assume that the bandwidth needed for pulse transmission is $-F$ to F and that there is noise power n_0 per unit bandwidth at

[1] K. W. Cattermole, Efficiency and Reciprocity in Pulse-Amplitude Modulation, *J. Inst. Elec. Engrs. (London)*, vol. 105B, pp. 449–462, 1958.

the receiver input. Each recovered signal sample is then accompanied by a noise sample from a noise ensemble of mean power $2Fn_0$. The frequency range occupied by the noise ensemble may extend much farther than the signal band, but, as may be seen from Eq. (6-1-5), the out-of-band noise components will be reproduced in the signal-output circuit as in-band components having the beat frequency between the original noise frequencies and the nearest harmonic of the sampling rate. Signal and noise samples are thus indistinguishable in frequency content and must be accepted by the channel-output circuit on an equal basis. To calculate the full-load signal-to-noise ratio, we assume that a full-load test tone produces pulses at the receiver input of heights varying between $+A$ *and* $-A$. The mean-square value of the pulse height for a sine-wave signal is $A^2/2$, while the mean-square value of the noise samples in a 1-ohm circuit is $2Fn_0$. Note that these averages are taken discretely over the samples and not continuously over the time. The signal-to-noise ratio for a 1-ohm receiver is then

$$\frac{S}{N} = \frac{A^2}{4Fn_0} \tag{6-1-11}$$

Let the Fourier transform of the standard received pulse $g(t)$ be $G(\omega)$. If all samples were of unit height, the average power in a 1-ohm circuit would be the average of the squared ordinates of $g(t)$ over the interval T between successive samples from one channel. This would give

$$P_1 = \frac{1}{T} \int_{-\infty}^{\infty} g^2(t)\, dt = \frac{1}{T} \int_{-\infty}^{\infty} |G(\omega)|^2\, df \tag{6-1-12}$$

We have made use of Parseval's formula which expresses the relation between the total area of a squared time function and the corresponding area of the squared absolute value of its Fourier transform. The average full-load signal power P_s is $A^2P_1/2$. Since the standard pulse can be transmitted in bandwidth $-F$ to $+F$, the limits on the second integral in Eq. (6-1-12) can be made $-F$ and F.

Then
$$\frac{S}{N} = \frac{TP_s}{2n_0F \int_{-F}^{F} |G(\omega)|^2\, df} \tag{6-1-13}$$

If we use Nyquist's minimum bandwidth for complete suppression of intersymbol interference, we set $F = 1/(2T)$ and

$$G(\omega) = \begin{cases} \dfrac{1}{2F} & |f| < F \\ 0 & |f| > F \end{cases} \tag{6-1-14}$$

Substituting these values, we obtain

$$\frac{S}{N} = \frac{P_s}{2Fn_0} \tag{6-1-15}$$

Equation (6-1-15) shows that PAM and baseband-signal transmission have equivalent signal-to-noise ratios for the same average power transmitted through white Gaussian noise with Nyquist's ideal minimum bandwidth. The PAM system becomes inferior when more than the Nyquist bandwidth is used per channel.

Companding. Time division as a means of multiplexing speech channels suffers in comparison with FDM because no use is made of the nonsimultaneous multiplex load advantage shown in Table 4-7-1. A partial offset is furnished by the greater ease of applying companding to a PAM system. In speech transmission it is found that the important signal-to-noise ratio is that of full-load speech power to noise power in the absence of speech. An increase in noise during strong speech sounds is found tolerable. Advantage of this is taken in companding technique, in which transmitter gain is made to decrease with signal strength and the receiver gain made to increase. The range of transmitted signal power is thereby compressed and the range of received power is correspondingly expanded. This enables the weak signals to be transmitted at a value of gain which would cause overload if allowed for strong signals. Instantaneous companding is not recommended for continuous speech transmission because the resulting harmonics and modulation products in the transmitted wave greatly widen the required band. Syllabic companding in which the gain is made to vary slowly as dictated by the envelope of the speech syllables is acceptable but requires duplication of equipment in all the channels. PAM and the various pulse systems derived therefrom have the advantage that instantaneous companding of the samples can be performed without widening the required transmission band. The bandwidth of a pulse train is not affected by the pulse heights but only by the waveshapes. Any nonlinear relation between pulse height and signal samples merely results in a different set of pulse heights on the line. If these pulse heights are converted at the receiver to obtain the original signal samples before the samples are passed through channel filters, the nonlinearity can be exactly compensated.

6-2. Pulse Time Modulation[1]

In order to obtain an advantage from the increased bandwidth consumed by pulses, it is desirable to represent the signal samples by some property of the pulse other than by amplitude. In pulse duration modulation (PDM), the samples of the signal wave control the width of the individual pulses. Generation and detection of duration-modulated pulses can be done with simple terminal apparatus. However, since all

[1] An extensive treatment of many forms of pulse time-modulated waves has been given in a paper by M. Sánchez and F. Popert, Über die Berechnung der Spektren modulierter Impulsfolgen, *Arch. Elekt. Übertragung*, vol. 9, pp. 441–452, 1955.

the signal information is contained in the instants at which the pulses terminate, a considerable amount of transmitted pulse power is wasted. Pulse position modulation (PPM), in which the signal samples are represented by displacement of the pulses from equally spaced reference times, is more efficient in utilizing the transmitted power. A PPM pulse train can be constructed from a PDM transmitter by differentiating the PDM pulses and suppressing the initial pulses by half-wave rectification.

Pulse Position Modulation (PPM) and Pulse Duration Modulation (PDM). Correct reproduction of the signal from samples requires that the signal must be sampled at regularly spaced instants of time and that the detector must deliver uniformly spaced samples. This uniformity is easily obtained in PAM but is not so simply accomplished in PPM and PDM. The rigorously correct way of making the conversion from amplitude to time and from time back to amplitude requires (1) sampling and holding the signal during the time the pulse length or position is being controlled, (2) sampling and holding of the detected amplitude corresponding to the length or position of the received pulse, and (3) uniform resampling of the sampled-and-held pulses from the detector. In practice it is often found expedient to omit one or more of these theoretically essential steps. A certain amount of distortion then occurs, which may be acceptable, for example, in speech transmission if high fidelity is not important. Allowing the signal sample to be taken at the times dictated by the pulse occurrence leads to what is called "natural sampling" in contrast to uniform sampling. Natural sampling distorts the recovered signal by phase-modulating its components.

Departures from uniformly spaced sampling times can lead to serious impairments of the recovered signal if the exact shape of the waveform has critical significance. Severe requirements on freedom from sampling jitter have been demonstrated in the literature[1,2] for the cases in which pulse-transmission methods are applied to signals such as that representing color television or a band of frequency-division multiplexed channels.

Figure 6-2-1 shows an elementary circuit for a PPM transmitter with natural sampling. The signal input is impressed in series with a sawtooth sweep voltage on the base of a transistor normally biased beyond cutoff. In the absence of signal, the sweep voltage V carries the base voltage E_b from a very negative value, which suppresses the collector current I_c, to a positive value at which I_c is large. The result is that at some time during the sweep a rapid increase of collector current occurs and a corresponding rapid fall in the collector voltage takes place because of the voltage drop in the external resistor R_0. This causes a negative pulse in

[1] O. E. DeLange, The Timing of High-Speed Regenerative Repeaters, *Bell System Tech. J.*, vol. 37, pp. 1455–1486, November, 1958.

[2] W. R. Bennett, Statistics of Regenerative Digital Transmission, *Bell System Tech. J.*, vol. 37, pp. 1501–1542, November, 1958.

the output through the capacitor C. A corresponding positive pulse also occurs during the flyback of the sweep, but this can be eliminated by a half-wave rectifier. The presence of a signal voltage in series with the sawtooth source adds a variable bias which changes the time at which the negative pulse appears during the forward sweep. The resulting waveform is indicated in Fig. 6-2-2. The center lines at t_1, t_2, t_3, . . . are drawn at the times the negative pulses would occur in the absence of

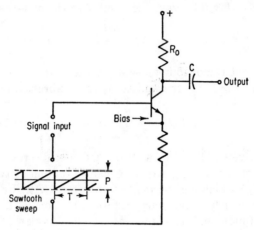

FIG. 6-2-1. Elementary circuit for PPM transmitter.

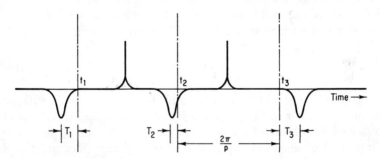

FIG. 6-2-2. Output wave of PPM transmitter.

signal. The signal displaces the times of occurrence by the amounts $-T_1$, $-T_2$, T_3, . . . depending on the magnitude of the signal. The values of time $-T_1$, $-T_2$, T_3, . . . thus constitute samples of the signal wave taken at a nonuniform rate dependent on signal magnitude. In the absence of signal, the pulses occur at a regular rate equal to the frequency of occurrence of the sweep.

Let T be the period of the sweep and represent the signal by a single-frequency component $Q \cos (qt + \theta)$. The sweep voltage V during the

rth sweep is given by

$$V = \frac{2P}{T}(t - rT) \qquad rT - \frac{T}{2} < t < rT + \frac{T}{2} \qquad (6\text{-}2\text{-}1)$$

Assume for simplicity that the pulses occur when the sum of signal and sweep voltages is zero. Then in the absence of signal the pulses occur at $t = rT$. Let t_r represent the time at which the rth pulse occurs when the signal is present. The signal sample is then represented by the time displacement $t_r - rT$. The value of t_r satisfies the equation

$$Q \cos(qt_r + \theta) + \frac{2P}{T}(t_r - rT) = 0 \qquad (6\text{-}2\text{-}2)$$

Let $g(t)$ represent the output pulse if produced at $t = 0$. The complete output wave of the PPM transmitter is then expressed by

$$E(t) = \sum_{r = -\infty}^{\infty} g(t - t_r) \qquad (6\text{-}2\text{-}3)$$

We can resolve the PPM wave train $E(t)$ into discrete sinusoidal components by first considering a more general function of two independent variables $F(x,y)$ which can be made to represent $E(t)$ by constructing a special case in which x and y are suitable functions of t. We note that there are two fundamental frequencies present, the signal frequency q and the sweep frequency $p = 2\pi/T$ both expressed in radians per second. We keep in mind in defining the function $F(x,y)$ that we are ultimately going to apply our result to the special case $x = pt$, $y = qt + \theta$. The values of x and y which we finally use therefore lie along the straight line

$$y = \frac{q}{p}x + \theta \qquad (6\text{-}2\text{-}4)$$

The function $F(x,y)$ will be defined to be periodic in x and y with period 2π in each. Values of $F(x,y)$ on the line defined by Eq. (6-2-4) can then be obtained equally well from points on any parallel line in which x and y are increased or decreased by any multiples of 2π. We can, therefore, determine $F(x,y)$ completely from any region in the xy plane containing a complete period in both x and y. Let (x_r,y_r) represent a point in the xy plane such that when we introduce the special values of x and y in terms of t the resulting value $t = t_r$ satisfies Eq. (6-2-2). Then $F(x,y)$ is characterized by pulses centered at points (x_r,y_r) satisfying the equation

$$Q \cos y_r + \frac{P}{\pi}(x_r - 2r\pi) = 0 \qquad (6\text{-}2\text{-}5)$$

The pulses occur along straight lines with slope q/p and are defined by the function $g[(x - x_r)/p]$. The analysis is simplified if we assume pulses of very short duration.   The solution for pulses of any other waveform can then be obtained by applying the Fourier transform of the actual pulse as a frequency-response function to the solution for short pulses.   That is, we base our preliminary analysis on pulses representable in the limit as δ functions.   The function $F(x,y)$ is, therefore, defined to be zero everywhere except in the neighborhood of the points on the multibranched curve with coordinates satisfying Eq. (6-2-5).   The branches of the curve are parallel and have horizontal spacing 2π.

Figure 6-2-3 shows the behavior of the function $F(x,y)$ in a period square in the xy plane including the range $-\pi$ to π in both variables.

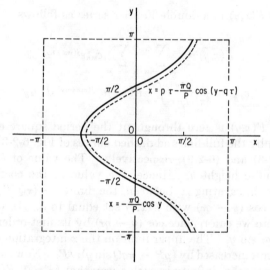

FIG. 6-2-3. Region of integration for PPM with natural sampling.

This square is traversed by the branch $r = 0$ of the family of curves defined by Eq. (6-2-5).   The equation of the branch is

$$x = \frac{-\pi Q}{P} \cos y \qquad (6\text{-}2\text{-}6)$$

The pulses start on this curve and continue on straight lines extending to the right with slope q/p.   We assume the pulses to be rectangular with height h and duration τ.   Their horizontal and vertical projections are $p\tau$ and $q\tau$, respectively.   To find the equation of the locus of their end points, consider the typical pulse starting at the point (x_0, y_0).   The point-slope equation of the straight line passing through this point with slope q/p is

$$y - y_0 = \frac{q}{p}(x - x_0) \qquad (6\text{-}2\text{-}7)$$

Since x_0 and y_0 are values of x which satisfy Eq. (6-2-6), we can substitute x_0 in terms of y_0 from Eq. (6-2-6) to rewrite Eq. (6-2-7) in the form

$$y - y_0 = \frac{q}{p}\left(x + \frac{\pi Q}{P}\cos y_0\right) \tag{6-2-8}$$

The pulses end at $y = y_0 + q\tau$ since $q\tau$ is the vertical projection of the pulse base. Making this substitution we obtain for the equation of the dashed curve of Fig. 6-2-3 representing the locus of the pulse terminations

$$x + \frac{\pi Q}{P}\cos(y - q\tau) = p\tau \tag{6-2-9}$$

We expand $F(x,y)$ in a double Fourier series as follows

$$F(x,y) = \sum_{m=-\infty}^{\infty}\sum_{n=-\infty}^{\infty} c_{mn}e^{j(mx+ny)} \tag{6-2-10}$$

$$c_{mn} = \frac{1}{4\pi^2}\int_{-\pi}^{\pi}\int_{-\pi}^{\pi} F(x,y)e^{-j(mx+ny)}\,dx\,dy \tag{6-2-11}$$

The value of $F(x,y)$ is zero throughout the period square except in the strip bounded by the full-line and dashed curves of Fig. 6-2-3 representing the Eqs. (6-2-6) and (6-2-9), respectively. The value of $F(x,y)$ on the strip is the pulse height h. Hence, the value of the coefficient c_{mn} is calculated by integrating x between the limits $-(\pi Q/P)\cos y$ and $p\tau - (\pi Q/P)\cos(y - q\tau)$ with $F(x,y)$ set equal to h. In the limit as τ approaches zero we can replace $\cos(y - q\tau)$ by its first-order approximation $\cos y + q\tau \sin y$. The upper limit on the x integration is then equal to the lower limit increased by $(pP - \pi qQ \sin y)\tau/P$. Now as τ approaches zero and h approaches infinity in such a way that $h\tau = 1$, $F(x,y)$ becomes an impulse of weight $(pP - \pi qQ \sin y)/P$ at values of x satisfying Eq. (6-2-6). Hence,

$$c_{mn} = \frac{1}{4\pi^2 P}\int_{-\pi}^{\pi}(pP - \pi qQ \sin y)e^{-jny}\,dy\int_{-\pi}^{\pi}\delta\left(x + \frac{\pi Q}{P}\cos y\right)e^{-jmx}\,dx$$

$$= \frac{1}{4\pi^2 P}\int_{-\pi}^{\pi}(pP - \pi qQ \sin y)e^{-j(nPy - m\pi Q \cos y)/P}\,dy \tag{6-2-12}$$

Evaluating the integral and replacing x and y by their special representations in terms of time, we find that when $g(t) = \delta(t)$, the PPM wave can be resolved in the form:

$$E(t) = \frac{p}{2\pi} - \frac{qQ}{2P}\sin qt$$

$$+ \sum_{m=1}^{\infty}\sum_{n=-\infty}^{\infty}\frac{mp + nq}{m\pi}J_n\left(\frac{m\pi Q}{P}\right)\cos\left[(mp + nq)t + \frac{n\pi}{2}\right] \tag{6-2-13}$$

If $g(t)$ is a pulse having the Fourier transform

$$G(\omega) = A(\omega)e^{jB(\omega)} \tag{6-2-14}$$

with $A(\omega)$ and $B(\omega)$ real,

$$E(t) = \frac{p}{2\pi} A(0) - \frac{qQ}{2P} A(q) \sin[qt + B(q)]$$

$$+ \sum_{m=1}^{\infty} \sum_{n=-\infty}^{\infty} \frac{mp + nq}{m\pi} J_n\left(\frac{m\pi Q}{P}\right) A(mp + nq) \cos\left[(mp + nq)t\right.$$

$$\left. + B(mp + nq) + \frac{n\pi}{2}\right] \tag{6-2-15}$$

The first term of Eq. (6-2-15) is a d-c component equal to the average value of the pulses. The second term is proportional to the derivative of the signal modified by the aperture effect associated with the pulse shape. The remaining terms are cross-modulation products between the sampling and signal frequencies. Many of them fall in the signal band and cannot be separated from the detected signal. The fact that there is a signal component in the pulse train could easily be overlooked by careless analysis. Although the differentiated form emphasizes high-frequency components and shifts all phases by 90°, the resulting signal component in the case of speech is quite intelligible. Integration of the pulse train restores the signal component to its original waveshape.

A greater signal amplitude with less distortion can be obtained at the receiver by conversion from PPM to PDM. This can be done by using a train of regularly spaced pulses at the sweep frequency p to turn on a flip-flop circuit which is then turned off by the PPM pulse. By substituting $m = 1$, $n = 0$ in Eq. (6-2-15), we see that there is a component of frequency p in the PPM pulse train. A narrow bandpass filter centered at p isolates this component which can then be used to generate the regularly spaced pulses. The pulses should be phased to occur half way between the positions the PPM pulses would have in the absence of signal modulation. The output of the flip-flop is a train of lengthened pulses which begin at equally spaced instants and end when the PPM pulses arrive. The appropriate function $G(x,y)$ for the resulting PDM output playing the same role as the function $F(x,y)$ did for the PPM pulse train is shown in Fig. 6-2-4. The pulses begin on the vertical line $x = -\pi$ and end on the curve defined by Eq. (6-2-6), which defines the starting points of the PPM pulses. The value of $G(x,y)$ is equal to a constant h in the shaded regions of the period square and is equal to zero in the remainder of the square. Expanding $G(x,y)$ in a double Fourier series in the same way we previously expanded $F(x,y)$, we obtain for a typical coefficient

$$c_{mn} = \frac{h}{4\pi^2} \int_{-\pi}^{\pi} e^{-jny}\, dy \int_{-\pi}^{\frac{-\pi Q}{P}\cos y} e^{-jmx}\, dx \tag{6-2-16}$$

The complete solution for the PDM wave expressed as a function of time is then

$$E(t) = \frac{h}{2} - \frac{hQ}{2P} \cos qt + \frac{h}{\pi} \sum_{m=1}^{\infty} \left[(-)^m - J_0\left(\frac{m\pi Q}{P}\right) \right] \frac{\sin mpt}{m}$$
$$- \frac{h}{\pi} \sum_{m=1}^{\infty} \sum_{n=1}^{\infty} \frac{J_n(m\pi Q/P)}{m} \left[\sin\left(mpt + nqt + \frac{n\pi}{2}\right) \right.$$
$$\left. \mp \sin\left(mpt - nqt + \frac{n\pi}{2}\right) \right] \quad (6\text{-}2\text{-}17)$$

The second term of the expansion represents the original signal in undistorted form with an unimportant polarity reversal. The undistorted

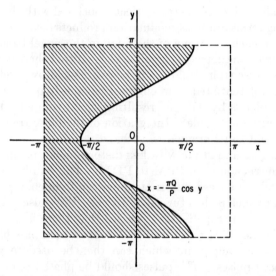

FIG. 6-2-4. Region of integration for PDM wave derived from naturally sampled PPM.

signal is, however, accompanied by numerous distortion products falling within the signal band. If the signal band extends from q_1 to q_2, the distortion products which must be accepted are those terms in the double summation with frequencies $mp - nq$ falling in the range from q_1 to q_2.

The average pulse-repetition frequency should be at least twice the highest signal frequency in order to obtain the minimum number of samples necessary for satisfactory signal recovery. The distortion product of frequency $p - q$, therefore, usually falls well above the signal band. The products which fall within the signal band are typically those with frequencies $p - 2q$, $p - 3q$, . . . etc. If we designate by D_n the ratio of the amplitude of the product of frequency $p - nq$ to the amplitude of the signal component, we find from Eq. (6-2-17)

$$D_n = \frac{2}{\pi\mu} |J_n(\pi\mu)| \tag{6-2-18}$$

where $\mu = Q/P$ is the *modulation index*. When $\mu = 1$ the pulse is shifted by the maximum amount possible without spilling over into the adjacent time slot. In a PPM time-division multiplex system the sampling interval must be subdivided into time slots for the individual channels and the index of modulation must be correspondingly reduced. Figure 6-2-5 shows graphs of the principal distortion products which can fall in

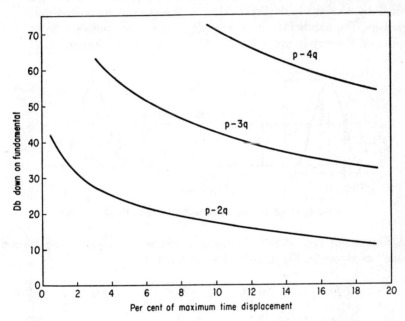

Fig. 6-2-5. Distortion products in signal band from transmission by PPM with natural sampling and PPM-PDM detection.

a signal band for the case of PPM with natural sampling and detection by conversion to PDM.

If we compare the expression for the nth-order side frequencies on the nth harmonic of the sampling rate in Eq. (6-2-17) with Eq. (5-3-2) for the resolution of an angle-modulated wave, we can draw the important conclusion that the harmonics of the PPM wave are phase-modulated by the signal. It is in fact possible to derive a PM wave by inserting a bandpass filter around one of the harmonics. An FM wave can be derived by appropriate preemphasis of the signal. This method has been used in FM transmitters for military communication.[1]

[1] L. R. Wrathall, Frequency Modulation by Non-Linear Coils, *Bell Lab. Record*, vol. 24, No. 3, pp. 102–105, March, 1946.

Noise affects PPM and PDM signals by falsifying the time at which the pulses are judged to begin or end. In the case of PPM, the time of occurrence of the pulses is registered at the receiver by means of a threshold detector. Superimposed noise causes the threshold to be exceeded before or after the instant the pulse value itself crosses the threshold. Immunity to effect of noise can be approached by making the pulse build up very steeply so that the time interval during which noise can exert any perturbation is short. Displacement of the pulse position by noise in effect inserts noise samples in the receiver output which add directly to the signal samples. The slope of the pulse is limited by the available bandwidth of the transmission medium. By increasing the bandwidth it is possible to use short pulses with steeper slopes and thereby improve the signal-to-noise ratio in the output.

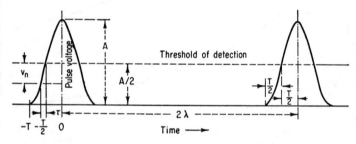

Fɪɢ. 6-2-6. Displacement of pulse by noise in PPM system.

A convenient type of pulse to use as a means of analysis is the "raised cosine" as shown in Fig. 6-2-6. Its equation is

$$g(t) = \frac{A}{2}(1 + \cos \pi f_b t) \qquad -T < t < T \qquad f_b = \frac{1}{T} \quad (6\text{-}2\text{-}19)$$

The corresponding Fourier transform is

$$G(\omega) = \int_{-T}^{T} \frac{A}{2}(1 + \cos \pi f_b t)e^{-j2\pi f t}dt$$

$$= \frac{A \sin (2\pi f/f_b)}{2\pi f(1 - 4f^2/f_b^2)} \qquad (6\text{-}2\text{-}20)$$

The transform has its first nulls at $f = \pm f_b$ and is small outside this range. For practical purposes the bandwidth required for transmission of the pulse can be taken as the range between first nulls.

As shown in the figure, the slicing level for pulse recognition is set at $A/2$, which is half the peak pulse height. A noise wave of relatively small instantaneous value v_n displaces the time of detection by τ, where

$$\frac{v_n}{\tau} = g'\left(-\frac{T}{2}\right) = \frac{\pi f_b A}{2} \qquad (6\text{-}2\text{-}21)$$

The peak-to-peak position swing is represented by 2λ. A full-load sine-wave signal component modulates the pulse position by $\pm\lambda$ and has mean-square deviation $\lambda^2/2$. The mean-square deviation produced by noise of spectral density w_0 is

$$\langle \tau^2 \rangle = \frac{4\langle v_n^2 \rangle}{(\pi f_b A)^2} = \frac{8w_0}{\pi^2 f_b A^2} \qquad (6\text{-}2\text{-}22)$$

The mean-square value of the PPM wave is

$$P_s = \frac{1}{2\lambda} \int_{-T}^{T} g^2(t)\, dt = \frac{3A^2}{8\lambda f_b} \qquad (6\text{-}2\text{-}23)$$

Hence the signal-to-noise ratio is given by

$$\frac{S}{N} = \frac{\pi^2 f_b \lambda^2 A^2}{16 w_0} = \frac{\pi^2 f_b^2 \lambda^3 P_s}{6 w_0} \qquad (6\text{-}2\text{-}24)$$

For an n-channel multiplex PPM system in which each channel has bandwidth W and is sampled $2W$ times per second,

$$2n(\lambda + T) = \frac{1}{2W} \qquad \text{or} \qquad \lambda = \frac{1}{4nW} - \frac{1}{f_b} \qquad (6\text{-}2\text{-}25)$$

In terms of the average pulse power P_s, the signal-to-noise ratio in each channel is

$$\frac{S}{N} = \frac{\pi P_s}{6 f_b w_0} \left(\frac{f_b}{4nW} - 1 \right)^3 \qquad (6\text{-}2\text{-}26)$$

In terms of peak power $P_m = A^2$,

$$\frac{S}{N} = \frac{\pi^2 P_m}{16 f_b w_0} \left(\frac{f_b}{4nW} - 1 \right)^2 \qquad (6\text{-}2\text{-}27)$$

For large ratios of pulse bandwidth f_b to original signal-channel bandwidth W, the signal-to-noise power ratio in the output of the PPM receiver is similar to that obtained by FM in that the improvement follows the square of the transmission bandwidth. The analysis neglects false pulses produced by high noise peaks, which have a finite though small probability of occurrence when the noise is Gaussian, no matter how small the rms value is. As the bandwidth is increased indefinitely the accompanying increase in total noise power eventually causes a sufficient number of false pulses to prevent further improvement by band widening.

In the case of PDM with low noise, a slicer operating at half the peak removes all noise effects except the time shift similar to that we have evaluated for PPM. We assume that one edge of the pulse is fixed by a noise-free reference. The average transmitted power is increased relative to PPM because duration of the pulse extends to the fixed reference time. The waveform is as shown in Fig. 6-2-7 in which a portion of constant height A and duration D is preceded and followed by rising and falling segments identical with the leading and trailing halves of the PPM pulse. For fixed duration, the average power is that for the PPM pulse plus the amount contributed by the rectangular portion, that is, for fixed D

$$P_s = \frac{3A^2}{8\lambda f_b} + \frac{A^2 D}{2\lambda} \qquad (6\text{-}2\text{-}28)$$

For a full-load test tone of angular frequency q

$$D = \lambda(1 + \sin qt) \qquad (6\text{-}2\text{-}29)$$

We, therefore, obtain for the average value of pulse power for a full-load test tone

$$P_s = \frac{3A^2}{8\lambda f_b} + \frac{A^2}{2} \qquad (6\text{-}2\text{-}30)$$

The resulting signal-to-noise ratio in the detector output is

$$\frac{S}{N} = \frac{\pi^2 f_b{}^2 \lambda^3 P_s}{2w_0(3 + 8f_b\lambda)} = \frac{\pi^2 P_s(f_b/4nW - 1)^3}{6f_b w_0[1 + \tfrac{4}{3}(f_b/4nW - 1)]} \qquad (6\text{-}2\text{-}31)$$

In terms of peak pulse power the signal-to-noise ratio for PDM is the

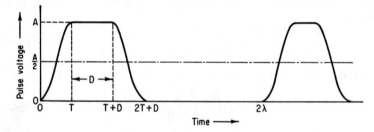

Fig. 6-2-7. Waveform in PDM system.

same as PPM. In terms of average power the PDM system is inferior because no information is furnished during the portion of the pulse with constant height.

Pulse Frequency Modulation (PFM). If we remove the restriction that the index of modulation Q/P in a PPM system cannot exceed unity, we are no longer constrained to one and only one pulse for each cycle of the sweep. This extension leads to a form of modulation called pulse frequency modulation (PFM) or pulse density modulation. Roughly speaking we say that in PFM the number of pulses transmitted per unit of time is proportional to the signal voltage. More precisely a PFM wave is one which consists of one pulse for every complete oscillation of an FM wave. Thus detection of FM by a cycle counter is equivalent to converting FM to PFM and selecting the low-frequency components of the PFM wave by a low-pass filter. If the cycle counter is inserted at the FM transmitter and the complete output pulse train is transmitted, we have a PFM transmission system. Multiplexing of channels by time division is not feasible for PFM because there are no fixed time slots. For single-channel systems PFM has the attraction that no synchronizing of the terminal with the transmitter is required. In fact the only apparatus needed for detection is a low-pass filter.

Theoretical analysis of PFM is identical with that of PPM with natural sampling. To obtain an undistorted signal component in the receiver, it is necessary to integrate the signal wave either before it is impressed upon the transmitter or after it has been recovered at the receiver. It is not difficult to see why a PFM wave should contain a signal component when we picture the wave with condensations and rarefactions in the pulse train corresponding to amplitude variations in the signal. If we decrease the amount of frequency variation, the condensations and rarefactions become less pronounced. We finally reach a condition like PPM in which the pulses merely shift their relative spacings. There is no sharp dividing line causing the signal component to disappear, and hence PPM, which is somewhat like weakly modulated PFM, retains a signal component even though it may be relatively small. We also note that PFM shares with naturally sampled PPM the disadvantage of a detected signal contaminated by $p - nq$ modulation products.

6-3. Pulse Code Modulation (PCM)

A method of transmitting an approximate but adequate representation of a continuous signal wave by sending a succession of discrete numerical values was proposed by Rainey[1] in 1926. A patent applying Rainey's principle to speech transmission was obtained by Reeves[2] in 1939. The system, which has since come to be known as pulse code modulation (PCM), is basically quantized PAM. Instead of sending the actual values of the samples, a PCM transmitter selects the nearest approximations from an allowable discrete set of values. In the actual transmission the resulting sequence of discrete numbers can be expressed in whatever notation is most convenient. The simplest and most widely used form is a binary representation. In the binary system the numbers 0 and 1 retain the same form as in the decimal system, but 2 becomes 10, 3 is 11, 4 is 100, 5 is 101, etc. If m positions are available, 2^m different numbers can be represented. Transmission is accomplished by assigning m time slots in which the symbols 0 and 1 correspond, respectively, to absence or presence of a pulse in the slot. An m-digit binary PCM system requires m pulse positions per sample of the signal. If the signal has bandwidth f_s, the sampling rate must be at least $2f_s$ and the pulse rate at least $2mf_s$.

[1] P. M. Rainey, United States Patent 1,608,527, Nov. 30, 1926.
[2] A. H. Reeves, French Patent 853,183, Oct. 23, 1939.

The advantage of PCM lies chiefly in the ability to regenerate the pulse train and thereby remove completely the effect of noise in the transmission medium. To do this requires the insertion of regenerative repeaters at sufficiently close spacing to prevent any ambiguity in recognizing the discrete pulse values. In binary PCM with on-off pulsing the repeater makes a decision in each time slot as to whether or not a pulse is present. If the decision is "yes" a clean new pulse is sent to the next repeater. If the decision is "no" a clean base line is sent. The outgoing train of pulses is also retimed to maintain the correct spacing. Accumulation of noise and distortion in a repeater span is thereby removed provided that the disturbance is not sufficiently great to cause an error in any decision. The requirement on a single repeater span is the same as that on a complete system.

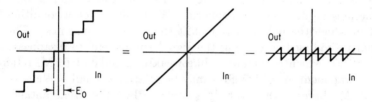

FIG. 6-3-1. Analog-to-digital conversion characteristic.

The principal distortion in a detected PCM signal is the rounding-off error introduced by quantizing the signal samples. In effect the signal samples are applied as input to a *staircase transducer* with input-output characteristic such as shown in Fig. 6-3-1. When the steps are of equal size the characteristic can be expressed as the difference between a linear response and a sawtooth response, as shown. The quantizing error is represented by the sawtooth portion, which is a periodic function $F(E_1)$ with period E_0, where E_1 is the input voltage and E_0 is the step size. We write

$$F(E_1) = E_1 - rE_0 \qquad \frac{(2r-1)E_0}{2} < E_1 < \frac{(2r+1)E_0}{2}$$

$$= \frac{E_0}{\pi} \sum_{n=1}^{\infty} \frac{(-)^{n+1}}{n} \sin \frac{2n\pi E_1}{E_0} \tag{6-3-1}$$

We can regard a PCM system as a perfect PAM system which transmits the sum of two signal waves which are (1) the original signal, and (2) the error wave $-F(E_1)$. Even though the original signal is band-limited to half the sampling rate, the error component extends over a wider band. However, it is converted at the detector to a band-limited wave defined by the same samples and containing cross-modulation products involving the sampling frequency and its harmonics.

If we represent the signal by a sinusoidal component $E_1(t) = Q \cos qt$, we can resolve the error component into a Fourier series

$$F(E_1) = \sum_{r=0}^{\infty} A_{2r+1} \cos (2r + 1)qt \qquad (6\text{-}3\text{-}2)$$

The value of A_{2r+1} can be calculated in two ways using either the first or second forms of $F(E_1)$ given in Eq. (6-3-1). The first form gives the result

$$A_{2r+1} = \frac{4E_0}{\pi(2r + 1)} \sum_{s=1}^{k} \sin\left[(2r + 1) \arccos \frac{(2s - 1)E_0}{2Q} \right]$$

$$= \frac{4E_0}{\pi(2r + 1)} \sum_{s=1}^{k} \left[1 - \frac{(2s - 1)^2 E_0{}^2}{4Q^2} \right]^{1/2} U_{2r}\left[\frac{(2s - 1)E_0}{2Q} \right] \qquad (6\text{-}3\text{-}3)$$

The value of k is defined by the condition that $2k - 1$ is the largest odd integer equal to or less than $2Q/E_0$. The symbol U_n represents an nth-order Chebyshev polynomial of the second kind.

If we use the second form, we obtain a series of Bessel functions:

$$A_{2r+1} = \frac{2E_0}{\pi} \sum_{n=1}^{\infty} \frac{(-)^n}{n} J_{2r+1}\left(\frac{2n\pi Q}{E_0} \right) \qquad (6\text{-}3\text{-}4)$$

When the error wave is sampled at rate f_r, the corresponding wave finally delivered to the low-pass filter has the original components multiplied by the sampling function $y(t)$ of Eq. (6-1-6). The accepted error signal is, therefore, composed of the low-frequency part of

$$F_0(t) = \sum_{m=0}^{\infty} \sum_{r=0}^{\infty} A_{2r+1} \cos [m\omega_r - (2r + 1)q]t \qquad (6\text{-}3\text{-}5)$$

The principal components falling in the signal band are the odd harmonics of the signal frequency obtained by setting $m = 0$ and the lower side frequencies on the sampling frequency which are obtained by setting $m = 1$. The third harmonic has the same amplitude as the modulation product of frequency $\omega_r - 3q$, the fifth harmonic has the same amplitude as the product of frequency $\omega_r - 5q$, etc. There is also a variation in the signal level itself, which can be calculated by subtracting the coefficient A_{01} from Q.

Curves calculated from Eq. (6-3-5) are shown in Figs. 6-3-2 to 6-3-4. Figure 6-3-2 shows the gain variation versus signal amplitude for a six-digit PCM system with equal steps. Figure 6-3-3 shows the variation of the third harmonic and the product $\omega_r - 3q$ for the same case, and Fig. 6-3-4 shows the fifth harmonic and the $\omega_r - 5q$ product. Figures 6-3-3 and 6-3-4 can also be applied to other numbers of digits by increasing the magnitudes of the abscissa scale by 6 db for each added digit. The amplitudes of the individual harmonics and products oscillate with signal

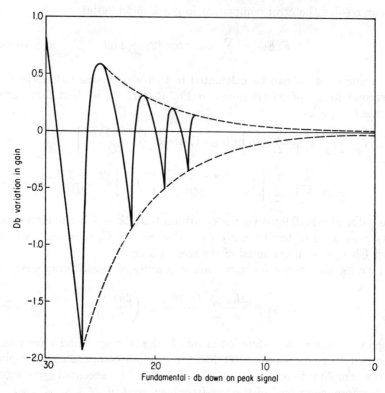

FIG. 6-3-2. Single-frequency gain variation in six-digit binary PCM system; 32 positive and 32 negative steps, no preliminary compression.

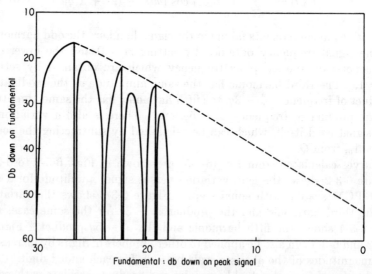

FIG. 6-3-3. Third harmonic and $(\omega_r - 3q)$ product in six-digit binary PCM system.

amplitude. Null values occur at various levels for the different components, but of course not all of the terms vanish at any one given signal level. When an analyzer measurement is made of the components of various frequencies present in the output of a PCM receiver with a single-frequency signal applied at the transmitter, a myriad of response peaks are found with various magnitudes. Slight changes in the amplitude or frequency of the modulating signal cause relatively large changes in the magnitudes and frequencies of the products. Such behavior of

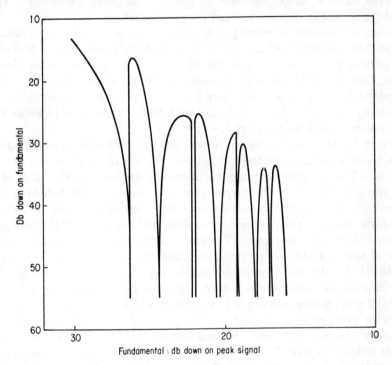

FIG. 6-3-4. Fifth harmonic and $(\omega_r - 5q)$ product in six-digit binary PCM system.

modulation measurements on PCM systems with sine-wave signals is unsatisfactory for rating of performance.

A simple way of estimating the mean-square value of the error samples applies when both the number of discrete steps and the rate of signal change are sufficiently high to make adjacent errors independent of each other. The errors are then equally likely to fall anywhere in the range $-E_0/2$ to $E_0/2$. The mean-square value of error is then given by

$$\langle F^2 \rangle = \frac{1}{E_0} \int_{-E_0/2}^{E_0/2} F^2 \, dF = \frac{E_0^2}{12} \qquad (6\text{-}3\text{-}6)$$

A full-load sine wave for an m-digit binary PCM system would have amplitude $2^{m-1}E_0$ and mean-square value $2^{2m-3}E_0^2$. Hence, regarding the error as the noise in the system, we obtain for the full-load signal-to-noise ratio

$$\frac{S}{N} = 3 \cdot 2^{2m-1} \tag{6-3-7}$$

For a six-digit system $S/N = 6{,}144$, which is equivalent to 37.9 db. This is on the assumption that the error spectrum is flat, which it is if the error samples are independent. It is also assumed that the receiver accepts the full band from zero to half the sampling frequency. The noise in a smaller band is reduced proportionately.

Since the number of pulses per sample is equal to the number of binary digits, the bandwidth of the transmission medium must increase in direct proportion to the value of m in Eq. (6-3-7). The equation shows, therefore, that in PCM the signal-to-noise ratio varies exponentially with bandwidth. This is a much more powerful exchange of bandwidth for signal-to-noise ratio than is obtained with FM, for example, in which the improvement follows a square law.

When PCM is used for speech transmission, the principle of companding can be used to improve the signal-to-noise ratio for a given number of digits. The compandor could be inserted externally in the form of a compressor preceding the transmitter and an expander following the receiver. Practically it is found most convenient to compress the instantaneous samples just before quantizing and to expand the samples immediately after decoding. The effect can be described equally well as one of tapering the size of the quantizing steps. More steps are made available for the more vulnerable low-level part of the signal range. If the number of steps is reasonably large, the mean-square error is still $E_0^2/12$ when the signal sample is in a step of width E_0, but it is now necessary to average over all values of E_0 weighted in accordance with the probabilities of occurrence. If the quantizer is preceded by a compressor with output voltage $E_2 = G(E_1)$, where E_1 is the input voltage, equal steps E_0 of the output are equivalent approximately to steps of size $E_0/G'(E_1)$ in the input. Then if the probability density function of the signal input values is $p(E_1)$ between $E_1 = Q_1$ and $E_1 = Q_2$, comprising the range of levels to be quantized, the mean-square quantizing noise is given by

$$N = \frac{E_0^2}{12} \int_{Q_1}^{Q_2} \frac{p(E_1)\, dE_1}{[G'(E_1)]^2} \tag{6-3-8}$$

The spectral density of the quantizing errors must eventually depart from flatness at some high frequency. A convenient signal for which the variation can be studied is band-limited Gaussian white noise. It is convenient to perform the calculation by inserting $E_1 = v(t)$ in Eq. (6-3-1) and evaluating the autocorrelation function of $F[v(t)]$ on the assumption that $v(t)$ is a member of a band-limited white Gaussian noise ensemble. We write

$$R_F(\tau) = \langle F[v(t)]F[v(t + \tau)]\rangle$$

$$= \frac{E_0{}^2}{\pi^2} \sum_{m=1}^{\infty} \sum_{n=1}^{\infty} \frac{(-)^{m+n}}{mn} \left\langle \sin \frac{2m\pi v(t)}{E_0} \sin \frac{2n\pi v(t + \tau)}{E_0} \right\rangle \quad (6\text{-}3\text{-}9)$$

It has been shown in a paper by Bennett, Curtis, and Rice,[1] that if $x(t)$ is a member of a Gaussian ensemble with zero mean

$$\langle e^{j[ax(t)+bx(t+\tau)]}\rangle = \exp\left[-\frac{a^2 + b^2}{2} R_x(0) - abR_x(\tau)\right] \quad (6\text{-}3\text{-}10)$$

Applying the cosine addition formula to express the product of sines in Eq. (6-3-9) as the difference of cosine terms to which we apply Eq. (6-3-10), we obtain

$$R_F(\tau) = \frac{k\sigma^2}{\pi} \sum_{m=1}^{\infty} \sum_{n=1}^{\infty} \frac{(-)^{m+n}}{mn} \exp\left[-\frac{2\pi^2(m^2 + n^2)}{k}\right] \sinh \frac{4mn\pi^2\alpha}{k}$$

$$(6\text{-}3\text{-}11)$$

where σ^2 is the mean-square value of $v(t)$, $k = E_0{}^2/\sigma^2$, and $\alpha = R_v(\tau)/\sigma^2$. The spectral density[2] of the complete error wave is shown in Fig. 6-3-5 for various numbers of binary digits. Since Gaussian noise has a nonzero probability of exceeding any finite magnitude no matter how large, the analysis based on a finite number of steps neglects overload conditions of small probability. The maximum signal has arbitrarily been taken as four times rms in the calculations. The total distortion power falling in the signal band at the receiver output is shown in Fig. 6-3-6.

Another problem of interest is the spectral resolution of the pulse train. It might seem at first thought that the coded pulses would have little in common with the original signal until a decoding operation is performed. Actually in the case of speech transmission by PCM, the transmitted pulse train is quite intelligible although severely distorted. This comes about because there is a partially systematic relationship between pulse density and signal magnitude.

We shall demonstrate the presence of a signal component in the PCM wave train by calculating the spectrum for a sinusoidal signal. Assume a signal $Q \cos (qt + \theta)$ with an added bias $Q_0 > Q$. Let the input range of the coder be zero to NE_0, where N is the number of steps and E_0 is the step size. In the case of binary coding, a signal voltage E satisfying the inequality

$$sE_0 < E < (s + 1)E_0 \qquad s = 0, 1, 2, \ldots, N - 1 \quad (6\text{-}3\text{-}12)$$

[1] W. R. Bennett, H. E. Curtis, and S. O. Rice, Interchannel Interference in FM and PM Systems Under Noise Load Conditions, Bell System Tech. J., vol. 34, pp. 601–636, May, 1955.

[2] W. R. Bennett, Spectra of Quantized Signals, Bell System Tech. J., vol. 27, pp. 446–472, July, 1948.

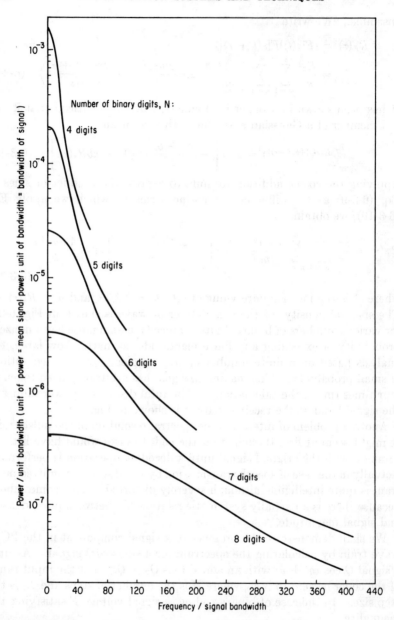

FIG. 6-3-5. Spectrum of distortion from quantizing the magnitude of a random-noise wave. (*From W. R. Bennett, BSTJ, vol. 27, July, 1948, p. 451.*)

is represented by the voltage

$$sE_0 = E_0 \sum_{k=1}^{r} D_k 2^{r-k} \qquad (6\text{-}3\text{-}13)$$

where D_k has the proper value, either 0 or 1, to represent the number s in binary notation. The number of binary digits is r, and the values of k begin with the most significant digit. We code instantaneous samples of the signal voltage

$$E = Q_0 + Q \cos (qt + \theta) \qquad (6\text{-}3\text{-}14)$$

at regularly spaced instants of time

$$t_\mu = \mu T = 2\pi \frac{\mu}{p} \qquad \mu = 0, \pm 1, \pm 2, \ldots \qquad (6\text{-}3\text{-}15)$$

The inequality of Eq. (6-3-12) determines the value of the integer s for

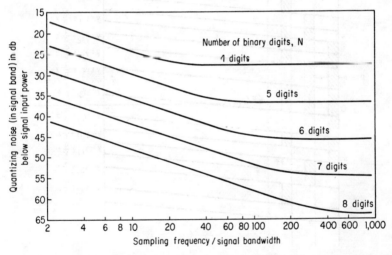

FIG. 6-3-6. Total distortion in signal band from quantizing and sampling a random-noise wave. (From W. R. Bennett, BSTJ, vol. 27, July, 1948, p. 453.)

each sample. The number s is expressed in binary notation to determine the values of D_k. In a series of r consecutive time slots, a pulse is transmitted in the kth slot if $D_k = 1$. No pulses are sent in the slots for $D_k = 0$. The r time slots occupy a total interval γT where γ is the reciprocal of the number of PCM channels multiplexed by time division. As in previous examples we shall calculate a function $F(x,y)$ for which $F(pt, qt + \theta)$ defines the pulse train just described.

The quantization condition of Eq. (6-3-12) is defined along the y axis by the lower and upper bounds, respectively.

$$Q_0 + Q \cos y = sE_0 \qquad Q_0 + Q \cos y = (s + 1)E_0 \qquad (6\text{-}3\text{-}16)$$

In Fig. 6-3-7 we have used Eq. (6-3-16) to mark off division points along the y axis. These occur at

$$y = \arccos \frac{sE_0 - Q_0}{Q} \qquad s = 0, 1, 2, \ldots, s_0 \qquad (6\text{-}3\text{-}17)$$

where s_0 is the largest integer satisfying the relation

$$s_0 E_0 - Q_0 < Q \qquad (6\text{-}3\text{-}18)$$

Through the division points, straight lines are drawn with slope q/p.

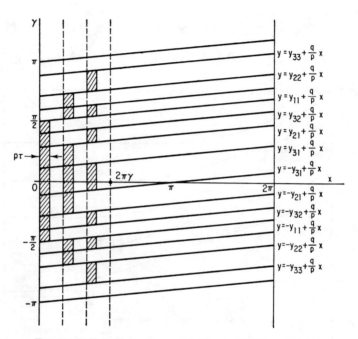

Fig. 6-3-7. Function of two variables for PCM wavetrain.

Boundaries between code values must fall along these lines. In the interior of the strip between the line corresponding to s and the line corresponding to $s + 1$, pulses occur in accordance with the values of D_k in the binary representation of s. Thus if $D_k = 1$, a pulse begins at $x = 2\pi k\gamma/r$. If $D_k = 0$, there is no pulse at this value of x. We note that the value of D_1 is zero when s lies in the lower half of N and is unity when s is in the upper half. Likewise, D_2 is zero for s in the first and third quarters of N and is unity for the second and fourth quarters. These conditions enable us to fix the boundary in the xy plane between occurrence and nonoccurrence of particular pulses. Thus the condition under which the first pulse occurs is $s > N/2$, and the boundary between occurrence is a straight line of slope q/p and intercepts

$$\pm y_{11} = \arccos \frac{NE_0 - 2Q_0}{2Q} \qquad 2Q > NE_0 - 2Q_0 \qquad (6\text{-}3\text{-}19)$$

If the inequality is not satisfied the first pulse never occurs. Likewise'
the boundaries between occurrence and nonoccurrence of the second pulse
are straight lines with slope q/p and intercept

$$\pm y_{22} = \arccos \frac{NE_0 - 4Q_0}{4Q}, \ \pm y_{11}, \ \pm y_{21} = \arccos \frac{3NE_0 - 4Q_0}{4Q}$$

$$(6\text{-}3\text{-}20)$$

provided these intercepts exist. The intercepts for the remainder of the
pulses are determined in similar fashion. A convenient value to take for
the bias Q_0 is $NE_0/2$, which places an a-c signal symmetrically with respect
to the midpoint of the available coding range. The maximum sinusoidal
signal amplitude without overload is then Q_0.

Figure 6-3-7 shows the regions in the xy plane for which pulses exist in
the illustrative case $r = 3$ and $Q/Q_0 = 0.8$. The coefficients in the
double Fourier-series expansion of $F(x,y)$ are found by integrating over
the shaded regions. As in the earlier cases it is convenient to evaluate
the limiting form of the coefficient when the width of the pulses is infinitesimal and apply aperture admittance functions to obtain the result for
generalized pulse forms.

In particular if we let $\lambda = Q_0/Q$ and M represent the largest integer
contained in the ratio $2^k/\lambda$, we calculate for the component in the output
of the same frequency as the signal:

$$c_{01}e^{jy} + c_{0,-1}e^{-jy} = A_{01} \cos y \qquad (6\text{-}3\text{-}21)$$

$$A_{01} = \frac{pr}{\pi^2} \left\{ \frac{2}{r} - 1 - \frac{2}{r} \sum_{k=1}^{r-1} \sum_{\mu=1}^{M} (-)^\mu \left[1 - \left(\frac{\mu\lambda}{2^k} \right)^2 \right]^{\frac{1}{2}} \right\} \qquad (6\text{-}3\text{-}22)$$

The amplitude A_{01} of the signal component in the binary PCM wave
train is plotted in Fig. 6-3-8 as a function of $1/\lambda$, the ratio of input signal
amplitude to full-load input, for $r = 2, 3, 4,$ and 5 digits. It appears that
a definite although severely compressed component of the original signal
is present in a PCM pulse train coded in the natural binary system. The
signal content of the message can be reduced by translating to a coding
plan which changes in a less orderly fashion as signal strength is increased.

The development of solid-state components of small size, wideband
response, long life, low cost, and low power consumption has made the use
of PCM attractive for extending the capabilities of existing transmission
facilities. The fact that the digital signal can be regenerated[1] at points
sufficiently close together to avoid accumulation of distortion and noise

[1] B. M. Oliver, J. R. Pierce, and C. E. Shannon, The Philosophy of PCM, *Proc.
IRE*, vol. 36, pp. 1324–1332, November, 1948.

enables utilization of a wide frequency range in a cable over much greater distances than would be feasible in an analog system. For example, the Bell System operates a 24-channel PCM voice-transmission system[1,2] sending 1,544,000 pulses/sec over 19- or 22-gauge cable pairs with transistorized regenerative repeaters spaced 6,000 ft apart.

Delta Modulation (DM). Delta modulation or unit increment modulation[3-5] is a form of digital transmittion in which discrete increments relative to previous approximations are transmitted. A simple form of delta modulation is shown in Fig. 6-3-9. At regularly spaced instants of time, a comparator decides which of two inputs has the greater value. One input is the signal and the other is an approximation obtained by

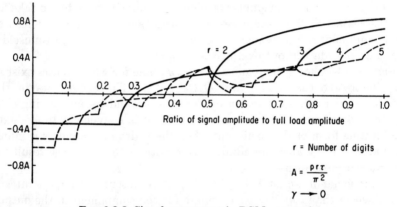

Ratio of signal amplitude to full load amplitude

r = Number of digits

$$A = \frac{pr\tau}{\pi^2}$$

$$\gamma \longrightarrow 0$$

FIG. 6-3-8. Signal component in PCM wavetrain.

summing the previous output pulses. When the signal sample is greater, the comparator delivers a positive pulse tending to increase the approximated signal. When the signal sample is smaller, the comparator delivers a negative pulse to reduce the approximate signal. The approximator thus does the best it can to track the signal by one unit step at a time. The sequence of plus and minus pulses constitutes the transmitted digital information. The receiver reconstructs the approximate signal wave by summing the pulses in a network identical with that used at the transmitter. The approximation can be improved indefinitely by increasing the sampling rate with a corresponding increase in transmission band-

[1] D. F. Hoth, The T1 Carrier System, *Bell Lab. Record,* vol. 40, pp. 358–363, November, 1962.

[2] H. Cravis and T. V. Crater, Engineering of T1 Carrier System Repeatered Lines, *Bell System Tech. J.,* vol. 42, pp. 431–486, March, 1963.

[3] F. de Jager, Delta Modulation: A Method of PCM Transmission Using the 1-unit Code, *Philips Res. Rept.,* vol. 7, pp. 442–466, 1952.

[4] H. Van de Weg, Quantizing Noise of a Single Integration Delta-Modulation System with an N-digit Code, *Philips Res. Rept.,* vol. 8, pp. 367–385, 1953.

[5] F. K. Bowers, What Use Is Delta Modulation to the Transmission Engineer?, *Trans. AIEE,* part 1, vol. 76, pp. 142–147, May, 1957.

width. The staircase alternations above and below the true signal are smoothed out by a low-pass filter in the receiver. Regenerative repeaters can be used in the line to hold the distortion to that caused by quantizing.

In a simple delta-modulation system the trade between bandwidth and signal-to-noise ratio follows a square law and is, therefore, like that obtained in FM and PPM. By using a more elaborate network than an integrator in the feedback path of the delta modulator, it is possible to obtain a power law higher than the square. The question of whether it is possible for DM to compete with PCM in the same bandwidth and still

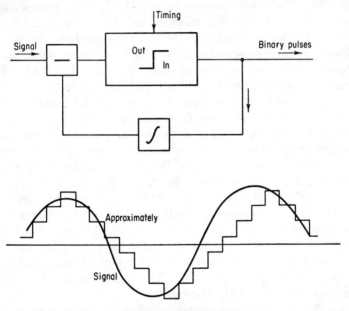

FIG. 6-3-9. Delta-modulation system.

retain the simplicity of the same decoding law for all pulses is a difficult one. The main advantages offered by DM are simple coders and decoders for single-channel systems. The simplicity is lost when channels are multiplexed because the past history has to be restored in each channel separately. Multiple-digit delta modulation, in which the comparator is replaced by an m-level quantizer, can be advantageous when the signal has predominant low-frequency components. Such a system is more properly designated as differential PCM since in effect it is the difference between successive samples which is quantized and since digit framing is required at the receiver as in PCM.

6-4. Compound Pulse-modulation Systems

The pulse trains produced by the various kinds of modulation described can in turn be used as signals in a second modulation process. Modulation systems can thus be cascaded in successive stages to form an unlimited number of compound types. Two-stage systems are common in radio transmission. Beginning with PAM, for example, we could use the PAM pulse train to modulate either the amplitude or the frequency of a radio-frequency carrier. The first case is called PAM-AM. It consists of a simple translation from the frequencies contained in the PAM wave to upper and lower sidebands on the carrier. The second case called PAM-FM has some interesting properties in its own right since it offers an exchange of added bandwidth for improved signal-to-noise ratio.

PAM-FM. The signal-to-noise ratio in PAM-FM systems has been analyzed in papers by Rauch,[1] Landon,[2] and by Feldman and Bennett.[3] More recently it has been rediscovered by various authors who have given it the less descriptive designation PFM which they apply indiscriminately to systems which in our notation are PAM-FM and PCM-FM. A block diagram for a time-division-multiplex PAM-FM system is shown in Fig. 6-4-1. Samples of the signals from the n channels are taken in sequence at the rate of f_r samples per second per channel. The samples are shaped by a network in the common path to produce pulses with bandwidth f_b and heights proportional to the values of the signals at the sampling instants. The shaped pulse train frequency-modulates an oscillator. The resulting FM wave is limited to a band of width B by a bandpass filter. The output of the bandpass filter constitutes the transmitted PAM-FM wave. The receiver selects the same band of frequencies and detects the instantaneous frequency of the resulting wave. The baseband output of the frequency detector is selected by a low-pass filter cutting off at f_b and connected successively to the inputs of individual low-pass filters for each of the n channels. The switching at the receiver is synchronous with that at the transmitter.

The analysis given in the references cited shows that the signal-to-noise ratio increases with the square of the bandwidth when the bandwidth is made sufficiently large. PAM-FM is thus capable of trading excess bandwidth for signal-to-noise ratio in a manner similar to ordinary FM and at the same time provides for time-division multiplexing of channels.

Other forms of pulse modulation can also be transmitted by either amplitude or frequency modulation of a carrier. The case of PPM-AM does not present new features of interest other than the doubling of the baseband width. PCM-AM is likewise a straightforward application of carrier methods, but related systems such as double-sideband suppressed carrier and vestigial sideband have some interesting characteristic

[1] L. L. Rauch, Fluctuation Noise in Pulse-Height Multiplex Radio Links, *Proc. IRE*, vol. 35, pp. 1192–1197, November, 1947.

[2] V. D. Landon, Theoretical Analysis of Various Systems of Multiplex Transmission, *RCA Rev.*, vol. 9, pp. 287–351, June, 1948, and pp. 438–482, September, 1948.

[3] C. B. Feldman and W. R. Bennett, Bandwidth and Transmission Performance, *Bell System Tech. J.*, vol. 28, pp. 490–595, July, 1949.

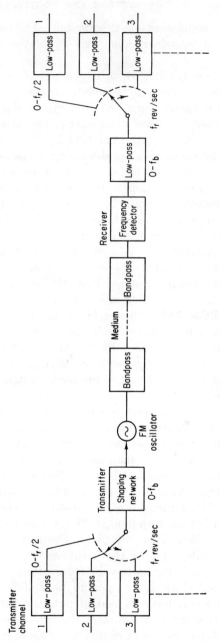

Fig. 6-4-1. PAM-FM system.

features when the modulating signal is digital. The cases of PPM-FM and PCM-FM also introduce some new properties worth a special treatment.

PPM-FM. In this system, which is also analyzed in the references cited, the pulse produces a change in radio frequency from f_1 to $f_1 + \beta$ and back again. The resultant signal-to-noise ratio contains two improvement factors obtained by excess bandwidth. The first one depends on the ratio of r-f bandwidth to pulse bandwidth. The second depends on the ratio of the pulse bandwidth to the total signal channel width. Each improvement ratio varies with the square of the appropriate bandwidth ratio when these ratios are large. In the limit the pulse bandwidth cancels and the signal-to-noise ratio becomes proportional to the square of the ratio of r-f bandwidth to signal bandwidth. In order to obtain these results, it is necessary to preserve two thresholds. First the radio-frequency carrier amplitude must be sufficiently above the r-f band noise peaks to keep the limiter from being broken by noise. Second the detected pulses must be sufficiently stronger than the accompanying noise to prevent the slicer from registering false pulses.

PCM-AM and PCM-FM. Since a PCM signal is digital, the quality of its transmission is properly evaluated in terms of error probabilities rather than signal-to-noise ratios. PCM-AM is equivalent to amplitude keying and PCM-FM to frequency-shift keying. These systems are discussed in detail in Chap. 7 and in the book on data transmission by Bennett and Davey.[1]

FDM-PCM. Compound modulation systems also exist in which a CW method precedes pulse modulation. We consider here one example, FDM-PCM, in which the composite wave from a group of channels multiplexed by frequency division is quantized and transmitted by pulse code modulation. Assume a single-sideband suppressed-carrier system with n channels of equal bandwidth f_s. The total bandwidth occupied by the baseband signal to be quantized is nf_s. The simplest case is that in which the baseband extends from zero to nf_s. The baseband can then be represented by samples taken at a rate $2nf_s$. The mean-square quantizing error $E_0{}^2/12$ is distributed over the n channels, and the mean-square noise accepted by each channel is $E_0{}^2/12n$. Here E_0 represents the quantizing interval, which is assumed to be uniform throughout the signal range. A nonsimultaneous load advantage is obtained in the case of speech channels because the peak of the composite signal does not increase as fast as the number of channels. This effect is illustrated in Fig. 6-4-2 which shows the variation of signal-to-noise ratio in each channel versus number of channels for seven-digit binary PCM.

Companding is not very effective in FDM-PCM when applied to the

[1] W. R. Bennett and J. R. Davey, "Data Transmission," McGraw-Hill Book Company, New York, 1965.

composite FDM signal. The reason for this is that strong signals in a few channels can dictate large quantizing steps which are very disadvantageous for simultaneously occurring weak signals in other channels. A small amount of companding giving an advantage of 3 db or less can

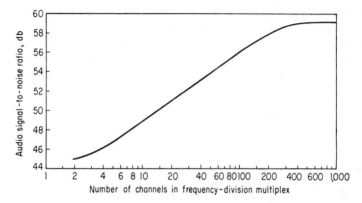

Fig. 6-4-2. Quantizing noise in each channel when seven-digit binary PCM is applied to an FDM group. (*From C. B. Feldman and W. R. Bennett, BSTJ, vol. 28, July, 1949, p. 499.*)

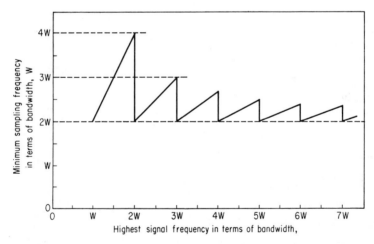

Fig. 6-4-3. Minimum sampling rate without overlap as a function of ratio of highest sampled frequency to bandwidth. (*From C. B. Feldman and W. R. Bennett, BSTJ, vol. 28, July, 1949, p. 594.*)

be justified by theory but would hardly be worth the additional complications in a practical system. Addition of another binary digit which reduces the rms quantizing error by a factor of 2 and hence secures a 6-db improvement in signal-to-noise ratio at the cost of a relatively small percentage increase in bandwidth, appears more attractive than instantaneous companding.   In the case of speech, it is possible to use syllabic companding in the individual channels to improve the signal-to-noise ratio at the cost of n slow-acting compandors.

If the bandwidth occupied by the FDM channels is elevated from zero frequency, it may still be possible to use a sampling rate $2nf_s$ without shifting the baseband frequency range downward.   Certain critical ranges exist in which the sidebands produced by sampling do not overlap the baseband.   Freedom from overlap occurs when the baseband is located between adjacent multiples of f_s.   The minimum sampling frequency for other cases is shown in Fig. 6-4-3 in terms of the bandwidth $W = nf_s$.

PART III

Seymour Stein

CHAPTER 7

BASIC BINARY COMMUNICATIONS TECHNIQUES

In Chap. 2, particularly Sec. 2-5, the transmission of digital information was considered from the viewpoint of general decision theory. Some specific examples were presented in the context of idealized situations, including ideal matched filtering, to illustrate the decision-theoretic limitations imposed by various assumptions on signal design and on knowledge of the possible received signals. It is also useful to develop these results from an engineering viewpoint, particularly as they can then be applied to the design and analysis of suboptimum systems.

In this and succeeding chapters, we shall discuss binary signaling from such an alternative "engineering" point of view. We shall define generic models for signaling and reception and establish for these models the basic dependences of error-rate performance upon signal design, noise level, and the reception process. In these models, matched filtering will then enter naturally as the optimized linear-system reception technique for minimizing error rate through maximizing the signal-noise ratio (as in Sec. 2-4). The fact is that matched filtering was originally noted on just this basis.

While minimizing the error rate is the criterion underlying maximum-likelihood receivers (decisions on the basis of highest posterior probability), our error-rate approach will be based on certain reception models. Hence the corresponding optimization is only with respect to these models. The maximum-likelihood approach is more general in that it *shows* that these *are* the optimum reception "structures." As it happens the results are the same: these optimum structures are not different from the basic models of our engineering intuition. It is often important to know that these matched-filter operations are optimum structures, so that their performance represents the best achievable. On the other hand, our engineering viewpoint will emphasize calculations for suboptimum systems and systems subject to effects not always included in present decision-theory models.

Before entering into these models, we shall briefly discuss some relevant aspects of the communication systems in which digital signaling appears.

7-1. Carrier Telegraphy

Telegraphy means the transmission of a message to a remote location. While this originally implied a language message, and also does not necessarily imply *electrical* transmission, the term has more loosely come to be used to mean electrical transmission of information encoded in binary form. Some semantic distinction is still made between telegraphy, as implying alphanumerics, and more general binary data communications. Digital data communication more generally also includes multiple-state, so-called M-ary (or N-ary, or P-ary) systems, which transmit more than one information bit per symbol.

Our basic consideration here will be of binary (two-state) communication signals. In simplest form, such a signal may utilize on-off (1 or 0), or bipolar ($+1$ or -1) voltage waveforms. Generalizing, the binary signal also can be visualized as a sequence of pulses, each of which has associated with it two possible voltages, the choices of successive voltages being determined by the information to be transmitted. Other possible techniques include modulation of pulse length. Also the pulses may be shaped, carrying the telegraph information as their peak values, for example.

Simple *carrier telegraphy* is the use of a telegraph waveform to modulate a sinusoidal carrier. The common forms of such modulation are AM, FM, and phase modulation. The AM form usually corresponds to 100 per cent modulation with a bipolar voltage waveform; the carrier is "keyed" on and off to describe the two telegraph states.[1] The system is referred to as amplitude keying (AK) or on-off keying (OOK). The FM form corresponds usually to bipolar modulation of the frequency of a carrier; the telegraph states are described by the sense of the frequency shift over the pulse. With rectangular modulation, the states are described by which of a pair of possible frequencies is transmitted. The system is commonly known as frequency-shift keying (FSK). Phase-shift keying (PSK) is the analog of phase modulation. Its simplest form, choice of a 0° or 180° phase shift on a carrier, has been increasingly used in recent years.

Simple carrier telegraphy involves perhaps the most readily analyzed of all radio signals. Fortunately, most of the more complex systems involve only simple generalizations of carrier telegraphy, such that either analytical results for the latter apply directly or useful qualitative extrapolations can often be made.

The extensions from simple carrier telegraphy arise when one considers the multiplexing, or simultaneous transmission, of a number of telegraph signals by use of a single radio carrier. Standardly two multiplexing

---

[1] In all these forms, nonrectangular modulation may be used to minimize spectral occupancy. Sinusoid shapes are often used for this purpose.

techniques are identified, known as frequency-division (FDM) and time-division (TDM) multiplexing, respectively.

Typically, time-division multiplexing utilizes sequenced sampling of each of the telegraph waveforms to be transmitted, at a uniform rate such that each waveform is sampled precisely once during each of its states (pulses). A composite telegraph waveform, with correspondingly shorter states, is then constructed from the sequence of samples (Fig. 7-1-1) and this composite telegraph waveform is then transmitted by a standard technique of carrier telegraphy. For example, suppose a typical telegraph waveform of the set to be multiplexed has pulses 20 msec long. Then time-division multiplexing of two, three, four, or six telegraph channels

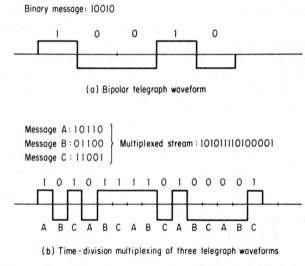

Binary message: 10010

(a) Bipolar telegraph waveform

Message A : 10110
Message B : 01100   } Multiplexed stream : 101011110100001
Message C : 11001

(b) Time-division multiplexing of three telegraph waveforms

Fig. 7-1-1. Time-division multiplexing of telegraph signals.

would result in a signal with pulses 10, 6.7, 5, or 3.3 msec long, respectively. Time-division multiplexing may also involve interleaving of blocks of bits from each component stream. For example, in TDM of several voice channels to be transmitted via PCM, one may sequence the analog-digital converter itself over the several voice channels, each sample obtained being converted to a several-bit PCM word.

In terms of results presented in this book, the analysis of performance (error rate) of any one channel in a time-division multiplex telegraph system is still just the problem of determining the probability of error for each pulse associated with that channel, and this problem is of course the same (except for the change in pulse parameters) as the analysis of a non-multiplexed telegraph signal transmitted by the same carrier-modulation technique.

The more common, older multiplexing technique is frequency-division multiplexing. In FDM, each of the telegraph waveforms is modulated in some standard fashion onto a different subcarrier, with the subcarriers (normally in the audio range) sufficiently spaced so that there is negligible overlap among the subbands occupied by the several signals.[1] The set of modulated carriers, each occupying a disjoint segment of the frequency band, is then added together to form a composite, so-called baseband signal. The latter is then modulated onto a radio carrier by some standard technique. At the receiving end, after the initial demodulation down to baseband, the individual modulated subcarriers are demultiplexed (separated out) by appropriate filtering, and subsequently demodulated individually. Frequency-division multiplexing is commonly employed in transmission of teleprinter information, typically with 12 to 24 telegraph channels multiplexed into a single voice-channel bandwidth (300–3300 cps). The voice channel in turn may be sent as part of a frequency-division multiplexed group of voice channels.

When used in h-f radio, where there is severe fading selectivity (Sec. 9-3), the FDM signal is usually transmitted by single-sideband AM rather than FM. Since the receiver is then linear down through the demultiplexing point, the analysis of performance (calculation of error rate) for each telegraph signal is again essentially that of a simple carrier telegraph signal. In contrast, when FM techniques are employed for the radio transmission, as is common in UHF carrier systems, the receiver is nonlinear and the carrier telegraph results can no longer be applied so readily.

In this description of multiplexing, it should be clear that TDM is simply a parallel-to-serial conversion of information. To some extent, certain M-ary systems can also be viewed as simply a parallel-to-serial conversion, but where the serial stream comprises M-ary rather than binary symbols. For example, if one is using 0 vs. 180° phase-shift keying for a binary stream, a second binary stream can be transmitted by modulating a carrier in quadrature, hence using the same carrier frequency but the 90 vs. 270° phase positions. If two such signals, of equal strength, are added together for transmission, the transmitted signal is simply a carrier whose phase appears to shift among the four phase positions 45°, 135°, −135°, and −45°. The two binary streams may be derived by two separate appropriate detections of the arriving signal, or by detection of the 45°, etc., positions followed by appropriate logic circuitry. It should also be apparent that an M-ary signal can be derived from a single serial message stream, by replacing a sequence of binary pulses by a single M-ary pulse. There has been some use, or suggestions of use, of M-ary signaling, with either multiple-phase PSK, multiple-tone FSK, or (closely related to the latter) the use of a set of orthogonal or biorthogonal waveforms as M-ary symbols. In this book, our dominant emphasis will be on binary signal-

---

[1] See also Sec. 4-7.

ing, with any significant discussion of M-ary techniques precluded by space limitations. The reader should find, however, that just as the decision-theoretic formulation is easily extended to M-ary signaling (Sec. 2-7), the literature on M-ary techniques is readily comprehended once one has a firm grasp on the binary problem.

7-2. Relation of Character or Code Performance to Binary Error Rate

In many binary transmissions, particularly those originating from teleprinter or PCM operation, individual binary symbols are used by the system only in groups or sequences. The same is true when error-control (error-correction or error-detection) codes are in use. As an example, automatic printer codes normally employ 5-bit characters to represent the full set of alphanumerics plus printer control instructions. Synchronization bits may be added, so that 7 bits per character is quite common. The relation between binary error rate and sequence error rate can be relatively simple when there is no statistical dependence between the occurrence of errors in different bits of a sequence and when all bits are equally significant in determining whether a sequence error occurs. In practical systems, this is often not the case. Errors may cluster due to some time-varying property of the channel such as radio fading; or a single synchronization bit error may produce many successive character errors. There is insufficient space here to enter into the wide variety of such problems. They are in any case hardly as amenable to theoretical analysis as are the binary error probabilities, and in many cases, resort must be made to extensive test results and empirical models.[1]

In effect, we shall concentrate in this book on the characterization of the binary communication link only, considering the error-rate in the individual binary decisions. Each individual application (as in the teleprinter case) can in turn be described in terms of the digital error rate allowable for satisfactory overall operation in that application. For example, typical acceptable character error rates for teleprinter operation are of the order of 5×10^{-3} (average of five characters in error per thousand). The corresponding binary error rates are of the order of 10^{-3}. In other applications (transmission of computer data, for example), binary error-rate requirements may be of the order of 10^{-5} to 10^{-10}. At the other extreme, in transmission of voice by PCM or deltamodulation techniques, sufficient intelligibility for, say, a tactical military application may still be possible with binary error rates of 0.1 or even higher, although high-quality voice communication may still require error rates of the order of 10^{-5}.

The problem of character or sequence synchronization was raised.

---

[1] The interested reader will find some discussion and references in W. R. Bennett and J. R. Davey, "Data Transmission," McGraw-Hill Book Company, New York, 1965.

Often, such synchronizing information is simply an additional bit, or a particular sequence, inserted regularly, as mentioned.   As the electronic art advances, fully synchronous systems tend to become feasible, in which the transmitter and receiver can be timed by extremely stable clocks, which are only very occasionally synchronized or are synchronized from sources other than the communications transmission.   Nevertheless, in radio propagation when fading or multipath media are involved, the path delay may be subject to changes which can best be monitored by regular transmittal of synchronizing pulses, or pulses from which synchronization data can be inferred.

In addition to sequence synchronization, there is the problem of "bit synchronization," of establishing a timing chain in the receiver relative to the start of successive individual pulses as received.   It is very important in this connection to note that a large portion of the theoretical analysis in communications, such as the decision-theoretic analysis of Chap. 2, as well as much of the analysis in this chapter and those following, is based upon the assumption of perfect bit synchronization.   For example, the matched-filter conception (but almost all other analyses as well) assumes perfect knowledge of the time of arrival of the individual symbol waveforms.   Techniques for achieving and maintaining synchronization are an important part of the communications art.   However, it appears to be a practical truism that synchronization per se can be maintained well under conditions where the channel is already useless as a communications link because of high error rates.   Hence, except where particularly specified otherwise, we also shall assume perfect synchronization in the receiving process.

7-3. Representations of Bandpass Signals, Noise, and Filtering

The object of this chapter is to introduce the physical and mathematical models of carrier telegraph signaling.   To some extent, this chapter will cover ground already covered in Chaps. 1 and 2, but with the analysis developed from an engineering operational point of view.   Thus, the earlier results for on-off keying are repeated here for completeness, placing them in a common framework with additional important results for non-coherent FSK and differential PSK.   The reader will note, for example, that as distinct from certain "effective signal-noise ratios" conveniently defined in Chap. 2, the SNR here will always be defined with a common operational interpretation.   In addition, this common framework will be used as the basis for the extended results of later chapters.

In these results, we shall always be assuming narrow-bandpass signals and corresponding filtering of the signals and noise.   For convenience, this section summarizes a number of useful definitions and results contained or simply implied in Secs. 1-6 and 1-7.

Representation of Narrowband Signal.

$$s(t) = \text{Re} \left[u(t) \exp (j\omega_0 t) \right] \qquad (7\text{-}3\text{-}1)$$

where ω_0 = nominal carrier radian frequency

$u(t)$ = complex envelope, or modulation component, with bandwidth $\ll \omega_0/2\pi$

$|u(t)|$ = signal envelope $\qquad (7\text{-}3\text{-}2a)$

$\arg u(t)$ = signal r-f phase $\qquad (7\text{-}3\text{-}2b)$

Representation of Narrowband Bandpass Filter.

Filter impulse response:

$$k(t) = \int_{-\infty}^{\infty} \exp (j\omega t) K(\omega) \, df \qquad (7\text{-}3\text{-}3a)$$

Filter transfer function:

$$K(\omega) = \int_{-\infty}^{\infty} \exp (-j\omega t) k(t) \, dt \qquad (7\text{-}3\text{-}3b)$$

$K(\omega)$ is two-sided, centered at $+\omega_0$ and $-\omega_0$.

Physically realizable filter:

$$k(t) = \begin{cases} 0 & t < 0 \\ \text{real} & t > 0 \end{cases} \qquad (7\text{-}3\text{-}4a)$$

$$K^*(-\omega) = K(\omega) \qquad (7\text{-}3\text{-}4b)$$

Representation in terms of "equivalent low-pass filter":

$$H(\omega) = \begin{cases} K(\omega + \omega_0) & \omega > -\omega_0 \\ 0 & \omega < -\omega_0 \end{cases} \qquad (7\text{-}3\text{-}5a)$$

Narrowband: $\qquad H(\omega) = 0 \qquad$ except when $\left| \dfrac{\omega}{\omega_0} \right| \ll 1 \qquad (7\text{-}3\text{-}5b)$

$$h(t) = \int_{-\infty}^{\infty} \exp (j\omega t) H(\omega) \, df \qquad (7\text{-}3\text{-}5c)$$

$$k(t) = 2 \, \text{Re} \left[h(t) \exp (j\omega_0 t) \right] \qquad (7\text{-}3\text{-}5d)$$

Note $h(t)$ is not necessarily real; it is real only if filter response is properly symmetric about ω_0.

Bandpass Filtering of Narrowband Signal.

Response of filter represented by $k(t)$ to signal represented by $s(t)$ is

$$q(t) = \int_{-\infty}^{\infty} k(t - \tau) s(\tau) \, d\tau = \text{Re} \left[v(t) \exp (j\omega_0 t) \right] \qquad (7\text{-}3\text{-}6a)$$

where $\qquad v(t) = \int_{-\infty}^{\infty} h(t - \tau) u(\tau) \, d\tau \qquad (7\text{-}3\text{-}6b)$

Note that if interest is in a single value, say some instant of time t_0, the form

$$v(t_0) = \int_{-\infty}^{\infty} h(t_0 - \tau) u(\tau) \, d\tau \qquad (7\text{-}3\text{-}7a)$$

is mathematically indistinguishable from any more general expression of the form

$$v(t_0) = \int_{-\infty}^{\infty} c(\tau, t_0) z(\tau) \, d\tau \qquad (7\text{-}3\text{-}7b)$$

The latter formally includes cross-correlation, the operation implied in many matched-filter systems. In the sense of (7-3-7), one can assert that filtering and cross-correlation are mathematically equivalent operations; there exists an equivalent (not necessarily physically realizable) filter corresponding to any cross-correlation. Without further ado, our later discussions in terms of bandpass filtering can be regarded to apply to cross-correlation systems as well.

Corresponding to (7-3-6b) is the useful transform relation

$$V(\omega) = H(\omega)U(\omega) \tag{7-3-8}$$

so that the effect of filtering on the modulation components of the signal is described directly in terms of the equivalent low-pass filter.

Representation of Narrowband Bandpass Noise.

$$n(t) = \text{Re}\ [z(t) \exp\ (j\omega_0 t)] \tag{7-3-9a}$$
$$z(t) = x(t) + jy(t) \tag{7-3-9b}$$

For (wide-sense) stationary Gaussian noise, the quadrature components $x(t)$ and $y(t)$ are distributed as a bivariate zero-mean Gaussian process,[1]

$$\langle x(t) \rangle = \langle y(t) \rangle = 0 \tag{7-3-10a}$$
$$\langle x(t)x(t + \tau) \rangle = \langle y(t)y(t + \tau) \rangle = R_c(\tau) \tag{7-3-10b}$$
$$\langle x(t)y(t + \tau) \rangle = -\langle x(t + \tau)y(t) \rangle = R_s(\tau) \tag{7-3-10c}$$
$$R_c(-\tau) = R_c(\tau) \tag{7-3-10d}$$
$$R_s(-\tau) = -R_s(\tau) \tag{7-3-10e}$$
$$\langle z(t) \rangle = 0 \tag{7-3-11a}$$
$$\tfrac{1}{2}\langle z^*(t)z(t + \tau) \rangle = R(\tau) = R_c(\tau) + jR_s(\tau) \tag{7-3-11b}$$
$$\tfrac{1}{2}\langle z(t)z(t + \tau) \rangle = 0 \tag{7-3-11c}$$
$$\langle n(t)n(t + \tau) \rangle = R_n(\tau) = \text{Re}\ [R(\tau) \exp\ (j\omega_0 \tau)] \tag{7-3-12}$$

One may also define cross-covariances for complex envelopes in complete analogy to (7-3-11).

Power Density Spectra and Filtering of Narrowband Bandpass Noise.

$$G_n(f) = \int_{-\infty}^{\infty} R_n(\tau) \exp\ (-j\omega\tau)\ d\tau \tag{7-3-13a}$$

$$G(f) = \int_{-\infty}^{\infty} R(\tau) \exp\ (-j\omega\tau)\ d\tau \tag{7-3-13b}$$

$$G_n(f) = \frac{G(f - f_0)}{2} + \frac{G(f + f_0)}{2} \tag{7-3-13c}$$

For bandpass filtering by a filter with equivalent low-pass transfer function $H(f)$, the input and output noise complex envelopes are related by

$$z_{\text{out}}(t) = \int_{-\infty}^{\infty} h(t - \tau)z_{\text{in}}(\tau)\ d\tau \tag{7-3-14}$$
$$G_{\text{out}}(f) = |H(\omega)|^2 G_{\text{in}}(f) \tag{7-3-15}$$

A special result based on (7-3-13c) and (7-3-15) and often useful in analysis is the following: Often one can regard the input noise (prior to receiver filtering) as spectrally flat over the bandwidth of any subsequent filtering. That is, in (7-3-15), $G_{\text{in}}(f)$ has a constant value n_0 over all the spectral band over which $|H(\omega)|^2$ is non-vanishing. It is then often convenient mathematically, in expressions like (7-3-15), to regard $G_{\text{in}}(f)$ as having infinite width with the same constant value n_0. While this is inconsistent with the original spectral definitions of $G_{\text{in}}(f)$, it clearly leads to no mathematical inconsistencies so long as a narrowband filtering operation is involved, as in (7-3-15). This is the sense in which such a "white-noise" input approximation is made in most bandpass analyses in the literature. It is also obvious

[1] Here, and throughout Chaps. 7 to 11, the angle brackets denote an ensemble average.

from (7-3-13c) that the value n_0 for the power density spectrum of $G_{in}(f)$ is to be taken as twice the value in the positive side of the defined two-sided spectrum of the physical, bandpass input process. Equivalently, if the physical process is redefined to have a one-sided spectrum, n_0 is the value over this one-sided spectrum (the equivalent low-pass spectrum $G_{in}(f)$ is still two-sided).

Finally, we shall often speak of an *instantaneous* signal-noise ratio, in processes where both the signal terms and noise terms are actually time-varying. By the instantaneous power in a bandpass voltage, we shall always mean *no more nor less* than half the square of the instantaneous value of the envelope. For example, the signal described in (7-3-1) and (7-3-2) has instantaneous power

$$P_s = \tfrac{1}{2}|u(t)|^2 \tag{7-3-16}$$

Similarly, using the description of a noise process in (7-3-9) and those following, the instantaneous power in a particular realization of the noise process (a particular member of the ensemble) is

$$P_N = \tfrac{1}{2}|z(t)|^2$$

and the mean noise power (averaged over the ensemble of realizations) is

$$N = \langle P_N \rangle = \tfrac{1}{2}\langle |z(t)|^2 \rangle = R(0) = R_c(0) \tag{7-3-17}$$

7-4. On-off Keying

While on-off keying is no longer widely used in communications, for reasons which will be discussed later, it is a useful model for introducing

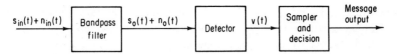

FIG. 7-4-1. Generic form of simple binary receiver.

certain concepts. An on-off-keyed radio system can be described as transmitting pulses[1]

$$s_T(t) = \begin{cases} u_T(t) \cos(\omega_0 t + \phi_T) & \text{for Mark} \\ 0 & \text{for Space} \end{cases} \tag{7-4-1}$$

where $u_T(t)$ is some low-pass pulse waveform, often, but not necessarily, a rectangular pulse. We shall assume at this point that the medium introduces no distortions on the signal waveform. In our model of the receiver (Fig. 7-4-1), the signal is contaminated at the receiver input with additive Gaussian noise, originating either as pickup by the antenna (antenna noise) or as receiver thermal noise in the first amplifiers or mixer stages. The combined waveform is then translated to some convenient frequency and filtered. Frequency translations are assumed not to

---

[1] The simple keyed tones which will be the basis for discussions in Secs. 7-4 to 7-6 are essentially those used in practice. A discussion of more general waveforms is given in Sec. 7-7. The terms Mark and Space are used here and later as convenient descriptors of the pair of binary states.

affect the relative levels or waveforms of signal or noise and hence are not included in our analytical model. For this and the two subsequent sections, we shall not comment on the details of the filtering action. We shall assume all filters to be bandpass, attempting to limit the band of the noise to that band needed for appropriate processing of the signaling waveform. After examining detection results in a number of cases, we shall return in Sec. 7-7 to discuss the implications of filter parameters.

At the output of the receiver filter, the signal term has the form

$$s(t) = \begin{cases} u(t) \cos \omega_0 t & \text{Mark being received} \\ 0 & \text{Space being received} \end{cases} \qquad (7\text{-}4\text{-}2)$$

The reader will readily verify that there is no loss of generality in the arbitrary choice of phase reference implied in (7-4-2). The noise term, from (7-3-9), will have the form

$$n(t) = x(t) \cos \omega_0 t - y(t) \sin \omega_0 t \qquad (7\text{-}4\text{-}3)$$

Considering for the moment only the case of a Mark signaled, the filter output will be a superposition of the signal and noise terms

$$e(t) = s(t) + n(t) = [u(t) + x(t)] \cos \omega_0 t - y(t) \sin \omega_0 t \qquad (7\text{-}4\text{-}4)$$

This signal is now applied to a detector and decision circuit, the object of which is to determine whether a Mark is present or a Space. The receiver is assumed to know the timing of the succession of binary waveforms (i.e., perfect synchronization is maintained). It is also assumed that the binary decisions are made on the basis of *sampling* the detector output at some appropriate *instant*, once per information pulse. The sampled voltage will, for example, determine the setting of a printer relay or some equivalent operation. The detectors themselves, as will be noted later, are all essentially zero-memory devices.[1] All integration, smoothing, etc., is accomplished as part of the *predetection filtering;* and there is *no postdetection* filtering in this model. There are communication systems which employ smoothing of the information–bearing voltages after the detection process. But in general rigorous or even dependable analyses do not appear to exist for binary error-rate performance of such systems.

The most common method for detection of on-off radiotelegraph signals is noncoherent detection, involving measurement of the amplitude of the *envelope* of the bandpass filter output. Coherent detection methods also can be employed in principle. However, as noted later, once coherent detection techniques are admitted, one can easily achieve higher performance by other than on-off keying techniques. Both forms of detection

---

[1] The device output is the instantaneous value of the desired quantity, rather than a smoothing over recent values. While the actual detector implementation may include filters to remove undesired components generated by the basic nonlinear process, these are merely part of the realization of the desired "zero-memory detector."

will be considered below (note also the related discussions in Chaps. 1 and 2).

Noncoherent Detection. From (7-4-4), the instantaneous envelope of the bandpass filter output is given by

$$r(t) = \sqrt{[u(t) + x(t)]^2 + y^2(t)} \qquad (7\text{-}4\text{-}5)$$

Recalling the Gaussian nature of $x(t)$ and $y(t)$ and the formulas in Sec. 1-4, the probability density function for this instantaneous value of the envelope is given by

$$p(r) = \frac{r}{N} \exp\left(-\frac{r^2 + u^2}{2N}\right) I_0\left(\frac{ru}{N}\right) \qquad (7\text{-}4\text{-}6)$$

where u is the signal envelope and N is the (ensemble) mean-square value (mean power) of the output noise *at that instant.*

The statement that the envelope will be sampled once per pulse to determine whether the pulse was Mark or Space implies a number of assumptions for ideal operation. One already stated is that "synchronous" timing is available at the receiver. Thus we assume an accurate knowledge of the interval occupied by each received information pulse and hence of appropriate timings for the successive envelope samplings and binary decisions. Secondly, the envelope value involved in each sample is assumed to include only the voltages associated with a single information pulse plus noise. We thus ignore at this time the possibility of intersymbol interference, in which the binary decisions may be confused by residual voltages in the filter output remaining from previous pulse inputs. In part, this implies practically that the information pulses are of finite length. Thus, for a Mark starting at time $t = 0$, $u(t)$ is such that $u(t) = 0$ both for $t < 0$ and for $t > T$, where T is the spacing between successive pulse starts. If the sampling instant occurs at $T_S(T_S < T)$ following the start of each pulse, the further implication is that the filter has, over an interval of length T_S, completely discharged all currents or voltages remaining from the previous pulses. This problem is discussed in greater detail in Sec. 7-7. However, it is useful to introduce some preliminary remarks here. Based on the discussion above, if a passive filter is in use, its rise time (and decay time) ideally must be shorter than T_S. For a simple one-pole (RLC) filter, for example, if rise time is interpreted in terms of the 10 to 90% points on the envelope of the filter response, the 3-db bandwidth will have to exceed $0.7/T_S$.

An alternative approach for avoiding intersymbol interference involves rapid discharging of the filter, by auxiliary circuitry, at the end of each pulse. The resulting circuit is no longer truly a "continuous linear filter," even though the filter acts in an "ordinary" manner *between* discharge intervals. However, for such a regularly discharged filter, the filter bandwidth is no longer critical as far as intersymbol interference is concerned and can be as narrow a bandwidth as desired.   Indeed, if one goes to the limit of extremely narrow bandwidths, the result is an ideal integrating bandpass filter whose impulse response is a step function.   The effect of discharge every T sec is to convert the effective impulse response to a rectangle of duration T.   Such an "integrate-and-dump" filter, as it is often termed, is then a proper matched filter for optimal reception of constant amplitude pulses of length T, and indeed is the one outstanding instance where matched-filter detection has been routinely achieved in applications (see also Sec. 7-7).

Returning to (7-4-5) and (7-4-6), it is intuitively clear that for the on-off signal, the Mark-Space decision can only be based on comparing $r(t)$ at the sampling instant against some threshold.   This was also shown in Chap. 2 to be the theoretically optimum decision procedure when signal phase is not known.   The optimum threshold level was also derived.   The latter result will be rederived below, based directly on the "practical" approach of minimizing the probability of error.

Specifically, let b denote the threshold level.   Then when at a sampling instant $r(t) \geq b$, the decision is Mark; and when $r(t) < b$, the decision is Space.   Then using (7-4-6), for a Mark transmitted, the probability of an error is

$$
\begin{aligned}
P_{eM} = \text{Prob } (r < b) &= \int_0^b p(r)\, dr = 1 - \int_b^\infty p(r)\, dr \\
&= 1 - \int_b^\infty \frac{r}{N} \exp\left(-\frac{r^2 + u^2}{2N}\right) I_0\left(\frac{ru}{N}\right) dr \\
&= 1 - Q(\sqrt{2\gamma}, b_0) \qquad\qquad (7\text{-}4\text{-}7)
\end{aligned}
$$

where
$$
b_0 = \frac{b}{\sqrt{N}} \qquad\qquad (7\text{-}4\text{-}8)
$$

is the threshold level normalized to the rms noise;

$$
\gamma = \frac{u^2}{2N} \qquad\qquad (7\text{-}4\text{-}9)
$$

is the signal-noise ratio (SNR) in the filter output at the sampling instant; and $Q(a,b)$ is the Q function introduced in Chap. 1 (see also Appendix A),

$$
Q(a,b) = \int_b^\infty \exp\left(-\frac{a^2 + x^2}{2}\right) I_0(ax)x\, dx \qquad\qquad (7\text{-}4\text{-}10)
$$

Assuming no intersymbol interference, $u = 0$ when a Space is transmitted (no signal).   In this case, an error occurs if $r > b$, that is,

$$
\begin{aligned}
P_{eS} = \int_b^\infty \frac{r}{N} \exp\left(-\frac{r^2}{2N}\right) dr &= Q(0,b_0) \\
&= \exp\left(-\frac{b_0^2}{2}\right) \qquad\qquad (7\text{-}4\text{-}11)
\end{aligned}
$$

Assuming further that Marks and Spaces occur with equal frequency (each with probability $\frac{1}{2}$), the average probability of an error is

$$P_e = \tfrac{1}{2}P_{eM} + \tfrac{1}{2}P_{eS} = \tfrac{1}{2}[1 - Q(\sqrt{2\gamma}, b_0)] + \tfrac{1}{2}\exp\left(-\frac{b_0{}^2}{2}\right) \quad (7\text{-}4\text{-}12)$$

A general plot of this formula for probability of error (or synonymously, in the large-sample sense, the *error rate*) versus SNR is shown in Fig. 7-4-2 for various threshold levels.

It is clear from Fig. 7-4-2 that at each SNR there is a threshold level which would produce minimum error rate; the larger the SNR, the larger

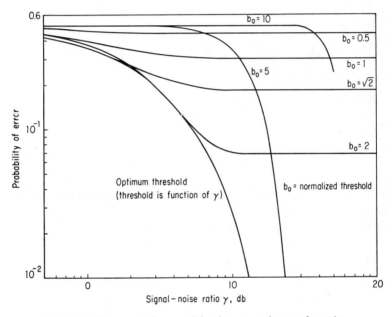

FIG. 7-4-2. Error rate for on-off keying, noncoherent detection.

the optimum threshold. Analytically, one can find for each SNR the value of b_0 which minimizes the error rate by setting $\partial P_e / \partial b_0 = 0$. Using (7-4-12), this leads readily to the transcendental equation

$$\exp(-\gamma)I_0(b_0\sqrt{2\gamma}) = 1 \quad (7\text{-}4\text{-}13)$$

which is the same equation derived in Sec. 2-1. As there noted, the optimum b_0 ranges monotonically from a value of $\sqrt{2}$ for very small γ ($\gamma \ll 1$) to the asymptotic dependence $\sqrt{\gamma/2}$ (for the nonnormalized threshold, $b \to u/2$ as $\gamma \to \infty$. The relation

$$b_0 = \sqrt{2 + \frac{\gamma}{2}} \quad (7\text{-}4\text{-}14)$$

is an excellent analytic approximation to the solution of (7-4-13). Both

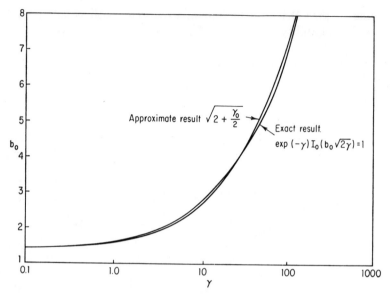

FIG. 7-4-3. Optimum threshold versus SNR for noncoherent detection of on-off keying.

the exact solution of (7-4-13) for b_0 versus γ, and the approximation of (7-4-14) are shown in Fig. 7-4-3. The error rate (minimum achievable for noncoherent detection of OOK) when the optimum threshold is used at each SNR is shown as the lowest curve in Fig. 7-4-2.

We also note some useful asymptotic forms for high SNR. For a, b large we have (see Appendix A)

$$Q(a,b) \approx 1 - \frac{1}{2}\,\mathrm{erfc}\left(\frac{a-b}{\sqrt{2}}\right) \qquad (7\text{-}4\text{-}15)$$

Then the error rate in (7-4-12) is well approximated by

$$P_e \approx \frac{1}{2}\left[\frac{1}{2}\,\mathrm{erfc}\left(\sqrt{\gamma} - \frac{b_0}{\sqrt{2}}\right) + \exp\left(-\frac{b_0{}^2}{2}\right)\right] \qquad (7\text{-}4\text{-}16)$$

With optimum threshold at high SNR, $b_0 = \sqrt{\gamma/2}$, and with the asymptotic form for the complementary error function

$$x \to \infty \qquad \mathrm{erfc}\,x \approx \frac{\exp(-x^2)}{x\sqrt{\pi}} \qquad (7\text{-}4\text{-}17)$$

$$P_e \approx \frac{1}{2}\exp\left(-\frac{\gamma}{4}\right)\left(1 + \frac{2}{\sqrt{\pi\gamma}}\right) \to \frac{1}{2}\exp\left(-\frac{\gamma}{4}\right) \qquad (7\text{-}4\text{-}18)$$

Note the implication of this last result. In an on-off system with noncoherent detection, with optimized threshold, the error rate for steady signaling in additive Gaussian noise decreases exponentially with SNR, at error rates of practical interest. Furthermore, at optimum threshold, note that the errors occur predominantly because of noise alone exceeding the threshold rather than signal plus noise failing to exceed threshold.

Coherent Detection.   In ideal coherent detection, one assumes that there is available in the receiver an exact replica of the possible arriving signal, exact even to the timing of r-f phase.   The receiver then in effect cross-correlates this replica against the sum of the received signal and the additive noise.   (The specific question of deriving such a replica for use in the receiver is deferred to Sec. 7-6, where it is discussed within the more important application context of phase-shift keying.)

In general, for any bandpass signal, there is another signal whose complex envelope has a Fourier transform (spectrum) shifted by 90° in all components.   This signal is orthogonal to the first.   Additive Gaussian noise occupying the same band as either of these signals can be considered to have its energy equally divided between these orthogonal components. Then coherent detection of a signal can be viewed as the extraction of this signal from a background of noise and interference, along with whatever portion of the background is "in phase" with the desired signal, while rejecting that part in "phase quadrature."   It is the latter rejection operation which tends to diminish the perturbations which can be caused by a given amount of noise energy in the band of the signal and which produces the advantages over noncoherent reception.   However, as already noted in Chap. 2 and as will also be seen later in Sec. 7-6, the fullest advantage of coherent detection is obtained in binary transmission by taking advantage of the presumed knowledge of signal phase to encode the binary information as the phase of a single *continuous* waveform (as in phase-shift keying).

As has been noted several times in previous chapters, coherent or synchronous detection is equivalent to bandpass filtering of the received signal and noise followed by a multiplier–low-pass filter operation.   Thus, with the signal plus noise at the bandpass filter output described again as in (7-4-4),

$$e(t) = [u(t) + x(t)] \cos \omega_0 t - y(t) \sin \omega_0 t \qquad (7\text{-}4\text{-}19)$$

the multiplication operation corresponds to multiplying by $\cos \omega_0 t$.   (The reference signal is then ideally in phase with the signal component.)   The subsequent low-pass filtering removes the double-frequency components but passes the zero-frequency terms.

The net result (ignoring a factor of $\frac{1}{2}$ which can be lumped into receiver gain constants) is a detector output

$$v(t) = u(t) + x(t) \qquad (7\text{-}4\text{-}20)$$

Since $x(t)$ is zero-mean Gaussian with $\langle x^2 \rangle = N$, where N is the *total* mean noise power in the bandpass filter output, $v(t)$ is simply a biased Gaussian variable, with mean value u and variance N.

The problem of distinguishing between Mark and Space (for Space,

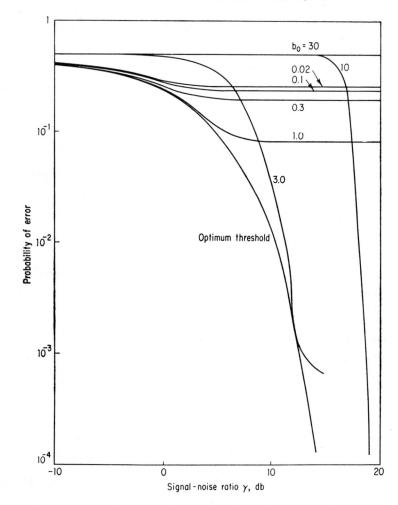

Fig. 7-4-4. Error rate for on-off keying, coherent detection.

$u = 0$) is then essentially that treated in the example of Sec. 2-5. For equal frequency of Marks and Spaces, and setting a normalized threshold as in (7-4-8), $b_0 = b/\sqrt{N}$, such that the decision is Mark if $v \geq b$ and Space if $v < b$, the probability of error is

$$P_e = \frac{1}{2}\left[1 - \frac{1}{2}\operatorname{erfc}\left(\frac{b_0}{\sqrt{2}} - \sqrt{\gamma}\right)\right] + \frac{1}{2}\left(\frac{1}{2}\operatorname{erfc}\frac{b_0}{\sqrt{2}}\right) \quad (7\text{-}4\text{-}21)$$

Since
$$\operatorname{erfc}(-x) = 2 - \operatorname{erfc}(x) \quad (7\text{-}4\text{-}22)$$

the error rate can be rewritten as

$$P_e = \frac{1}{2}\left[\frac{1}{2}\operatorname{erfc}\left(\sqrt{\gamma} - \frac{b_0}{\sqrt{2}}\right) + \frac{1}{2}\operatorname{erfc}\frac{b_0}{\sqrt{2}}\right] \quad (7\text{-}4\text{-}23)$$

It is apparent from the symmetry of the problem in this simple case (or is easily proved) that the optimum threshold is given by

$$b_0 = \sqrt{\frac{\gamma}{2}} \qquad b = \frac{u}{2} \qquad (7\text{-}4\text{-}24)$$

Then with threshold optimized at each SNR, the probability of error is just

$$P_e = \frac{1}{2} \operatorname{erfc} \frac{\sqrt{\gamma}}{2} \qquad (7\text{-}4\text{-}25)$$

This is shown plotted against SNR in Fig. 7-4-4, along with plots of (7-4-23) versus SNR for various fixed nonoptimized thresholds.

At the optimum threshold in this coherent-detection case, the probability of error is identical for Marks and Spaces transmitted. (As discussed earlier, this is not the case in envelope detection.)

At high SNR, recall the asymptotic form of (7-4-17). Then for b_0 large,

$$\operatorname{erfc} \frac{b_0}{\sqrt{2}} \approx \frac{\exp(-b_0^2/2)}{b_0 \sqrt{\pi/2}} \qquad (7\text{-}4\text{-}26)$$

Comparing (7-4-23) with (7-4-16) at high values of γ (where the exponentials dominate) there is no significant difference between envelope and coherent detection at the same threshold setting, whether optimized or not. Such blurring of the performance difference between noncoherent and coherent detection is observed quite generally whenever high SNR and/or high thresholds are involved.

7-5. Frequency-shift Keying (FSK)

As will be observed later (Sec. 9-5), on-off keying is particularly susceptible to signal fading. This early led communications engineers to search for signaling techniques which would be less affected by fading. An obvious answer was also available in the form of the amplitude-insensitive *frequency modulation* techniques (assuming, implicitly, operation above the FM threshold). Thus, frequency-shift keying was originally based on the simple concept of using a telegraph signal to frequency-modulate a carrier, with such frequency deviation (or modulation index) as appeared to give a useful FM improvement in SNR. Within the usual FM practice, the overall bandwidths so chosen would tend to be several times the telegraph signal (modulation) bandwidth; the receiving system would be the usual FM limiter-discriminator.

However, the instantaneous frequency actually shifts quite rapidly (the rapidity depending on transmitter bandwidth) between just two frequencies, one representing transmission of Mark and the other, Space. For wide deviations, it becomes apparent that two filters, one centered on the Mark frequency and one on the Space frequency, may provide a less noisy discrimination than the "conventional" linear discriminator. Likewise, from the more recent statistical decision-theory viewpoint (Sec. 2-5), the optimum detector for an FSK signal involves a pair of cross-correlators which, for particular signal classes, can be replaced by realizable matched filters. For both reasons, the two-filter receiver model is the one more commonly encountered in communications applications and is the one we shall emphasize in most of our discussions. The reader is referred to Sec. 8.5 for a discussion of the ideal frequency detector in FSK reception.

Also, while we shall emphasize frequency shifting, it is worthwhile noting that most of the related analyses (the discussion in Sec. 8-5 of ideal frequency detectors being one exception) apply equally well to the general problem of reception of binary transmissions employing a pair of at least partially distinguishable waveforms to denote the two message states. One can visualize in the matched-filter case, for example, that the detection operation takes place *after* a bandpass matched filter or cross-correlator. The bandpass signal applied to the detector can then be thought of again as basically sinusoidal (see also Sec. 7-7).

As in the on-off case, either noncoherent or coherent detection of FSK is possible. While we shall point out below the results for both cases, coherent detection of FSK signals is not often encountered in practice. The simple reason, mentioned earlier, is that it is usually just as easy and more profitable to operate a coherent system with phase-shift keying on a single tone (see Sec. 7-6) rather than using two tones.

The simplest FSK radio system is one with rectangular frequency modulation and constant amplitude. This can be described as ideally transmitting signal pulses of the form

$$s(t) = \begin{cases} A \cos \omega_M t & \text{for Mark} \\ A \cos \omega_S t & \text{for Space} \end{cases} \quad 0 < t < T \qquad (7\text{-}5\text{-}1)$$

where A is a constant and ω_M or ω_S is constant over any single information pulse. Conventionally, this is generated by a reactance-tube modulator or equivalent FM device. While we shall primarily discuss "rectangular" tone pulses as defined by (7-5-1), in some systems there is an emphasis on optimum design of the signal so as to minimize spectral tails. In this case, the modulating telegraph waveform (instantaneous frequency of the transmitted carrier) is not a rectangular wave with sharp transitions between bipolar levels but rather one in which cosinusoidal or other conveniently shaped transitions are made.[1] As noted later, if such a signal is detected by a dual-filter pair, such as discussed below, the analysis of performance follows also from the results below, limited only by one's ability to calculate the effects of the bandpass filters upon the FM signal. The alternative method for generating FSK is the selective "gating" of

[1] See, e.g., W. Lyons, Design Considerations for FSK Circuits, *IRE Nat. Conv. Record*, pt. 8, pp. 70–73, 1954.

one of a pair of appropriate oscillators. (This system, with the oscillators stable, would have to be employed for a coherent detection system to be possible, as noted later.) In either case, the transmitter bandwidth is usually wide enough so that the carrier amplitude remains effectively a constant, although even this is not in principle necessary.

In this section, we shall discuss only the simplest examples of the use of a pair of filters for reception, with both noncoherent and coherent detection. In a two-filter system, filters designed to be centered on one tone may partially respond to pulses of the other tone. In addition to such *crosstalk* on the signaling tones, any spectral overlap of the filters will produce some correlation between the portions of front-end noise passed by the two filters, the degree of correlation depending on the degree of overlap. In matched-filter systems, there is an equivalent problem if the pair of transmission waveforms (and hence filter response functions) are nonorthogonal. In the present section, by way of introduction, we shall only consider the important special case in which there is no crosstalk or overlap, and defer to the analysis of Chap. 8 a discussion of such disturbing effects, along with other interference problems.

Noncoherent FSK. In noncoherent detection of FSK using a pair of bandpass filters, one filter is tuned to "peak up" on Marks, the other is tuned to Spaces. The two filter outputs are envelope-detected and sampled once per information pulse, and the Mark-Space decision is made according to whichever detected output is the larger. As stated above, our assumption in this section will be that both signals and filtering are ideal (no crosstalk, etc.). Hence the representations of Sec. 7-3 describe the filter outputs in terms of their inputs. In particular, let N be the mean noise power in the filter output at the instant of sampling, assumed the same for both filters, and let u be the signal level at the same instant in the filter containing the signaled tone (the other containing zero signal component). Then, as previously, the probability density function (pdf) for the envelope r_1 at the output of the filter containing the signal is given by

$$p(r_1) = \frac{r_1}{N} \exp\left(-\frac{r_1{}^2 + u^2}{2N}\right) I_0\left(\frac{r_1 u}{N}\right) \qquad 0 \le r_1 < \infty \qquad (7\text{-}5\text{-}2)$$

For the other filter, containing noise alone in the output, the pdf for the envelope r_2 is correspondingly given by

$$p(r_2) = \frac{r_2}{N} \exp\left(-\frac{r_2{}^2}{2N}\right) \qquad 0 \le r_2 < \infty \qquad (7\text{-}5\text{-}3)$$

By our assumptions of statistically independent noises in the two filter outputs, r_1 and r_2 are also statistically independent. An error occurs whenever $r_2 > r_1$. Thus, the probability of error is given by

$$P_e = \int_{r_1=0}^{\infty} p(r_1) \left[\int_{r_2=r_1}^{\infty} p(r_2)\, dr_2\right] dr_1 \qquad (7\text{-}5\text{-}4)$$

Since the inner integral is just exp $(-r_1^2/2N)$,

$$P_e = \int_0^\infty \frac{r_1}{N} \exp\left(-\frac{r_1^2}{N}\right) \exp\left(-\frac{u^2}{2N}\right) I_0\left(\frac{r_1 u}{N}\right) dr_1 \qquad (7\text{-}5\text{-}5)$$

If we set $r_1/\sqrt{N} = x/\sqrt{2}$ and again identify the signal-noise ratio as[1]

$$\gamma = \frac{u^2}{2N} \qquad (7\text{-}5\text{-}6)$$

then $\qquad P_e = \exp\left(-\gamma\right) \frac{1}{2} \int_0^\infty x \exp\left(-\frac{x^2}{2}\right) I_0(x\sqrt{\gamma})\, dx \qquad (7\text{-}5\text{-}7)$

and this integrates directly (e.g., see Appendix A) into

$$P_e = \frac{1}{2} \exp\left(-\frac{\gamma}{2}\right) \qquad (7\text{-}5\text{-}8)$$

This simple and well-known result is shown plotted as the upper curve in Fig. 7-5-1.

It is interesting to compare this result with that for noncoherent detection of on-off keying, at high SNR, and with optimized threshold, as given in (7-4-18). It is apparent that the same error rate (at low error rates) is achieved in noncoherent FSK with only half the value of γ required for noncoherent OOK. For equal information rates, the SNR in both cases is defined with respect to the same filter bandwidths and hence the same level of noise N (see also Sec. 7-7). On the other hand, in OOK, γ is defined in terms of the power transmitted only during the Marks; zero power is transmitted during the Spaces. The *average* power used in OOK is then only *half* the value used in defining γ. Thus, at low error rates, noncoherent OOK and noncoherent FSK achieve equivalent error rate at the *same average SNR*. The only significant disadvantage of OOK is the need for optimizing the detection threshold at each SNR; no such problem exists in FSK. We shall see later in discussing fading (Sec. 9-5) that this in fact accounts for the difference in performance of conventional versions of these systems when operated over fading circuits.

Coherent FSK. By coherent (or synchronous) detection of an FSK signal, we again mean that there is available in the receiver an exact knowledge of each of the possible received signals, particularly including their r-f phase. Coherent detection again has the effect of rejecting a portion of the bandpass noise in each filter output. As we shall see, coherent FSK operation involves much the same difficulties as phase-shift keying, but as already noted in Chap. 2, achieves lesser performance. (The result below will of course be the same as that in Sec. 2-5.) At the same time, we shall observe below that coherent detection of FSK (in our

---

[1] Note γ in (7-5-6) is particularly the signal-noise ratio at the output of *that* filter containing the signal in its output.

present model of zero crosstalk) is significantly better than noncoherent reception only at relatively low signal-noise ratios, i.e., relatively high error rates. Despite all this, there are practical applications in which FSK may be convenient because of particular operational problems and

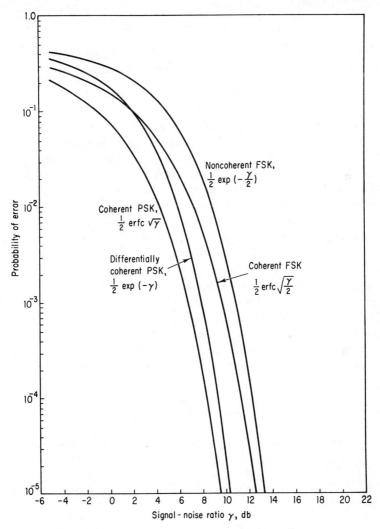

FIG. 7-5-1. Error rates for several binary systems.

in which coherent detection may still be available, for whatever additional advantage it provides.

Extending the coherent-detection analysis of Sec. 7-4, we consider synchronous detection of the sinusoidal signal-plus-noise outputs of a pair of bandpass filters. The filter containing the signal has a sinusoidal output component of envelope u, hence its output voltage can be written as

$$e(t) = [u(t) + x_1(t)] \cos \omega_1 t - y_1(t) \sin \omega_1 t \qquad (7\text{-}5\text{-}9)$$

The other filter, at frequency ω_2, has output (in the absence of crosstalk or interference) containing only noise,

$$e_2(t) = x_2(t) \cos \omega_2 t - y_2(t) \sin \omega_2 t \qquad (7\text{-}5\text{-}10)$$

The coherent-detection processes, using reference signals $\cos \omega_1 t$ and $\cos \omega_2 t$, respectively, give as the corresponding detector outputs,

$$\begin{aligned} v_1(t) &= u(t) + x_1(t) \\ v_2(t) &= x_2(t) \end{aligned} \qquad (7\text{-}5\text{-}11)$$

As an aside, we point out that if there is subsequent low-pass filtering which modifies the signal and noise voltages, its modifications to the signal and noise voltage can be accounted for in the usual manner from the filter transfer characteristic, leaving a form exactly like (7-5-11). In Sec. 7-6 we point out that this applies rigorously only in the case of the ideal noiseless-reference coherent detector being discussed here. Within this limitation, there is no loss in regarding (7-5-11) as the basic description of the output after postdetection filtering at the point where the Mark-Space decision is to be made. In this case, then, bandpass filtering prior to coherent detection is completely equivalent mathematically to low-pass filtering following synchronous detection.

In (7-5-11), we now consider the output at some appropriate sampling instant for a typical information pulse, letting u, x_1, x_2 represent the voltages at that instant. We assume u is positive (it is readily verified that the result below is identical if the opposite is true); hence we expect v_1 to be *algebraically* larger than v_2. If it is not, an error is made. Thus the probability of an error is given by

$$\begin{aligned} P_e = \text{Prob }(v_1 < v_2) &= \text{Prob }(u + x_1 < x_2) \\ &= \text{Prob }(u < x_2 - x_1) \qquad (7\text{-}5\text{-}12) \end{aligned}$$

Since x_1 and x_2, representing components of noise in the respective filter outputs, are independent zero-mean Gaussian variates with equal variance N, their difference $x = x_1 - x_2$ is also zero-mean Gaussian, with variance $2N$. Clearly, P_e is the probability that this Gaussian variable x exceeds u, that is,

$$P_e = \frac{1}{2} \operatorname{erfc} \left(\frac{1}{\sqrt{2}} \frac{u}{\sqrt{2N}} \right) = \frac{1}{2} \operatorname{erfc} \sqrt{\frac{\gamma}{2}} \qquad (7\text{-}5\text{-}13)$$

with γ defined again as in (7-5-6). The result is shown as a second curve on Fig. 7-5-1.

If this result is compared with that for coherent detection of OOK with optimized threshold in (7-4-25), it is seen that the same error rate occurs in the FSK case at a 3-db lower value for γ than in the OOK case. Again, we recall that this implies that the same performance is obtained at *equal average* power, when the 50-per-cent duty cycle of OOK is considered.

We shall also note in the next section (see also Fig. 7-5-1) that the same form of result is obtained for ideal phase-shift keying, except that identical error-rate performance is then obtained at 3 db lower signal-noise ratio. This simply reflects a doubled noise level associated with the use of orthogonal waveforms in coherent FSK, as opposed to "anti-parallel" waveforms in the PSK case.

Another interesting comparison is coherent versus noncoherent FSK at high SNR. Using (7-4-17), at high SNR the probability of error in coherent FSK is well approximated by

$$P_e \approx \frac{1}{\sqrt{2\pi\gamma}} \exp\left(-\frac{\gamma}{2}\right) \qquad (7\text{-}5\text{-}14)$$

Because the behavior is dominated by the exponential, there is a vanishingly small difference (for increasingly large γ) between the SNR γ required to achieve a certain error rate in coherent FSK, (7-5-14), and that required in noncoherent FSK as given earlier by (7-5-8). This is also apparent in the corresponding curves of Fig. 7-5-1.

Optimum Tone-spacing in Coherent FSK. It is appropriate at this point to note some additional remarks in Sec. 2-5 regarding optimization of coherent FSK. All the results of the present chapter are presented in terms of γ, the SNR at the output of a bandpass filter, prior to a final detector. The choice of filter to minimize the probability of error is that filter which maximizes γ; as shown in Chap. 2, this leads to specifying the appropriate matched filter. While the general aspects will all be further discussed in Sec. 7-7, the particular coherent FSK discussion in Sec. 2-5 is relevant here. In the result above, our assumption of "no crosstalk" is tantamount to assuming orthogonal signaling waveforms. In Sec. 2-5, it was in fact shown that for rectangular tone pulses and matched filtering, this implies certain spacings between the pair of tones. It was also shown that at other spacings, the cross-correlation of the two waveforms would be negative. With the two waveforms then partially "antiparallel," greater discrimination is possible between the two waveforms than when they are orthogonal. However, at the minimum such spacing,[1] giving the greatest discriminability, the gain in effective SNR as indicated by (2-5-48) or (2-5-49) is about 1.2, or less than 1 db. This performance is still not as good as that of phase-shift keying which, under the same qualitative assumptions and with simpler implementation,

[1] In Sec. 2-5, the result (2-5-48) implies that the minimum spacing for orthogonality is $0.5/T$, where T is the pulse length, and that the "best" spacing for discrimination is $0.7/T$. In fact, as pointed out there, the limitations of "practical" matched-filter implementations indicate that for practical systems, the respective numbers should be $1/T$ and approximately $1.4/T$.

performs 3 db better than orthogonal-waveform coherent FSK, as shown in the next section. Thus, only an unusual set of conditions (distinct from the communications requirement, per se) requiring somehow the use of distinguishable waveforms but yet allowing coherent detection would lead to the use of coherent FSK.

7.6. Phase-shift Keying (PSK)

Ideal Coherent PSK. Just as FSK can be regarded as a form of frequency modulation, phase-shift keying (PSK) can be considered to be the digital analog of phase modulation. In addition, one may recall the decision-theory results in Chap. 2 on the optimum (minimum error rate) binary signaling/receiving technique, utilizing a sequence of pulsed waveforms. It was shown that each information bit should be encoded as the algebraic sign of a single pulsed waveform, with detection by cross-correlation against a perfect replica of this waveform. Phase-shift keying of a constant-amplitude carrier, with sharp keying transitions between two phase states separated by π radians (hence the signal has the form of a sequence of plus-minus rectangular pulses), exactly fulfills the requirements for optimum signaling.

In some applications, one may use a more complex pulse waveform. A common example is the use of a pseudorandom, noiselike phase modulation,[1] with information still encoded as the algebraic sign. In that case, commonly, the first operation in reception will be to mix against a local reference waveform having the same complex modulation as the transmitted waveform but offset in frequency. For a constant-amplitude signal, the difference-frequency term in the mixer output is then readily observed to be a sinusoidal waveform with its phase (0 or π radians, say) containing the binary information. Thus, the remainder of the receiving operation can be identical with that for simple PSK. Hence, while we confine our discussion to the latter case, phase-modulated sinusoidal CW waveforms, the basic results apply much more generally.

In this case that we analyze, then, the coherent detector is a synchronous detector, requiring a reference waveform accurate in frequency and phase. An exactly similar reference waveform would be required to implement a *phase detector* as a means of detecting the binary information. The phase detector, by our definition, is a zero-memory device whose output is independent of the envelopes of the detector inputs; it specifically measures the cosine of this phase difference.[2] The coherent

---

[1] E.g., to facilitate synchronization in telemetry from deep-space probes; or, as in some versions of the Rake technique (Chap. 11), to utilize the wider signaling bandwidth as a means of resolving multipath in the transmission channel.

[2] The usual balanced phase-detector *circuit* yields the cosine of the phase difference between the two input signals. Usually, as part of a phase detector, one of the

detector, on the other hand, is also a zero-memory device, but its output is proportional to the input envelopes and to the cosine of the phase difference (see also Eq. 7-6-13). In *either* case, however (and assuming no postdetection filtering), the binary decision is based on the algebraic *sign* of the detector output; hence in this problem, both types of detectors will render the identical binary decision with the same input signals. Thus, unlike the analogs in FSK, there will be no performance difference between the coherent detector suggested by decision theory, and the phase detector suggested by the analogy to demodulation of phase-modulated carriers.

The mathematical model for ideal coherent detection is essentially the same as in the previous sections, except that now only a single waveform is involved. Thus as in (7-5-9) to (7-5-11), the output of the coherent detector has the form

$$v(t) = u(t) + x(t) \tag{7-6-1}$$

and, in analogy to (7-5-12), the probability of error, assuming $u > 0$, is simply the probability that $v(t)$ is negative at the sampling instant,

$$P_e = \text{Prob} \ (v < 0) = \text{Prob} \ (u + x < 0) \tag{7-6-2}$$

Since x is a zero-mean Gaussian variate, one obtains quickly

$$P_e = \frac{1}{2} \, \text{erfc} \, \frac{u}{\sqrt{2N}} = \frac{1}{2} \, \text{erfc} \, \sqrt{\gamma} \tag{7-6-3}$$

where again the SNR at the filter output at the sampling instant is denoted by

$$\gamma = \frac{u^2}{2N} \tag{7-6-4}$$

This is of course the same result presented in Chap. 2. It is shown as the lowest curve in Fig. 7-5-1.

Comparing with (7-5-13) for ideal coherent FSK, it is seen that a particular probability of error occurs at exactly 3 db lower SNR in ideal PSK than in coherent FSK. Thus for system-design purposes where one is attempting to operate below some specified error rate, there is a very real 3-db design advantage for ideal coherent PSK over ideal coherent FSK. This is also evident in the curves of Fig. 7-5-1.

---

signals is first given an additional 90° phase shift. Then the overall detector-circuit output becomes the sine of the phase difference. For differences small relative to 1 radian, this approximates to the phase difference itself, and this is the usual desired output in phase-modulation systems. However, we shall rather consider throughout here that a "phase detector" is only the balanced detection circuit giving the *cosine* of the phase difference between the input signals. Thus a phase difference of 0° results in a +1, and of 180° in −1, which is the kind of bipolar output desired for detection in binary systems.

Effect of Phase Error. We have continually identified our model above as *ideal* coherent PSK. In practical implementation, there are two important restrictions which apply to coherent detection in general. One would be a possible phase error in the stored reference with respect to the incoming signal. Since coherent detection always picks out that component of the additive noise in phase with the receiver reference and rejects the component in quadrature with it, the nature of the noise term in formulas such as (7-6-1) does not change. However, if the phase error is $\Delta\phi$, it is easy to show that the signal term is diminished by the factor $\cos \Delta\phi$. With the actual SNR prior to coherent detection defined by γ in (7-6-4), the error rate would then be

$$P_e = \tfrac{1}{2}\,\text{erfc}\,(\sqrt{\gamma}\,\cos \Delta\phi) \qquad (7\text{-}6\text{-}5)$$

In operation, such phase errors ($\Delta\phi$) may result from relative drifts between the master oscillators at transmitter and receiver or from changes induced by the propagation medium, which appear as apparent drifts or fluctuations in the relative frequency or phase of the received signal. In either case, these changes can only be compensated by "correcting" the receiver oscillator, and this correction can only be derived by operations on the received signal. Usually, the latter requires relatively long-term smoothing to diminish the additional apparent fluctuations caused by receiver noise. For example, this can be achieved by the use of phase-locked loops. The result (7-6-5) can be used to estimate the time scale in which such correction must be accomplished. For example, to suffer no more than a 1-db loss in performance (again meaning a requirement of 1 db higher SNR to achieve the same error rate) as compared with ideal coherent PSK requires

$$\cos^2 \Delta\phi > 0.8 \qquad (7\text{-}6\text{-}6a)$$

Or approximately

$$|\Delta\phi| < 0.45 \text{ radian (or } 25°) \qquad (7\text{-}6\text{-}6b)$$

If one knows the approximate rate and magnitude of variations in phase and/or frequency, one can use the result above, for example, to estimate the time constants required in the correction loops.

The other restriction in detection of PSK is the additive noise associated with deriving the reference signal in the receiver. This is discussed in generality in Chap. 8. A special, but important, example is discussed immediately below.

Differentially Coherent PSK (DPSK). An interesting alternative to attempting ideal coherent PSK, with the required long-term stability and/or high-quality correction loops, is so-called differential phase-shift keying (DPSK).[1] In this technique, it is assumed simply that there is

---

[1] Probably best known in practice at this time as incorporated by Collins Radio Co. in a variety of applications under the name "Kineplex." Usually these systems

enough stability in the oscillators and the medium so that there will be negligible change in phase from one information pulse to the next. Information is then encoded, not by absolute identification of say, 0° phase with Mark and 180° with Space, but rather by *differentially* encoding the information in terms of the phase change between successive pulses. For example, *no* (0°) phase shift from the previous pulse could designate Mark, and 180° phase shift could designate a Space (see Fig. 7-6-1*a*). A coherent detector or phase detector is still used, one input being the "current" pulse, and the other being the previous pulse appropriately delayed. An example of a possible implementation is shown in Fig.

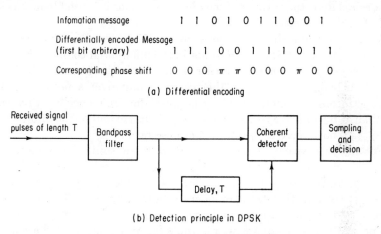

(a) Differential encoding

(b) Detection principle in DPSK

FIG. 7-6-1. Differential phase-shift keying.

7-6-1*b*. It should be noted that differential encoding, by itself, can be used in any digital system, and is not particularly tied to DPSK. However, in detection systems such as we have discussed earlier, additional decoding logic would be required at the receiver output to recover the original message. Hence, differential encoding is employed only where it has some particular usefulness as part of the signaling-transmission-detection scheme.[1]

One common receiver implementation for rectangular keyed DPSK involves integrate-and-dump matched filtering. The reader will recall (or see Sec. 7-7) that such a filter utilizes a narrowband, or extremely high-Q (long ringing time) resonant circuit, artificially discharged after

---

have employed four or eight phases per pulse rather than two; we shall confine our discussion here to the two-phase case. See, e.g., M. L. Doelz, E. T. Heald, and D. L. Martin, Binary Data Transmission Techniques for Linear Systems, *Proc. IRE*, vol. 45, pp. 656–661, May, 1957.

[1] An interesting non-DPSK example is described in A. Lender, The Duobinary Technique for High-Speed Data Transmission, *Communications and Electronics*, vol. 82, no. 66, pp. 214–218, May, 1963.

the desired sampling has taken place. If the input to such a circuit is gated off, but the circuit is not discharged, it will hold at its last output value. When such filters are used, the delay circuit in Fig. 7-6-1b can be replaced by using these ringing properties.[1] The sequence of input pulses of length T is commutated, at intervals T, between two such integrate-and-dump filters. Alternately, each charges up with an input signal pulse over a period T, then holds for a second period of length T, and is then discharged and ready for new input. During the second interval, the other filter is being charged up with the next signal pulse. If the two filter outputs are connected to a coherent detector, it is readily seen that the desired detector output for the binary decisions is available just at the end of each time interval T.

Again, the major difference between DPSK as described and the ideal coherent reference PSK system is not in the differential coding, which can be employed in any case. Rather it lies in the "reference" signal for detection being derived from the receiver input over a previous pulse. The performance difference arises because the "reference" is thus contaminated by additive thermal noise to the *same* extent as the information pulse, i.e., both have the same signal-noise ratio.

For analysis, we can assume that a Mark is transmitted and hence that in the absence of noise both the "signal" and the "reference" portions of the filter outputs have the same phase (and same frequency, of course). It is easy to show that the subsequent results apply as well if Space were transmitted and hence the two signals were of opposite phase. Including the noise, the two bandpass filter outputs for Mark transmitted are of the form

$$e_1(t) = [u(t) + x_1(t)] \cos \omega_0 t - y_1(t) \sin \omega_0 t$$
$$e_2(t) = [u(t) + x_2(t)] \cos \omega_0 t - y_2(t) \sin \omega_0 t \qquad (7\text{-}6\text{-}7)$$

Since the noises are assumed to arise from different input-pulse intervals, they will ideally be uncorrelated but of equal mean power. Thus x_1, y_1, x_2, y_2 are all zero mean, mutually uncorrelated, and each has variance N, where N is the mean noise power associated with *each* voltage at the sampling instant. It is convenient to rewrite (7-6-7) in terms of redefined, nonzero-mean Gaussian processes which have u as their mean value,

$$e_1(t) = x_1(t) \cos \omega_0 t - y_1(t) \sin \omega_0 t = \operatorname{Re} [z_1 \exp (j\omega_0 t)]$$
$$e_2(t) = x_2(t) \cos \omega_0 t - y_2(t) \sin \omega_0 t = \operatorname{Re} [z_2 \exp (j\omega_0 t)] \qquad (7\text{-}6\text{-}8)$$

where x_1, x_2, y_1, y_2 represent the complete quadrature components of the inputs to the phase detector or coherent detector. Accordingly,

$$\operatorname{Re} \langle z_1 \rangle = \operatorname{Re} \langle z_2 \rangle = \langle x_1 \rangle = \langle x_2 \rangle = u$$
$$\operatorname{Im} \langle z_1 \rangle = \operatorname{Im} \langle z_2 \rangle = \langle y_1 \rangle = \langle y_2 \rangle = 0 \qquad (7\text{-}6\text{-}9a)$$
$$\tfrac{1}{2}\langle |z_1 - \langle z_1 \rangle|^2 \rangle = \langle (x_1 - \langle x_1 \rangle)^2 \rangle = \langle y_1^2 \rangle = \tfrac{1}{2}\langle |z_2 - \langle z_2 \rangle|^2 \rangle$$
$$= \langle (x_2 - \langle x_2 \rangle)^2 \rangle = \langle y_2^2 \rangle = N \qquad (7\text{-}6\text{-}9b)$$

[1] Doelz, Heald, and Martin, *loc. cit.*

and the fluctuation components of z_1 and z_2 are mutually uncorrelated. One can also introduce envelope and phase of the detector inputs,

$$z_1(t) = R_1(t) \exp [j\theta_1(t)] \qquad (7\text{-}6\text{-}10a)$$
$$z_2(t) = R_2(t) \exp [j\theta_2(t)] \qquad (7\text{-}6\text{-}10b)$$

Then
$$e_1(t) = R_1(t) \cos [\omega_0 t + \theta_1(t)]$$
$$e_2(t) = R_2(t) \cos [\omega_0 t + \theta_2(t)] \qquad (7\text{-}6\text{-}11)$$

With these as inputs to a synchronous detector, the detector output at the instant of sampling (again ignoring gain or conversion factors) is

$$v_s = R_1 R_2 \cos (\theta_1 - \theta_2) = x_1 x_2 + y_1 y_2 = \mathrm{Re}\,(z_1 z_2{}^*) \qquad (7\text{-}6\text{-}12)$$

while the output of a phase detector would be simply

$$v_p = \cos (\theta_1 - \theta_2) = \frac{x_1 x_2 + y_1 y_2}{R_1 R_2} = \frac{\mathrm{Re}\,(z_1 z_2{}^*)}{|z_1 z_2{}^*|} \qquad (7\text{-}6\text{-}13)$$

Clearly, in either case, the decision is based on the algebraic sign of $\cos (\theta_1 - \theta_2)$. Thus either the multiplier detector, whose output is v_s, or the phase detector, with output v_p, would render identical binary decisions.

As a practical matter, reference has often been made to the phase-detector interpretation of implementation. As a result, most of the published performance analyses of DPSK systems have been based upon studying the distributions of the phase.[1] However, at least in the binary case, there is available a simpler analysis based on the coherent-detection model, using the scalar-product representation on the right-hand side of (7-6-12). Thus, on the assumption that the same phase has been signaled in both $e_1(t)$ and $e_2(t)$, the probability of error is given by

$$P_e = \mathrm{Prob}\,(x_1 x_2 + y_1 y_2 < 0) = \mathrm{Prob}\,[\mathrm{Re}\,(z_1 z_2{}^*) < 0] \qquad (7\text{-}6\text{-}14)$$

There are several simple ways to evaluate this last probability conveniently. Our technique, closely related to the general analysis of the next chapter, involves a particular coordinate rotation, or diagonalization of the quadratic form in the scalar product of (7-6-14). In terms of complex envelopes, this is the almost trivial algebraic identity

$$\mathrm{Re}\,(z_1 z_2{}^*) = \left| \frac{z_1 + z_2}{2} \right|^2 - \left| \frac{z_1 - z_2}{2} \right|^2 \qquad (7\text{-}6\text{-}15)$$

Since the sign of the quantity on the right-hand side here can be regarded

[1] J. G. Lawton, Comparison of Binary Data Transmission Systems, *Proc. 2nd Nat. Conf. Mil. Electronics*, pp. 54–61, 1958; J. G. Lawton, Theoretical Error Rates of "Differentially Coherent" Binary and "Kineplex" Data Transmission Systems, *Proc. IRE*, vol. 47, pp. 333–334, February, 1959; C. R. Cahn, Comparison of Coherent and Phase-Comparison Detection of a Four Phase Digital Signal, *Proc. IRE*, vol. 47, p. 1662, September, 1959; C. R. Cahn, "Performance of Digital Phase-Modulation Communication Systems, *IRE Trans. Commun. Systems*, vol. CS-7, pp. 3–6, May, 1959.

as determining the larger envelope of two obviously defined bandpass Gaussian processes, our DPSK analysis can be directly related to the earlier noncoherent FSK analysis.   To be more specific, one can introduce into (7-6-14) the new stationary complex Gaussian processes w_1 and w_2 defined by

$$w_1 = \frac{z_1 + z_2}{2} \qquad w_2 = \frac{z_1 - z_2}{2} \qquad (7\text{-}6\text{-}16)$$

These are jointly Gaussian.   Using (7-6-9), they are quickly observed to be uncorrelated and to have the following statistics:

$$\langle w_1 \rangle = u \qquad \langle w_2 \rangle = 0 \qquad (7\text{-}6\text{-}17)$$

$$\tfrac{1}{2}\langle |w_1 - \langle w_1 \rangle|^2 \rangle = \tfrac{1}{2}\langle |w_2|^2 \rangle = \frac{N}{2} \qquad (7\text{-}6\text{-}18)$$

From (7-6-15) and (7-6-14), the probability of error for DPSK is now defined by

$$P_e = \text{Prob } (|w_1|^2 - |w_2|^2 < 0) = \text{Prob } (|w_2|^2 > |w_1|^2)$$
$$= \text{Prob } (|w_2| > |w_1|) \qquad (7\text{-}6\text{-}19)$$

But the statistics and the problem statement are now *identical in form* with those involved in the analysis of the noncoherent detection of FSK in Sec. 7-5.   Namely, the probability is that the envelope of one zero-mean Gaussian process (noise alone) exceeds the envelope of a second, nonzero-mean Gaussian process (signal plus noise), with the two processes uncorrelated and each of variance $N/2$.   Thus one can apply directly the result in (7-5-8), to obtain

$$P_e = \frac{1}{2} \exp \left[-\frac{1}{2}\left(\frac{u^2}{2N/2}\right) \right] = \frac{1}{2} \exp \left(-\frac{u^2}{2N} \right) = \frac{1}{2} \exp (-\gamma) \qquad (7\text{-}6\text{-}20)$$

where γ is as defined earlier in (7-6-4).   The well-known result (7-6-20) is thus obtained here in a mathematical form which indicates an extremely close relationship to the noncoherent FSK envelope-detection problem. In some of the literature, where DPSK is analyzed by a phase-detector model, the formal similarity of the DPSK error-rate result to that for noncoherent FSK is noted as a curiosity but a probable coincidence.   On the contrary, as the analysis above shows, there is a very real basis for this similarity.

The result (7-6-20) has also been plotted in Fig. 7-5-1.   It is clear from the formula itself that at all error-rate levels, DPSK requires exactly 3 db less SNR than noncoherent FSK for the same error rate.   Recalling the asymptotically exponential behavior of coherent detection, it is clear that at high SNR, as shown in Fig. 7-5-1, DPSK performs almost as well as ideal coherent PSK.

The equivalence expressed by (7-6-15) has useful physical interpretation,

as well.   Thus one could actually form the sinusoidal signals and associated noises implied by (7-6-16) and detect by envelope comparison.
Thinking of the actual sequence of phase-shift keyed pulses transmitted
in DPSK, it is clear that the relations (7-6-16) really imply processing
(predetection filtering) over successive pairs of pulses (each individual
pulse then entering into two successive pairs).   Because of the differential
encoding, the pairs with phases $0° - 0°$ or $180° - 180°$ form continuous
sinusoidal waveforms, *either* of which represents the *same* information
element in the original message.   The other information state is represented by either the sequence $0° - 180°$ or its negative, $180° - 0°$; the
total waveform for this sequence has a $180°$ phase shift between its two
halves.   It is then clear that $0° - 0°$ (or its negative) and $0° - 180°$ (or
its negative) are *orthogonal* waveforms over the total two-pulse period.
Thus, applying the decision-theory principles of Chap. 2, to regain our
message we should noncoherently matched-filter detect which one of the
pair of orthogonal waveforms has been transmitted.   This is precisely the
implication already contained in (7-6-19).   In this sense, the 3-db
advantage over noncoherent FSK at the same information rate (in the
same additive Gaussian noise environment) arises because in DPSK the
total energy in the message-bearing waveforms is twice that in the FSK
case, because in DPSK the waveforms are *twice* as long.   The matched
filters for the envelope-detection of DPSK are integrate-and-dump filters,
one running continuously over the two-pulse period, the other with a phase
inversion inserted at its input halfway through the interval.   Because of
the need for processing over successive pairs, it may be noted that practical
implementation would require two pairs of matched filters operating in
alternation.

With these observations, it becomes no longer clear whether DPSK
really should be regarded as a member of the coherent-detection family or
rather as a particularly useful kind of orthogonal waveform signaling.
It is true that the right-hand side of (7-6-15) can be operationally identified
with the output of a balanced detector, with the signal and local reference
as its inputs and square-law devices in the sum-and-difference arms.
This is, of course, one well-known scheme for implementing a multiplier
and is very similar (save possibly in the detector law) to a common class
of phase detectors.   Nevertheless, the orthogonal-waveform point of view
is quite real and often provides the most useful intuitive basis for viewing
the system (see also Sec. 7-7).   Furthermore in Sec. 8-5, we shall cite
results which show that a DPSK signal, suitably designed, can be very
efficiently detected by appropriate filtering followed by a *limiter-discriminator*, and this is certainly a strongly noncoherent operation.

Because of the partial overlap of signal and noise components involved
in successive binary decisions, there is a significant tendency for errors
in DPSK to occur in clusters of two, at least for the case under considera-

tion of steady signals in additive Gaussian noise.[1] This occurs because, especially under high-SNR low-error-rate operation, an error is likely to be caused by a momentarily high noise level associated with a single pulse completely distorting its phase. Since any such single pulse is involved in two successive binary decisions, both may have a high likelihood of error. Such a clustering of errors may be of major significance if error-control coding of any type is used in the binary transmissions, since the coding must then be designed to cope with the clusters of errors rather than random single errors. Unfortunately, while the associated probabilities can be reduced to the evaluation of a single integral, no closed form appears to be currently available.[2]

7-7. Suboptimum versus Matched Filters

We have now examined the class of basic signaling-detection systems, all in terms of bandpass-filtering operations followed by zero-memory detectors (and no postdetection filtering). In each case the error probability is related *solely* to the *SNR* in the appropriate filter outputs. In this section, we discuss further aspects of these filtering operations.

Comparing Systems on an SNR Basis. First, despite the differences among the several systems, the SNR γ has been consistently defined so that the systems are directly comparable. The underlying assumption here is that the systems are to be compared when used at the same information (keying) rate. Then, in a comparison, all may be visualized as using the same individual pulse waveform shapes, hence the *same* bandpass filtering will be appropriate to all the systems (in FSK, such filtering is applied at *each* tone frequency). In turn, the latter statement assumes that with the "random" nature of message-bearing pulse sequences, the bandpass filtering in each case is defined with the common goal of a best (in some sense) processing of each individual pulse in the sequence. If one now assumes the same signal power and the same receiver noise power density spectrum, it is clear that the systems are indeed directly comparable, in terms of the SNR corresponding to a particular error rate. If any of the above assumptions are weakened, for reasons of engineering implementation or channel characteristics, then the SNR in each case must of course be related further to the basic signal power and noise parameters in order to achieve a realistic comparison.

Relation to Matched Filtering. The SNRs in the formulas of this chapter are all defined at the *outputs* of the bandpass filters. With only this as the basis, a reasonable next question is whether these filters can themselves be selected to maximize the SNR produced in each case and

---

[1] Such clustering may be less common under conditions of signal fading (see Chap. 11).

[2] Some numerical results are given in J. Salz and B. R. Saltzberg, Double Error Rates in Differentially Coherent Phase Systems, *IEEE Trans. Commun. Systems*, vol. CS-12, pp. 202–205, June, 1964.

thereby minimize the error rate. As shown in Sec. 2-4, this variational problem leads directly to defining the matched filter, a filter whose impulse response is a time-reversed version of the pulse waveform. The operation is further equivalent to cross-correlation against a replica of the transmitted waveform, and, as shown in Sec. 2-5, this can also be shown to be the optimum processing on a decision-theory basis.

In discussing matched-filter or cross-correlation operations, as in Sec. 2-5, the operations defined usually include *both* filtering and detection. For example, optimum reception of a sinusoidal pulse involves correlation against an exact replica. The phasing of this reference already corresponds to the coherent detection portion of the receiver process, and the integration to the filtering process. Such a view leads to defining *effective* SNR's, as in Sec. 2-5, which partially include the effect of the detection process. In practice, however, the filtering and detection operations are more usually separated along the lines of the generic models studied in this chapter. With this in mind, it is usually preferable to define the SNR more along the lines of this chapter, as the SNR after "bandpass matched filtering" or "bandpass cross-correlation." This leads to a common form, in terms of the symbol energy-noise power-density ratio, which is also more easily compared with results for alternative, suboptimum, but possibly more easily implemented, bandpass filtering.

The SNR for Matched Filtering. Section 2-4, on matched filtering, indicated the very significant result that the maximum SNR attainable at the output of a linear filter, with a pulsed signal plus white noise applied to the input, depends solely upon the input-signal energy and the noise spectral density. Specifically, at the filter output the ratio of squared envelope to mean-squared noise was given, by (2-4-8), as $2E/n_0$ with E the energy in the input signal and $n_0/2$ the two-sided noise spectral density. The result can be similarly derived from a complete bandpass representation.[1] In terms of our definition of γ as ratio of mean-squared signal to mean noise power at the filter output, we have

$$\gamma = E/n_0 \qquad (7\text{-}7\text{-}1)$$

It is worth emphasizing again that this result is independent of any details of the signal waveshape. It is readily verified that use of (7-7-1) in the appropriate probability-of-error formulas derived in this chapter gives exactly the results derived in Sec. 2-5 for particular models.

In the case of rectangular pulses, (7-7-1) reduces to the simple form,

$$\gamma = \frac{ST}{n_0} \qquad (7\text{-}7\text{-}2)$$

where S is the power level over the pulse and T is its length.

These results are for isolated single pulses. In a continuous communications format, the SNR's above will apply provided that at each decision

[1] E.g., C. W. Helstrom, Resolution of Signals in White, Gaussian Noise, *Proc. IRE*, vol. 43, pp. 1111–1118, September, 1955.

instant, the matched filter contains no residual energy from prior pulses. For a rectangular pulse the matched-filter realization given by an integrate-and-dump circuit provides this desirable property.

Performance with an _RLC_ Filter. As suggested several times earlier, problems of implementation may often weigh against use of the matched-filter or equivalent cross-correlator. Any filter used in practice will have to represent a compromise between the relatively narrow matched-filter bandwidth required to optimize the discrimination against noise in detection and the requirement of sufficiently rapid time response (decay) to avoid intersymbol interference. As an example, consider a rectangular pulse stream. From Fig. 2-4-4 the optimum time constant for detecting a single isolated pulse with a simple _RC_ filter (_RLC_ for the bandpass case) is roughly $4T$, with T the rectangular pulse width. However this time constant gives a high level of intersymbol interference. A simple calculation shows that decreasing the time constant to $(\pi/1.15)T = 2.73T$ reduces intersymbol interference to about -20 db. The resultant loss in SNR, as compared with matched filtering, is only 1.5 db (Fig. 2-4-4).

Spectral Aspects of Matched Filtering. An additional important practical aspect of matched filtering involves spectral occupancy. Thus, let us again examine the matched filter for rectangular pulses, as defined by the equivalent low-pass impulse response

$$h(t) = \begin{cases} 1 & 0 < t < T \\ 0 & \text{elsewhere} \end{cases} \qquad (7\text{-}7\text{-}3)$$

If the filter is centered at frequency f_0, and we examine its output with respect to a pulse at frequency $f_0 + f$, starting with the filter uncharged at time $t = 0$, it is readily found (assuming $f \ll f_0$) that the output envelope has the form

$$v_0(t) = K \frac{\sin \pi f T}{\pi f} \qquad (7\text{-}7\text{-}4)$$

where K is a constant including gain factors and the like. In particular, just prior to discharge at $t = T$, where T is the pulse length, the envelope value can be written in the form

$$v_0(T) = K \frac{\sin \pi f T}{\pi f} = KT \frac{\sin \pi f T}{\pi f T} \qquad (7\text{-}7\text{-}5)$$

Thus, the _effective_ transfer function at the _sampling instants_, as measured by the output envelope, has nulls at frequencies displaced by integer multiples of $1/T$ from the filter center frequency. In FSK, for example, with matched filtering of rectangular pulses, the tone spacing could be just $1/T$ and there would be _no crosstalk_ between the filter outputs at the _sampling instants._[1] Similarly, in frequency-division multiplexing of

---

[1] In coherent FSK, as noted earlier, such crosstalk could add slightly to signal discriminability. However, in most practical systems, such as noncoherent FSK, crosstalk is undesirable.

digital signals using rectangular pulses and matched filters, and *with all channels synchronized in pulse timing*, all tones can be spaced as close as $1/T$. In decision-theory parlance, both the signals and their matched filters are orthogonal. We note that this $1/T$ spacing is quite a close spectral spacing and interesting for exactly this reason. For example, the bandwidth defined by the -3-db points on the power spectrum of a bandpass rectangular pulse of length T is approximately $1/T$. Thus pulses of length T at tone spacing $1/T$ would have their spectra overlapping at the -3-db points—and yet there will be no crosstalk with matched-filter reception. This close-packing feature of matched-filter systems has been of considerable interest in recent communications-system design studies.

Matched-filter Reception versus Signal Fidelity. Matched filtering represents perhaps the ultimate in decision-processing of a signal. For every pulse, it gives at some appropriate instant a voltage which can be used to make the minimum-probability-of-error binary decision. However, the matched-filter output waveform generally bears no resemblance whatsoever to the input waveform. For example, for rectangular pulses, the matched-filter output envelope will be triangular during the course of the pulse.

On the other hand, in many applications in radiotelegraphy, there is emphasis on radio receiving systems which do not of themselves include telegraph-terminal (decision-using) equipment. In these systems, the reception goal of the radio system may *not* be to make binary decisions with minimum error rate, but rather to *reconstitute the transmitted telegraph modulation*, for further relaying (e.g., via land lines) to the users who have the telegraph terminals. Indeed, the radio receiving system of itself may have no equipment which is in any sense "aware" of the timing of the telegraph signal pulses. In such operation, the desired reconstitution of the telegraph signal may be most easily accomplished by demodulating the radio signal with a maximum *fidelity* and then "sharpening" the resulting noisy telegraph signal by hard limiting or some equivalent. Such "maximum fidelity" requires a filter which has a sufficiently fast response, or wide bandwidth, that there is very little rounding or other distortion of the telegraph signal. This can only be accomplished at a cost in noise reduction. With the random telegraph transitions occurring T sec apart, or at multiples of T, the radio signal can be regarded as having a sideband structure extending out to well beyond $1/T$ on either side of the radio carrier, and near-faithful reproduction requires that the filter be wide enough to pass a major part of this sideband structure. Typically, total-bandpass filter bandwidths of the order of $5/T$ may be used in such demodulation.

CHAPTER 8

GENERAL ANALYSIS OF SINGLE-CHANNEL BINARY
SYSTEMS IN ADDITIVE NOISE[1]

8-1. Generalized Models

The previous chapter introduced the basic concepts of binary signaling and reception techniques and analysis of their operation in terms of certain idealized models. The assumptions in the analyses generally included:

1. Lack of intersymbol (adjacent symbol) interference, such as might arise either from filter transients, or imperfect synchronization, or both.

2. Lack of external interference, such as might arise from spectral sidebands of other signaling channels nearby in frequency.

3. Additive Gaussian noise, independent between filter outputs whenever more than one output is involved (two-filter operation in either FSK or differential PSK) and with equal intensity in both outputs.

4a. No crosstalk in noncoherent two-filter FSK (signal components present in only *one* of the two filter outputs).

4b. Identical signal-noise statistics for the two filter outputs in DPSK.

5. Steady signal level, i.e., the error rate is averaged only over the ensemble of the additive Gaussian noise fluctuations.

These idealizations often do not exist in practice. In this chapter, we shall present an analysis of the signal binary channel which largely removes all the above restrictions, except that the noise will still be assumed additive and Gaussian and the signal level will be assumed to be steady. Specifically we shall generalize the noncoherent FSK model and the coherent PSK (perhaps more accurately, DPSK) model with noisy reference. In each case, two voltages are involved, each contaminated by additive Gaussian noise. The noises will be assumed to be arbitrarily *correlated* and with possibly *unequal* intensity. We shall also assume *both* voltages to contain deterministic components, of generally unequal level. These arbitrary deterministic components are visualized to be the sum of signal, crosstalk, and interference components. In this chapter, the deterministic components will be assumed to be steady, and the prob-

---

[1] The material of Secs. 8-1 through 8-3 is largely adapted from S. Stein, Unified Analysis of Certain Coherent and Non-Coherent Binary Communications Systems, *IEEE Trans. Inform. Theory*, vol. IT-10, pp. 43–51, January, 1964.

ability of error will be derived for the indicated binary models by averaging over the noise ensembles. Later (Sec. 9-6) it will be shown that these results also directly apply when the signal components involved are undergoing fading characteristic of long-distance radio channels.

In the remainder of this section, the generalized models are described in detail, partially reviewing the discussions of Chap. 7. In Sec. 8-2, the mathematical statements are reduced to a single "canonical" problem, for which a relatively straightforward solution can be demonstrated. The results are illustrated in Sec. 8-3 by specialized examples, including essentially all the results of Chap. 7. Additionally (Secs. 8-4 and 8-5), we shall be able to apply the formulas developed to analysis of the practically important operation of frequency detection in noncoherent FSK and subsequently compare performance against dual-filter operation.

Noncoherent Detection (FSK). In binary communication employing noncoherent detection, the successive binary symbols are represented by choosing between two different pulsed waveforms. These are received through a pair of bandpass filters (or cross-correlators), so designed that for each pulse, a greater amount of signal energy appears at one output than at the other. The output decision is usually made by comparing the detected *envelopes* of the filter outputs. Errors arise because of additive Gaussian noise when it causes a larger output from the "wrong" filter. The computation of probability of error is the computation of the probability that the noises will have such an effect.[1]

The actual binary decision is made by sampling the detector outputs at some *instant*, once per pulse, usually near the end of the pulse. Ideally, at this instant the filter outputs depend solely on the input during the course of the "current" information pulse. Otherwise, intersymbol (adjacent symbol) interference occurs. Since detectors are zero-memory devices, the level of such interference is determined by the filter parameters. Such interference may also arise for reasons of imperfect synchronization. There may also be other spurious voltages in the filter outputs, such as that due to interference from other signals.

Usually, one also attempts to use orthogonal signals and orthogonal filters. Each waveform then produces output in a corresponding one of the filters at the sampling instant but zero output in the other. However, it may not prove possible to use orthogonal signals, or even if the signals are orthogonal, other requirements on the filter design (e.g., to avoid intersymbol interference) may cause the filters to be nonorthogonal.

---

[1] Note that with external interference in FSK, for example, the probability of an error when Mark is transmitted may no longer be the same as when Space is transmitted. The two may have to be calculated separately and averaged (assuming, say, Marks and Spaces occur with equal probability). Such averaging, when necessary, is trivial; it will be implicit below that we are indicating only the basic probability-of-error computations to be used with such averaging when required.

There will then usually be some signal energy ("crosstalk") in the output of the "wrong" filter; there will also be some common spectral components of the input noise processed by both filters, hence their noise outputs will be partially correlated.

For the generalized FSK noncoherent detection analysis problem, then, we have two bandpass-filter outputs, which can be regarded as narrow-bandpass signals having the forms

Filter 1: $e_1(t) = x_1(t) \cos \omega_1 t - y_1(t) \sin \omega_1 t$

$$= \mathrm{Re}\,[z_1(t) \exp (j\omega_1 t)] \quad (8\text{-}1\text{-}1a)$$

Filter 2: $e_2(t) = x_2(t) \cos \omega_2 t - y_2(t) \sin \omega_2 t$

$$= \mathrm{Re}\,[z_2(t) \exp (j\omega_2 t)] \quad (8\text{-}1\text{-}1b)$$

The noncoherent (envelope) detectors form the voltages

$$R_1(t) = \sqrt{x_1{}^2(t) + y_1{}^2(t)} = |z_1(t)| \qquad R_2(t) = |z_2(t)| \quad (8\text{-}1\text{-}2)$$

respectively, and the binary decision is made by deciding which of these is larger *at the sampling instant.*[1] Since the detector is a zero-memory device, we are concerned with the values of z_1 and z_2 at *that instant* and write these henceforth as complex variates, with no time dependence. As amply discussed in Chap. 7, we can thus also ignore details of the filters for our detection analysis, since calculations of signal voltages and noise powers and correlations (and any other terms) at the filter outputs in terms of their transfer functions and the input waveforms are standard.

Additive bandpass Gaussian noise, when represented in the form (8-1-1), has zero-mean Gaussian quadrature components. Any deterministic voltages (the desired signal, or undesired interference components, in whatever mixture is present) bias these Gaussian quadrature components. We assume these deterministic voltages to have a steady value. Hence

---

[1] Note that from a decision-theory viewpoint, envelope comparison of two filter outputs is optimum for equiprobable waveforms only when the filter output-noise powers are equal *and* the received energy in the two binary waveforms are equal. The latter statement excludes a situation such as selective fading, in which unequal energy is associated with receiving the two possible waveforms and this selective fading has set in slowly enough for the receiver to have knowledge of the fading state. In such cases, a form of biased envelope comparison is readily shown to be optimum. If filter noise-output powers are unequal for some reason of receiver design, the optimum receiver can be regarded as one in which the relative gains of the two filters are adjusted to make the noise outputs equal, followed by the optimum comparison just mentioned to take into account the subsequent unbalancing of the signal energies at the filter outputs.

The general results of this chapter may rather be taken to apply to practical cases of engineering design where, despite such unbalances, the receiver is implemented on a straightforward envelope comparison. In this case, the average probability of error is given (assuming both binary message states occur with equal probability) by averaging the respective probabilities of error associated with reception of each of the two binary waveforms, including the appropriate noise levels, signal energies, and crosstalk levels for each of the two cases.

for stationary additive noise, the statistics of x_1, y_1, x_2, y_2 in (8-1-1) are jointly Gaussian, with generally nonzero mean.   In the complex notation, we may write their relevant moments as follows (the first representing the deterministic voltages in the filter outputs):

$$\langle z_k \rangle = m_{kf} + j\mu_{kf} \qquad k = 1, 2 \tag{8-1-3}$$

$$\left.\begin{array}{l} \frac{1}{2}\langle |z_k - \langle z_k \rangle|^2 \rangle = \sigma_{kf}{}^2 \\[4pt] \frac{1}{2}\langle (z_k - \langle z_k \rangle)^2 \rangle = 0 \end{array}\right\} \quad k = 1, 2 \qquad \begin{array}{l} (8\text{-}1\text{-}4a) \\[4pt] (8\text{-}1\text{-}4b) \end{array}$$

$$\begin{array}{l} \frac{1}{2}\langle (z_1 - \langle z_1 \rangle)^*(z_2 - \langle z_2 \rangle) \rangle = \sigma_{1f}\sigma_{2f}\rho_f \\[4pt] \frac{1}{2}\langle (z_1 - \langle z_1 \rangle)(z_2 - \langle z_2 \rangle) \rangle = 0 \end{array} \tag{8-1-5}$$

Here
$$\rho_f = \rho_{cf} + j\rho_{sf} \tag{8-1-6}$$

is the normalized complex cross-covariance between the two complex Gaussian processes, determined by the filter characteristics.   Considering mean-square values over a carrier-frequency period in (8-1-1), the instantaneous signal powers in the respective filter outputs (actually the powers in the nonrandom components) are

$$S_{1f} = \frac{1}{2}|\langle z_1 \rangle|^2 = \frac{m_{1f}{}^2 + \mu_{1f}{}^2}{2} \qquad S_{2f} = \frac{1}{2}|\langle z_2 \rangle|^2 = \frac{m_{2f}{}^2 + \mu_{2f}{}^2}{2} \tag{8-1-7}$$

Similarly, the instantaneous signal phases are

$$\theta_{1f} = \tan^{-1}\left(\frac{\mu_{1f}}{m_{1f}}\right) \qquad \theta_{2f} = \tan^{-1}\left(\frac{\mu_{2f}}{m_{2f}}\right) \tag{8-1-8}$$

and the total noise power in each is

$$N_{1f} = \frac{1}{2}\langle |z_1 - \langle z_1 \rangle|^2 \rangle = \sigma_{1f}{}^2 \qquad N_{2f} = \frac{1}{2}\langle |z_2 - \langle z_2 \rangle|^2 \rangle = \sigma_{2f}{}^2 \tag{8-1-9}$$

respectively.   The cross-covariance properties in (8-1-5) are the usual ones for stationary bandpass Gaussian noise (e.g., Chap. 1 or Sec. 7-3) expressed in the complex notation.

Rather than comparing the envelopes in (8-1-2), one may equally well compare any monotonic function of the envelopes.   A particularly useful one for analysis (corresponding practically to use of a square-law rather than linear envelope detector) is to compare $R_1{}^2$ and $R_2{}^2$.   The probability of error can then be calculated as the probability, averaged over the jointly Gaussian ensemble statistics of the z_k, that $R_2{}^2 > R_1{}^2$,

$$P_{ef} = \text{Prob } (R_2 > R_1) = \text{Prob } (R_2{}^2 > R_1{}^2)$$
$$= \text{Prob } (|z_2|^2 > |z_1|^2) \tag{8-1-10}$$

This is the probability of error when m_{1f}, μ_{1f} represent a signaled pulse plus "undesired" components and m_{2f}, μ_{2f} represent only undesired components (including effects of nonorthogonality).[1]

---

[1] We do not attempt here to further separate the effects due to undesired components.   Interference, for example, may have a fluctuating characteristic, and results such as (8-1-10) would have to be further averaged over changes in the parameters m_{kf}, μ_{kf}.   This also is true for determining average performance when a signal is fading (e.g. see Secs. 9-5 and 9-6).

We note, as a special case of (8-1-3) to (8-1-6), that $\sigma_{2f} = 0$ corresponds in (8-1-10) to determining the probability that R_1 is less than some non-fluctuating threshold given by $\sqrt{m_{2f}^2 + \mu_{2f}^2}$, and hence represents the probability of error for a keyed pulse noncoherently detected by comparison of envelope level against a threshold.

Coherent Detection (PSK). We next derive a corresponding mathematical statement for the generalized coherent detection model. We consider coherent signaling with the binary information encoded as the algebraic sign of a single waveform (for example, $0° - 180°$ phase-shift keying). The waveform resulting from filtering the received signal plus noise is coherently detected by multiplication against an appropriate reference waveform followed by low-pass filtering to remove all but the zero-beat component. The latter is then sampled, once per pulse, to make the binary decision.

However, in actual practice, the reference waveform may be noisy. For example, because of vagaries of the channel, the reference waveform will often have to be derived by relatively long-term filtering (smoothing) of the received signals, such as by use of phase-locked loops. The smoothed signal being used as the "coherent" detection reference will then inevitably still contain some of the noise associated with the reception process. The common phase-detection implementation of DPSK is another example of a noisy reference system.

Thus, we have a filter output which we can write generally as

$$e_1(t) = x_1(t) \cos \omega_0 t - y_1(t) \sin \omega_0 t = \text{Re} \left[z_1(t) \exp (j\omega_0 t) \right] \quad (8\text{-}1\text{-}11)$$

and a noisy reference signal at the same frequency which has the form

$$e_2(t) = x_2(t) \cos \omega_0 t - y_2(t) \sin \omega_0 t = \text{Re} \left[z_2(t) \exp (j\omega_0 t) \right] \quad (8\text{-}1\text{-}12)$$

Coherent (multiplicative) detection then produces the output at the sampling instant (again ignoring constant factors which do not affect the signal-noise ratio),

$$w = x_1 x_2 + y_1 y_2 = \text{Re} (z_1 z_2^*) = R_1 R_2 \cos (\theta_1 - \theta_2) \quad (8\text{-}1\text{-}13)$$

where we have introduced also the envelope and phase notation

$$z_1 = R_1 \exp (j\theta_1) \qquad z_2 = R_2 \exp (j\theta_2) \quad (8\text{-}1\text{-}14)$$

In a phase-shift-keyed system with perfect reference, in the absence of noise, the transmitted phase θ_1 is identical either with θ_2 or with $\theta_2 + \pi$. In the noisy case, the decision is made on the assumption (best knowledge) that this is still true of the received signal. Thus the decision is based only on the *sign* of w in (8-1-13) and equivalently can be based just on the phase difference $(\theta_1 - \theta_2)$, or on $\cos (\theta_1 - \theta_2)$. Either of the latter can be obtained by utilizing the reference signal and filter output in an appropriate phase detector rather than the multiplier mentioned initially. The major difference is that a phase detector normally does not respond to the size of the envelopes R_1, R_2. However, since the envelopes (R_1, R_2) are by definition always positive, in both cases it is only the *sign* of the term cos $(\theta_1 - \theta_2)$ which is used to make the decision, and performance (probability of error) is *identical* for both practical kinds of detection. As mentioned earlier in discussing DPSK in Sec. 7-6, approaching the problem from the viewpoint of coherent (multiplicative) detection exposes simple and useful relationships to the envelope-detection problem, which will be importantly employed in the later analysis.

We shall not here discuss the generalized coherent FSK problem (including coherent detection of on-off-keyed signals as a limiting case) which involves coherent detection of a pair of different (usually orthogonal) binary waveforms. The coherent FSK problem appears to involve an extension of the present analysis.

Returning now to (8-1-11) and (8-1-12), the statistics of the stationary jointly Gaussian quadrature components can be written in exactly the form given in (8-1-3) to (8-1-9). We shall distinguish the two cases by appending the subscript p rather than f to the statistical parameters whenever we are referring now to the PSK problem. The case of an ideal noiseless phase reference then corresponds to $\sigma_{2p}{}^2 = 0$. Perfect phase lock in the deterministic part of the reference (with or without added noise fluctuations) corresponds to $m_{1p}/\mu_{1p} = m_{2p}/\mu_{2p}$. The DPSK system (with no intersymbol interference effects) is the special case

$$S_{1p} = S_{2p} \quad \text{and} \quad N_{1p} = N_{2p} \tag{8-1-15}$$

that is

$$|\langle z_{1p}\rangle|^2 = |\langle z_{2p}\rangle|^2 \quad \text{and} \quad \langle|z_{1p} - \langle z_{1p}\rangle|^2\rangle = \langle|z_{2p} - \langle z_{2p}\rangle|^2\rangle \tag{8-1-16a}$$

Also, since noise at the filter output associated with one pulse is ideally independent of that associated with an adjacent pulse, the usual DPSK case involves

$$\rho_{cp} = \rho_{sp} = 0 \tag{8-1-16b}$$

A less noisy phase reference than in DPSK for use in detecting one information pulse might be achieved by averaging over many previous information pulses (if one can delete the phase changes due to their information content). Assuming this can be done, (8-1-16b) would still ideally hold since the noise associated with the previous pulses should be independent of that associated with the current pulse. However, because of the greater smoothing, one achieves a better signal-noise ratio in the reference signal than in the information pulse, i.e.,

$$\frac{S_{2p}}{N_{2p}} > \frac{S_{1p}}{N_{1p}} \tag{8-1-17}$$

the limit being the ideal noiseless reference, when $\dfrac{S_{2p}}{N_{2p}} \to \infty$. Our analysis below includes all these cases, as well as those for which (8-1-16b) no longer holds.

To write the basic probability of error expression, we use the multiplier output

$$P_{ep} = \text{Prob } (w < 0) = \text{Prob } (x_1 x_2 + y_1 y_2 < 0)$$
$$= \text{Prob } [\text{Re } (z_1{}^* z_2) < 0] \quad (8\text{-}1\text{-}18)$$

This is the probability of error when the signaled value of phase is the same as that supposedly contained in the reference signal. In the absence of interference or other unwanted deterministic components, this implies

$$\frac{m_{1p}}{\mu_{1p}} = \frac{m_{2p}}{\mu_{2p}} \qquad \text{or} \qquad \arg \langle z_{1p} \rangle = \arg \langle z_{2p} \rangle \quad (8\text{-}1\text{-}19)$$

This last equation is used later in interpreting the results but is not an assumption in deriving them. It is readily verified that if the opposite phase were signaled, the probability of error would be the same. (There are only trivial changes in the expressions involved.)

Note that use of any positive real multiplicative factor in the inequality in (8-1-18) does not alter the error-probability obtained. We have already noted that the presence or absence of envelope factors R_1, R_2 will not alter the probabilities. This observation will later be useful in simplifying our mathematics.

8-2. A Unified Formulation and Its Solution

Reduction to a Unified Formulation. We shall now show that the two problem statements of (8-1-10) and (8-1-18), while apparently relating to two different types of systems, are closely equivalent mathematically. The nature of the connection is evident if we recall the algebraic identity (7-6-15),

$$\text{Re } (z_1{}^* z_2) = \left| \frac{z_1 + z_2}{2} \right|^2 - \left| \frac{z_1 - z_2}{2} \right|^2 \quad (8\text{-}2\text{-}1)$$

Thus, the simple mathematical transformations

$$u_1 = \frac{z_1 + z_2}{2} \qquad \text{and} \qquad u_2 = \frac{z_1 - z_2}{2} \quad (8\text{-}2\text{-}2)$$

replaces a generalized PSK problem by a mathematically equivalent FSK problem,

$$\text{Prob } [\text{Re } (z_1{}^* z_2) < 0] = \text{Prob } [|u_1|^2 < |u_2|^2] \quad (8\text{-}2\text{-}3)$$

The transformation (8-2-2) corresponds to a 45° rotation in each of the cartesian coordinate systems defined by the process quadrature components (and, by our choice of factors, to an irrelevant change in metric).

Alternatively, the transformations (again basically the same 45° rotation)

$$u_1' = z_1 + z_2 \quad \text{and} \quad u_2' = z_1 - z_2 \tag{8-2-4}$$

will transform a generalized FSK problem into a mathematically equivalent PSK problem. Fundamentally, the connection is that both problems involve the sign of a Hermitian quadratic form in a pair of correlated, nonzero-mean Gaussian variates. Our solution then, while phrased particularly in the context of the specific problems (8-1-10) and (8-1-18), is readily extended to the probability that any more general Hermitian quadratic form in a pair of such variates is positive (or negative).

For convenience in ultimate solution, one can determine more general transformations than (8-2-2) or (8-2-4), to reduce both problems to a convenient mathematically equivalent noncoherent FSK problem. The latter is defined in terms of two *completely uncorrelated* nonzero-mean complex Gaussian variates t_1 and t_2 with the desired probability of error stated as

$$P_e = \text{Prob} \left(|t_1|^2 < |t_2|^2 \right) \tag{8-2-5}$$

The required linear transformations, in terms of the original variates (using subscripts f or p to distinguish the FSK or PSK starting models, respectively), are

$$
\begin{aligned}
t_1 &= \frac{z_{1f}(1 + K) + z_{2f}(1 - K) \exp(-j\phi)}{2} \\
&= \frac{(z_{1p} + z_{2p})(1 + K) + (z_{1p} - z_{2p})(1 - K) \exp(-j\phi)}{4}
\end{aligned}
\tag{8-2-6a}
$$

$$
\begin{aligned}
t_2 &= \frac{z_{1f}(1 - K) + z_{2f}(1 + K) \exp(-j\phi)}{2} \\
&= \frac{(z_{1p} + z_{2p})(1 - K) + (z_{1p} - z_{2p})(1 + K) \exp(-j\phi)}{4}
\end{aligned}
\tag{8-2-6b}
$$

The value of ϕ in the two respective cases is

$$\cos \phi = \frac{\rho_{cf}}{\sqrt{\rho_{cf}^2 + \rho_{sf}^2}} = \frac{\sigma_{1p}^2 - \sigma_{2p}^2}{\sqrt{(\sigma_{1p}^2 - \sigma_{2p}^2)^2 + 4\sigma_{1p}^2\sigma_{2p}^2\rho_{sp}^2}} \tag{8-2-7a}$$

$$\sin \phi = \frac{\rho_{sf}}{\sqrt{\rho_{cf}^2 + \rho_{sf}^2}} = \frac{-2\sigma_{1p}\sigma_{2p}\rho_{sp}}{\sqrt{(\sigma_{1p}^2 - \sigma_{2p}^2)^2 + 4\sigma_{1p}^2\sigma_{2p}^2\rho_{sp}^2}} \tag{8-2-7b}$$

and the value of K in the respective cases is

$$
\begin{aligned}
K &= \left(\frac{\sigma_{1f}^2 + \sigma_{2f}^2 + 2\sigma_{1f}\sigma_{2f}|\rho_f|}{\sigma_{1f}^2 + \sigma_{2f}^2 - 2\sigma_{1f}\sigma_{2f}|\rho_f|} \right)^{1/2} \\
&= \left[\frac{\sigma_{1p}^2 + \sigma_{2p}^2 + \sqrt{(\sigma_{1p}^2 - \sigma_{2p}^2)^2 + 4(\sigma_{1p}\sigma_{2p}\rho_{sp})^2}}{\sigma_{1p}^2 + \sigma_{2p}^2 - \sqrt{(\sigma_{1p}^2 - \sigma_{2p}^2)^2 + 4(\sigma_{1p}\sigma_{2p}\rho_{sp})^2}} \right]^{1/2}
\end{aligned}
\tag{8-2-8}
$$

While the use of linear transformations to simplify analyses is not uncommon, these are often diagonalizing transformations which basically preserve the metric. It is interesting to note that (8-2-6) involves a deliberate distortion of the metric.

We shall not set down in detail the statistics of t_1, t_2. It is apparent from the linearity of transformation that they are nonzero-mean complex Gaussian processes; it is easy to verify that their fluctuation components are uncorrelated, hence independent. Rather, we shall solve in terms of the general properties of t_1, t_2 and subsequently use (8-2-6) to relate the solution back to statistics such as (8-1-3) to (8-1-9).

Solution of the Canonical Problem. Since t_1 and t_2 are independent nonzero-mean complex Gaussian processes, their envelopes R_1 and R_2 are independently distributed, with the well-known probability density functions (e.g., Sec. 1-4),

$$p(R_k) = \frac{R_k}{\mu_k^2} \exp\left(-\frac{a_k^2 + R_k^2}{2\mu_k^2}\right) I_0\left(\frac{a_k R_k}{\mu_k^2}\right) \quad \begin{matrix} 0 < R_k < \infty \\ k = 1, 2 \end{matrix} \quad (8\text{-}2\text{-}9)$$

where $\qquad a_k = |\langle t_k \rangle| \qquad \mu_k^2 = \frac{1}{2}\langle |t_k - \langle t_k \rangle|^2 \rangle \qquad k = 1, 2 \quad (8\text{-}2\text{-}10)$

The probability of error in (8-2-5) is now simply

$$P_e = \text{Prob }(R_1^2 < R_2^2) = \text{Prob }(R_1 < R_2) \quad (8\text{-}2\text{-}11)$$

In Appendix A, it is shown that this probability is given by (among other forms)[1]

$$P_e = \frac{1}{2}[1 - Q(\sqrt{b}, \sqrt{a}) + Q(\sqrt{a}, \sqrt{b})] - \frac{A}{2} \exp\left(-\frac{a+b}{2}\right) I_0(\sqrt{ab}) \quad (8\text{-}2\text{-}12)$$

with $\qquad\qquad a = \dfrac{a_2^2}{\mu_1^2 + \mu_2^2} \qquad\qquad (8\text{-}2\text{-}13a)$

$$b = \frac{a_1^2}{\mu_1^2 + \mu_2^2} \qquad\qquad (8\text{-}2\text{-}13b)$$

$$A = \frac{\mu_1^2 - \mu_2^2}{\mu_1^2 + \mu_2^2} \qquad\qquad (8\text{-}2\text{-}13c)$$

[1] Excellent machine computation routines exist for calculating formulas of the type given in (8-2-12) with high accuracy. For such purposes it is convenient to introduce the complement of the Q function,

$$R(\alpha,\beta) = 1 - Q(\alpha,\beta) \qquad R(\alpha,\beta) \geq 0$$

Then if A is negative (or zero) in (8-2-12), the computation consists of a sum of three positive quantities, each of which can be calculated with the same *relative* accuracy. Interrelated routines, preserving 10^{-5} relative accuracy in all terms, were given in D. E. Johansen, New Techniques for Machine Computation of the Q-functions, Truncated Normal Deviates, and Matrix Eigenvalues, Applied Research Laboratory, Sylvania Electronic Systems, AFCRL-556, July, 1961.

When A is positive, or usefully in all cases, one can preserve relative accuracy in computing the probability by computing from the nonsymmetric equivalent form [Appendix A, Eq. (A5-5)],

$$P_e = \frac{1+A}{2} R(\sqrt{b}, \sqrt{a}) + \frac{1-A}{2} Q(\sqrt{a}, \sqrt{b})$$

where, since $|A| < 1$, both terms are always positive.

From (8-2-6) to (8-2-8), one can calculate these parameters in terms of the original statistics.   The latter were stated in (8-1-3) to (8-1-9) for the generalized FSK model, with formally similar statistics for the PSK model (the latter written again below with subscript p rather than f, as a notational reminder).   After the required algebra, one obtains

$$A = \begin{cases} \dfrac{\sigma_{1f}{}^2 - \sigma_{2f}{}^2}{\sqrt{(\sigma_{1f}{}^2 + \sigma_{2f}{}^2)^2 - 4\sigma_{1f}{}^2\sigma_{2f}{}^2|\rho_f|^2}} & \text{(FSK)} \qquad (8\text{-}2\text{-}14a) \\[4mm] \dfrac{\rho_{cp}}{\sqrt{1 - \rho_{sp}{}^2}} & \text{(PSK)} \qquad (8\text{-}2\text{-}14b) \end{cases}$$

$$\begin{Bmatrix} a \\ b \end{Bmatrix} = \frac{1}{2}\left[\frac{(\sigma_{1f}{}^2 + \sigma_{2f}{}^2)(|\langle z_{1f}\rangle|^2 + |\langle z_{2f}\rangle|^2) - 4\sigma_{1f}\sigma_{2f}\,\mathrm{Re}\,(\langle z_{1f}\rangle\langle z_{2f}{}^*\rangle\rho_f)}{(\sigma_{1f}{}^2 + \sigma_{2f}{}^2)^2 - 4\sigma_{1f}{}^2\sigma_{2f}{}^2|\rho_f|^2}\right.$$
$$\left.\mp \frac{|\langle z_{1f}\rangle|^2 - |\langle z_{2f}\rangle|^2}{\sqrt{(\sigma_{1f}{}^2 + \sigma_{2f}{}^2)^2 - 4\sigma_{1f}{}^2\sigma_{2f}{}^2|\rho_f|^2}}\right] \qquad \text{(FSK)} \qquad (8\text{-}2\text{-}15)$$

$$\begin{Bmatrix} a \\ b \end{Bmatrix} = \frac{1}{4(1 - \rho_{sp}{}^2)}\left[\frac{|\langle z_{1p}\rangle|^2}{\sigma_{1p}{}^2} + \frac{|\langle z_{2p}\rangle|^2}{\sigma_{2p}{}^2} + \frac{2\rho_{sp}}{\sigma_{1p}\sigma_{2p}}\,\mathrm{Im}\,(\langle z_{1p}\rangle\langle z_{2p}{}^*\rangle)\right.$$
$$\left.\mp \frac{2\sqrt{1 - \rho_{sp}{}^2}}{\sigma_{1p}\sigma_{2p}}\,\mathrm{Re}\,(\langle z_{1p}\rangle\langle z_{2p}{}^*\rangle)\right] \qquad \text{(PSK)} \qquad (8\text{-}2\text{-}16)$$

where in each case the upper sign gives a and the lower sign b.

In terms of signal and noise power, the results can also be written as

$$\begin{Bmatrix} a \\ b \end{Bmatrix}$$
$$= \frac{(N_{1f} + N_{2f})(S_{1f} + S_{2f}) - 4\sqrt{S_{1f}S_{2f}}\sqrt{N_{1f}N_{2f}}\,|\rho_f|\cos(\theta_{1f} - \theta_{2f} + \phi)}{(N_{1f} + N_{2f})^2 - 4N_{1f}N_{2f}|\rho_f|^2}$$
$$\mp \frac{S_{1f} - S_{2f}}{\sqrt{(N_{1f} + N_{2f})^2 - 4N_{1f}N_{2f}|\rho_f|^2}} \qquad \text{(FSK)} \qquad (8\text{-}2\text{-}17)$$

$$\begin{Bmatrix} a \\ b \end{Bmatrix} = \frac{1}{2(1 - \rho_{sp}{}^2)}\left[\frac{S_{1p}}{N_{1p}} + \frac{S_{2p}}{N_{2p}} + 2\rho_{sp}\sqrt{\frac{S_{1p}}{N_{1p}}\frac{S_{2p}}{N_{2p}}}\,\sin(\theta_{1p} - \theta_{2p})\right.$$
$$\left.\mp 2\sqrt{1 - \rho_{sp}{}^2}\sqrt{\frac{S_{1p}S_{2p}}{N_{1p}N_{2p}}}\,\cos(\theta_{1p} - \theta_{2p})\right] \qquad \text{(PSK)} \qquad (8\text{-}2\text{-}18)$$

8-3. Specializations, Including Previous Results

In Tables (8-3-1) and (8-3-2), we indicate how all the results discussed in Chap. 7, for both PSK and noncoherent FSK, are contained as special cases of these results.   By and large, the derivation of the specialized results from the more general forms is quite straightforward.   In Table 8-3-2, the term $\theta_{1p} - \theta_{2p}$ always refers to an *error* between the signaled phase and the desired component in the reference; i.e., the detection process is based upon the assumption that this phase difference is zero. As commented earlier, if the signaled phase is opposite to that of the reference, the corresponding probability of error in detection is readily

TABLE 8-3-1. SPECIAL CASES: FSK, NONCOHERENT DETECTION

| Conditions | | | | |
Noise levels	Noise correlation	Signals	A	$\begin{Bmatrix}a\\b\end{Bmatrix}$
$N_{1f} = N_{2f} = N_f$	Arbitrary	Arbitrary	0	$\dfrac{1}{2N_f}\left[\dfrac{S_{1f} + S_{2f} - 2\lvert\rho_f\rvert\sqrt{S_{1f}S_{2f}}\cos(\theta_{1f} - \theta_{2f} + \phi)}{1 - \lvert\rho_f\rvert^2} \mp \dfrac{S_{1f} - S_{2f}}{\sqrt{1 - \lvert\rho_f\rvert^2}}\right]$
Arbitrary	$\rho_f = 0$	Arbitrary	$\dfrac{N_{1f} - N_{2f}}{N_{1f} + N_{2f}}$	$a = \dfrac{2S_{2f}}{N_{1f} + N_{2f}} \qquad b = \dfrac{2S_{1f}}{N_{1f} + N_{2f}}$
$N_{1f} = N_{2f} = N_f$			0	$a = \dfrac{S_{2f}}{N_f} \qquad b = \dfrac{S_{1f}}{N_f}$
Arbitrary	$\rho_f = 0$	$S_{2f} = 0$	$\dfrac{N_{1f} - N_{2f}}{N_{1f} + N_{2f}}$	$a = 0 \qquad b = \dfrac{2S_{1f}}{N_{1f} + N_{2f}}$ $P = \dfrac{N_{2f}}{N_{1f} + N_{2f}}\exp\left(-\dfrac{S_{1f}}{N_{1f} + N_{2f}}\right)$
$N_{1f} = N_{2f} = N_f$			0	$a = 0 \qquad b = \dfrac{S_{1f}}{N_f}$ $P = \tfrac{1}{2}\exp\left(-\dfrac{1}{2}\dfrac{S_{1f}}{N_f}\right)$
Matched-filter detection $N_{1f} = N_{2f} = N_f \quad \rho_f = \dfrac{S_{2f}}{S_{1f}}\lvert \exp\,[i(\theta_{2f} - \theta_{1f})]$			0	$\dfrac{S_{1f}}{2N_f}(1 \mp \sqrt{1 - \lvert\rho_f\rvert^2})$
On-off keying (probability of not exceeding threshold) $N_{2f} = 0$	—	Arbitrary; S_{2f} represents threshold level	1	$a = \dfrac{2S_{2f}}{N_{1f}} \qquad b = \dfrac{2S_{1f}}{N_{1f}}$ $P = 1 - Q\left(\sqrt{\dfrac{2S_{1f}}{N_{1f}}}, \sqrt{\dfrac{2S_{2f}}{N_{1f}}}\right)$

TABLE 8-3-2. SPECIAL CASES: PSK

(Note: Same phase assumed signaled as nominally in reference)

Conditions				
Noise levels	Noise cross-correlation	Signal	A	$\left\{\begin{array}{c}a\\b\end{array}\right.$
Arbitrary	$|\rho_c| = 0$	Arbitrary	0	$\frac{1}{2}\left[\frac{S_{1p}}{N_{1p}} + \frac{S_{2p}}{N_{2p}} \mp 2\sqrt{\frac{S_{1p}}{N_{1p}}\frac{S_{2p}}{N_{2p}}}\cos(\theta_{1p} - \theta_{2p})\right]$
		S_{1p}, S_{2p}, arbitrary θ_{1p}, θ_{2p}	0	$\frac{1}{2}\left(\sqrt{\frac{S_{1p}}{N_{1p}}} \mp \sqrt{\frac{S_{2p}}{N_{2p}}}\right)^2$
Differentially coherent PSK: $N_{1p} = N_{2p} = N_p$	$|\rho_c| = 0$	$S_{1p} = S_{2p} = S_p$ θ_{1p}, θ_{2p} arbitrary	0	$\frac{S_p}{N_p}[1 \mp \cos(\theta_{1p} - \theta_{2p})]$
		$\theta_{1p} = \theta_{2p}$	0	$a = 0 \quad b = 2\frac{S_p}{N_p}$ $P = \frac{1}{2}\exp\left(-\frac{S_p}{N_p}\right)$
Ideal nonnoisy reference $N_{2p} = 0$	—	Arbitrary	0	$(a,b) \to \infty$ such that* $\frac{a}{b} \to 1$ and $\sqrt{\frac{b}{2}} - \sqrt{\frac{a}{2}} = \sqrt{\frac{S_{1p}}{N_{1p}}}\cos(\theta_{1p} - \theta_{2p})$ $P = \frac{1}{2}\text{erfc}\left[\sqrt{\frac{S_{1p}}{N_{1p}}}\cos(\theta_{1p} - \theta_{2p})\right]$
		$\theta_{1p} = \theta_{2p}$	0	$P = \frac{1}{2}\text{erfc}\left(\sqrt{\frac{S_{1p}}{N_{1p}}}\right)$

* See, e.g., Appendix A.

shown to be the same; in this case $\theta_{1p} - \theta_{2p}$ refers to any error by which the signaling phase is not exactly in opposition to that of the appropriate component of the reference.

It is apparent in the specialized results that in a large number of practical cases of interest with steady (nonfading) signals, the parameter A in (8-2-14) vanishes. In the FSK envelope-comparison case, this corresponds to the usual practical circumstance that equal noise intensity is associated with the pair of filtered voltages. In the generalized PSK case, the noise associated with the "reference" is uncorrelated with that associated with the "current" signal pulse. Again, since the reference is usually derived only from the signal received over previous pulses, this is a common practical condition for reception with steady signal levels in additive Gaussian noise.[1]

In this important $A = 0$ case, the probability-of-error expression (8-2-12) reduces to the form

$$A = 0 \qquad P_e = \tfrac{1}{2}[1 - Q(\sqrt{b},\sqrt{a}) + Q(\sqrt{a},\sqrt{b})] \qquad (8\text{-}3\text{-}1)$$

This equation can be described by a set of universal curves describing P_e as a function of the parameters a and b. A set of such curves is shown in Fig. 8-3-1.

As one example of the results, consider the case in Table 8-3-1 of dual-filter FSK, with equal noise intensities in both filter outputs, but with noises independent, and with signal terms in both outputs,

$$a = \frac{S_{2f}}{N_f} \qquad b = \frac{S_{1f}}{N_f} \qquad (8\text{-}3\text{-}2)$$

where S_{1f} is the filter output corresponding to the signaled symbol and S_{2f} is an undesired component. The latter might arise as intersymbol (adjacent-symbol) interference because of incomplete filter discharge from the previous pulse (assuming, say, the current pulse is a Mark and the previous one was a Space). In Sec. 7-7, in discussing possible use of an RLC filter rather than a matched filter, we postulated that an intersymbol-interference level of -20 db seemed to be small enough that its presence could be ignored. On the other hand, with Fig. 8-3-1, we can now estimate the effect accurately. Thus, the locus of all points such that $a/b = 0.01$ (-20 db) is a straight line through the origin of slope 0.01, while the horizontal axis ($a = 0$) is the exponential error-rate formula when no intersymbol interference is present. At the value $b = 12.5$, corresponding to $P_e = 10^{-3}$ when $a = 0$, the change in P_e when $a = 0.125$ is indeed negligible for all practical purposes. On the other hand, at $b = 40$, corresponding to $P_e = 10^{-9}$, the value $a = 0.4$ instead of $a = 0$ will increase the error rate to $P_e = 10^{-8}$. We may also note

[1] In extending these models to Rayleigh fading of the signals, Sec. 9-6, the zero-correlation assumption is usually no longer valid.

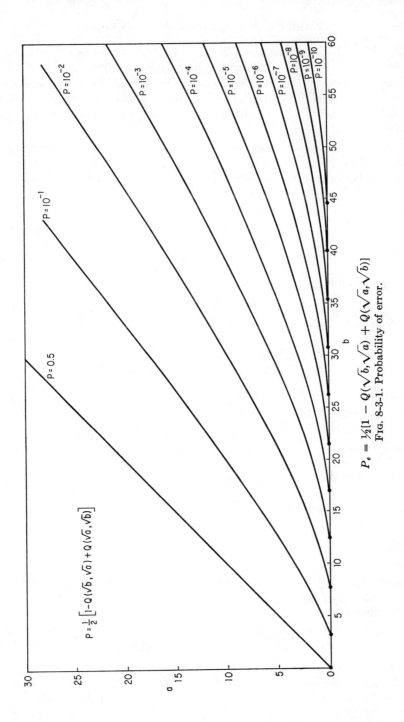

$$P = \frac{1}{2}\left[1 - Q(\sqrt{b}, \sqrt{a}) + Q(\sqrt{a}, \sqrt{b})\right]$$

$$P_e = \frac{1}{2}[1 - Q(\sqrt{b}, \sqrt{a}) + Q(\sqrt{a}, \sqrt{b})]$$

Fig. 8-3-1. Probability of error.

that at $b = 12.5$, a value $a = 1.25$ (-10 db intersymbol interference) will increase the error rate a full order of magnitude, to 10^{-2} rather than 10^{-3}. Note, in other words, that with the curves of Fig. 8-3-1, the effect on error rate of intersymbol interference (or of imperfect synchronization, which will lead to similar phenomena) can be estimated accurately for practical FSK systems.

Likewise, in extensions of DPSK where the "reference" is derived over many pulses rather than just one and hence is relatively less noisy than the signal pulse voltage, the appropriate forms from Table 8-3-2 can be used to determine the improvement.[1]   In this case, setting

$$\gamma_1 = \frac{S_{1p}}{N_{1p}} \tag{8-3-3a}$$

$$\gamma_2 = \frac{S_{2p}}{N_{2p}} \tag{8-3-3b}$$

we can assume

$$\gamma_2 > \gamma_1 \tag{8-3-3c}$$

that is, γ_2 refers to the "reference."   In this case

$$\frac{a}{b} = \left(\frac{\sqrt{\gamma_1} - \sqrt{\gamma_2}}{\sqrt{\gamma_1} + \sqrt{\gamma_2}}\right)^2 = \left(\frac{\sqrt{\gamma_2/\gamma_1} - 1}{\sqrt{\gamma_2/\gamma_1} + 1}\right)^2 \tag{8-3-4}$$

For a given value of $\sqrt{\gamma_2/\gamma_1}$, the locus of values of a/b is again a straight line with slope determined by $\sqrt{\gamma_2/\gamma_1}$.   The horizontal axis $a = 0$ corresponds to the DPSK case $\sqrt{\gamma_2/\gamma_1} = 1$.   For example, consider the value $S_{1p}/N_{1p} = \gamma_1 = 12.5/2 = 6.25$, which in DPSK gives the error rate 10^{-3}.   If instead $S_{2p}/N_{2p} = \gamma_2 = 18.75$ (an improvement of 5 db in the SNR of the "reference"), one obtains

$$a = \tfrac{1}{2}(\sqrt{18.75} - \sqrt{6.25})^2 = 1.67$$
$$b = \tfrac{1}{2}(\sqrt{18.75} + \sqrt{6.25})^2 = 23.33$$

and the error rate is approximately $P_e = 2(10)^{-4}$.   From Fig. 7-5-1, it is clear that 5db improvement in SNR of the reference suffices to almost completely achieve the performance of coherent PSK at the same SNR ($\gamma_1 = 6.25 = 8$db).

Another interesting example is noncoherent matched-filter detection in white noise of generalized FSK involving a pair of nonorthogonal, equal-energy waveforms, for which the results are indicated in the appropriate

---

[1] This result for this generalization of DPSK is believed to have first been derived by Leon Lewandowski, Derivation of the Probability of Error in a PSK System Employing Phase Locked Loop, Sylvania Electronic Systems, Buffalo, N.Y., Feb. 7, 1962.   The results were there derived by intricate complex-plane transformations. Lewandowski in this note recognized and emphasized the utility of using scalar product forms in analyzing the generalized PSK problem.

entry of Table 8-3-1.[1] Since the two matched filter response functions are identical with the two signalling waveforms, the noise cross-covariance is intimately related to the waveforms, as indicated in Table 8-3-1. From the results for a and b, one then obtains the useful relations

$$a + b = \frac{S_{1f}}{N_f} \tag{8-3-5a}$$

$$\frac{a}{b} = \frac{1 - \sqrt{1 - |\rho_f|^2}}{1 + \sqrt{1 - |\rho_f|^2}} \tag{8-3-5b}$$

Thus the lines $a = K_1 b$ form a family with only $|\rho_f|$ as the parameter determining K_1; the lines $a + b = K_2$ form another family with only signal-noise ratio as the parameter determining K_2. (S_{1f}/N_f is identical to the E/n_0, or bit energy-noise power-density ratio, for matched filters.) Drawing these two sets of straight lines, as shown in Fig. 8-3-2, then gives a complete picture of the result.

In other problems, such "load lines" as shown in Fig. 8-3-2 would generally no longer be straight. Nevertheless, since the computations of a, b are filter computations, the curves of Fig. 8-3-1 may be useful in engineering calculations of the effects of various particular system parameters upon error-rate performance. Again, we remind the reader that the curves of Fig. 8-3-1 apply only when $A = 0$ in (8-2-12). While this applies in many practical systems, it is not universally true.

8-4. Distribution of Instantaneous Frequency for Signal Plus Noise[2]

One can also apply the results of Sec. 8-2 to obtain results for performance of an FSK receiver based on an ideal frequency detector or limiter-discriminator. This mode of reception for FSK is quite common in practice, but was excluded from discussion in Chap. 7 because of the need for the results of Sec. 8-2 for a useful mathematical discussion. The performance will be discussed in detail in Sec. 8-5 as a special case of a more general result, presented immediately below, on the probability distribution of the instantaneous frequency of an arbitrary signal plus additive Gaussian noise.

Using complex envelope notation as introduced earlier, a bandpass voltage comprising a signal plus additive stationary Gaussian noise can

---

[1] The solution, for this matched-filter case only, was first given in C. W. Helstrom, Resolution of Signals in White, Gaussian Noise, *Proc. IRE*, vol. 43, pp. 1111–1118, September, 1955. Several important generalizations appear in G. L. Turin, Error Probabilities for Binary Symmetric Ideal Reception Through Nonselective Slow Fading and Noise, *Proc. IRE*, vol. 46, pp. 1603–1619, September, 1958.

[2] The material of this section is largely adapted from J. Salz and S. Stein, Distribution of Instantaneous Frequency for Signal Plus Noise, *IEEE Trans. Inform. Theory*, vol. IT-10, pp. 272–274, October, 1964.

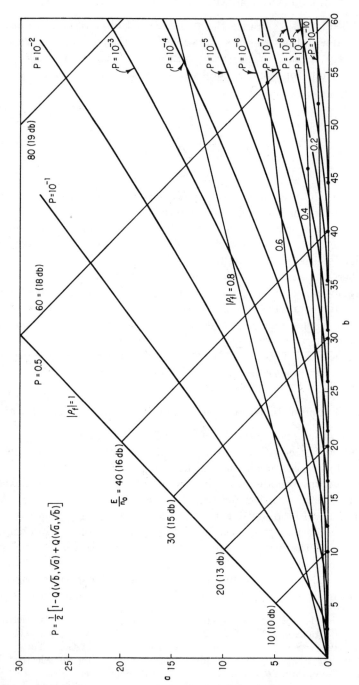

Fig. 8-3-2. Probability of error for matched-filter FSK.

be written as

$$u(t) = \text{Re}\,[z(t)\exp\,(j\omega_0 t)] \qquad (8\text{-}4\text{-}1)$$

The ensemble mean $\langle z(t)\rangle$ then represents the signal component, and $[z(t) - \langle z(t)\rangle]$ is the additive zero-mean bandpass Gaussian noise component. Thus $z(t)$ is a complex, *nonzero*-mean Gaussian process. The nominal carrier frequency f_0 is again assumed much larger than the bandwidth of $z(t)$.

The instantaneous radian frequency relative to ω_0, very closely approximating the output of a practical wideband limiter-discriminator, is then defined as the derivative of the instantaneous r-f phase in (8-4-1) relative to ω_0,

$$\nu(t) = \frac{d}{dt}\arg z(t) = \frac{d}{dt}\text{Im}\,[\ln z(t)] = \text{Im}\left[\frac{\dot{z}(t)}{z(t)}\right] \qquad (8\text{-}4\text{-}2)$$

For later convenience, we further rewrite the instantaneous frequency as[1]

$$\nu(t) = \frac{\text{Im}\,[z^*(t)\dot{z}(t)]}{|z(t)|^2} = \frac{\text{Re}\,[-jz^*(t)\dot{z}(t)]}{|z(t)|^2} \qquad (8\text{-}4\text{-}3)$$

Recall that stationary narrowband bandpass Gaussian noise fluctuation components have covariance properties describable by

$$\tfrac{1}{2}\langle[z(t) - \langle z(t)\rangle]^*[z(t + \tau) - \langle z(t + \tau)\rangle]\rangle = N\rho(\tau) \qquad (8\text{-}4\text{-}4a)$$

where $\rho(\tau)$ is the normalized complex autocovariance function and

$$\tfrac{1}{2}\langle|z(t) - \langle z(t)\rangle|^2\rangle = N \qquad (8\text{-}4\text{-}4b)$$

is the mean noise power. Furthermore, $\dot{z}(t)$ is then also a complex, nonzero-mean stationary Gaussian process, with $z(t)$ and $\dot{z}(t)$ satisfying a joint distribution. The statistical properties which we shall need are well-known,[2] or easily derived from (8-4-4). These are

$$\tfrac{1}{2}\langle|\dot{z}(t) - \langle\dot{z}(t)\rangle|^2\rangle = -N\ddot{\rho}(0) = N(2\pi f_2)^2 \qquad (8\text{-}4\text{-}5)$$

$$\tfrac{1}{2}\langle[z(t) - \langle z(t)\rangle]^*[\dot{z}(t) - \langle\dot{z}(t)\rangle]\rangle = N\dot{\rho}(0) = j2\pi f_1 N \qquad (8\text{-}4\text{-}6)$$

In the above, with $G(f)$ the normalized power density spectrum of $z(t) - \langle z(t)\rangle$ and hence the Fourier transform of $\rho(\tau)$, f_1 and f_2 are respectively the "mean" and "rms" frequencies in $G(f)$,

$$\rho(\tau) = \int_{-\infty}^{\infty}\exp\,(j\omega\tau)G(f)\,df \qquad (8\text{-}4\text{-}7a)$$

$$f_1 = \int_{-\infty}^{\infty}fG(f)\,df \qquad (8\text{-}4\text{-}7b)$$

$$f_2 = \left[\int_{-\infty}^{\infty}f^2 G(f)\,df\right]^{1/2} \qquad (8\text{-}4\text{-}7c)$$

[1] At low envelope values, $\nu(t)$ defined by (8-4-3) becomes infinite. This does not affect the cumulative distribution calculated below but makes this mathematical model inappropriate as an approximation to a real discriminator in calculating output power spectra or other second moments. See p. 132.

[2] R. Arens, Complex Processes for Envelopes of Normal Noise, *IRE Trans. Inform. Theory*, vol. IT-3, pp. 204–207, September, 1957; S. O. Rice, Statistical Properties of a Sine Wave Plus Random Noise, *Bell System Tech. J.*, vol. 27, pp. 109–157, January, 1948.

The probability distribution for the instantaneous frequency ν defined by (8-4-3) can now be written as

$$\text{Prob} \; (\nu < \eta) = \text{Prob} \left[\frac{\text{Re} \; (-jz^*\dot{z})}{|z|^2} < \eta \right]$$

$$= \text{Prob} \left[\frac{\text{Re} \; (-jz^*\dot{z} - \eta|z|^2)}{|z|^2} < 0 \right] \quad (8\text{-}4\text{-}8)$$

The functional dependence on t has been suppressed in all the variates here and below, with the understanding that all are being taken at some particular instant of time. Since the denominator in (8-4-8) is always positive, the probability statement can be rewritten further as

$$\text{Prob} \; (\nu < \eta) = \text{Prob} \; [\text{Re} \; (-jz^*\dot{z} - \eta|z|^2) < 0]$$

$$= \text{Prob} \; [\text{Re} \; (z^*\xi) < 0] \quad (8\text{-}4\text{-}9a)$$

where

$$\xi(t) = -j\dot{z}(t) - \eta z(t) \quad (8\text{-}4\text{-}9b)$$

Then $\xi(t)$ is also a nonzero-mean complex Gaussian process. From (8-4-4) to (8-4-6), its relevant first and second moments are defined, along with the variance of $z(t)$, by

$$\langle \xi(t) \rangle = -j\langle \dot{z}(t) \rangle - \eta \langle z(t) \rangle \quad (8\text{-}4\text{-}10a)$$

$$\sigma_1{}^2 = \tfrac{1}{2}\langle |z(t) - \langle z(t) \rangle|^2 \rangle = N \quad (8\text{-}4\text{-}10b)$$

$$\sigma_2{}^2 = \tfrac{1}{2}\langle |\xi(t) - \langle \xi(t) \rangle|^2 \rangle = N[\eta^2 + (2\pi f_2)^2 - 4\pi\eta f_1] \quad (8\text{-}4\text{-}10c)$$

$$\sigma_1\sigma_2(\rho_c + j\rho_s) = \tfrac{1}{2}\langle [z(t) - \langle z(t) \rangle]^*[\xi(t) - \langle \xi(t) \rangle] \rangle = (2\pi f_1 - \eta)N \quad (8\text{-}4\text{-}10d)$$

From this last equation,

$$\rho_s = 0 \quad (8\text{-}4\text{-}10e)$$

$$\rho_c = \frac{2\pi f_1 - \eta}{\sqrt{\eta^2 + (2\pi f_2)^2 - 4\pi\eta f_1}} \quad (8\text{-}4\text{-}10f)$$

The probability in (8-4-9) is now formally analogous to that involved earlier in the generalized PSK problem, (8-1-18). We employ the form of solution described by (8-2-12), (8-2-14b), and (8-2-16)

$$\text{Prob} \; (\nu < \eta) = \tfrac{1}{2}[1 - Q(\sqrt{b}, \sqrt{a}) + Q(\sqrt{a}, \sqrt{b})]$$

$$- \frac{A}{2} \exp\left(-\frac{a+b}{2}\right) I_0(\sqrt{ab}) \quad (8\text{-}4\text{-}11)$$

where

$$A = \frac{\rho_c}{\sqrt{1 - \rho_s{}^2}} \quad (8\text{-}4\text{-}12a)$$

$$\begin{Bmatrix} a \\ b \end{Bmatrix} = \frac{1}{4(1 - \rho_s{}^2)} \left[\frac{|\langle z \rangle|^2}{\sigma_1{}^2} + \frac{|\langle \xi \rangle|^2}{\sigma_2{}^2} + \frac{2\rho_s}{\sigma_1\sigma_2} \text{Im} \; (\langle z \rangle \langle \xi^* \rangle) \right.$$

$$\left. \mp \frac{2\sqrt{1 - \rho_s{}^2}}{\sigma_1\sigma_2} \text{Re} \; (\langle z \rangle \langle \xi^* \rangle) \right] \quad (8\text{-}4\text{-}12b)$$

In addition to inserting the statistics of (8-4-10), let us describe the signal term in its varying amplitude and phase factors,

$$\langle z(t) \rangle = R(t) \exp [j\psi(t)] \tag{8-4-13a}$$

$$\langle \dot{z}(t) \rangle = R(t) \exp [j\psi(t)] \left[\frac{\dot{R}(t)}{R(t)} + j\dot{\psi}(t) \right] \tag{8-4-13b}$$

Then the parameters of (8-4-12) can be shown to reduce to

$$A = \frac{2\pi f_1 - \eta}{\sqrt{\eta^2 + (2\pi f_2)^2 - 4\pi\eta f_1}} \tag{8-4-14}$$

$$\begin{Bmatrix} a \\ b \end{Bmatrix} = \frac{R^2}{4N} \left\{ \left(\frac{\dot{R}}{R} \right)^2 \frac{1}{\eta^2 + (2\pi f_2)^2 - 4\pi\eta f_1} \right.$$
$$\left. + \left[1 \mp \frac{\dot{\psi} - \eta}{\sqrt{\eta^2 + (2\pi f_2)^2 - 4\pi\eta f_1}} \right]^2 \right\} \tag{8-4-15}$$

The quantity

$$\gamma = \frac{R^2}{2N} \tag{8-4-16}$$

in (8-4-15) is the "instantaneous" signal-noise ratio at the same instant of time at which the probability of instantaneous frequency is given by (8-4-11).

In most applications, the spectrum of the additive noise will be symmetric about its center frequency, and then f_1 will vanish. On the other hand, even if the system is designed on this basis, frequency-drift effects may serve to uncenter the spectrum about the nominal center frequency, and then the parameter f_1 will be important in assessing the effects of the offset.

In practical applications the instantaneous frequency is measured by a limiter-discriminator or, equivalently, a zero-crossing-rate counter. These usually have a design bandwidth, within which they correspond excellently to an ideal detector of instantaneous frequency. However, the mathematical results above correspond to a frequency detector with an infinite bandwidth capability. Usually this mathematical over-idealization of the physical detector would be of no consequence, because the voltages applied to the detector are of limited bandwidth. However, one practical case of interest which cannot be analyzed because of this overidealization is that where the additive noise corresponds to white noise passed through a bandpass single-pole (RLC) filter. In this case, its frequency spectrum $G(f)$ falls off as $1/f^2$, with f measured from the center frequency, and then in (8-4-7), $f_2 \to \infty$. In (8-4-14) and (8-4-15) for this condition,

$$A \to 0$$

$$a = b = \frac{\gamma}{2}$$

and (8-4-11) becomes

$$\text{Prob} \ (\nu < \eta) = \frac{1}{2}$$

Thus for this kind of additive noise, the instantaneous frequency is extremely (infinitely) large for a major portion of time. In fact, as seen in (8-4-5), the derivative process under these conditions has an infinite rms value. It is worth reemphasizing that the results break down in this single-pole filtering case because of the overidealization of the frequency detector, which attributes undue significance to far-out spectral components of the noise process. For higher-order processes (i.e., spectra decreasing as $1/f^4$), it is *assumed* that while far-out spectral components again contribute to the computations, their significance is negligible as far as frequency components beyond the range of the practical device being considered. From a calculation viewpoint, therefore, the formulas above are quite useful, but their application must be limited because of the overidealization of the frequency detector implicit in them.

The results of this section for the distribution of instantaneous frequency have application in many problems of digital communications,[1] as well as in other areas. We shall particularly apply them below to frequency detection of binary FSK. Within the digital communications field the distribution is also particularly applicable towards determining performance for multitone FSK systems with frequency detection. The latter case will not be discussed at all here, however, in keeping with our expressed limitation to results for binary systems.

8-5. Binary FSK with Frequency Detection

The results of the previous section can be applied to frequency detection of binary FSK, for steady signals in additive Gaussian noise. We assume as a model that the receiver comprises *one* bandpass filter wide enough to pass both Mark and Space waveforms in appropriate measure, followed by the frequency detector and a sampling and decision circuit. To use the mathematical results, we assume that the frequency detector is infinitely wideband, i.e., that it is a perfect instantaneous frequency detector in the sense discussed in the previous section.

Furthermore, we are assuming that there is no postdetection smoothing (filtering) prior to the binary decision device—the decisions are made on the basis of sampling the detector output once per binary element. It is not clear that this is truly a best procedure. It certainly is not the usual procedure in demodulation of FM. However, since we are only interested

---

[1] The literature contains several results equivalent to that presented here, but with the results presented as integrals of various types for which numerical integrations are accomplished: A. V. Balakrishnan and I. J. Abrams, Detection Levels and Error Rates in PCM Telemetry Systems, *IRE Intern. Conv. Record*, part 5, pp. 37–55, March, 1960; A. A. Meyerhoff and W. M. Mazer, Optimum Binary F-M Reception Using Discriminator Detection and IF Shaping, *RCA Rev.*, vol. 22, pp. 698–728, December, 1961; W. R. Bennett and J. Salz, Binary Data Transmission by FM Over a Real Channel, *Bell System Tech. J.*, vol. 42, pp. 2387–2426, September, 1963.

in a binary decision, we may draw upon our decision-theory intuition to suggest that an optimum predetector filtering will be relatively narrowband, aimed at maximizing the frequency-detector SNR at the decision instant. If all the available energy has thus been concentrated into the single instant of decision, one would not expect additional postdetection filtering to yield useful further improvement. (Note that decision theory itself cannot be used to reach any such conclusion, since it leads to the dual matched-filter receiver rather than the frequency detector.) Indeed, calculations mentioned below on this model of predetection but no post-detection filtering do indicate the optimum predetection bandwidth to be much narrower than would be conceived on the basis of usual FM signal-fidelity considerations. At the same time, no useful analyses appear to be available for postdetection integration or any other kind of filtering after a frequency detector. (The integration of instantaneous frequency would appear to yield an output proportional to the net phase change over the interval. Some published analysis based on this appear to have overlooked the fact that phase is invariably defined modulo 2π, whereas in this problem one must maintain track of the total number of cycles of phase change as well.) Thus, in addition to intuitive arguments in favor of not needing any postdetection filtering, we are here also faced with the absence of any results other than described below for the filter-detection-decision model.

In our model then, the results of the previous section describe the probability distribution at the binary decision point (immediately follow-ing the frequency detector) when the voltages are those at the filter output at the same instant. We can assume that the Mark and Space signals are so designed as to appear symmetrically disposed in frequency about the filter center frequency f_0. Then, since frequency is detected relative to f_0, the binary decisions are made according to whether the algebraic sign of the detector output is positive or negative. Assume for the moment that Mark is signaled and that this corresponds to a positive detector output. Then the probability of an error is the probability that the instantaneous frequency at the sampling instant is negative (relative to f_0). In (8-4-11) and (8-4-15), this is the special case $\eta = 0$, which we can write as

$$P_{eM} = \text{Prob } (\nu < 0) = \tfrac{1}{2}[1 - Q(\sqrt{b_M},\sqrt{a_M}) + Q(\sqrt{a_M},\sqrt{b_M})]$$
$$- \frac{A}{2} \exp\left(- \frac{a_M + b_M}{2}\right) I_0(\sqrt{a_M b_M}) \quad (8\text{-}5\text{-}1)$$

where
$$A = \frac{f_1}{f_2} \quad (8\text{-}5\text{-}2a)$$

(note f_1 may be either positive or negative, but f_2 is defined positive),

and
$$\begin{Bmatrix} a_M \\ b_M \end{Bmatrix} = \frac{\gamma_M}{2} \left[\frac{1}{(2\pi f_2)^2} \left(\frac{\dot{R}_M}{R_M}\right)^2 + \left(1 \mp \frac{\dot{\psi}_M}{2\pi f_2}\right)^2 \right] \quad (8\text{-}5\text{-}2b)$$

Here $\dot{\psi}_M$ is the instantaneous radian frequency at the filter output when Mark is signaled (the other parameters being similarly defined).

Likewise, with Space signaled, the probability of error will be

$$P_{eS} = \text{Prob } (\nu > 0) = 1 - \text{Prob } (\nu < 0)$$
$$= \tfrac{1}{2}[1 - Q(\sqrt{a_S},\sqrt{b_S}) + Q(\sqrt{b_S},\sqrt{a_S})]$$
$$+ \frac{A}{2} \exp\left(- \frac{a_S + b_S}{2}\right) I_0(\sqrt{a_S b_S}) \quad (8\text{-}5\text{-}3)$$

where
$$A = \frac{f_1}{f_2} \quad (8\text{-}5\text{-}4a)$$

$$\begin{Bmatrix} a_S \\ b_S \end{Bmatrix} = \frac{\gamma_S}{2}\left[\frac{1}{(2\pi f_2)^2}\left(\frac{\dot{R}_S}{R_S}\right)^2 + \left(1 \mp \frac{\dot{\psi}_S}{2\pi f_2}\right)^2\right] \quad (8\text{-}5\text{-}4b)$$

where now $\dot{\psi}_S$ (and all the other parameters) is appropriate to the filter output when Space is signaled.

In most practical instances, the filtering is designed to have a symmetric transfer function about the center frequency f_0. In this case, in (8-5-2a) and (8-5-4a),

$$\text{Symmetric filter} \quad \begin{cases} f_1 = 0 & (8\text{-}5\text{-}5a) \\ A = 0 & (8\text{-}5\text{-}5b) \end{cases}$$

Note the factor f_1 enters in binary FSK only through the factor A. Note also that f_1 is a property of the receiving filter only; even if the signal is not properly centered in the filter, e.g., because of Doppler shifts, the noise spectrum of the filter will still have $f_1 = 0$ if the filter has a symmetric bandpass response. Thus, while (8-5-1) and (8-5-3) provide a basis for calculating the error effects even when (8-5-5) does not hold, we shall assume it to be the case in all our further discussions. Thus we have

$$P_{eM} = \tfrac{1}{2}[1 - Q(\sqrt{b_M},\sqrt{a_M}) + Q(\sqrt{a_M},\sqrt{b_M})] \quad (8\text{-}5\text{-}6a)$$
$$P_{eS} = \tfrac{1}{2}[1 - Q(\sqrt{a_S},\sqrt{b_S}) + Q(\sqrt{b_S},\sqrt{a_S})] \quad (8\text{-}5\text{-}6b)$$

where (a_M,b_M) and (a_S,b_S) are given by (8-5-2b) and (8-5-4b), respectively. The curves of Fig. 8-3-1 then apply directly [note the interchange of labeling in applying it to (8-5-6b)], so long as we make the appropriate filter calculations to obtain (a_M,b_M) and (a_S,b_S).

If we examine (8-5-2b) and (8-5-4b) in the light of (8-5-6), we note one interesting result concerning the influence of $\dot{R}$ being nonvanishing at the decision instant: if $\dot{R}$ has a nonzero value, both a and b are increased by the same amount over the values they would have had, if *all other parameters remained the same*. Referring to Fig. 8-3-1, it is clear that increasing a and b by an equal amount (i.e., moving on a 45° line) always increases the probability of error. Hence, *all other parameters remaining the same*, the smaller the value of $\dot{R}$, the lower the probability of error. It is tempting to infer from this that the design goal should be a large enough ratio of filter bandwidth to keying rate that $\dot{R}$ indeed vanishes at each decision instant. However, a narrower filter bandwidth may also improve the SNR γ sufficiently (i.e., increase a and b in the *same ratio*, hence usually along a line inclined much more than 45°) as to more than overcome the effect of introducing a large value of $\dot{R}$. Thus with all other values correct, the computation assuming $\dot{R} = 0$ gives a lower bound to the error rate, with actual performance some amount poorer.

A further interesting specialization in (8-5-2b) and (8-5-4b) occurs when it can be assumed that the filter is exactly tuned to the signal and that the signal in turn is designed with symmetrical frequency shifts about the center frequency. Then the instantaneous frequency of the filter output $\dot{\psi}$ will have equal and opposite values in the Mark and Space cases, respectively, while $\dot{R}$ and R will have the same values. Thus, if Mark signaled gives a certain set of parameters (a_M, b_M) in (5-4-2b), there will be an exactly equivalent Space condition in which, comparing (5-4-4b) and (5-4-2b),

$$a_S = b_M \\ a_M = b_S \tag{8-5-7}$$

and thus in fact the two probabilities of error in (8-5-6) will be exactly identical. For simplicity, we shall assume this case below. Then it is sufficient to calculate on the basis of a Mark signaled, writing now simply

$$P_e = \frac{1}{2}[1 - Q(\sqrt{b}, \sqrt{a}) + Q(\sqrt{a}, \sqrt{b})] \tag{8-5-8}$$

$$\begin{Bmatrix} a \\ b \end{Bmatrix} = \frac{\gamma}{2}\left[\frac{1}{(2\pi f_2)^2}\left(\frac{\dot{R}}{R}\right)^2 + \left(1 \mp \frac{\dot{\psi}}{2\pi f_2}\right)^2\right] \tag{8-5-9}$$

where, recalling (8-5-1), $\dot{\psi}$ is so designed that in the absence of noise and with reasonable filtering, it would be positive at the sampling instant.

For example, with sufficiently wide filtering of the signal, the signal terms at the filter output (discriminator input) around the sampling instant might be characterized by

$$R(t) = \text{constant} \qquad \dot{R}(t) = 0 \tag{8-5-10a}$$
$$\psi(t) = 2\pi f_d t \qquad \dot{\psi}(t) = 2\pi f_d \tag{8-5-10b}$$
$$f_d > 0 \tag{8-5-10c}$$

In this notation, $2f_d$ is the total spacing between Mark and Space tones. Then in (8-5-9)

$$\sqrt{a} = \sqrt{\frac{\gamma}{2}}\left|1 - \frac{f_d}{f_2}\right| \tag{8-5-11a}$$

$$\sqrt{b} = \sqrt{\frac{\gamma}{2}}\left(1 + \frac{f_d}{f_2}\right) \tag{8-5-11b}$$

While this is an interesting case, generally it may be better to use a more restricted bandwidth, hence increasing the SNR γ at the cost of allowing some intersymbol interference (residual voltages due to previous pulses).

We return to this below, but for the moment examine further the result (8-5-11).

The Exponential Error-rate Formula. In (8-5-11), we note the particular case when

$$\frac{f_d}{f_2} = 1 \tag{8-5-12}$$

that is, the signaled frequency deviation from nominal center frequency is exactly equal to the "rms frequency" of the noise spectrum. For this special case, (8-5-11) then becomes

$$\begin{aligned} \sqrt{a} &= 0 \\ \sqrt{b} &= \sqrt{2\gamma} \end{aligned} \tag{8-5-13}$$

Recalling (Appendix A) the special forms of the Q function when one of its arguments is zero, one obtains in (8-5-8)

$$P_e = \tfrac{1}{2} \exp(-\gamma) \tag{8-5-14}$$

Note that in (8-5-14), γ is measured at the output of a filter wide enough to pass *both* tones. Recall that in Sec. 7-5, for noncoherent dual-filter detection of FSK we had the result

$$P_e = \frac{1}{2} \exp\left(-\frac{\gamma}{2}\right) \tag{8-5-15}$$

where here γ is the SNR at the output of a filter wide enough to pass *one* of the two tones. Roughly speaking, under equivalent signaling and reception conditions, the latter SNR will then be twice that involved in the γ of (8-5-14), hence the extra factor of $\frac{1}{2}$ in the exponent of (8-5-15) will serve to produce the *same* result with either kind of detection. Even though this is only a rough comparison, it is extremely interesting to note that frequency detection which is not at all suggested by decision theory (such as in Chap. 2) gives roughly the same result as the noncoherent dual-filter detection suggested by decision theory.

The exponential dependence of error probability upon SNR in (8-5-14) is also identical in form with a result due to Montgomery[1] which for many years was the only analytical estimate available for performance with frequency detection of FSK. Montgomery in effect made a "sharp FM threshold" assumption to achieve his result (this assumption is warranted only as a useful "first approximation"). Thus, it was assumed that in frequency detection of the receiver filter output, the *correct* decision is made whenever, at the sampling instant, the envelope of the filter-output noise is below that of the signal output, and that, on the other hand, a *purely random* choice occurs when the noise envelope is the larger. The envelope of the Gaussian *noise* $r(t)$ has the Rayleigh probability-density

[1] G. F. Montgomery, A Comparison of Amplitude and Angle Modulation for Narrow-Band Communication of Binary Coded Messages in Fluctuation Noise, *Proc. IRE*, vol. 42, pp. 447–454, February, 1954.

function

$$p(r) = \frac{r}{N} \exp\left(-\frac{r^2}{2N}\right) \tag{8-5-16}$$

Thus, Montgomery's assumption is that no errors occur when $r(t) < R(t)$ at the sampling instant and that when $r(t) > R(t)$, errors occur with probability $\frac{1}{2}$ (in a purely random decision, there is always a probability $\frac{1}{2}$ of accidentally making the correct choice). Thus the estimate of the error rate is

$$P_e = \frac{1}{2} \int_{R(t)}^{\infty} \frac{r}{N} \exp\left(-\frac{r^2}{2N}\right) dr = \frac{1}{2} \exp\left[-\frac{R^2(t)}{2N_0}\right] = \frac{1}{2} \exp\left(-\gamma\right)$$

$$\tag{8-5-17}$$

which, as stated earlier, is exactly the form in (8-5-14). It is apparent, however, based on the succession of specializations involved in arriving at (8-5-14), that Montgomery's result applies rigorously only under a very special set of system parameters. On the other hand, calculations based on the more rigorous results, as discussed below, seem to indicate that the best achievable reception performance is obtained by filtering the pre-discriminator signal to a noise bandwidth which closely gives (8-5-12) and (8-5-14). Hence Montgomery's result, with γ properly interpreted, may indeed closely represent the best performance available in discriminator reception of FSK.

Narrow-bandwidth Calculations. As we have implied several times above, engineering practice (based on experimental data) in the design of FSK systems with frequency detection implies that best performance is obtained with receiving-filter bandwidths of the order of, or less than, the tone spacing and/or the keying rate. Theoretical computations and experimental data must then be carefully presented in terms of fully understanding, and properly averaging, the intersymbol-interference effects. For each pulse, these clearly vary with the message sequences of the prior pulses. At this time, the amount of detailed data of this type is so sparse and difficult to interpret that we shall present only a very limited discussion.

The interpretations of experimental data reported in the literature[1] have primarily been with respect to the exponential error-rate formula. These experimental data, which do not clearly indicate the nature of any intersymbol interference in the experiments, seem to be well-approximated by error formulas of the form

$$\frac{1}{2} \exp\left(-k\gamma\right)$$

[1] E.g., H. B. Law, The Signal/Noise Performance Rating of Receivers for Long-Distance Synchronous Radiotelegraph Systems Using Frequency Modulation, *Proc. IEE*, vol. 104, pt. B, pp. 124–129, March, 1957. H. C. A. van Duuren, Error Probability and Transmission Speed on Circuits Using Error Detection and Automatic Repetition of Signals, *IRE Trans. Comm. Systems*, vol. CS-9, pp. 38–50, March, 1961.

where γ is as defined earlier and k is a factor usually less than unity by a factor of the order of 1 to 2 db. For parameters close to those which theoretically give rise to the exponential error-rate law, and in view of the logarithmic nature of the usual plots, such an approximate kind of fit seems not surprising.

The theoretical data are all based on numerical integrations for specific parameters of formulas equivalent to those derived above, or special cases thereof. One set of calculations is for Gaussian-shaped variation of frequency, as received with Gaussian-shaped filters[1] (see also discussion below of DPSK). Another set[2] covers a periodic message sequence (alternating Marks and Spaces), with both rectangular and sinusoidal frequency variations assumed at the receiving filter *output* and hence intersymbol interference apparently ignored. The most detailed published theoretical calculations taking intersymbol interference into account[3] have involved calculations for all possible 10-bit sequences prior to the "current pulse." Rectangular keying was assumed, with tone spacing equal to the keying rate. Cosine roll-off filters and an actual phone-line characteristic were considered, with nominal bandwidths equal to the keying rate. (No attempt was apparently made to choose an optimum filter bandwidth.) In the first case, the "worst" sequence is about 1 db poorer than the "best" sequence, and the latter performance about 2.5 db poorer than ideal coherent PSK (hence better than dual-filter reception of the same FSK pulses—see the discussion below on DPSK). In the second case, of a real filter, results were about 2 db poorer; measured results for a system claimed to be approximately equivalent were about 1 db poorer than the theoretical results.

Frequency Detection of DPSK. Earlier, in discussing binary differential phase-shift keying, we described a system using only two phases, say 0° and 180°. However, without any change in performance, one could visualize a more symmetric phase shifting in which each pulse utilizes a phase shift either +90° or −90° from the previous pulse to denote Mark and Space, respectively. The two possible binary states in each pulse are still 180° apart, so that the standard DPSK detection (with the previous pulse used now to set up phase-detection references at 90° lead, and at 90° lag) will yield the same probability of error discussed earlier. In this new form, however, one can regard the phase transitions between successive pulses ($+\pi/2$ or $-\pi/2$ radians) as impulsive changes in frequency. That is, instantaneous frequency is the derivative of the instantaneous phase (or phase is the integral of the instantaneous fre-

---

[1] Meyerhoff and Mazer, *loc. cit*; these calculations are made assuming an empirical tolerable level of intersymbol interference by which to choose the narrowest allowed bandwidth, with intersymbol interference ignored in the error-rate calculations.

[2] Balakrishnan and Abrams, *loc. cit.*

[3] Bennett and Salz, *loc. cit.*

quency). Since a typical (rectangular keyed) DPSK signal consists of a carrier at frequency f_0 with segments of constant phase separated by step jumps, the same waveform can be regarded as a carrier of frequency f_0, frequency-modulated (at the phase transitions) by impulses with impulse areas $+\pi/2$ or $-\pi/2$.

Thus, DPSK signals can be viewed as a particular kind of frequency-modulated signal, with differentially encoded binary information presented as positive or negative impulses of appropriate impulse area. In a study of frequency detection of binary frequency-modulated signals, this limiting case might suggest itself as one convenient for computation. Calculations have been carried out of impulse frequency modulation,[1] apparently in exactly this latter context of a simple limiting case. A Gaussian-shaped receiving filter was considered as the receiver filter. Its bandwidth was chosen on the empirical basis of an allowable intersymbol-interference level (-26 db), and then the error rate was calculated as if no intersymbol interference were present. The filter bandwidth is slightly greater than half the keying rate. In this error-rate calculation, it was shown that an approximately optimum impulse area for the frequency impulses is 83° (that it is not 90° presumably has to do with various approximations made), and that the performance with this signaling and filtering, with *frequency detection*, is within about 1 db of that obtained with "coherent" detection of DPSK *with* matched filtering.

Recalling the discussions in Sec. 7-6, this result is an interesting contribution to the "philosophical" question of whether DPSK should be viewed in terms of a coherent detection system or as a strategically designed noncoherent detection system. It seems clear that an FSK system based on somewhat broader modulation "impulses" would perform almost as well. Coupled with the discussion in Sec. 7-6 on a dual-filter noncoherent detection mode for DPSK, the philosophical situation seems to be the following: From the statistical decision-theory emphasis on regarding each information interval as distinct from every other, and from the practical concept of intersymbol interference as ordinarily being a destructive effect, a "folk theorem" grew to be accepted that in sending at a keying rate $1/T$ one could not do better than assigning an interval T to each information bit, with matched-filter reception over that time T. On the contrary, it appears that one can choose for each information bit a pair of orthogonal waveforms which are identical for as much as possible of the first half of their length and maximally different (180° out of phase) for as much as possible of the other half. In tone-shifted FSK, for example, this is accomplished by maintaining the frequency at carrier frequency f_0 most of the time and only deviating from f_0 during a brief period (the impulse) centered halfway through the interval. The impulse area should be such that the two waveforms are orthogonal or nearly so

[1] Meyerhoff and Mazer, *loc. cit.*

over the total interval (e.g., with sharp impulses, the two binary states differ by 180° during the second half of the interval). On this basis, the discrimination of the binary state associated with any particular impulse can be based upon integrating received signal and noise over all the time interval up to the impulses on each side, i.e., including all the time on each side of the impulse during which the carrier rests at f_0. (Note, as in DPSK, each time interval of carrier rest on f_0 is used twice, i.e., in connection with two consecutive decisions.) In effect the energy associated with a particular information decision is associated with a time duration of length up to $2T$, even though the keying rate is $1/T$. The limiting value $2T$ is achieved with true impulse frequency modulation, i.e., the DPSK signal; but it is clear that lengths from T to $2T$ are achievable. Presumably, the longer the intervals, the better the signal-noise discrimination in the decisions. The full implications of these suggestive results will, however, have to await more study results than are presently available.

CHAPTER 9

FADING COMMUNICATION MEDIA

The two preceding chapters have described performance for several basic digital communications techniques, under conditions of steady received signals and additive stationary Gaussian noise. In many important radio applications, the channel characteristics are often strongly nonstationary, as evidenced by "signal fading." The primary purpose of this chapter is to introduce the relevant channel models and their characteristics.

In the first section below, we shall outline briefly where in the radio spectrum some of these effects arise. A phenomenological discussion of fading channel models is given in Sec. 9-2, followed by brief descriptions in Secs. 9-3 and 9-4 of the two major physical channels (ionospheric high-frequency "skywave" and tropospheric scatter propagation) in which these problems are encountered in practice. Then, in Secs. 9-5 and 9-6, we extend to fading situations the earlier calculations of performance of the basic binary systems. In Chaps. 10 and 11, we then go on to describe diversity and related techniques for improving the performance of communication systems in these fading situations.

In some applications, the additive noise is also not stationary or not Gaussian. However, all the analyses described later are confined to models involving stationary additive Gaussian noise. One reason is that this accurately describes additive noise in the large portion of radio applications in which the dominant noise is that originating in receiver "front ends." Secondly, even when external noise is dominant, it is still often Gaussian in character within bandwidths of interest, with a relatively slowly changing noise power level. The latter is similar in effect to long-term signal fading in that both describe relatively slow changes in signal-noise ratio which must be compensated by providing adequate system margin. There remain some relatively specialized applications (especially at radio frequencies below 500 kc) in which the external noise may be significantly impulsive in nature; this has received only limited attention and lies outside the sphere of our discussion. (While there has been much recent work on the impulsive-noise problems associated with digital data transmission over the *telephone network*, it does not appear that the problems posed by radio impulsive noise are closely related either in form, or in reasonable solutions.)

343

There has also been increasing concern, because of the growing occupancy of the radio spectrum, with external noise from interfering signals. This has long been a familiar problem in high-frequency (h-f) communications, and is increasing in the higher bands. However, efforts have been mainly directed towards controlling and avoiding interference, rather than toward specialized signal/receiver design to cope with it. This problem also lies outside the scope of our discussion.

9-1. Role of Fading Channels within the Radio Spectrum

Historically, major early development for long-distance radio communications involved dominantly the h-f band, nominally 3 to 30 Mc. The propagation was achieved point to point by ionospheric reflections. Beginning in the late 1930s and greatly stimulated during World War II, the rapid developments of equipment for the vhf (30 to 300 Mc), uhf (300 to 3000 Mc) and higher bands, and associated propagation research, introduced greatly expanded spectrum usage for communications. Commercially, this has perhaps been most evident in the rapid evolution of private and common-carrier vhf and microwave relay systems, which achieve long-distance coverage by a chain of relatively short point-to-point transmissions between repeater stations.

While the engineering of line-of-sight systems is a technology in itself, these are basically steady-signal systems involving standard communication techniques; hence they are not a further subject for this book. This applies as well to the extension of line-of-sight relay techniques by the use of satellites as relay stations. However, one special case of proposed satellite relay, the orbital dipole belt (the "West Ford" experiment[1]), involves fading more severe than encountered in either the h-f skywave or tropospheric-scatter modes discussed below. Another special kind of "satellite" relay is the use of the moon as a passive reflector for special narrowband communications applications. This medium has been experimentally observed to undergo severe selective fading.[2] While possible applications of lunar or orbital dipole relay appear to be too specialized to be discussed in any detail below, our general considerations on reception of fading signals will be applicable.

The other interesting long-distance radio communications use of microwaves, which has occasioned a great deal of fading-channel research, is transhorizon propagation at uhf and above in the mode commonly termed

---

[1] A collection of papers on this experiment appears in *Proc. IEEE*, vol. 52, pp. 452–606, May, 1964.

[2] E.g., R. P. Ingalls, L. E. Bird, and J. W. B. Day, Bandpass Measurements of a Lunar Reflection Circuit, *Proc. IRE*, vol. 49, pp. 631–632, March, 1961; R. E. Anderson, Sideband Correlation of Lunar and Echo Satellite Reflection Signals in the 900 mc. Range, *Proc. IRE*, vol. 49, pp. 1081–1082, June, 1961.

tropospheric scatter. The equipment involved is to a great extent higher-powered higher-gain versions of microwave line-of-sight equipment. Beginning with the observation of "anomalous" beyond-the-horizon uhf propagation during and after World War II, it was established during the early 1950s that weak (but persistent and usable) fields, although characterized also by severe fading, could be used for *reliable* moderate-bandwidth point-to-point communications out to distances several hundred miles beyond the radio horizon. The associated problems of marginal signals and severe fading have been a major basis for much of the research to be discussed in Chaps. 10 and 11. As a prelude, some of the relevant technical aspects of tropospheric-scatter systems will be separately described in Sec. 9-4.

Returning now to the below-microwave frequency bands, the most important by far is the high-frequency band. Utilizing reflections from the ionosphere layers (skywave propagation), this band still serves as the major long-distance radio medium, particularly for long-distance radio-telegraphy of all types. The transmissions are also characterized by severe fading and have been the other (and historically senior) impetus for research into techniques for coping with signal fading. Some of the technical problems of the h-f medium, as it is often termed, will therefore also be separately described in greater detail, in Sec. 9-3.

Along with the tropospheric transhorizon propagation, it was also discovered in the early 1950s that irregularities in the ionospheric layers will also produce weak, fading, but persistent, scattered fields at frequencies *above* those at which ionospheric reflection fails.[1] A high-powered radio transmission in the 50 to 100 Mc band will provide fields by tropospheric scatter out to typically about 600 to 800 miles beyond the radio horizon, beyond which the fields observed appear to be those due to ionospheric scatter (the two are distinguishable by the variation of intensity with distance). Unfortunately, ionospheric-scatter transmissions are characterized by the same severe selectivity which characterizes h-f skywave propagation so that relatively small useful bandwidths (less than 10 kc) are obtained, at the expense of high-powered transmitters and high-gain antennas. Efficient ionospheric-scatter transmission has been indicated to be possible only in the 35 to 50 Mc band. While ionospheric scatter is largely independent of some of the disruptions which affect h-f systems, presumably because scatter does not require a well-defined layered structure, and perhaps more because it occurs at a sufficiently higher frequency that it is not affected by increased absorption, these other limitations have precluded any large-scale applications. Other than research links, a few

---

[1] For discussion and bibliography on ionospheric scatter and meteor-burst systems, see, for example, the report of the Joint Technical Advisory Committee, Radio Transmission by Ionospheric and Tropospheric Scatter, *Proc. IRE*, vol. 48, pp. 5–44, January, 1960.

ionospheric-scatter links have been built for obtaining the basic propagational reliability in special long-distance point-to-point links which would otherwise only be available with the (propagationally) less reliable h-f skywave mode.

In the course of ionospheric-scatter research, it was early realized that some of the contributory ionization might well be caused by meteor trails at ionosphere altitudes. Subsequent research indicated that both ionospheric irregularities and meteor-trail ionization are apparently present, often indistinguishably.[1] It was found that there are often very strong ("overdense") meteor trails having a duration or decay time measurable in fractions of seconds and that these act as sufficiently strong specular (and hence wideband) reflectors to support long-distance communications. Typically such trails are present as much as 10 per cent of the time, allowing a wideband, moderate-power communications mode with a duty cycle possibly as high as 0.1 but typically much lower. This has led to the elaboration of "meteor-burst" digital communications systems. These are essentially feedback communications systems in which both terminals are continuously monitoring for reception of the other's transmission, to determine the existence of a suitable trail. When one is discovered, both proceed to transmit digital data, for as long as a suitable trail is available. Like ionospheric scatter, the meteor-burst mode is largely independent of the disruptions which affect skywave propagation. On the other hand, the terminal equipment and synchronization requirements become complex, the net information rates available are relatively low, and the major useful applications considered have been for long-distance, low-data-rate requirements. Furthermore, the communication techniques are basically standard and thus again will receive no further special attention in the book.

Below the h-f band, the m-f band (300 to 3000 kc) is largely allocated to entertainment broadcasting, rather than communications. Lower bands (below 300 kc), where longer wavelengths tend to result in a very stable propagation phase, find important use in timing systems such as loran and other radionavigation systems.[2] They are also used for specialized low-data-rate communication applications in which the use of the longer wavelengths has an importance in itself (e.g., to penetrate earth to buried antennas).

As indicated during this brief review, the bulk of Chaps. 9 to 11 will

[1] See earlier reference to JTAC report. Also *Proc. IRE*, December, 1957, contains several papers describing the basic early work on meteor-burst systems.

[2] C. H. Looney, Jr., A Very Low Frequency (VLF) Synchronizing System, *Proc. IRE*, vol. 49, pp. 448–452, February, 1961; F. H. Reder, M. R. Winkler, and C. Bickart, Results of a Long-Range Clock Synchronization Experiment, *Proc. IRE*, vol. 49, pp. 1028–1032, June, 1961; R. H. Doherty, G. Hefley, and R. F. Linfield, Timing Potentials of Loran-C, *Proc. IRE*, vol. 49, pp. 1659–1673, November, 1961.

deal with problems involving severe fading of radio signals. To this end, in the next section we discuss the general phenomenology of signal fading, since this is somewhat independent (except in scale of parameters) of the specific medium. Subsequently, in Secs. 9-3 and 9-4, we describe the specific phenomenology of the two most important media of this type, ionospheric skywave and troposcatter, respectively.

9-2. Phenomenological Descriptions of Multipath and Fading

The use of a natural (not man-made) medium for radio communications implies unavoidable involvement with the random changeability which often accompanies natural phenomena. Thus, the attenuation experienced in propagation may fluctuate, or the path electrical length may change. More perversely, several slightly different transmission paths may exist where the engineer wants only one and where, furthermore, it may not be possible to avoid exciting the several paths simultaneously. Nature is not the only source of such difficulties. As mentioned earlier, the proposed use of a belt of orbiting dipoles contemplates an artificial reflecting medium which may exhibit even more severely fluctuating characteristics than most natural media. However, most of these problems, at least at present, are connected with natural media.

Variations in the channel which take place in a time interval much shorter than the shortest durations of interest to the communications application (e.g., *much* shorter than a pulse length in digital transmission) are usually evidenced in the receiver only in some averaged form. This averaged form would then be accepted per se as a perfectly satisfactory phenomenological description of some corresponding observable characteristic of the medium, and one would not be concerned with the details of the more rapid but unevidenced fluctuation.

At the opposite extreme are changes which occur relatively slowly. This may imply fractions of an hour for some systems; daily, monthly, or seasonally for others; and for still others, as long a time scale as the 11-year solar cycle. Communications systems are usually designed to maintain some minimum standard of performance even during the periods of poor propagation characteristics occurring in the course of such long-scale changes. Moreover, if these changes occur slowly enough that they cannot be alleviated by the detailed signal-modulation or receiving-system design, they represent unavoidable gradual variations in average signal-noise ratio (or other characteristics), for which there is generally no solution other than to provide sufficient design allowances ("margin"). For example, a seasonal change in average path loss would produce a corresponding change in seasonal average signal-noise ratio, for which an adequate design margin must then be available. For this reason, although such long-term changes are extremely important in the overall design and economics of operational communications systems, they are largely outside our purview here.

It is the range between the two extremes mentioned above with which we shall be concerned here—those variations which can be observed in the signal received within an individual message transmission or similar operating interval and whose effect on performance can depend upon our choice of modulation- or receiving-system design. As indicated later, these variations typically occur on a time scale of the order of seconds.

Multipath and Rayleigh Fading. Without referring to specific media, consider the nature of the propagation vagaries described by terms such as fading and multipath. The meaning of multipath is implicit in its name: The propagation medium contains several distinguishable "paths" connecting the transmitter to the receiver, which lie within the respective beam patterns, so that some fraction of the total received energy unavoidably arrives over each path. These paths are best regarded for communications purposes as ray paths along which the electromagnetic energy propagates. Despite its looseness from the point of view of electromagnetic wave theory, there is enough substance to this simple picture to make it appropriate and extremely useful for understanding communications problems.

The distinguishability of several paths implies that they are resolvable, i.e., their electrical lengths are sufficiently different that signals starting out simultaneously on each ray can be distinguished as arriving sequentially. The communications receiver correspondingly is faced with "echoes." More concretely, the situation usually described as "multipath" is one in which more than one propagation path exists, with the time differentials between the several paths large with respect to the time-scale characteristic of the signal modulation, i.e., significantly larger than the reciprocal bandwidth (or larger than the period of the highest "significant" frequency components of the signal). Note that the intuitive designation of a particular propagation environment as "multipath" depends crucially on signal bandwidth.

What is observed when several paths exist with time differentials smaller than the reciprocal signal bandwidth? To examine this, let us consider a limiting case. Suppose multipath is observed, but then the signal modulation is removed and only a continuous tone (unmodulated carrier) is transmitted. Several signals are still arriving "sequentially" at the receiver, but all are continuous sine waves and only the result of their superposition is actually seen. The only effect of the differential electrical-path delays will now be to introduce relative phase shifts on the component tones. The several different signals may then add either constructively or destructively, according to the values of the relative phase shifts. More to the point, changes in the relative path lengths by amounts of the order of the radio carrier wavelength will change the relative phasing among the several phasors and hence change their resultant. If such changes occur continually and randomly, the observed resultant "carrier" will correspondingly change randomly in envelope and radio-frequency phase (relative to some fixed phase reference). Statistically the problem of determining the resultant of a set of random phasors is familiar as that of a two-dimensional random walk; and when the number of components of the multipath is large, and all are of comparable magnitude, the resultant statistics are those of a Rayleigh fading envelope and a uniformly distributed r-f (carrier) phase. Actually, it has been noted[1]

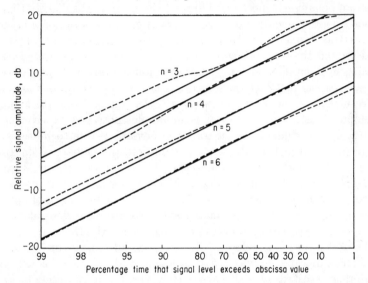

FIG. 9-2-1. Calculation of envelope distributions for n equal-amplitude random-phase phasors. Solid lines are Rayleigh distributions chosen to have same median value in each case.

that as few as six sine waves with independently fluctuating random phase will give a fluctuating resultant whose envelope closely follows Rayleigh statistics and whose phase is uniformly distributed. This is shown in Fig. 9-2-1.[2]

A more basic view of the two-dimensional random walk follows by regarding the constituent independently varying phasors to be resolved into quadrature components. The simultaneous values of the quadrature

[1] W. R. Bennett, Distribution of the Sum of Randomly Phased Components, *Quart. Appl. Math.*, vol. 5, pp. 385–393, January, 1948; M. Slack, Probability Densities of Sinusoidal Oscillations Combined in Random Phase, *J. IEE*, vol. 93, Part III, pp. 76–86, 1946; J. Greenwood and D. Durand, On the Distribution of Length and Components of the Sum of n Random Unit Factors, *Ann. Math. Stat.*, vol. 26, pp. 233–246, 1955.

[2] Based on data in Slack, *loc. cit.* See H. B. Law, F. J. Lee, R. C. Looser, and F. A. W. Levett, An Improved Fading Machine, *Proc. IEE*, vol. 104, part B, pp. 117–123, March, 1957.

components of the resultant at any instant are then readily shown to be uncorrelated, and, by the central-limit theorem, to independently approach Gaussian variates as the number of steps in the random walk (the number of contributing phasors) becomes large. Accordingly, in this limit, the resulting sum at any instant has all the characteristics of narrow-bandpass Gaussian noise, with corresponding Rayleigh-fading envelope and uniformly distributed phase. That Rayleigh fading is observed with as few as six contributing phasors indicates how quickly Gaussian behavior is approached. Furthermore, the central-limit approach of a sum to Gaussian behavior is most rapid around the mean of the distribution and becomes poorer towards the tails. For our case of a zero-mean bivariate process, this implies that the approach toward Gaussian behavior is most rapid around the origin of coordinates, i.e., where the resultant is small. Thus, even when there are only a few contributing randomly phased tones, one may expect *the Rayleigh statistics to be a very good approximation* for the resultant envelope *at low envelope levels*, but perhaps not at higher envelope levels. Such behavior is sometimes observed experimentally. (Although it is difficult to separate the deviations due to finite sample size from actual lack of Rayleigh distribution, the deviations do appear to be greater at the high-signal end.) More importantly, it is exactly the *low-level* statistics of the envelope which are of primary concern in system performance, and (fortunately) this is just the range of envelope levels at which the Rayleigh fading statistics are most dependable as a description of the fading process produced by multipath.

The above discussion does not imply that all fading can be ascribed phenomenologically to varying degrees of destructive or constructive interference created by multipath. However, Rayleigh fading or simply explained modifications thereof are encountered extremely often in experimental observations (e.g., the media discussed in Secs. 9-3 and 9-4); and the phenomenological origin described above is sufficiently consistent with physical intuition that in the absence of better evidence, most investigators have simply assumed it as fact. Indeed, for communication purposes, it suffices to accept the phenomenological model as a basis for predicting systems performance and for devising new or improved systems, so long as it does not conflict with experiment. There is no evidence that such contradictions have been observed in any of the physical systems for which the Rayleigh-fading models appear to agree with experimental observations.

This random-walk interpretation of the observed Rayleigh fading of envelopes is important in analysis because of the earlier mentioned equivalence to assuming that the simultaneous values of the quadrature components of the fading carrier have independent (uncorrelated) Gaussian distributions when a continuous tone is transmitted. As an *extrapolation* of this last remark, based upon physical intuition and the random-walk model, it is usually assumed that the quadrature components are Gaussian random processes, i.e., that the joint distribution for successive time samples of the quadrature components is *multivariate* Gaussian just as it is for bandpass Gaussian noise and that it can similarly be described in terms of a power density spectrum. Almost all the useful theory in discussing fading systems has been based upon this multivariate Gaussian assumption for the quadrature components, with reasonable success and experimental justification.

Selective Fading. The discussion above showed how a changing multipath can lead to a Rayleigh envelope fading and uniform random-phase characteristic for the envelope and phase of a single transmitted sine-wave tone. For transmission of intelligence, one must also consider what happens to a packet of frequencies, i.e., a bandpass signal such as is always involved in radio communications. As is shown later more quantitatively, it suffices to understand what occurs to a pair of spaced tones transmitted simultaneously.

Recall the representation of the multipath contributions as phasors in a two-dimensional random walk. If two transmitted tones are very close in frequency, the two corresponding sets of varying phasors are nearly alike and so are the resultants in both amplitude and phase. That is, the two tones fade in a highly correlated manner. However, since the angles of individual phasors are a measure of electrical path lengths, the *relative* phases among the set depend strongly upon frequency. Hence, as the spacing between the transmitted tones is increasingly widened, the *set* of phasors observed at one tone frequency tends to have decreasing relationship to the set observed at the other. The phasors become "jumbled" in their relative phase positions, particularly when the frequency spacing becomes much larger than $2\pi/T_M$, where T_M is a measure of the overall delay spread in the multipath. The resultant envelope and phase at one tone frequency will then generally be markedly different from that at the other. With sufficient tone spacing, the cross-correlation of fading fluctuations at the two tone frequencies decreases towards zero. The lack of correlation in fading of spaced tones, which implies distortion in the spectrum of a modulated signal, is called *selective fading*.

This frequency selectivity is closely related to a fading model. Frequency selectivity in principle can also occur independently of fading, implying only that a channel is "selective" in its response to various frequency components within the signal bandwidth. It is not even necessary that there be propagation (e.g., reflections due to mismatches on transmission lines might produce such effects) or a multipath situation in particular. Nevertheless, where we discuss selective fading, it will be in connection with the Rayleigh-fading model.

Deterministic Characterization of a Multipath Channel. To introduce a more quantitative expression to the channel descriptions above, we shall first consider a deterministic characterization of the channel response function. Using the complex envelope notation, a transmitted signal at some carrier frequency f_0, can be represented as

$$s_0(t) = \text{Re}\left[u_0(t)\exp\left(j2\pi f_0 t\right)\right] \tag{9-2-1}$$

where $u_0(t)$ has an equivalent low-pass spectrum $U_0(f)$,[1]

$$u_0(t) = \int_{-\infty}^{\infty} U_0(f)\exp\left(j2\pi ft\right)df \tag{9-2-2}$$

Using some convenient definition of the nominal bandwidth such as

$$B = \frac{\int |U_0(f)|^2\,df}{|U_0(0)|^2} \tag{9-2-3}$$

we have as the definition of a narrowband signal,

$$B \ll f_0 \tag{9-2-4}$$

Now consider what might be termed a *static* multipath situation where the several paths remain fixed in their characteristics and can be identified individually. Then the received signal will have the form

$$s(t) = \sum_k \alpha_k s_0(t - t_0 - \tau_k) \tag{9-2-5}$$

where t_0 is some conveniently chosen representative value of the total propagation time (say the average over all paths), τ_k is the additional relative delay on the kth path, and the real number α_k is the path transmission factor for the kth path. As discussed later, the sum would be replaced by an integral over any set of paths which define a continuous range of propagation times. Substituting (9-2-1),

$$s(t) = \text{Re}\left\{u(t - t_0)\exp\left[j2\pi f_0(t - t_0)\right]\right\} \tag{9-2-6}$$

where
$$u(t) = \sum_k \alpha_k u_0(t - \tau_k)\exp\left(-j2\pi f_0\tau_k\right) \tag{9-2-7}$$

The latter represents the received signal completely if the nominal average propagation delay t_0 is ignored (as it usually is in analysis). With (9-2-2), it can readily be rewritten as

$$u(t) = \int_{-\infty}^{\infty} U_0(f)\exp\left(j2\pi ft\right)\left\{\sum_k \alpha_k \exp\left[-j2\pi(f + f_0)\tau_k\right]\right\}df \tag{9-2-8}$$

---

[1] In previous chapters the notation $F(\omega)$, $H(\omega)$, etc., has been used specifically to represent Fourier transforms. The functional dependence on f has been utilized solely for power density spectra [$G_n(f)$, $G_x(f)$, etc.]. In this and in the chapters following, we choose to use the notation $U(f)$, $H(f)$, etc., for Fourier transforms, to be in closer conformity with the published literature on propagation phenomena and communication by fading media. In the integrals defining the Fourier transforms and their inverses we then also use $2\pi f$ in place of ω. [See for example Eqs. (9-2-2), (9-2-7).]

Thus, the *equivalent low-pass transfer function of the channel* is

$$H(f) = \sum_k \alpha_k \exp\left[-j2\pi(f + f_0)\tau_k\right] \tag{9-2-9}$$

in terms of which

$$u(t) = \int_{-\infty}^{\infty} U_0(f)H(f) \exp(j2\pi ft)\, df \tag{9-2-10}$$

The actual domain of integration in (9-2-10) is that frequency band occupied by the spectrum of the transmitted signal. While the latter will not usually be strictly band-limited in a mathematical sense, in fact there is some frequency domain $\mathfrak{B}$, of width greater than the nominal width B given by (9-2-3), which can be regarded as including *all* significant frequency components of $u_0(t)$. Note $\mathfrak{B}$ is centered around $f = 0$, when f represents frequencies measured with respect to f_0 as origin. If $H(f)$ is effectively a constant over $\mathfrak{B}$, then by (9-2-6) and (9-2-10), the received signal is identical in form to the original signal. It is received without distortion but with an overall attenuation given by $|H(0)|$ and a delay t_0 [and an irrelevant additional fixed phase shift of the r-f carrier given by arg $H(0)$].

More generally, within the form (9-2-9), the condition under which $H(f)$ can effectively appear to have such a constant value over $\mathfrak{B}$ is observed to be

$$|f\tau_k| \ll 1 \tag{9-2-11}$$

for f in $\mathfrak{B}$ and all k.[1] Examining the approximation involved more closely by expanding the exponentials in (9-2-9) and retaining only the leading terms,

$$H(f) = \left[\sum_k \alpha_k \exp\left[-j2\pi f_0\tau_k\right]\right] - j2\pi f\left[\sum_k \alpha_k\tau_k \exp\left(-j2\pi f_0\tau_k\right)\right] \tag{9-2-12}$$

Setting
$$H^{(0)} = \sum_k \alpha_k \exp\left[-j2\pi f_0\tau_k\right] \tag{9-2-13a}$$

and
$$H^{(1)}(f) = 2\pi f \sum_k \alpha_k\tau_k \exp\left(-j2\pi f_0\tau_k\right) \tag{9-2-13b}$$

the form of $H(f)$ to first order is given by

$$H(f) = H^{(0)} - jH^{(1)}(f) \tag{9-2-14}$$

Here, $H^{(0)}$ is a frequency-independent complex number which would correspond to distortionless propagation if it completely represented $H(f)$. In multipath, however, it is now apparent that a more accurate statement than just (9-2-11) for reception of undistorted signal would be

$$|f\tau_k| \ll 1 \qquad \text{for } f \text{ in } \mathfrak{B} \text{ and all } k \tag{9-2-15a}$$

and
$$\left|\frac{H^{(1)}(f)}{H^{(0)}}\right| \ll 1 \qquad \text{for all } f \text{ in } \mathfrak{B} \tag{9-2-15b}$$

---

[1] More accurately (9-2-11) should be written in terms of the extreme values of τ_k, as $|f[(\tau_k)_{\max} - (\tau_k)_{\min}]| \ll 1$ for all f in $\mathfrak{B}$.

The second condition above implies that while a basic condition for nonselective transmission is that the differential time delay over the several paths is small relative to the reciprocal width of $\mathcal{B}$, it may still be possible to observe selective effects when this condition is fulfilled but (9-2-15*b*) is not. Such a situation would occur when the particular *combination* of the phasors $\alpha_k \exp (-j2\pi f_0 \tau_k)$ in (9-2-13*a*) happens to be close to a zero resultant (destructive interference). In this condition the main nonselective channel, so to speak, is weak enough that the actual dominant signal arriving is governed by $H^{(1)}(f)$ and so contains the frequency-selective characteristics implied by $H^{(1)}(f)$, in this case a linear variation with frequency across the band (equivalent to differentiation of the transmitted modulation components). One can extend this argument to the possibility of observing even higher orders of selectivity, still in a basically nonselective situation. Under conditions which are obviously even more rare than those above, both $H^{(0)}$ and $H^{(1)}$ may be close to zero; utilizing the next term in the expansion, significant contributions to the transfer characteristic would then be represented by a term $H^{(2)}(f)$, involving a quadratic variation with frequency across the band (or double differentiation of the transmitted modulation).[1] In dynamic-fading situations, there is in fact always some (small) percentage of time during which the zero-order, and higher-order, terms become extremely small because of the "destructive" combinations occurring. In some systems, selective-fading distortion appears to degrade performance during "deep fades," at levels at which good performance would still be expected under nonselective propagation conditions.[2]

When (9-2-15*a*) is satisfied, operation is basically nonselective except for the situations noted. Returning to (9-2-9), one can now further identify the *basically selective* situations as those where $2\pi f \tau_k$ undergoes several radians variation as f varies within $\mathcal{B}$ and as τ_k varies over the

---

[1] A representation for analysis purposes of "mildly" selective fading channels by the leading terms of such a power-series expansion was suggested by P. Bello, and applied by Bello, J. Ekstrom, and D. Chesler to studies of techniques for signaling over such channels, as reported in Study of Adaptable Communications Systems, RADC-TDR-62-314, Applied Research Laboratory, Sylvania Electronic Systems, June, 1962.

[2] Some of the specific observations have been made on multichannel FDM-FM troposcatter systems, which will not be discussed in detail in these chapters because the multichannel FDM-FM technique introduces nonlinearities into the system which are beyond the scope of the models we use. FM systems are quite sensitive to echoes or to selective fading, which become evidenced as a form of intermodulation distortion. Analyses of operation of voice-frequency data channels in *nonselectively* fading FDM-FM systems appear in B. B. Barrow, Error Probabilities for Telegraph Signals Transmitted on a Fading FM Carrier, *Proc. IRE*, vol. 48, pp. 1613–29, September, 1960, and D. E. Johansen, Binary Error Rates in Fading FDM-FM Communications, *IRE Trans. Commun. Systems*, vol. CS-9, pp. 206–214, September, 1961. (In connection with our discussion above, note particularly Johansen's footnote 8.)

several paths. While some interesting statements can be made about the resulting form of $H(f)$ in the two-path case,[1] there is very little illuminating of a nonstatistical nature to be added about the more general case, other than that severe selective fading occurs (a statistical discussion is given later).

When the differences between the several τ_k become extremely large compared with the reciprocal of the largest effective modulation frequency $(\tau_k B \gg 1)$ for at least some k, one may as well use the form (9-2-7), expressing that discernible modulation echoes can be observed, as originally defined as observable multipath. For continuous transmission, the intrasignal interference represented by such echoes can also be regarded as an extreme form of selective propagation, but this would lose sight of the more physically direct interpretation. The term "selective" is thus usually reserved for the case described earlier, where the differential delay between paths is not readily observable for modulation elements, but frequency-selective destructive or constructive interference of the various spectral components still occurs.

Statistical Characterization of a Dynamic Multipath Channel. Referring to the fundamental representation (9-2-5), a dynamic situation occurs if either α_k or τ_k are time-varying. It becomes important now to identify more specifically what is being described physically by the k different paths. To regard the τ_k as varying implies that the paths have some intrinsic physical identification. For example, if a number of distinguishable physical scatterers are involved, one might identify a separate path with each individual scatterer; as the scatterer moves, the associated τ_k would change and, perhaps more gradually, so would the α_k. One might even find circumstances where such "paths" cross.

In most physical situations of interest, however, the paths cannot be distinguished physically. Rather, while some insight may exist into the physical processes of reflection or scatter which are taking place, one has no significant identification of the individual reflectors or scatterers. For example, suppose the propagation involves weak reflections (single scattering) from a distribution of scatterers or a distribution of thin platelets in otherwise homogeneous space. The total propagation time would then be identical for all paths involving scatterers or platelets located on a particular spheroidal surface of revolution (Fig. 9-2-2) generated by an ellipse with the receiving and transmitting antenna phase centers as foci. Each such confocal spheroidal surface defines a different transmitter-receiver propagation time. More realistically, space may be inhomogeneous and/or the propagation may be more akin to ray refraction than to reflections. Nevertheless, there are still a set of confocal surfaces,

---

[1] The two-path case is of major engineering importance in line-of-sight links. See, e.g., W. G. Albersheim and J. P. Schafer, Echo Distortion in the FM Transmission of Frequency-Division Multiplex, *Proc. IRE*, vol. 40, pp. 316–328, March, 1952.

"warped spheroids" as it were, for which the same properties would hold. Without knowing the shape of such surfaces (or even whether the shapes change), one can identify each with a propagation time delay τ_k and hence identify the *resultant* of contributions from all scatterers on this surface as α_k. As scatterers move, they become identified in this view with different τ_k. From a statistical point of view this description is more natural than trying to identify and follow the individual scatterers.

Furthermore, rather than refer to a confocal surface, it will be more relevant to refer to a density distribution of the multipath. Thus consider all propagation paths having a relative propagation delay in the range $(\tau, \tau + \Delta\tau)$, that is, paths defined by scatterers lying within a particular thin shell defined by two confocal surfaces with total (delay)

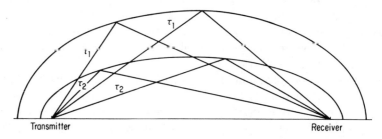

Fɪɢ. 9-2-2. Surfaces of constant propagation delay.

separation $\Delta\tau$. With regard to the transmitted signal as described by (9-2-1) and (9-2-3), let us take the size of $\Delta\tau$ to lie in the range

$$\frac{1}{f_0} < \Delta\tau \ll \frac{1}{B} \tag{9-2-16}$$

It is apparent from (9-2-4) that this range exists. Also, as seen above, this size of $\Delta\tau$ implies that the composite fading due to scatterers *within* such a shell will be basically nonselective. Using (9-2-16),

$$u_0(t - \tau - \Delta\tau) = u_0(t - \tau) - \Delta\tau \dot{u}_0(t - \tau) + \cdots$$
$$= u_0(t - \tau)[1 + 0(B\,\Delta\tau)] \tag{9-2-17}$$

That is, for all relative delays in the narrow range $(\tau, \tau + \Delta\tau)$, the contribution to the received signal is the same, to within quantities which are vanishingly small, of the order of $B\,\Delta\tau$.

On the other hand, for the delays in this shell varying by as much as $\Delta\tau$, the factor exp $(j2\pi f_0 t)$ in (9-2-1) undergoes a total possible variation of exp $(j2\pi f_0\,\Delta\tau)$. In other words, with (9-2-16) the *r-f phase* variation due to varied paths in the delay range $(\tau, \tau + \Delta\tau)$ may still cover *many* complete cycles. From our previous discussion, it is then clear that if there are a sufficient number of contributing scatterers randomly (and time-change-ably) located within the $(\tau, \tau + \Delta\tau)$ delay shell, the net *dynamic* effect of the shell of scatterers is to multiply $u_0(t - \tau)$ by a Rayleigh-fading envelope coefficient and to associate with the r-f carrier, to which we can assign a nominal phase factor exp $(-j2\pi f_0\tau)$, an additional uniformly distributed random phase shift. For the transmitted signal represented in (9-2-1),

$$s_0(t) = \text{Re} \, [u_0(t) \exp \, (j2\pi f_0 t)] \qquad (9\text{-}2\text{-}18)$$

the contribution from the $(\tau, \tau + \Delta\tau)$ shell can be written in the form

$$s_\tau(t) = \text{Re} \, \{\beta_\tau(t - t_0)u_0(t - t_0 - \tau) \exp \, [j\pi f_0(t - t_0 - \tau)]\} \qquad (9\text{-}2\text{-}19)$$

In these forms, $\beta_\tau(t - t_0)$ is a complex Gaussian process, with a Rayleigh-fading envelope and uniformly distributed phase, fluctuating with time because of dynamic changes in the multipath structure within the $\Delta\tau$ shell. The $t - t_0$ argument in $\beta_\tau(t - t_0)$ specifically refers these fluctuations to the nominal time at which the signals affected were transmitted. Because of the randomness of its phase, the phase factor exp $(-j2\pi f_0\tau)$ can also be absorbed into $\beta_\tau(t - t_0)$, if desired. Again, we emphasize that this statistical characterization of β_τ is crucially dependent on the assumption that a meaningful $\Delta\tau$ can be chosen (recall that the allowed values depend on signal bandwidth) so that a *sufficiently large number* of scatterers lie within the shell.

With the assumptions that $\beta_\tau(t - t_0)$ is Gaussian, and that $u_0(t - t_0 - \tau)$ in (9-2-19) is essentially unchanging throughout the shell, one can conveniently define another complex Gaussian process $\beta(\tau; t - t_0)$ such that

$$\beta_\tau(t - t_0) \exp \, (-j2\pi f_0\tau) = \int_\tau^{\tau+\Delta\tau} \beta(x; t - t_0) \, dx \qquad (9\text{-}2\text{-}20a)$$

and such that one can also write

$$s_\tau(t) = \text{Re} \left[\exp j2\pi f_0(t - t_0) \int_\tau^{\tau+\Delta\tau} \beta(\tau; t - t_0)u_0(t - t_0 - \tau) \, d\tau \right] \qquad (9\text{-}2\text{-}20b)$$

In other words, we are creating here the *useful mathematical fiction* of a more finely subdivided version of $\beta_\tau(t - t_0)$ exp $(j2\pi f_0\tau)$ as a function of τ, within each shell, and assuming that this finely divided subdivision is still a complex Gaussian process. If we consider $\beta_\tau(t - t_0)$ defined for various values of shell thickness $\Delta\tau$ we can regard the definition of $\beta(\tau; t - t_0)$ to be

$$\beta(\tau; t - t_0) = \lim_{\Delta\tau \to 0(1/f_0)} \left\{ \frac{1}{\Delta\tau} \, [\beta_\tau(t - t_0) \exp \, (-j2\pi f_0\tau)] \right\} \qquad (9\text{-}2\text{-}21)$$

where $\beta_\tau(t - t_0)$ implicitly contains $\Delta\tau$ as a parameter and where actually (9-2-21) is meant only to describe the statistics of $\beta(\tau; t - t_0)$. This *mathematical fiction* provides the convenient integral form (9-2-20b), with which the sum over the contributions from *all* the successive shells in the multipath can now be written

$$s(t) = \text{Re} \left\{ \exp \, [j2\pi f_0(t - t_0)] \int_{-\infty}^{\infty} \beta(\tau; t - t_0)u_0(t - t_0 - \tau) \, d\tau \right\} \qquad (9\text{-}2\text{-}22)$$

where $\beta(\tau; t - t_0)$ vanishes except over a range (or disjoint range segments) in τ defining the total range of multipath delays. The alternative to the notation of (9-2-22) would be to deal with a *sum* of terms like (9-2-19), with $\Delta\tau$ noninfinitesimal and the τ subscript in $\beta_\tau(t - t_0)$ merely indexing the successive shells. Actually, aside from the notational awkwardness of the latter, we assert that all our subsequent quantitative descriptions of the fading model can be derived equally well from such a sum representation.[1] No meaningful *physical* identity is claimed for $\beta(\tau;t - t_0)$, since for any shell of infinitesimal width $d\tau$, $f_0\,d\tau$ will also be an infinitesimal, and even a large number of scatterers within the shell would not provide the relative phasing required for the random-walk model to apply. On the other hand, once we *accept* $\beta_\tau(t - t_0)$ as a complex Gaussian process and assume it arises from multipath uniformly distributed over the range $(\tau, \tau + \Delta\tau)$, there is no difficulty in *defining* the complex Gaussian mathematical process $\beta(\tau;t - t_0)$ as essentially the "density" of $\beta_\tau(t - t_0)$, by (9-2-21).[2] Furthermore, if $\beta_\tau(t - t_0)$ is "continuous" in τ (over adjacent shells), $\beta(\tau;t - t_0)$ will be continuous over the entire range of multipath.

Accepting (9-2-22) with $\beta(\tau;t)$ as a complex Gaussian process, one can obviously rewrite it as

$$s(t) = \text{Re}\,\{u(t - t_0)\exp[j2\pi f_0(t - t_0)]\} \qquad (9\text{-}2\text{-}23)$$

where

$$u(t) = \int_{-\infty}^{\infty} \beta(\tau;t)u_0(t - \tau)\,d\tau = \int_{-\infty}^{\infty} \beta(t - \tau;t)u_0(\tau)\,d\tau \qquad (9\text{-}2\text{-}24)$$

Using (9-2-2) in (9-2-24), one arrives at the alternative statement

$$u(t) = \int_{-\infty}^{\infty} U_0(f)H(f;t)\exp(j2\pi ft)\,df \qquad (9\text{-}2\text{-}25)$$

where

$$H(f;t) = \int_{-\infty}^{\infty} \beta(\tau;t)\exp(-j2\pi f\tau)\,d\tau \qquad (9\text{-}2\text{-}26)$$

It is apparent that $\beta(\tau;t)$, in its *dependence on* τ, represents a "time-varying equivalent low-pass impulse response" for the channel. Likewise $H(f;t)$ is its "time-varying equivalent low-pass transfer function." The characterization of the medium by $\beta(\tau;t)$ and its transform is not unique. One could equally well characterize the medium in terms of τ and a variable $z = t - t_0 - \tau$ which would refer the characterization to

---

[1] In perhaps the earliest published detailed discussion on the statistical characterization of multipath models, G. L. Turin, Communication Through Noisy, Random-Multipath Channels, *IRE Nat. Conv. Record*, part 4, pp. 154–166, 1956, the discussion was carried out completely in terms of summations over separable paths. For media such as ionospheric reflections, where the multipath delays occur in clusters centered about very distinct values corresponding to basically different modes of travel (e.g., one-hop versus two-hop modes), a combined integration-summation model is actually the most realistic.

[2] Many of the macroscopic theories of classical physics (e.g., fluid flow) rest on defining "point functions" in a very analogous manner, even though these point functions have no physical microscopic reality.

the actual time at which the signal elements are emitted which each infinitesimal shell will affect. One could also describe the medium in terms of z and t, the instants of emission and reception. Such alternative characterizations and their interrelationships have been described in the literature.[1] For our purposes, the one representation already given will suffice.

It is interesting to verify from (9-2-25) that if $U_0(f) = \delta(f - f')$, that is a cw sine-wave tone is transmitted at the frequency $f_0 + f'$, the total response is $\text{Re}\{\exp[j2\pi(f_0 + f')t]H(f';t)\}$. Thus a physical interpretation for $H(f;t)$ is that it describes exactly the response of the medium, including its time-variability, to a transmitted sine wave of relative frequency f. Because of the time-variability implied by its t dependence, the received signal when the tone at $f_0 + f'$ is transmitted will involve a spectral band around $f_0 + f'$.

It should also be clear that the previous categorizations of selective versus nonselective fading apply directly to the representations in (9-2-24) and (9-2-25), as well. Specifically, the criterion for basic nonselectivity analogous to (9-2-15a) is now

$$|f\tau| \ll 1 \qquad (9\text{-}2\text{-}27)$$

where τ is the largest relative delay at which $\beta(\tau;t)$ is significantly nonzero and f is the largest relative frequency for which $U_0(f)$ is significantly nonzero. The kind of expansion discussed in (9-2-14) and (9-2-15) again applies, with the same comments applying to the possibility of observing selectivity during moments of deep fading.

Covariance Functions in the Statistical Model of Fading. With the *premise* that $\beta(\tau;t)$ is a complex Gaussian process as a function of t, it follows from (9-2-26) that $H(f;t)$, resulting from a linear operation on $\beta(\tau;t)$, is also complex Gaussian as a function of t. Particularly, for two or more different values of f and/or different values of t, the corresponding $H(f;t)$ are derived from the one complex Gaussian process $\beta(\tau;t)$ and hence are a joint complex Gaussian process. Such a joint process for $H(f;t)$ is completely described statistically by its general pairwise covariance, which we term the "frequency-time cross-variance," defined by

$$R_F(f_1,t_1;f_2,t_2) = \tfrac{1}{2}\langle H^*(f_1;t_1)H(f_2;t_2)\rangle \qquad (9\text{-}2\text{-}28)$$

When f_1 and f_2 represent two frequencies in the spectrum of a transmitted signal, (9-2-28) provides a statistical measure of the extent to which the signal is distorted by the multipath. Using (9-2-26)

$$R_F(f_1,t_1;f_2,t_2) = \int_{-\infty}^{\infty} \tfrac{1}{2}\langle \beta^*(\tau_1;t_1)\beta(\tau_2;t_2)\rangle \exp[j2\pi(f_1\tau_1 - f_2\tau_2)]\, d\tau_1\, d\tau_2$$

$$(9\text{-}2\text{-}29)$$

[1] E.g., T. Kailath, "Channel Characterization: Time-Variant Dispersive Channels," chap. 6 in "Lectures on Communication System Theory," E. Baghdady (ed.), Mc-Graw-Hill Book Company, New York, 1961.

The statistical average in the integrand is the general pairwise covariance for $\beta(\tau;t)$, which we term the "space-time cross-covariance" of the multipath, defined by

$$R_T(\tau_1,t_1;\tau_2,t_2) = \tfrac{1}{2}\langle \beta^*(\tau_1;t_1)\beta(\tau_2;t_2)\rangle \qquad (9\text{-}2\text{-}30)$$

Thus, there exists a two-dimensional Fourier-transform relationship,

$$R_F(f_1,t_1;f_2,t_2) = \int\limits_{-\infty}^{\infty}\!\!\int R_T(\tau_1,t_1;\tau_2,t_2)\,\exp\left[j2\pi(f_1\tau_1 - f_2\tau_2)\right]d\tau_1\,d\tau_2 \qquad (9\text{-}2\text{-}31)$$

In the generality of form in (9-2-31), aside from observing the two-dimensional Fourier-transform relation, there is little useful further to be said. However, the forms can be further specialized in line *with physical intuition* about the model (interpretations of experimental data and our general phenomenological picture). First, since our interest here is "short-term fading" (see Secs. 9-3 and 9-4), it is reasonable to assume that $\beta(\tau;t)$ is stationary, at least in a local-time sense. Then R_T, and hence also R_F, depend on t_1 and t_2 only through the difference $\Delta t = t_1 - t_2$. Redefining each in an obvious manner, we have, instead of the previous equations,

$$R_F(f_1,f_2;\Delta t) = \tfrac{1}{2}\langle H^*(f_1,t)H(f_2,t + \Delta t)\rangle \qquad (9\text{-}2\text{-}32)$$
$$R_T(\tau_1,\tau_2;\Delta t) = \tfrac{1}{2}\langle \beta^*(\tau_1;t)\beta(\tau_2;t + \Delta t)\rangle \qquad (9\text{-}2\text{-}33)$$

and

$$R_F(f_1,f_2;\Delta t) = \int\limits_{-\infty}^{\infty}\!\!\int R_T(\tau_1,\tau_2;\Delta t)\,\exp\left[j2\pi(f_1\tau_1 - f_2\tau_2)\right]d\tau_1\,d\tau_2 \qquad (9\text{-}2\text{-}34)$$

The next reasonable physical assumption is that the complex Gaussian process $\beta_r(t)$ in (9-2-19) or (9-2-20) is independent for different values of τ (from one $\Delta\tau$ shell to the next). This is based on an assumed independence of the relative dynamic behavior which gives rise to the Rayleigh fading in each $\Delta\tau$ shell of our earlier descriptions. Even if scatterers move from one shell to the next, they are assumed *not* to have a fixed relative ("rigid-body") motion; there is then little reason to expect fluctuation effects observed at one instant in one shell to have any relation to those observed at a later instant in another. This, however, is again an assumption to be justified,[1] along with even the complex Gaussian nature of $\beta_r(t)$. This assumption on independence of the $\beta_r(t)$ at different τ can be extended to the mathematically defined process $\beta(\tau;t)$ by assuming, specifically, that (9-2-33) has the form

$$R_T(\tau_1,\tau_2;\Delta t) = \tfrac{1}{2}\langle \beta^*(\tau_1;t)\beta(\tau_2;t + \Delta t)\rangle = r_T(\tau_1;\Delta t)\delta(\tau_1 - \tau_2) \qquad (9\text{-}2\text{-}35)$$

In this representation, we are making two statements: (1) There is zero

---

[1] There are some measurements of both ionospheric skywave and troposcatter phenomena which have been suggested as possibly indicating drift mechanisms in the media. There would be little difficulty in extending the model to cover such an assumption, but it does not appear warranted with present scanty data.

cross-correlation, at any time lag, between different "layers." (2) $r_T(\tau;\Delta t)$ represents the autocovariance with time lag Δt for a single layer defined by the delay range $(\tau,\tau + d\tau)$. Since the range is an infinitesimal, so is $r_T(\tau;\Delta t)$. A physically more meaningful interpretation follows by returning to our shell concept, defining the complex Gaussian process $\beta_\tau(t)$ for a shell of thickness $\Delta\tau$ as in (9-2-20a),

$$\beta_\tau(t) \exp\,(-j2\pi f_0\tau) = \int_\tau^{\tau+\Delta\tau} \beta(x;t)\,dx \qquad (9\text{-}2\text{-}36)$$

Then, with (9-2-35), the space-time autocovariance for a given shell is

$$\tfrac{1}{2}\langle\beta_\tau{}^*(t)\beta_\tau(t + \Delta t)\rangle = \iint_\tau^{\tau+\Delta\tau} \tfrac{1}{2}\langle\beta^*(x_1;t)\beta(x_2;t + \Delta t)\rangle\,dx_1\,dx_2$$

$$= \int_\tau^{\tau+\Delta\tau} r_T(x,\Delta t)\,dx \qquad (9\text{-}2\text{-}37)$$

If one assumes that $r_T(x,\Delta t)$ is the same for all delays within the small range of the integral, then specifically

$$\tfrac{1}{2}\langle\beta_\tau{}^*(t)\beta_\tau(t + \Delta t)\rangle = r_T(\tau,\Delta t)\,\Delta\tau \qquad (9\text{-}2\text{-}38)$$

Thus, if one again conceives $\beta_\tau(t)$ to be defined for a variety of different but meaningful values of $\Delta\tau$, $r_T(\tau,\Delta t)$ can be interpreted as the result of the mathematical limiting process,

$$r_T(\tau,\Delta t) = \lim_{\Delta\tau\to 0\left(\frac{1}{f_0}\right)} \left\{\frac{1}{\Delta\tau}\,[\tfrac{1}{2}\langle\beta_\tau{}^*(t)\beta_\tau(t + \Delta t)\rangle]\right\} \qquad (9\text{-}2\text{-}39)$$

in which $\beta_\tau(t)$ implicitly contains $\Delta\tau$ as a parameter.

We denote $r_T(\tau;\Delta t)$ as the "multipath autocovariance profile." The dependence on τ may imply a different shape of the autocovariance (or of the equivalent power density spectrum) for different τ. Later we shall discuss in detail the time changes of the medium and their statistical characterization. However, one can comment here that there is little detailed experimental evidence for common fading channels which would enable one either to affirm or to deny that there is any significant change with τ in the *shape* of the autocovariance function or power density spectrum.[1] A simpler implication of the τ dependence lies in the variation of the intensity associated with various path delays, as given by $r_T(\tau;0)$; this would enter as a scale factor on the multipath autocovariance profile, even if its shape did not change with τ. Specifically

$$r_T(\tau;0) = \tfrac{1}{2}\langle|\beta(\tau;t)|^2\rangle \qquad (9\text{-}2\text{-}40)$$

describes the intensity (averaged over the fading fluctuations) of the scattering or reflection process at relative propagation delay τ. This will be termed, as a special case of the multipath autocovariance profile, the

---

[1] At the time of writing, some unpublished data has become available which indicate that the autocovariance function is indeed τ-dependent for both of these media.

"multipath intensity profile," and one can clearly expect it to vary with τ (and to vanish outside a certain range of values of τ).

If we now assume no spatial correlation among various layers expressed by (9-2-35), the corresponding frequency-time cross-variance of (9-2-34) becomes

$$R_F(f_1,f_2;\Delta t) = \int_{-\infty}^{\infty} r_T(\tau;\Delta t) \exp\left[j2\pi(f_1 - f_2)\tau\right] d\tau \qquad (9\text{-}2\text{-}41)$$

Thus R_F then also has a specialized form,

$$R_F(f_1,f_1 + \Delta f;\Delta t) = r_F(\Delta f;\Delta t)$$

$$= \int_{-\infty}^{\infty} r_T(\tau;\Delta t) \exp\left[-j2\pi\tau \,\Delta f\right] d\tau \qquad (9\text{-}2\text{-}42)$$

That is, the assumption (9-2-35) leads to "stationarity" in the frequency domain, in the sense that the frequency-time cross-covariance is a *function of the frequency spacing only* and in fact is the Fourier transform of the multipath autocovariance profile. The definition of R_F in (9-2-32) implies that it is directly measurable (during intervals over which stationarity holds for the process) by transmitting pairs of spaced tones and carrying out cross-covariance measurements (at least for all but very narrow tone spacings for which receiver filters might not be able to separate the received fading tones). A number of experiments of this type have been carried out over the tropospheric-scatter fading medium[1] and for lunar reflections.[2] Similar detailed measurements for short-term fading in ionospheric skywave propagation do not appear to be available. It has always been assumed in interpreting these measurements that (9-2-42) holds, which would mean that the measured cross-covariances are independent of the exact location of the spaced tones and depend only on the spacing. This assumption in a sense directly follows physical intuition— in a bandpass situation at a relatively high carrier frequency, the actual detailed value of carrier frequency should not be important in describing propagation effects. These should depend only on *relative* frequencies within the transmitted band. Our derivation above indicates that this physically appealing assumption is intimately related to the spatial-layer independence described by (9-2-35). As is usual in a case like this, however, the assumption (9-2-35) can be relaxed and can be regarded only as

[1] L. G. Abraham, Jr., and J. A. Bradshaw, Tropospheric Scatter Propagation Study, AFCRC-TR-59-533, General Electric Res. Lab., October, 1959; A. B. Crawford, D. C. Hogg, and W. H. Kummer, Studies in Tropospheric Propagation Beyond the Horizon, *Bell System Tech. J.*, vol. 38, pp. 1067–1178, September, 1959; J. H. Chisholm, L. P. Rainville, J. F. Roche, and H. G. Root, Measurement of the Bandwidth of Radio Waves Propagated by the Troposphere Beyond the Horizon, *IRE Trans. Antennas and Propagation*, vol. AP-6, pp. 377–378, October, 1958.

[2] R. P. Ingalls, L. E. Bird and J. W. B. Day, Bandpass Measurements of a Lunar Reflection Circuit, *Proc. IRE*, vol. 49, pp. 631–632, March, 1961; R. E. Anderson, Sideband Correlation of Lunar and Echo Satellite Reflection Signals in the 900 mc Range, *Proc. IRE*, vol. 49, pp. 1081–1082, June, 1961.

the limiting statement of a slightly weaker assumption under which $R_F(f_1,f_2;\Delta t)$ may still be a function of only $f_1 - f_2$. An analogous example in system analyses is to assume a wide noise spectrum to be a white noise with a delta-function autocorrelation; this simplifies the mathematical analysis, and the system cannot tell the difference. Likewise, here, it can be shown from (9-2-34) that the frequency-time cross-covariance will be a function of frequency spacing only, so long as the space-time autocovariance $R_T(\tau_1,\tau_2;\Delta t)$ tends to vanish whenever $\tau_1 - \tau_2$ is of the order of (some fraction of) the reciprocal of the signal bandwidth (maximum frequency spacing of interest). This delay difference also defines the order of magnitude of the $\Delta\tau$ by which we originally defined our nonvanishing-thickness shells, hence it is tantamount to stating that independence of fading from shell to shell is the basic requirement. We also emphasize now that the latter condition appears to be a *necessary*, as well as a sufficient condition for $R_F(f_1,f_2;\Delta\tau)$ to be a function of $f_2 - f_1$ only.

The propagation measurements cited above have in fact not really measured $r_F(\Delta f;\Delta t)$, but only the cross-correlation or cross-covariance of the simultaneous envelope values on spaced tones. When $\Delta\tau = 0$, (9-2-42) becomes

$$r_F(\Delta f;0) = \int_{-\infty}^{\infty} r_T(\tau;0) \exp (j2\pi\tau \, \Delta f) \, d\tau \qquad (9\text{-}2\text{-}43)$$

Thus a measurement of $r_F(\Delta f;0)$ as a function of tone spacing would be also a measurement of the Fourier transform of the multipath intensity profile $r_T(\tau;0)$. However, in all these reported measurements, the cross-correlation actually measured has been on the *envelopes* simultaneously received for the two tones. Since it has also usually first been verified that each fading-tone envelope is Rayleigh distributed, which leads to the extrapolation that the Gaussian model is then correct, the measurement of envelope cross-correlation can be regarded[1] as a measurement of $|r_F(\Delta f;0)|$. Unfortunately this is the only aspect of $r_F(\Delta f;0)$ for which detailed measurements have been available. The additional assumption that $r_F(\Delta f;0)$ is real would enable the inversion of (9-2-43); but this assumption is tantamount to assuming that the real quantity (intensity) $r_T(\tau;0)$ has *even* symmetry in τ about some central point, and (see Secs. 9-3 and 9-4) this does not appear to be a realistic assumption for actual propagation media.

The other possibility for statistical measurement of the channel would be to transmit extremely short pulses to "sound" the medium, thus measuring $r_T(\tau;\Delta t)$ by correlation of values observed with successive pulses. This latter kind of measurement has been accomplished at h-f.[2] As an

---

[1] E.g., Davenport and Root, *op. cit.*, p. 170.

[2] M. Balser and W. B. Smith, Some Statistical Properties of Pulsed Oblique HF Ionospheric Transmissions, *J. Res. Natl. Bur. Stat.*, vol. 66D, pp. 721–730, November–December, 1962.

alternative to short pulses, any sort of interpretable wideband transmission, such as the noiselike signal used in the Rake technique (Sec. 11-5), also can be used for sounding.

Doppler Effects; Power Spectrum of Fading. The transfer function $H(f;t)$ describes the channel response to a *monochromatic* transmission at relative frequency f. As commented earlier, the t dependence here implies that the response is *not* monochromatic; more generally, the channel response to any signal contains frequencies *not present* in the transmission. This is generally characteristic of a time-varying filter. However, in our case the time variations or dynamic changes in the channel can be related directly to motions in the medium. Motion in turn implies Doppler effects, and we shall show below that it is in fact reasonable to interpret the time dependence of $H(f;t)$ in terms of Doppler shifts. Statistically, we are interested in physical interpretation of the time-lag dependence of the cross-covariances introduced above; again, it will be shown that this can be interpreted in terms of a Doppler spectrum.

By way of review, consider a single moving scatterer of unchanging reflection coefficient α but for which path length is changing at a velocity v. Using, for example, the notation of (9-2-9), the electrical path delay then changes at the rate

$$\tau(t) = \frac{v}{c} t \qquad (9\text{-}2\text{-}44)$$

where c is the velocity of light. The channel response for this single scatterer will be

$$H(f;t) = \alpha \exp\left[-j2\pi(f + f_0)\frac{v}{c} t \right] \qquad (9\text{-}2\text{-}45)$$

For a transmitted signal $s_0(t)$ with spectrum $U_0(f)$, the received signal then has the form

$$s(t) = \text{Re}\left\{ \exp\left[j2\pi f_0(t - t_0) \right] \int_{-\infty}^{\infty} \exp\left[j2\pi f(t - t_0) \right] U_0(f) \right.$$
$$\left. \exp\left[-j2\pi(f + f_0)\frac{v}{c} t \right] df \right\} \qquad (9\text{-}2\text{-}46)$$

Comparing with (9-2-2), it is apparent that the received signal can be written as

$$s(t) = s_0\left(t\left[1 - \frac{v}{c}\right] - t_0 \right) \qquad (9\text{-}2\text{-}47)$$

In words, aside from an overall time delay t_0, the received signal is a time-compressed (when $v < 0$) or time-expanded (when $v > 0$) version of the transmitted signal.

A useful interpretation arises by rewriting (9-2-46) so as to display the spectrum of $s(t)$ in a form

$$s(t) = \text{Re} \{[\int \exp (j2\pi\mu t) V(\mu) \, d\mu] \exp (j2\pi f_0 t)\} \qquad (9\text{-}2\text{-}48)$$

To accomplish this, in (9-2-49) we set

$$\mu = f\left(1 - \frac{v}{c}\right) \qquad \mu_0 = f_0\left(1 - \frac{v}{c}\right) \qquad (9\text{-}2\text{-}49)$$

Then
$$s(t) = \text{Re} \left\{ \exp\left[j2\pi\mu_0\left(t - \frac{t_0}{1 - v/c}\right)\right] \right.$$
$$\left. \int_{-\infty}^{\infty} \exp\left[j2\pi\mu\left(t - \frac{t_0}{1 - v/c}\right)\right] U_0\left(\frac{\mu}{1 - v/c}\right) \frac{d\mu}{1 - v/c} \right\} \qquad (9\text{-}2\text{-}50)$$

In other words, redefining the average time delay (which is only, all along, a constant defined for convenience) as

$$t_0' = \frac{t_0}{1 - v/c} \qquad (9\text{-}2\text{-}51)$$

it is clear that the spectrum of $s(t)$ is that of a bandpass signal, centered at frequency

$$\mu_0 = f_0\left(1 - \frac{v}{c}\right) \qquad (9\text{-}2\text{-}52)$$

and with the equivalent low-pass modulation spectrum

$$V(\mu) = U_0\left(\frac{\mu}{1 - v/c}\right) \qquad (9\text{-}2\text{-}53)$$

In general, the largest values of f of interest correspond to the highest modulation frequencies and are measured in order of magnitude by the bandwidth B. But values of v/c are limited by the speeds of dynamic motion in the atmosphere or ionosphere (or of a satellite); an exorbitant value, for example, would be $v/c = 3(10)^{-5}$, corresponding to path length changes at a rate of 10 km/sec. The effect on modulation components, even for bandwidths in the megacycle range, is essentially negligible. On the other hand, at a carrier frequency of 1 gc (1,000 Mc), the corresponding shift indicated by (9-2-52) would be 30 kc, a value which might be quite large with respect to the signaling bandwidth. If the changes within the modulation spectrum are ignored as just discussed, all components in the spectrum can be regarded as simply shifted by this amount. For a transmission which propagates by essentially a single path, the adjustment of tuning to compensate for shift of the carrier is generally the only compensation required for Doppler effects. (At least, this holds for most earthbound communications. When fast-moving satellites, or deep-space probes or interplanetary stations are involved in communications, the changes in modulation frequencies may have to be noted, as well. The time-domain representation in (9-2-47) indicates that fundamentally such changes amount to a time compression or expansion and can be so noted along with the basic change in carrier frequency, as long as basically a single transmission path is involved.)

Now we return to a multipath situation.   Let us momentarily again use the representation (9-2-9) which emphasizes the individual paths in the propagation channel and consider also the simple assumption that each path transmission coefficient α_k remains constant, but that the path delay is changing at some uniform rate v_k.   Then the relative delays have the form

$$\tau_k(t) = \tau_{k0} - \frac{v_k}{c} t \qquad (9\text{-}2\text{-}54)$$

and the equivalent time-varying low-pass transfer function becomes

$$H(f;t) = \sum_k \alpha_k \exp\left[-j2\pi(f + f_0)\left(\tau_{k0} - \frac{v_k}{c} t\right)\right] \qquad (9\text{-}2\text{-}55)$$

The spectral transfer function associated with the kth path is seen in this illustration to correspond to a frequency translation of the transmitted frequency $f_0 + f$ to the frequency $(1 + v_k/c)(f + f_0)$.   Moreover, since the v_k will generally be different for the various paths, any single transmitted spectral line at $f + f_0$ will have associated with it conglomerate Doppler effects or frequency shifts in the range

$$\left[\frac{(v_k)_{\min}}{c} (f + f_0), \frac{(v_k)_{\max}}{c} (f + f_0)\right]$$

We have indicated that unlike the idealized case above, physical fading channels are more realistically portrayed by statistical models in which all paths of the same length are lumped as a single path.   Then, however, the actual physical reflectors or scatterers contributing to a single path (lying within a single confocal shell, as discussed earlier) will generally have a variety of velocities, and then for *each* single path delay, the contributions will contain a variety of Doppler shifts.   Of course, because of the physical motion, each of the scatterers involved at some path delay at one instant will be involved at some other path length at some later instant.   However, the assumption of stationarity implies that *statistically* each shell will always be occupied by the same number and kind of scatterers, with the same distribution of velocities.   Thus, in these statistical models, which appear to be consistent with experimental data, we can expect a spectral broadening, due to the variety of Doppler shifts, at each path delay.   This spectral broadening for a single layer can be identified statistically with the Δt dependence of the multipath autocovariance profile $r_T(\tau;\Delta t)$.   Earlier, the dependence of $r_T(\tau;\Delta t)$ on τ was related to the frequency-time autocovariance $r_F(\Delta f;\Delta t)$ as a τ-Δf transform.   However, both of these are covariance functions, at time lag Δt, and both have associated power density spectra.   Particularly, with frequency denoted by μ, and τ regarded now as a fixed parameter, this power density spectrum for $r_T(\tau;\Delta t)$ is given by

$$V_T(\tau;\mu) = \int_{-\infty}^{\infty} r_T(\tau;\Delta t) \exp[j2\pi\mu(\Delta t)] \, d(\Delta t) \qquad (9\text{-}2\text{-}56)$$

$$r_T(\tau;\Delta t) = \int_{-\infty}^{\infty} V_T(\tau;\mu) \exp[-j2\pi\mu(\Delta t)] \, d\mu \qquad (9\text{-}2\text{-}57)$$

Again, recalling (9-2-39), $V_T(\tau;\mu)$ can be interpreted physically with respect to finite $\Delta\tau$ shells.

As stated earlier, for a *single tone* transmitted at relative frequency f', the received complex envelope is simply $\exp(j2\pi f't)H(f';t)$. With (9-2-32), and its specialization (9-2-42), the autocovariance of the received signal will be just

$$R_s(\Delta t) = \tfrac{1}{2}\langle H^*(f';t)H(f';t+\Delta t)\rangle = \exp(j2\pi f'\Delta t)r_F(0,\Delta t) \qquad (9\text{-}2\text{-}58a)$$

where $$r_F(0,\Delta t) = \int_{-\infty}^{\infty} r_T(\tau;\Delta t) \, d\tau \qquad (9\text{-}2\text{-}58b)$$

With (9-2-57) this becomes

$$R_s(\Delta t) = \exp(j2\pi f'\,\Delta t) \int_{-\infty}^{\infty} \exp[-j2\pi\mu(\Delta t)] \left[\int_{-\infty}^{\infty} V_T(\tau;\mu) \, d\tau\right] d\mu \qquad (9\text{-}2\text{-}59)$$

Hence $$V_s(\mu) = \int_{-\infty}^{\infty} V_T(\tau;\mu) \, d\tau \qquad (9\text{-}2\text{-}60)$$

is the (equivalent low-pass) power density spectrum of the received signal with a single tone transmitted relative to the frequency of the tone. Interpreted as Doppler effects, the functional dependence of $V_T(\tau;\mu)$ on μ describes the probability density function of velocity for all the scatterers at propagation delay τ. For this reason, in some of the literature, it is termed the *scattering function*. Thus, assuming that each scatterer in the layer is moving uniformly at some individual velocity v we can make the identification,

$$\mu = \frac{v}{c} f_0 \qquad (9\text{-}2\text{-}61)$$

The v have some probability density function over the layer, $p(\tau;v)$, such that $p(\tau;v)\,dv$ is the probability over the ensemble of scatterers associated with τ that v lies in the range $(v,v+dv)$. Assuming all the scatterers associated with τ have equal scattering coefficients [e.g., the α_k in (9-2-55)], or at least that the distribution of these over all scatterers having the same velocity is the same for each velocity, our model then leads to the conclusion that $V_T(\tau;\mu)$ is just proportional to $p(\tau;v)$, with μ and v related by (9-2-61). One example of the use of this concept was the prediction of the fading power spectra for the orbital dipole belt prior to any actual experiments.[1]

---

[1] *Proc. IEEE*, Westford issue, May, 1964.

Fading Rate. A gross parameter of the rapidity of fading, often used in measurements, is the fading rate. This is usually defined for a single tone transmitted as the average rate of excursions of the received envelope downward across its median level. For Rayleigh fading, it has been shown[1] that this average fade rate is given by

$$f_e = 1.475 f_N \qquad \text{crossings/sec} \qquad (9\text{-}2\text{-}62)$$

where f_N is the so-called rms frequency in $G(f)$, the equivalent low-pass power density spectrum of the process,

$$f_N = \left[\frac{\int_{-\infty}^{\infty} f^2 G(f)\, df}{\int_{-\infty}^{\infty} G(f)\, df} \right]^{1/2} \qquad \text{cps} \qquad (9\text{-}2\text{-}63)$$

The parameter f_N is clearly a rough measure of the width of $G(f)$. In our case, where measurements are made on the envelope received for a single tone transmission, the power density spectrum $G(f)$ in (9-2-63) is that defined above in (9-2-60). The average rate of fading across levels other than the median has been shown[2] for Rayleigh fading to be given in terms of f_e by

$$f(r) = 2r \exp\left(-0.693 r^2\right) f_e \qquad \text{fades/sec} \qquad (9\text{-}2\text{-}64)$$

where r is the ratio of the level concerned to the median level. Experimental data indicate this relation to be reasonably well observed.[3]

For some applications, interest may lie in the statistics of the durations of fades below certain threshold levels. The *mean* duration of fades can be derived quickly from (9-2-64), by writing the cumulative Rayleigh distribution in the similar form,

$$P(r) = \text{Prob (relative envelope} < r) = 1 - \exp\left(-0.693 r^2\right) \qquad (9\text{-}2\text{-}65)$$

Then the mean duration of fades at this level is simply

$$\bar{t} = \frac{P(r)}{f(r)} \qquad (9\text{-}2\text{-}66)$$

Note that the speed of fading has *nothing whatsoever to do with its selectivity*. The selectivity is governed by the transmitted *bandwidth* and the *multipath spread*, whereas the rapidity of fading describes the rate at which all observed effects change, because of dynamic changes in the multipath structure. Thus, earlier, we mentioned that most calculations

[1] S. O. Rice, Statistical Properties of a Sine Wave Plus Random Noise, *Bell System Tech. J.*, vol. 27, pp. 109–157, January, 1948.

[2] *Ibid.*

[3] E.g., A. B. Crawford, D. C. Hogg, and W. H. Kummer, Studies in Tropospheric Propagation Beyond the Horizon, *Bell System Tech. J.*, vol. 38, pp. 1067–1178, September, 1959; J. Grosskopf and L. Fehlhaber, Rate and Duration of Single Deep Fades in Tropospheric Scatter Links, *NTZ-CJ*, no. 3, pp. 125–131, 1962.

of fading have been based upon the assumption of nonselectivity (fading represented as multiplicative noise); and separately, that most analyses are based upon slow fading. These are *independent* assumptions. Thus, even where selectivity has been considered, slow fading has often been assumed; conversely, such analyses as exist of fast fading have usually assumed nonselectivity.[1] We shall discuss these in more detail in our later analyses.

By definition, in slow-fading models, the instantaneous transfer function of the medium $H(f;t)$ is assumed not to change during the course of an information pulse. Thus, if selectivity is an issue in a slow-fading case, it is essentially the values of $H(f;t)$ at the many different frequencies within the signal bandwidth, but at the *same instant of time*, which are of interest. The important frequency-time cross-covariance is then just $r_F(\Delta f;0)$, which as mentioned earlier, is the particular aspect of $r_F(\Delta f;\Delta t)$ which has been touched upon in measurements of fading selectivity. However, in a faster-fading case, one may need to relate the value of $H(f;t)$ at one frequency *and* at one instant to its value at another frequency at another instant (where both instants are within an information pulse length). For this, one needs to know $r_F(\Delta f;\Delta t)$ more fully. Short of a direct measurement (which, as commented earlier, has always been confined to the case $\Delta t = 0$), $r_F(\Delta f;\Delta t)$ can be estimated from (9-2-42), if $r_T(\tau;\Delta t)$ can be estimated. Most desirably, the latter would come from propagation experiments. If not available in this form, it can in turn be estimated by (9-2-57) if $V_T(\tau;\mu)$ can be determined or predicted. While this requires identification of the fading power spectrum for each τ, the assumption that the latter is described by the velocity distributions permits its possible estimation in turn from knowledge of the radio-physical processes.

A note of warning is again in order here. Severe selective fading implies that the multipath spread is of the same order of magnitude as the information pulse length (the spacing between successive pulses) in digital data transmission. In this case, the cross-covariances discussed above will still be useful in describing the distortion in a single received pulse. However, part of this distortion may then involve a significant pulse lengthening, which physically will produce significant intersymbol (adjacent symbol) interference. Often analyses of digital data transmission in fading still assume the so-called one-shot receiver, in which one discusses the effects of receiver processing on individual pulses as if no other pulses

---

[1] An excellent example of this dichotomy is furnished by comparing the models in two papers by P. Bello and B. D. Nelin: Predetection Diversity Combining with Selectively Fading Channels, *IRE Trans. Commun. Systems*, vol. CS-10, pp. 32–42, March, 1962, and The Influence of Fading Spectrum on the Binary Error Probabilities of Incoherent and Differentially Coherent Matched Filter Receivers, *IRE Trans. Commun. Systems*, vol. CS-10, pp. 160–168, June, 1962.

were present, thereby ignoring intersymbol interference. Of course, such analyses have dealt primarily with very slight selective fading situations. The warning is that in more severe selective fading, such intersymbol interference effects can no longer be ignored in performance calculations (see also Sec. 11-3).

Resolvability of Multipath; Spread Factor. It is already clear that to distinguish between signal components arriving by time delays differing by an infinitesimal amount would require a signal, and receiver, of infinite bandwidth. This is certainly not available. Rather, for any given modulated-signal bandwidth, the resolvable differential multipath delay (observable echoes) is roughly the reciprocal of the nominal bandwidth. This statement is meant to indicate order of magnitude. It also indicates that within a total spread of multipath delay, the *effective* number of *independent* observable paths is roughly the product of this multipath delay spread by the signal bandwidth (note it is a function of signal *bandwidth*).

In principle, the channel multipath can be measured continuously by transmitting a sequence of pulses (of constrained bandwidth). However, if the multipath spread is T_M, this is also the time required for each pulse to traverse the multipath and hence is the minimum measurement time required to establish the total channel *state*. On the other hand, the channel is changing dynamically at a rate measured by its fading power density spectrum. If the width of the latter is B_D (cps), then $1/B_D$ (sec) is a time span characteristic of the period in which *changes* occur in the multipath amplitudes and phases. Hence, only if $T_M \ll 1/B_D$ can one define in a measurable sense the *instantaneous* state for the channel multipath. The concept of measuring the channel state plays an important role in certain adaptive systems, such as Rake (Sec. 11-5), and leads to defining as another channel parameter the so-called *spread factor*,

$$S = T_M B_D \qquad (9\text{-}2\text{-}67)$$

In general, the requirement is that $S \ll 1$ in order to define an instantaneous state for the multipath structure. Nevertheless, note that the size of S is not a limitation on *resolvability* of the channel structure. If the requirement is only to estimate the individual multipath strengths *as they arrive* at the receiver, the size of the spread factor no longer defines a limitation on operation. (However, it still enters as a parameter in the performance of such systems).

To indicate some physical dimensions on the resolvable multipaths, let us assume that for a signal bandwidth B, the delay separation

$$\Delta\tau \sim \frac{0.1}{B} \qquad (9\text{-}2\text{-}68)$$

defines distinguishable (resolvable) modulation echoes. Some typical bandwidths and the corresponding $\Delta\tau$ are indicated in Table 9-2-1.   We can next consider several particular altitudes typical of the "reflection" zones involved in various types of communications circuits and calculate

TABLE 9-2-1

B	$\Delta\tau$
1 kc	100 μsec
10 kc	10 μsec
100 kc	1 μsec
1 Mc	100 nsec
10 Mc	10 nsec

the thickness of the "shell of resolvability" at the path midpoint as a function of the distance separating the transmitting and receiving terminals.   The results are shown in Fig. 9-2-3 for $\Delta\tau = 1$ μsec.   (To excellent approximation the shell thickness is directly proportional to $\Delta\tau$ for any

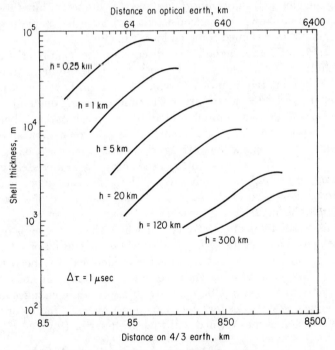

FIG. 9-2-3. Typical shell thicknesses.

other $\Delta\tau$.)   Note that since the velocity of light is 300 m/sec, even for vertical incidence (up and down propagation) the resolvable shell thickness for $\Delta\tau = 1$ μsec is 150 m and that the resolvable thickness rapidly increases for oblique incidence, essentially as the cosecant of the incidence angle. The computations in Fig. 9-2-2 have been done using the geometric earth's radius for ionospheric heights of 300 and 120 km, and using the so-called 4/3 earth radius for the lower heights where tropospheric propagation is solely involved.   The upper limits on these curves occur when, for each height involved, the ray is leaving the earth tangentially.

It is seen that the shell thicknesses are quite large, and not by any stretch of the imagination infinitesimal.   Thus "points" from a communications (time delay) viewpoint typically involve huge volumes of space.   This observation alone, relating as it does to typical signaling bandwidths which are our only concern, is the major basis for expecting the dynamic situation to be that portrayed in our phenomenological model.   (Recall the statistical characterization depends on the two-dimensional random-walk situation.)   It is clear, however, that with *very* wide bandwidths, one might observe individual shells thin enough *never* to cause Rayleigh fading by themselves, but it is not clear that any such effects have ever been observed in these media.   On a statistical ensemble basis, some of the physical realizations of the ensemble (i.e., momentary states of the channel) may *appear* to have this property, but these cases would have to be shown to be inconsistent with a statistical picture before the latter could be assumed to be no longer in effect.

Fading Plus Steady Signal.   In discussing the characteristics of a general multipath channel, we have been tacitly assuming a number of paths of approximately identical strengths.   Often, however, a medium may be characterized at least part of the time as having one major strong stable path, with perhaps a number of additional weak paths.   The stable path often appears to arise as a result of a stable reflection, as in ionospheric-skywave propagation, giving rise to the term "specular component."   This terminology is often used to apply to any steady signal in a fading situation.[1]   In such a case, the composite signal will then appear to be composed of the sum of a steady signal and of a Rayleigh-fading signal, the latter having the usual Gaussian quadrature components.   Leaving aside the issue of selectivity, for which the extension is obvious, the signal envelope resulting from a transmitted continuous tone will fluctuate according to statistics which are identical to those for the envelope of a sine wave plus additive bandpass Gaussian noise.   Such statistics were discussed in Chap. 2.   With appropriate changes in notation, the envelope statistics for "specular-plus-Rayleigh" fading or "Rice" fading as it is sometimes termed will then be described by

$$p(v) = \exp\left(-\frac{S_0}{S_R}\right) \frac{2v}{S_R} \exp\left[-\frac{v^2}{S_R}\right] I_0\left(\frac{2v\sqrt{S_0}}{S_R}\right) \qquad (9\text{-}2\text{-}69)$$

where S_R = mean-square value of fading component
S_0 = mean-square value of specular (steady) component
v = "instantaneous" rms value of composite signal

---

[1] Note that the "specular" component in a fading channel will often be Doppler-shifted from the transmitted frequency, so that while its envelope is stable, its phase may be continually changing with respect to a phase reference at the transmitted frequency.

The situation in which $K = S_0/S_R$ is somewhat larger than unity is often particularly encountered in h-f propagation, as will be discussed in the next section. When the ratio is either smaller or somewhat larger, the respective extremes of a Rayleigh-fading signal, or of a very slightly perturbed steady signal, are observed. This is shown graphically in the

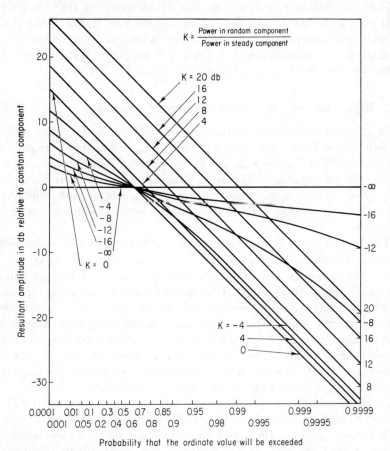

FIG. 9-2-4. Distribution of the resultant amplitude of a constant vector plus a Rayleigh-distributed vector.

curves of Fig. 9-2-4.[1] In particular, when S_0 becomes small relative to S_R, it is quickly "buried" as just another one of the multipath components giving rise to the Rayleigh law. At the other extreme, when S_0 becomes large, the distribution of signal level becomes concentrated about the value of the steady component; the major remaining perturbations in that

[1] Taken from K. A. Norton, L. E. Vogler, W. V. Mansfield, and P. J. Short, The Probability Distribution of the Amplitude of a Constant Vector Plus a Rayleigh-Distributed Vector, *Proc. IRE*, vol. 43, pp. 1354–1361, October, 1955.

case are evidenced as phase fluctuations. This latter case is of some interest in understanding the phase fluctuations which occur in vhf or uhf line-of-sight systems but is not generally of concern in any of the characteristically fading media to which most of our attention will be directed here.

For analytical purposes, a more important comment than (9-2-69) is that for a continuous transmitted tone, the received signal is describable directly as a nonzero-mean complex Gaussian process. Important use can be made of this mathematical description in analyzing systems subject to such specular-plus-Rayleigh fading, as indicated in Sec. 9-6.

9-3. High-frequency Ionospheric-skywave Propagation

In this and in the next section, we briefly discuss the characteristics of two major fading radio-propagation media. For our purposes, the emphasis will be on the fading and multipath parameters which affect the choice of signaling techniques. Therefore, we shall at best touch only very lightly upon many important engineering and radiophysical aspects associated with these media, leaving this to the extensive literature.

The first of these two media is the ionospheric-skywave mode, usable for long-distance communications from 2 Mc to as high as 60 Mc at times, but primarily used in the 3-to-30 Mc h-f band. While this band is also used for relatively short-range ground-wave propagation, its major importance has been for long-distance communications. (In addition, the fading and multipath characteristics of vhf ionospheric scatter are quite similar to those discussed below for the ionospheric-reflection mode.) Several excellent publications, on all levels of sophistication,[1] can provide the interested reader with a more comprehensive account of the properties of this skywave propagation mode than is possible here.

Four significant ionosphere "layers" are identified, denoted the D, E, F_1 and F_2 layers. Their heights and electron densities are closely related to solar radiation, so that there are important diurnal variations (day versus night) as well as important pathological effects ("magnetic storms" and "sudden ionospheric disturbances") related to phenomena such as sunspots and solar flares. For example, ionospheric character-istics and related properties of the earth's magnetic field offer one of the

---

[1] E.g., a very useful and readable introduction is K. Davies, "Ionospheric Radio Propagation," 1965, a publication of the National Bureau of Standards. Another comprehensive coverage appears in Y. L. Alpert, "Radio Wave Propagation and the Ionosphere," USSR, 1960, trans. by Consultants Bureau, New York, 1963. An excellent indication of the status of recent ionospheric radiophysics research appeared in W. J. G. Beynon (ed.), "Monograph on Ionospheric Radio," (13th General Assembly of URSI, London, September, 1960), American Elsevier Publishing Company, New York, 1962.

most striking sets of observations of the impact of the 11-year sunspot cycle. The D layer, at about 60 km altitude, acts primarily as an absorbing medium and very little as a reflector. It is usually formed under the influence of sunlight, being most intense diurnally at local noon, tending to vanish during local night. Propagation blackouts due to solar storms or flares are often related to unusually intense ionization of the D layer.

The other layers, however, act predominantly as reflectors. Antenna radiation obliquely incident upon these ionospheric layers is "reflected" down to earth at a distant point, enabling long-distance point-to-point radio connections. The density of ionization at which reflection occurs depends both upon the frequency and the angle of incidence, according to an appropriate version of Snell's law. In fact, with the ionosphere index changing continuously with altitude, a continual turning of the wave, rather than sharp reflection, more truly represents the "reflection" process. A frequency which is not reflected from a given ionosphere level at vertical incidence may still be reflected from that level when a more grazing oblique incidence is used. This accounts, for example, for the skip-distance phenomenon, where only points beyond a certain distance from a transmitter can receive ionospherically reflected waves at a given frequency. Furthermore, at frequencies above those at which there are no reflections at vertical incidence, the higher the angle of incidence (the more grazing the ray) required at a given ionosphere level in order to obtain reflection with increasing frequency. Since this in turn implies larger skip distances, it is apparent that for every transmitter-receiver separation, there is some maximum usable frequency (the so-called MUF) beyond which the receiving antenna lies in a skip zone with respect to the transmitter.

Ionospheric absorption tends to increase as frequency decreases. This leads to the desire to operate as close to the MUF condition existing at any time as can be achieved within frequency allocations. Thus, in communications practice, it is also common to define a lowest usable frequency (LUF) based on absorption, as well as such parameters as the frequency of optimum transmission. Elaborate prediction services are maintained by the U.S. National Bureau of Standards, and other agencies internationally, to assist communication users in optimizing their operations (operating stations will often have several frequency assignments among which to choose, depending on ionospheric conditions). In addition, there have been strong suggestions for extensive use of oblique-incidence sounder networks to achieve a more accurate "real-time" picture of the state of the ionosphere for communication purposes.

Of the reflecting layers themselves, the lowest is the E layer, at about 90 to 110 km. Because of its height, single E-layer reflection can account for propagation over distances up to about 1,200 miles (at this limit, the rays are tangent to the earth at transmitter and receiver).   The F_1 layer, at about 150 km, and the F_2 layer, at about 250 to 300 km, usually appear as two distinct layers in the daytime and are responsible for longer distance propagation.   At night, the E layer weakens, sometimes disappearing altogether (there is no longer any significant concentration in electron density at E-layer heights) while the F_1 and F_2 layers appear to merge into a single F layer.   Because of the greater height, single F-layer reflections can account for reception at ranges up to about 2,500 miles; the electron densities are such as to be often effective at frequencies up to about 25 to 30 Mc and sometimes even exceeding 60 Mc.

At the MUF for a given path, there is a unique ray path, i.e., a unique value of incidence angle associated with the propagation.   But below the MUF, it is often possible to find *two* possible paths, involving different incidence angles and different reflection heights.   These are often called the "low" and "high" rays, respectively.   As one approaches the MUF from below, these two paths tend to approach each other in length, so that just at the MUF there is a kind of focusing action and enhancement of the signal level, just before, at still higher frequencies, skipping occurs.

Moreover, the earth itself is a reasonable reflector for down-coming radio waves, so that an oblique-incidence ionosphere-reflected wave may be further reflected (or "scattered") forward again at its incidence upon the earth, and reflected again in a second ionospheric reflection at a much further distance, etc.   There may also be repeated bounces between the E and F layers.   Such multiple-hop propagation accounts for all propagation at ranges beyond about 2,500 miles and for all E-layer propagation beyond 1,200 miles; quite often it is encountered well within these ranges.   The fact that radiation may reach a distant point both by a large number of hops at some relatively high angle (small angle of incidence) and a smaller number of hops at more grazing incidence, possibly by paths involving different layers, accounts for most of the more widely separated multipath observed in long-distance h-f propagation.   Some of the more characteristic multihop trajectories are sketched in Fig. 9-3-1.

Additionally, although the earth's magnetic field is relatively weak, it produces significant effects in ionospheric propagation because of the circular motion imposed upon electrons by a magnetic field.   The gyromagnetic resonance effects result in different phase velocity (index of refraction) and absorption for the two opposite senses of circular polarization.   Since any linear polarization can be regarded as a sum of two counterrotating circularly polarized components, which then propagate with different velocities and may be differentially absorbed, there is a tendency for linear-polarized waves to be converted after interaction with the ionosphere to elliptic polarization (i.e., a more arbitrary combination of counterrotating circularly polarized waves of unequal magnitude and general phase relationship). When, in addition, there tend to be slight continuous random changes in the relative overall times of travel of the waves, the magnetoionic effects tend to result in randomly rotating polarization, so-called "polarization fading." That is, a linearly polarized receiving antenna will tend to observe a fading signal, while a

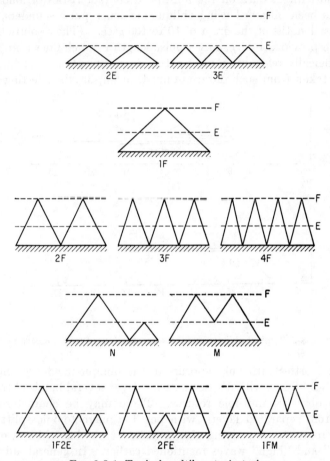

FIG. 9-3-1. Typical multihop trajectories.

second linearly polarized antenna orthogonally oriented will also observe a fading signal, with some tendency for the two fadings to be anticorrelated (i.e., as the signal on one antenna increases, the other decreases). Note, however, that in multihop reception, any such anticorrelation associated with any single-ray trajectory may be heavily masked by the independence among the several trajectories.

Another aspect of the magnetoionic interaction is that, since the counterrotating circularly polarized components interact differently with electrons, they will in general be reflected at different heights (different electron densities) for any given frequency. The two resulting waves are designated the ordinary and extraordinary waves. Because of the different overall path lengths, such ray-splitting tends further to add to the multipath nature of the medium.

The most direct data on the multipath characteristics of ionospheric paths has been obtained using oblique-incidence pulse sounders, which have pulse lengths of the order of 10 to 100 μsec. (The resolution of the multipath provided by so short a pulse length is much finer than is phenomenologically relevant to most actual communications systems.) An example taken from such data, obtained during daytime testing over a

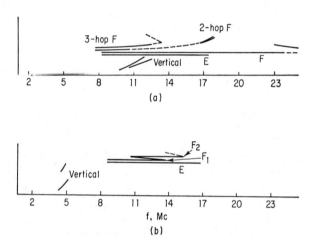

FIG. 9-3-2. Typical oblique incidence records traced from ionograms.

1,600-km North-South link, appears in the oblique-incidence ionogram of Fig. 9-3-2,[1] taken with 35-μsec pulses. Over several bands of frequencies, one observes multiple returns. These may be characterized as coming from separated layers, with possible magnetoionic splitting on each, or from returns arriving after a different number of hops, or from the "low" and "high" waves mentioned earlier. In general, all single-hop returns, which are distinguishable primarily as a consequence of their differing virtual heights, lie within a few hundred microseconds of each other (recall also Fig. 9-2-3), often within a fraction of this value. Multiple-hop returns, on the other hand, may differ by time delays of several milliseconds, depending upon the differences in the number of hops and upon the geometry of the path. Some typical data are shown in Fig. 9-3-3.

[1] From M. Balser and W. B. Smith, Some Statistical Properties of Pulsed Oblique HF Ionospheric Transmissions, *J. Res. Natl. Bur. Std.*, vol. 66D, pp. 721–730, November–December, 1962.

From these data, it is apparent that any attempt to transmit serial digital streams over long distances via the ionosphere at a rate exceeding 100 to 200 pulses/sec will tend to result in a severe intersymbol (adjacent-symbol) interference problem. That is, energy associated with one signaling pulse will still be arriving at the receiving point by the longer delayed paths, at the same time that energy associated with the subsequent signaling pulse begins to arrive via the shorter paths. In h-f communication systems, operators attempt to minimize such undesirable effects by judicious selection of operating frequency, such as by operation near the MUF. Generally, an operational system will have more than one operating frequency allocated to it. At the very least, different

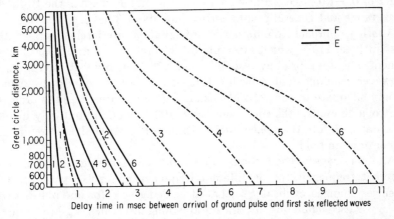

FIG. 9-3-3. Time of arrival of multihop waves. (Numbers refer to order of reflection.)

frequencies will usually be employed for day and night use, often on a regular schedule; but whenever propagation distortion effects become severe, the operators will attempt to determine whether another of their allocated frequencies would yield a better transmission. The potential use of oblique-incidence sounder networks aims at providing routinely an improved basis for making such decisions.

Another approach towards relieving severe multipath conditions is use of directional antenna arrays which preferentially receive certain (adjustable) vertical angles of arrival and discriminate against others. This is the principle behind the MUSA (Multiple-unit Steerable Antenna), which was introduced on transoceanic h-f circuits during the 1930s[1], and also has been the subject of more recent research interest.[2] Such an

[1] F. A. Polkinghorn, A Single-Sideband MUSA Receiving System for Commercial Operation on Transatlantic Radio Telephone, *Proc. IRE*, vol. 28, pp. 157–170, April, 1940.

[2] H. Brueckmann and R. Silberstein, HF Propagation Test of ISCAN, *IEEE Trans. Antennas and Propagation*, vol. AP-11, pp. 454–458, July, 1963.

antenna system will discriminate against certain multiple-hop paths in favor of others.

Measures such as these tend to narrow down the number of different multiple-hop modes by which energy arrives. However, even within a single multihop mode, there still remains the 100-μsec order of multipath due to the roughness of the ionospheric layers, the nonzero antenna beamwidths, etc. This leads to some residual multipath, no matter how "clean" the mode. Thus, in the absence of specific antimultipath measures, minimum reasonable pulse lengths for long distance circuits are of the order of 5 to 20 millisec; and even with the kind of antimultipath measures mentioned above, the minimum reasonable signal pulse length is of the order of 0.5–1.0 msec. Pulse lengths commonly used are in the 10-to-20-msec range and generally not shorter than about 3 msec.

Another approach to eliminating intersymbol interference is the Rake system (Sec. 11-5), which attempts to "resolve" the multiple-path components and appropriately recombine them for time-diversity advantages. However, as implemented for h-f, Rake utilizes a 10-kc bandwidth, which is only adequate to control wide-separation multipaths, i.e., the range of controllable multipaths runs from about 100 μsec on up, but only in 100-μsec steps. Thus, the *symbol-rate* limitations expressed above would tend to continue to hold.

Another suggested solution is to transmit successive signaling pulses at different frequencies or in different frequency channels,[1] with the frequencies changed cyclically so that after being used for one pulse, a frequency is used again only after a suitably long interval, say 20 to 25 msec. In principle, signaling pulses can then be as short as desired. However, the set of frequencies or frequency channels being used must be spaced by at least the bandwidth of the individual signaling pulses, i.e., by some amount q/T where T is the length of each transmitted pulse and q is a factor exceeding unity, perhaps as large as 5 to 10. For example, with the use of a total bandwidth F and a total cycling time T_c (exceeding the longest multipath spread), with pulses of length T, we find

$$\text{Number of pulses per frequency-change cycle} = \frac{F}{(q/T)} = \frac{T_c}{T}$$

or

$$T = \sqrt{\frac{qT_c}{F}} \tag{9-3-4}$$

Thus, even if $q = 2$ is a reasonable factor and T_c is as short as 1 msec, even with F as large as 1 Mc, T must exceed 45 μsec so the signaling rate will be

---

[1] J. L. Hollis, An Experimental Equipment to Reduce Teleprinter Errors in the Presence of Multipath, *IRE Trans. Commun. Systems*, vol. CS-7, pp. 185–188, September, 1959; A. R. Schmidt, A Frequency Stepping Scheme for Overcoming the Disastrous Effects of Multipath Distortion on High-Frequency FSK Communications Circuits, *IRE Trans. Commun. Systems*, vol. CS-8, pp. 44–47, March, 1960.

less than 25,000 pulses/sec. This is achieved at a huge cost in spectrum utilization and potential interference with other users. The same total signaling rate is in principle available within a bandwidth of 50 to 75 kc by signaling in parallel, using a large number of, say, 50-bit/sec FSK channels. The only saving then is in equipment complexity by serial rather than parallel transmission.

Now let us return to the pulse-sounder oblique-incidence returns described earlier and discuss fading effects. First, considering the particular successive pulse returns corresponding to a given propagation path, how does this return vary over successive sounding pulses? Remembering that the experiments used short (35 μsec) sounding pulses, the following results were obtained[1] on daytime tests over this 1,600-km link, in which a total of 146 records covering fixed intervals of time of the order of 5 to 15 minutes were examined (each record covering only the pulses being received via *one* mode in the resolved multipath):

On 35 per cent of the records the observed distribution of envelopes matched well to a Rayleigh distribution.

On 14 per cent of the records, the distribution fit well to that for a steady wave (specular component) plus a Rayleigh-fading component (to one of the curves in Fig. 9-2-4, for example), by assuming an appropriate ratio for the two components. A wide range of ratios of specular to Rayleigh component was observed down to low ratios at which the specular component was no longer apparent in the probability distribution.

On 6 per cent, it appeared that two interfering sine waves were being observed.

On 35 per cent of the records, none of the above kinds of match were possible. Rough estimates strongly suggested that the fading statistics were Rayleigh (or Rayleigh plus specular) but with a nonstationary intensity over these intervals. That is, during the period of observation, either the mean-square value of the fading component changed significantly, or its ratio to a specular component appears to have changed appreciably.

On the remaining records (10 per cent), the data was either scanty or very irregular, and no identification at all could be made.

The shortness of the sounding pulses was emphasized above. For longer pulses, such as used in communications (say, over 1 msec long), most of the paths described individually above will contribute constructively or destructively interfering components within the long pulse (Sec. 9-2). Thus, even a set of specular components measured with short pulses can be expected to tend to combine into Rayleigh fading on the longer pulses. Hence Rayleigh fading, with occasionally a strong specular component, can be very much expected to characterize the *short-term*

---

[1] Balser and Smith, *loc. cit.*

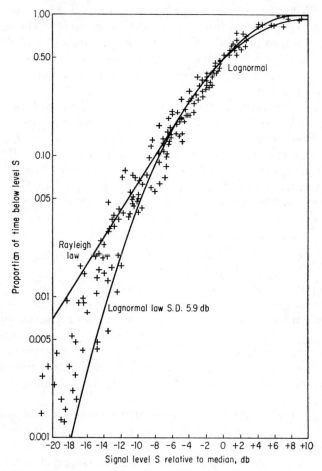

FIG. 9-3-4. Measured probability distribution for h-f fading.

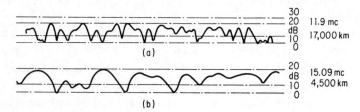

FIG. 9-3-5. Typical h-f envelope-fading records.

fading in h-f propagation.   This bears out many more observations made with signals on communication circuits.   Some very typical characteristics of this type are shown in Figs. 9-3-4 to 9-3-6.[1]   Figure 9-3-4 shows a

[1] From G. L. Grisdale, J. G. Morris, and D. S. Palmer, Fading of Long-Distance Radio Signals and a Comparison of Space- and Polarization-Diversity Reception in the 6-18 Mc/s Range, *Proc. IEE.*, vol. 104, part B, pp. 39–51, January, 1957.

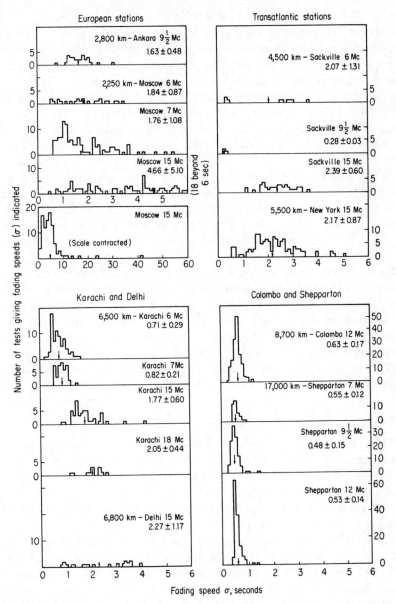

FIG. 9-3-6. Fading speeds in h-f propagation. (Distances are with respect to receiving sites in England.)

typical composite distribution, measured over a set of 10-minute periods for several circuits involving distances of 2,250 to 16,000 km. Over a wide range of the distribution, down to probabilities of the order of 0.05, a Rayleigh law appears to be observed. Below this there is a scatter of the points, probably due to the short length of sampling interval for such data. There is a slight trend for this latter data to follow the log-normal law shown; a log-normal law is often followed over long periods over which the short-term fading is nonstationary. Combining this fact and the effect of measurement inaccuracies, the interpretation is that a Rayleigh law is still reasonably indicated for the short-term fading. Figure 9-3-5 shows typical fading envelope records and Fig. 9-3-6 some histogram data on typical fading speeds at h-f.[1] Recent experimental data appear to suggest that fading speeds tend to be relatively slow, of the order typically of 0.1/sec or less, when only a single set of hops are involved in the propagation. Further, when multiple sets of hops are involved, such as both one- and two-hop modes, it appears that these often involve different *mean* doppler shifts (because of the different number of reflections), and it is this difference in mean doppler shift which then dominantly determines the overall width in the spectrum of fading of the total received signal. The latter widths then may correspond to fade rates of the order of 1/sec or even 10/sec.

To complete the discussion of h-f fading, we should show some experimental results relating to the degree of selectivity in h-f fading. Unfortunately, detailed data, of the kind presented in Sec. 9-4 for troposcatter, do not seem to be available here. Rather, one can only quote the literature[2] that for typical long-distance paths, selective fading effects set in at frequency spacings well below 1 kc and are quite pronounced at spacings of 5 to 10 kc. This is consistent with the multipath spreads which we have been discussing and with the interpretations in Sec. 9-2.

9-4. Tropospheric-scatter Propagation

The second medium which we shall describe in some detail is beyond-the-horizon propagation at vhf and above, termed "tropospheric scatter" or "troposcatter." This terminology derives from the earliest detailed model proposed for explaining the phenomenon. Again, we shall first discuss general aspects of the medium and then the specific characteristics relating to multipath fading.

Probably the most straightforward introduction to troposcatter is to cite the experimental data on point-to-point signaling at transhorizon distances, for frequencies ranging from 100 Mc through the microwave band (beyond 10 gc, atmospheric absorption limits routine use of the spectrum for communication purposes). A summary compiled by the

---

[1] The fade speed σ defined by Grisdale, et al, is such that $0.4/\sigma$ represents the average number of envelope fades per second at the level exceeded 60 per cent of the time; this can be shown for Rayleigh fading to be very closely equal (within about 2 per cent) to the fade rate at median level.

[2] E.g., J. W. Allnatt, E. D. Jones, and H. B. Law, Frequency Diversity in the Reception of Selectively Fading Binary Frequency Modulated Signals, *Proc. IEE*, vol. 104, part B, pp. 98–110, March, 1957.

U. S. National Bureau of Standards[1] is shown in Fig. 9-4-1. The data represent median path loss, averaged over long periods of time, for a variety of ground-to-ground radio circuits. The measured path loss is defined as the ratio of transmitted to received power, reduced by the transmitting antenna gain and the receiving cross section of the receiving

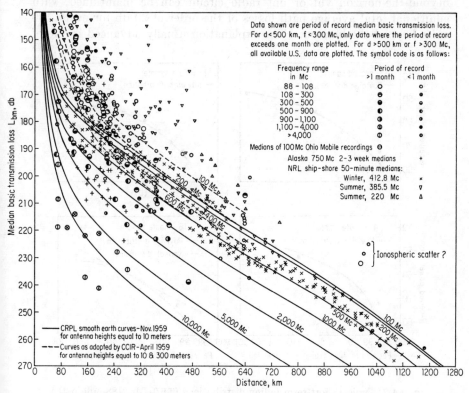

FIG. 9-4-1. Average tropospheric propagation path loss versus distance.

antenna. However, no attempt was made in the compilation to correct for antenna heights, climatological factors, so-called antenna gain degradation, frequency dependence of path loss, etc. All these factors are quite

[1] Report of USA National Committee to 13th General Assembly of URSI, *J. Res. Natl. Bur. Std.*, vol. 64D, November–December, 1960; particularly p. 616. For the reader interested in propagation-theory aspects, several excellent review articles are available: H. Staras and A. D. Wheelon, Theoretical Research on Tropospheric Scatter Propagation in the U.S., 1954–1957, *IRE Trans. Antennas and Propagation*, vol. AP-7, pp. 80–86, January, 1959; Report of the USA National Committee, etc., *J. Res. Natl. Bur. Std.*, vol. 64D, pp. 612–615, November–December, 1960; and a series of articles published as J. A. Saxton (ed.), "Monograph on Radiowave Propagation in the Troposphere," (Proc. of 13th Gen. Assembly, URSI, London, 1960), American Elsevier Publishing Company, New York, 1962.

relevant to the detailed behavior of any particular circuit; their omission is taken to be largely responsible for the scatter of the data shown.

As seen from Fig. 9-4-1, once sufficiently high effective radiated power and receiving antenna gain can cope with a path loss of about 60 db over and above the inverse-square loss (or so-called "free-space loss"), a beyond-the-horizon vhf or uhf radio circuit can be maintained, with additional total average path losses of the order of 20 db for every 100 miles beyond the horizon. The explanation usually advanced is one of

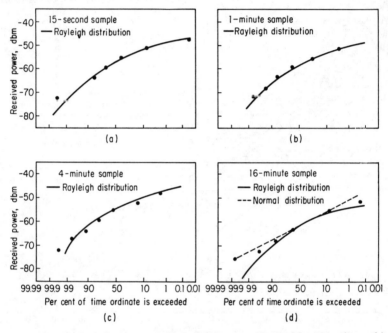

Fig. 9-4-2. Typical short-term fading distributions (3,670 Mc, 188-mile path).

scattering or reflection by inhomogeneities distributed through the common volume intersection of the transmitting and receiving beams. However, these weak persistent fields are obtained only with the accompaniment of continuous fluctuations (fading) in the field strength. When an unmodulated tone is transmitted, the fading envelope is typically observed to obey a Rayleigh law over periods of time ranging to several minutes, often perhaps an hour. A series of measured fading distributions illustrating this behavior is shown in Fig. 9-4-2.[1] In the case shown, the Rayleigh law was apparently observed over periods of one minute and

[1] From J. H. Chisholm, P. A. Portmann, J. T. de Bettencourt, and J. F. Roche, Investigations of Angular Scattering and Multipath Properties of Tropospheric Propagation of Short Radio Waves Beyond the Horizon, *Proc. IRE*, vol. 43, pp. 1317–1335, October, 1955.

perhaps up to four minutes duration. Short-term fading distributions such as in Figs. 9-4-2a and b are found in a wide variety of experimental data reported in the literature.

Over longer periods of time, the signal levels obey a more complicated distribution, already indicated in Fig. 9-4-2d. This long-term distribution is usually described by measuring the median level over intervals of time of the order of one hour, or often 15-minute periods. The troposcatter medians thus measured over a long period of time (a month, or a year) are found to obey a log-normal distribution. That is, the values measured in decibels appear to follow a Gaussian law. Some typical long-term distributions are shown in Figs. 9-4-3 and 9-4-4.[1]

For system design, it is common to distinguish between long- and short-term fading. Thus, the short-term Rayleigh distribution is a one-parameter probability law, with the median typically taken to be this parameter. During a period over which the median remains constant, the performance or quality of any particular system can be regarded as a function of the median level. For example, most of the antimultipath or antifading measures in use (see Chaps. 10 and 11) are oriented towards improving just such short-term quality by optimizing the configuration (e.g., minimizing the transmitter power, or antenna sizes) needed to achieve a given quality. Specifying some minimally acceptable quality over a short period is accordingly tantamount, for any given system configuration, to specifying the minimum short-term median fading level which provides acceptable short-term operation. The long-term performance is then commonly specified by requiring that this minimal quality be achieved over some minimal percentage of the total short-term periods, for example 99 per cent of the total hours of the years, or 95 per cent of the hours of the worst month. Knowing the minimal short-term median and the long-term distribution of the relative values of the median, one can then determine the required long-term median (i.e., the median of such distributions as given in Fig. 9-4-3). The latter in turn is given by design equations which include, for example, its dependence on distance through the kind of experimental data shown in Fig. 9-4-1.

As already indicated, the short-term fading is usually observed to obey Rayleigh-law envelope statistics. Some non-Rayleigh short-term fading observations are apparently due to additional propagation mechanisms, such as ducting,[2] so that the fading has the form of one or two strong specular components along with a Rayleigh-law component. Other times, non-Rayleigh behavior may be caused by nonstationarity ("long-

---

[1] From Chisholm, et al., *loc. cit.*, and from J. H. Chisholm, W. E. Morrow, Jr., B. E. Nichols, J. F. Roche, and A. E. Teachman, Properties of 400 Mcps Long-Distance Tropospheric Circuits, *Proc. IRE*, vol. 50, pp. 2464–2482, December, 1962.

[2] Interesting discussions of such experimental data are found in J. A. Saxton, *loc. cit.*

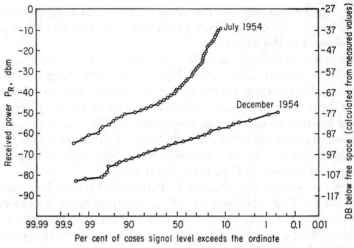

(a) Monthly distributions of hourly medians, 3,670 Mc, 188-mile path

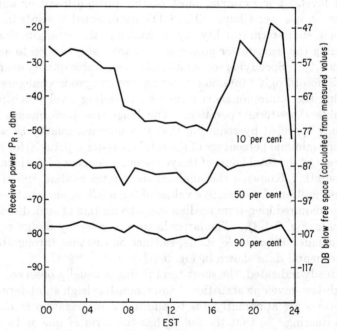

(b) Diurnal variation of hourly medians, averaged over 6-month period,
3,670 Mc, 188-mile path

FIG. 9-4-3. Typical long-term fading distributions.

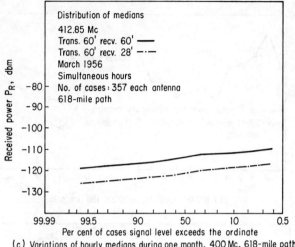

(c) Variations of hourly medians during one month, 400 Mc, 618-mile path

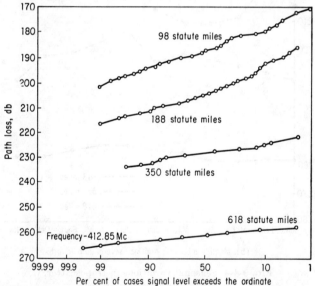

(d) Distribution of hourly medians during typical winter month, 400 Mc, several path lengths

FIG. 9–4–3. (*Continued*)

term'') fading during the measurement interval (say, several minutes), which does not contradict the assumption of Rayleigh-law envelope fading within shorter subintervals (again, recall Fig. 9-4-2). To the present time, it has therefore seemed reasonable and realistic for troposcatter communication system design purposes (e.g., for estimating diversity

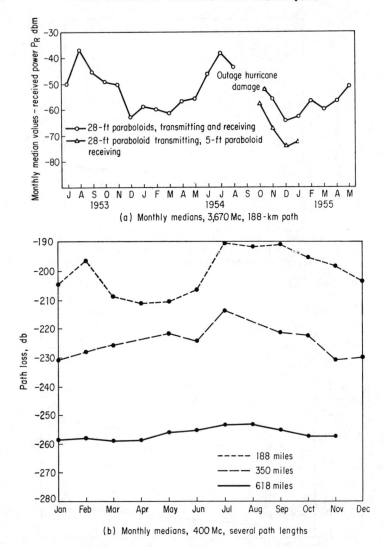

(a) Monthly medians, 3,670 Mc, 188-km path

(b) Monthly medians, 400 Mc, several path lengths

Fig. 9-4-4. Seasonal variations in troposcatter.

performance, as in Chap. 10) to assume that at least during weak signal periods (the depths of the long-term fading), the short-term fading is Rayleigh-law.[1] We shall be following this line closely in the extensive analyses which follow, using the phenomenological interpretations of Sec. 9-2.

In Sec. 9-2 the kind of information required to fully describe multipath fading was outlined.   It was mentioned that available experimental data

[1] An interesting relevant note is R. G. Finney, Short-Time Statistics of Tropospheric Radio Wave Propagation, *Proc. IRE*, vol. 47, pp. 84–85, January, 1959.

are largely confined to fading power spectrum, fade rate, and fading selectivity with spaced tones. For most of the experimental results cited below, the experimenters have also verified that the envelope distribution does reasonably follow a stationary Rayleigh law over each measurement interval.

It will be recalled (Sec. 9-2) that the width of the fading power spectrum can be regarded as determined by the range of Doppler frequencies associated with the dynamic changes in the medium. Accordingly, this width is expected to be proportional to operating (carrier) frequency. Correspondingly, all fading processes can be expected to occur also at a rate proportional to the operating frequency. This is reasonably con-

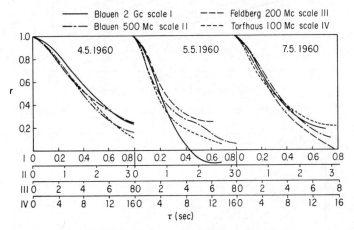

FIG. 9-4-5. Fading envelope autocorrelations.

sistently observed in the experimental data,[1] which for troposcatter covers almost two decades of frequency. For example, Fig. 9-4-5 shows some experimental observations[2] of normalized envelope-fading autocorrelations, taken on several paths approximately 250 km long. These were obtained with cw tones transmitted, at several frequencies as indicated. While there is some variation between the three days shown, the autocorrelations are essentially alike on all frequencies within each day's test when the time scale is normalized to the reciprocal of the cw frequency, consistent with our comment above. In connection with these autocorrelations, it may be emphasized (Sec. 9-2) that for our assumed model of Rayleigh fading, the normalized envelope autocovariance is very closely the square of the magnitude of the normalized autocovariance of the complex Gaussian process describing fading on a single tone. Hence, the power

[1] There is, incidentally, some evidence that the speed of fading may tend to be higher at weaker median levels. Some data to this effect are given by F. du Castel in J. A. Saxton, *op. cit.*, p. 22.

[2] Reported by J. Grosskopf in J. A. Saxton, *op. cit.*, p. 44.

spectra of the autocovariances in Fig. 9-4-5 are *not* the same as these involved in later calculations where the properties of the complex Gaussian process are used.

Typically, observed troposcatter fading rates range from 0.1 to 1.0 fades/sec at 400 Mc, to 1 to 10 fades/sec at 4,000 Mc.   However, in

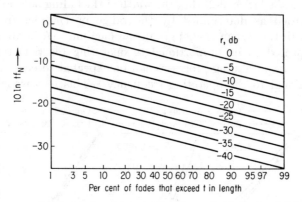

(a) Compilation of data at several frequencies (Grosskopf and Fehlhaber)

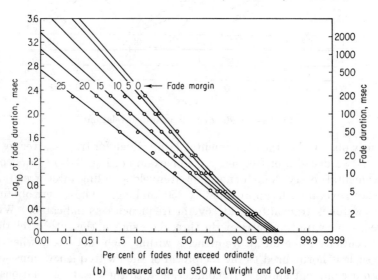

(b)   Measured data at 950 Mc (Wright and Cole)

FIG. 9-4-6. Short-term distributions of fade durations.

individual experiments, the fade rates may vary from these values by a factor of 10, in either direction.[1]

Detailed experimental data on the statistical distribution of fade durations are sparse.   Such data as are available are reasonably consistent

[1] J. Grosskopf and L. Fehlhaber, Rate and Duration of Single Deep Fades in Tropospheric Scatter Links, *NTZ-CJ*, no. 3, pp. 125–131, 1962.

as to trend and order of magnitude, but not in good detailed agreement on the shape of the distributions.   One set of data described as summarizing extensive tests at several frequencies[1] is shown in Fig. 9-4-6a.   Another set of data,[2] taken at 950 Mc, is shown in Fig. 9-4-6b (however, envelope distributions published as part of these latter measurements leave doubt as to the character or stationarity of the fading over the observation intervals).

The other important characteristic of the short-term fading is its selectivity or multipath profile.   The sketch in Fig. 9-4-7 illustrates the

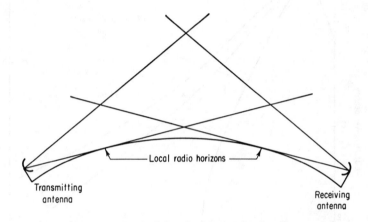

Fig. 9-4-7. Typical sketch of scattering geometry.

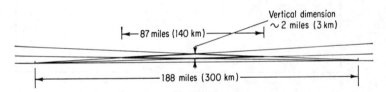

Fig. 9-4-8. Scale diagram of scatter geometry.

"common volume" geometry which roughly defines the troposcatter multipath spread insofar as it is controlled by antenna beamwidths and transmitting-receiving site separation.   While Fig. 9-4-7 is typical of such sketches in the literature, it is illuminating to show in Fig. 9-4-8 a typical case drawn to scale for a 188-mile (300 km) path with 1° beamwidth antennas.   This sketch emphasizes the actual physical extent of the volume within which interaction takes place.   It is clear that each "shell"

---

[1] Grosskopf and Felhaber, *loc. cit.*

[2] K. F. Wright and J. E. Cole, Measured Distribution of the Duration of Fades in Tropospheric Scatter Transmission, *IRE Trans. Antennas and Propagation*, vol. AP-8, pp. 594–598, November, 1960.

or "layer" defining the multipath (Sec. 9-2) is physically of great "hori-zontal" extent. Taking into account the overall "width" of the individual "shells," antenna beam patterns, and variation of the "scattering" cross section (as a function of the scattering angle and of atmospheric density variation with altitude) throughout the common volume, one typically

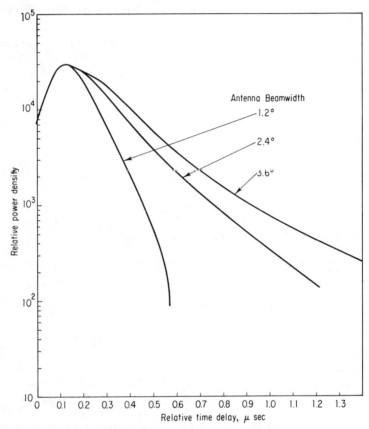

FIG. 9-4-9. Typical multipath intensity profiles.

arrives at a multipath intensity profile such as shown in Fig. 9-4-9,[1] cal-culated for a 300-km path. As seen, the estimated multipath spread for contributions within 10 db of the peak is several tenths of a microsecond for these beamwidths and this length of path. This appears consistent with experimental data.

Direct pulse-sounding measurements of the multipath spread have been

[1] B. B. Barrow, Time-Delay Spread with Tropospheric Propagation Beyond the Horizon, Applied Research Laboratory, Sylvania Electronic Systems, Res. Note 364, October, 1962. The calculation was based upon idealized conical beam patterns, and formulas of the layer-reflection theory for estimating the variation of scattering cross section.

accomplished over paths up to 800 miles length.[1] However, generally the pulses have been no shorter than 1 μsec duration, so that only fractional elongation of the sounding pulses is observed on paths about 200 miles long, by an amount which can only be estimated as a few tenths of microseconds. For typical beamwidths, the maximum elongation increases to 4 to 8 μsec on paths 800 miles long. One more detailed set of data, taken with 0.1-μsec pulses over a 188-mile path at 2,290 Mc,[2] indicated a multipath spread on that path of the order of 0.3 to 0.4 μsec.

Alternative to the pulse-sounding measurements, there have been several experimental investigations of the selective-fading properties of the troposcatter channel, using either rapidly sweeping transmitters,[3] or transmission of spaced tones with measurement of cross-correlation on the received envelopes as a function of the frequency spacing.[4] Some typical data at 975 Mc are shown in Fig. 9-4-10.[5] It will be recalled from Sec. 9-2 that the envelope covariance data on spaced tones are not adequate to describe the multipath intensity profile unless the latter is symmetric. It is quite clear from Fig. 9-4-9 that symmetry is typically not expected in troposcatter. Hence, at best, one can only infer from such selective-fading data an order of magnitude for the multipath spread, as the reciprocal of, say, the spacing at which the normalized envelope cross-covariance falls to 0.5. On this basis, such data as in Fig. 9-4-10 are generally consistent with multipath spread data obtained from pulse measurements.

One may also note some experiments with rapid sweeping of a voltage-tunable transmitter across a wide bandwidth,[6] yielding "candid" shots of the instantaneous transfer characteristic over a wide frequency range. The observation has been that over a wide bandwidth (for example, 150 Mc centered on 3 gc) there is almost always at least one frequency at which the instantaneous path transmission is several db *above* the median over the band, with relatively wide instantaneous transmission bandwidth. It has been suggested that useful adaptive operation could accordingly be

[1] Chisholm, Morrow, et al., *op. cit.* and Chisholm, Portmann, et al., *loc. cit.*

[2] J. F. Roche and J. Chisholm, Measurements Over a 188-Mile Path at 2290 mc/s, Using 0.1 Microsecond Pulse Transmissions, URSI-IRE Fall Meeting, 1962, Ottawa, Canada.

[3] J. H. Chisholm, L. P. Rainville, J. F. Roche, and H. G. Root, Measurement of the Bandwidth of Radio Waves Propagated by the Troposphere Beyond the Horizon, *IRE Trans. Antennas and Propagation*, vol. AP-6, p. 377, October, 1958.

[4] L. G. Abraham, Jr., Effective Bandwidth of Tropospheric Propagation, URSI Spring Meeting, Wash., D.C., 1959; also L. G. Abraham, Jr., and J. A. Bradshaw, Tropospheric Scatter Propagation Study, AFCRC-TR-59-533, General Electric Research Lab., October, 1959; A. B. Crawford, D. C. Hogg, and W. H. Kummer, "Studies in Tropospheric Propagation Beyond the Horizon, *Bell System Tech. J.*, vol. 38, pp. 1067–1178, September, 1959.

[5] From Abraham and Bradshaw, *loc. cit.*; the path length was 135 miles.

[6] du Castel, in J. A. Saxton, *loc. cit.*

based upon continual monitoring over a wide band, with the operating communication frequency controlled to follow the instantaneous optimum frequency. This seems likely to provide performance equivalent to a high order of frequency diversity (frequency diversity is discussed in Chap. 10, although there will be no further references to this frequency-tracking technique). However, along with implementation problems,

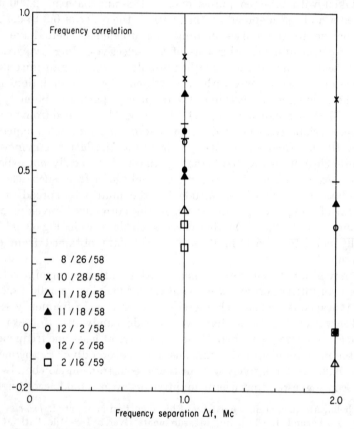

FIG. 9-4-10. Typical envelope cross-correlations on spaced tones.

use of an extremely wide frequency band may imply severe problems of frequency allocation and potential interference with other services, so that such a system concept seems likely to be employed at most for very special applications.

9-5. Single Binary Channels in Slow, Nonselective Rayleigh Fading

Having discussed mathematical models for fading channels and the parameters of the two most important of these media, we now return to our main topic, analysis of performance for digital signaling over these channels. We shall first examine the model mentioned near the end of Sec. 9-2, which has received most attention in the literature: slow, nonselective, purely Rayleigh fading. Somewhat more general fading models are discussed in Sec. 9-6. Both these sections, however, will confine attention to the single binary channel, leaving to Chaps. 10 and 11 the important subject of diversity operation.

As discussed in Sec. 9-2, the idealized assumption of nonselective fading implies that the fading can be described completely as a multiplicative complex Gaussian process. It also implies that the medium introduces no significant pulse lengthening and hence that there is no intersymbol interference due to the medium. We will also assume here that no intersymbol interference is introduced by the receiver filters. In assuming purely Rayleigh fading in this section we also specifically exclude models involving an additional specular component. Hence the multiplicative Gaussian process is taken to be zero-mean.

The assumption of slow fading further implies that the multiplicative fading process varies so slowly compared with signal keying rates that it may be regarded to be effectively constant during the course of each signal pulse, although varying over a long succession of such pulses. Combined with the other assumption, this implies that each transmitted pulse is received undistorted, except for a complex multiplier consisting of a Rayleigh-distributed envelope and an additive, uniformly distributed carrier phase shift. This same complex multiplier will then also appear directly as a multiplier on the output voltage of receiver filters acting upon that pulse.

Within these assumptions, one can then directly apply the steady signal results of Chap. 7 to write the probability that additive Gaussian noise will produce an error on a particular pulse. The functional dependence of the error probability on signal level is viewed now as describing a probability of pulse error *conditional* on the value of the complex multiplier for that pulse. The average performance over fading is obtained by further averaging this result over the Rayleigh distribution for the envelope factor and (if it enters) the uniform distribution for the phase. This technique, which we illustrate below, is convenient when the probability of error has already been calculated for steady signal in additive Gaussian noise and when the resulting expression can be conveniently averaged over the ensemble of values of the multiplicative noise.

On the other hand, each filter output involved in detection/decision in our model for the Rayleigh-fading channel is at most the sum of a complex zero-mean Gaussian variate representing the signal, plus a complex zero-mean Gaussian additive noise variate. That is, each filter output is totally just a complex zero-mean Gaussian variate whose statistics involve both signal and noise parameters; hence for Rayleigh-fading signal, the total detection/decision problem then involves only zero-mean Gaussian processes.   In simple FSK, for example, the probability of error becomes just the probability that the envelope of one zero-mean complex Gaussian process (the filter output containing no signal) exceeds the envelope of another (the filter output containing signal plus noise).   The derivations of probability-of-error formulas are usually correspondingly simpler from this viewpoint, which will also be illustrated below and used extensively in Chap. 11.

Both approaches above apply equally well to calculating the probability that any *single* information pulse, chosen completely at random, will be in error.   Many calculations, however, involve a sequence of pulses, e.g., to determine the probability of character error in radioteletype or to determine the probability of correct decoding for code blocks when redundant coding is being employed.   Most calculations along these lines have been based upon extending the slow-fading model to the *assumption* that the multiplicative noise remains constant over the *entire* character or sequence.   Clearly, this becomes less and less realistic as the sequence length increases.   Within this assumption, however, one rests on the first calculation technique: All pulses in the sequence are assumed to have the same multiplicative factor but to be associated with independent additive noises.   Accordingly, one can calculate a probability of *sequence* error conditional on the value of the multiplicative process.   This is then averaged over the distribution of the multiplicative noise to obtain the overall average probability of sequence error.   Since the individual binary decisions in the sequence are not statistically independent (the multiplicative noise is "completely correlated" over all pulses in the sequence), there appears in this case to be no useful application of the alternate mode of calculation.

At the other extreme in dealing with pulse sequences is the assumption that every pulse error in a sequence occurs independently of every other pulse error.   This appears realistic, when coupled with the assumption of slow-fading for each individual pulse, only when "interleaving" or "interlacing" is being employed (the pulses of the sequence are transmitted with wide spacings between them, so that they encounter independent fading conditions; they are interleaved with pulses from other sequences).   This results in error independence within a sequence essentially without regard to fading rate.

As already indicated, however, our purposes preclude detailed study of pulse sequences.   In the remainder of this section, we shall examine the effects of slow, nonselective Rayleigh fading on only bit error rates, for the basic systems introduced in Chap. 7.   While we have emphasized the importance of FSK and PSK systems in current applications, we shall for completeness first present results for on-off keying.

On-off Keying with Noncoherent Detection.   We refer back to Sec. 7-4. Under the assumptions above, and assuming Mark transmitted, the envelope of the *signal* at the filter output at the sampling instant, u, is a statistical variate with a Rayleigh Law p.d.f.,

$$p(u) = \frac{2u}{u_0^2} \exp\left(-\frac{u^2}{u_0^2}\right) \qquad 0 < u < \infty \qquad (9\text{-}5\text{-}1)$$

where
$$u_0^2 = \langle u^2 \rangle \qquad (9\text{-}5\text{-}2)$$

is the mean-square value of u, averaged over the fading. The filter output-noise intensity at every sampling instant is still the factor N, unchanged from pulse to pulse. Hence one may also regard the SNR at the sampling instant

$$\gamma = \frac{u^2}{2N} \qquad (9\text{-}5\text{-}3)$$

as a statistical variable from pulse to pulse. With (9-5-1) and N thus regarded as a constant, the p.d.f. for γ is then the exponential distribution

$$p(\gamma) = \frac{1}{\gamma_0} \exp\left(-\frac{\gamma}{\gamma_0}\right) \qquad 0 < \gamma < \infty \qquad (9\text{-}5\text{-}4)$$

where
$$\gamma_0 = \langle \gamma \rangle = \frac{u_0^2}{2N} \qquad (9\text{-}5\text{-}5)$$

is the mean SNR (over fading) at the sampling instants at the filter output. For a *fixed threshold* b normalized with respect to N as

$$b_0 = \frac{b}{\sqrt{N}} \qquad (9\text{-}5\text{-}6)$$

the conditional probability of error for each decision when Mark and Space are equally likely is given from (7-4-12),

$$P_\gamma = \tfrac{1}{2}[1 - Q(\sqrt{2\gamma}, b_0)] + \tfrac{1}{2} \exp\left(-\frac{b_0^2}{2}\right) \qquad (9\text{-}5\text{-}7)$$

The overall probability of error is obtained by averaging over (9-5-4)

$$P = \int_0^\infty P_\gamma \, p(\gamma) \, d\gamma \qquad (9\text{-}5\text{-}8)$$

The required integrals are readily carried out (e.g., Appendix A), giving

$$P = \frac{1}{2}\left[1 - \exp\left(-\frac{b_0^2}{2}\frac{1}{1+\gamma_0}\right)\right] + \frac{1}{2}\exp\left(-\frac{b_0^2}{2}\right) \qquad (9\text{-}5\text{-}9)$$

A set of curves of P versus mean SNR γ_0 is given in Fig. 9-5-1, for various values of b_0. Again, as in (7-4-13), one can find a value of *fixed threshold* which minimizes the error probability for each γ_0, as is apparent in Fig. 9-5-1. Analytically, the optimum fixed threshold is found by differentiating (9-5-9) with respect to b_0; the result is

$$b_0 = \sqrt{2\left(1 + \frac{1}{\gamma_0}\right)\ln(1 + \gamma_0)} \qquad (9\text{-}5\text{-}10)$$

A graph of b_0 versus the mean SNR γ_0 is presented in Fig. 9-5-2. For large γ_0 (large mean SNR over fading),

$$b_0 \rightarrow \sqrt{2\ln\gamma_0} \qquad (9\text{-}5\text{-}11)$$

The value of P as a function of γ_0, using the appropriate value of b_0 from Fig. 9-5-2, is also shown in Fig. 9-5-1.

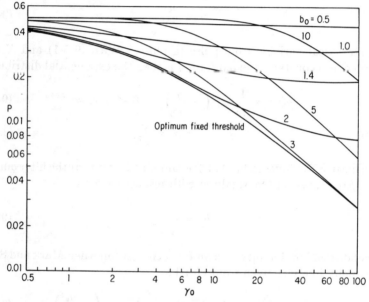

FIG. 9-5-1. Probability of error versus mean SNR, noncoherent on-off keying, Rayleigh fading.

The curve of error rate versus SNR for the optimum fixed b_0 corresponding to each value of mean SNR γ_0 is redrawn in Fig. 9-5-3. Along with it is shown for comparison (from Fig. 7-4-2) the error rate with optimum threshold for each γ_0, for *steady* (nonfading) signals in thermal noise. The destructive effect of signal fading is obvious. With Rayleigh fading covering the entire range of values $(0, \infty)$, no *fixed* threshold can properly discriminate signal (Mark) from noise (Space) over the variety of levels. When the signal is weak (deep fading), it will fall below the threshold; when it is very strong, far exceeding threshold, an even higher threshold would more suitably discriminate against falsely identifying noise as signal.

This observation leads one to consider a possible adaptive system.

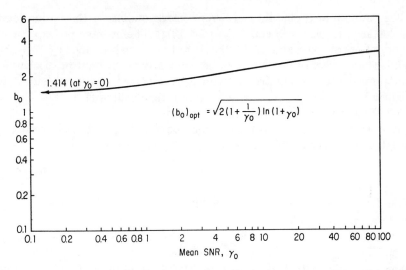

FIG. 9-5-2. Optimum fixed threshold versus mean SNR, noncoherent on-off keying, Rayleigh fading.

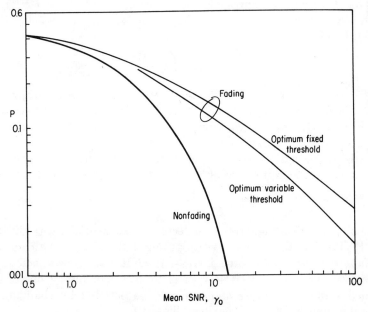

FIG. 9-5-3. Probability of error for noncoherent on-off keying under various conditions.

Under the assumption of sufficiently slow fading, one may visualize some relatively noiseless monitoring of the fading state, for example through integration of the received signal (plus noise) level over many Mark pulses. In that case, with *sufficiently slow* fading, one might consider the possibility of continually adjusting the threshold at each "instant" to the optimum value (minimum probability of error) corresponding to the fading level at that instant, as given earlier by (7-4-13). The average probability of error follows by averaging (7-4-12) over fading, with b_0 defined by (7-4-13). While these integrations cannot be conveniently carried out precisely, one can employ the close approximation in (7-4-14); this gives a result only slightly higher than with the true optimum threshold of (7-4-13). Figure 9-5-3 shows the results of the calculation.

At very large γ_0 ($\gamma_0 \to \infty$), the error rate in fading with (approximate) variable optimized threshold asymptotically approaches

$$P_{var} = \frac{1.63}{\gamma_0} \qquad (9\text{-}5\text{-}12a)$$

while for the optimum fixed threshold, using (9-5-9) and (9-5-10), it can be shown to approach

$$P_{fixed} = \frac{1}{2} \frac{\ln \gamma_0}{\gamma_0} \qquad (9\text{-}5\text{-}12b)$$

Thus, at sufficiently low error rate, the fixed optimized and variable optimized thresholds both give an error rate inverse with SNR. On the other hand, with a fixed threshold (not adjusted even to mean SNR), one may observe the much poorer behavior shown in Fig. 9-5-1. From (9-5-9), this is given for large γ_0 (and fixed b_0) by

$$P \to \frac{1}{2} \exp\left(-\frac{b_0^2}{2}\right) \qquad (9\text{-}5\text{-}12c)$$

In other words, in a system with a fixed threshold, the effect of fading is to place a minimum value upon the achievable probability of error; at large mean SNR, the system approaches a fixed error rate *independent* of SNR, as in the nonfading case.

The behavior with optimum threshold is especially to be compared with the earlier asymptotic results in (7-4-18) for a *steady* signal in noise,

$$P_{steady} = \frac{1}{2} \exp\left(-\frac{\gamma}{4}\right) \qquad (9\text{-}5\text{-}13)$$

In the absence of fading, error rate decreases *exponentially* with SNR, at large SNR. In fading, even with optimized thresholds, the error rate still falls only inversely with increasing SNR. As shown below, the inverse variation with SNR is typical in Rayleigh fading of all well-designed digital techniques and can only be bettered by changing the fading distribution, as by diversity (Chap. 10).

It is useful to indicate the simplicity of the alternative derivation of (9-5-9). Thus, the *p.d.f. for the envelope* at the filter output at the sampling instant, with signal present, is the Rayleigh law for the envelope of a complex Gaussian process composed of the sum of one process of intensity N (the additive noise) and another of intensity $\gamma_0 N$ (the fading signal). The probability that the envelope exceeds some threshold b is then directly given by

$$\text{Prob } (r > b) = \int_b^\infty \frac{r}{N(1 + \gamma_0)} \exp\left(-\frac{r^2}{2N}\frac{1}{1 + \gamma_0}\right) dr$$

$$= \exp\left(-\frac{b^2}{2N}\frac{1}{1 + \gamma_0}\right) = \exp\left(-\frac{b_0{}^2}{2}\frac{1}{1 + \gamma_0}\right) \quad (9\text{-}5\text{-}14)$$

This leads, again, directly to (9-5-9).

On-off Keying with Coherent Detection. In this case, one can refer to the result in (7-4-23), regarded again as conditional on γ. This result

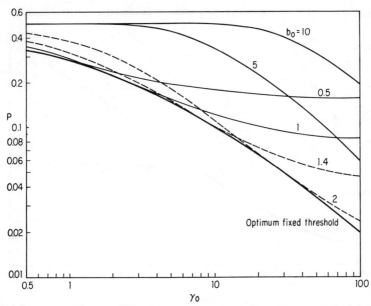

FIG. 9-5-4. Probability of error versus mean SNR for coherent on-off keying, Rayleigh fading.

assumed a perfect, noiseless reference for coherent detection. If the fading is slow enough, it is reasonable to assume that this can still be accomplished (e.g., through phase-locked loops, integrating over the arriving phases in many successive Marks). We shall here assume this case (see later comments in the discussion of PSK). Thus, averaging (7-4-23) over the fading distribution gives

$$P = \frac{1}{2} - \frac{1}{4}\frac{1}{\sqrt{1 + 1/\gamma_0}} \exp\left[-\frac{b_0{}^2}{2(1 + \gamma_0)}\right] \text{erfc}\left[-\frac{b_0}{\sqrt{2(1 + 1/\gamma_0)}}\right]$$
$$(9\text{-}5\text{-}15a)$$

where again $\quad \text{erfc } x \equiv \dfrac{2}{\sqrt{\pi}} \displaystyle\int_x^\infty \exp\left(-t^2\right) dt \quad (9\text{-}5\text{-}15b)$

A plot of P versus γ_0 for various fixed values of threshold b_0 is shown in Fig. 9-5-4.

Again one can seek the value of fixed threshold which minimizes the probability of error, leading to the implicit relation

$$\gamma_0 = b_0 \sqrt{\frac{\pi \gamma_0}{2(1 + \gamma_0)}} \exp\left[\frac{b_0^2 \gamma_0}{2(1 + \gamma_0)}\right] \operatorname{erfc}\left[-b_0 \sqrt{\frac{\gamma_0}{2(1 + \gamma_0)}}\right] \quad (9\text{-}5\text{-}16)$$

The value of b_0 versus γ_0 given by (9-5-16) is plotted in Fig. 9-5-5. For $\gamma_0 \to 0$, $b_0 \to \sqrt{(2/\pi)\gamma_0}$, while for $\gamma_0 \to \infty$, $b_0 \to \sqrt{2 \ln \gamma_0}$. The corresponding probability of error in fading with the optimum fixed threshold is shown in Fig. 9-5-4, as a function of γ_0.

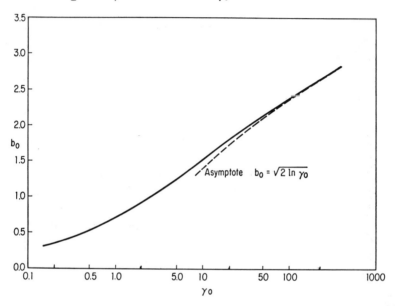

FIG. 9-5-5. Optimum fixed threshold versus mean SNR for coherent on-off keying, Rayleigh fading.

One can also again contemplate a variable-threshold case, in which fading is assumed slow enough that at each instantaneous level γ the threshold can be set at an associated local optimum, as given by (7-4-24), with the resulting conditional probability of error given by (7-4-25). Averaged over fading, one then obtains as the probability of error for this case,

$$P_{\text{var}} = \int_0^\infty \frac{1}{\gamma_0} \exp\left(-\frac{\gamma}{\gamma_0}\right) \frac{1}{2} \operatorname{erfc} \frac{\sqrt{\gamma}}{2} \, d\gamma = \frac{1}{2}\left(1 - \frac{1}{\sqrt{1 + 4/\gamma_0}}\right) \quad (9\text{-}5\text{-}17)$$

This is shown plotted as a function of γ_0 in Fig. 9-5-6, along with the curve for optimum fixed threshold redrawn from Fig. 9-5-4. For comparison, the curve in Fig. 7-4-4 for steady signals in thermal noise with optimum threshold, as given by (7-4-25), has been redrawn here as well.

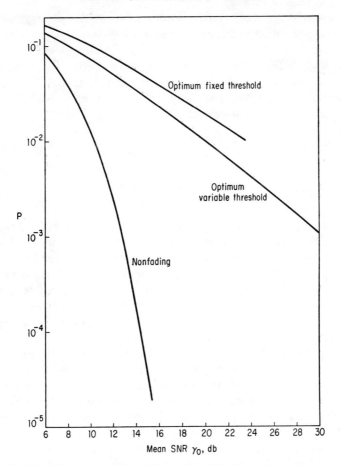

Fig. 9-5-6. Probability of error for coherent on-off keying under various conditions.

Asymptotically, for large γ_0, the quantities plotted in Fig. 9-5-6 approach

$$P_{\text{fixed}} \approx \frac{1}{2} \frac{\ln \gamma_0}{\gamma_0} \qquad (9\text{-}5\text{-}18a)$$

$$P_{\text{var}} \approx \frac{1}{\gamma_0} \qquad (9\text{-}5\text{-}18b)$$

$$P_{\text{steady}} \approx \frac{1}{\sqrt{\pi \gamma_0}} \exp\left(-\frac{\gamma_0}{4}\right) \qquad (9\text{-}5\text{-}18c)$$

Again, as in the noncoherent case, the error rate varies exponentially with decreasing SNR in the nonfading case but only linearly (inversely) when Rayleigh fading occurs.

This discussion of on-off keying, supplementing that given earlier in Sec. 7-4, is all that will be said here about on-off keying. In the remainder of our material we shall confine attention to FSK and PSK systems, representing the dominant present applications in radio transmission of digital data.

FSK and PSK. Within the slow, nonselective Rayleigh-fading assumption, one can deal simultaneously with FSK and PSK. Thus, from Secs. 7-5 and 7-6, there are only two forms of conditional probability of error on the individual pulses:

$$P_\gamma^{(1)} = \tfrac{1}{2} \exp\left(-\alpha\gamma\right) \qquad \begin{cases} \alpha = \tfrac{1}{2} & \text{noncoherent FSK} \\ \alpha = 1 & \text{differentially coherent PSK} \end{cases}$$

$$(9\text{-}5\text{-}19)$$

$$P_\gamma^{(2)} = \tfrac{1}{2} \operatorname{erfc}\left(\sqrt{\alpha\gamma}\right) \qquad \begin{cases} \alpha = \tfrac{1}{2} & \text{coherent FSK} \\ \alpha = 1 & \text{ideal coherent PSK} \end{cases} \qquad (9\text{-}5\text{-}20)$$

In light of the preceding discussion of on-off keying, it is apropos to note that these conditional error probabilities depend only on SNR but do not involve any such additional parameter as a threshold. More precisely, recalling Chap. 7, we can recognize that in all these FSK and PSK systems, the threshold is effectively a *zero* level, *independent* of SNR. That is, either a voltage is compared against zero level to determine its sign, or the *difference* in two voltages is so compared against a zero level. Since this *zero* threshold is *independent* of SNR, it is clear that under the conditions of slow, nonselective fading the threshold for these systems is in effect at its optimum value at all levels of signal fading. Thus, one way of viewing the advantages of these systems over on-off keying when used on a fading channel is that, *without requiring any actual adaptation*, they inherently contain the performance of a continuously optimized variable-threshold system. This is indeed the case; as will be seen, for the slow, nonselective Rayleigh-fading channel, the asymptotic error probabilities for all the systems vary inversely as the mean SNR.

There is no problem in averaging (9-5-19) or (9-5-20) over fading to describe the average probability of single-pulse error for noncoherent FSK. However, for either ideal PSK or coherent FSK, one again encounters the issue of establishing a phase reference in view of the random fluctuations of carrier phase implied by the fading. The earlier, superficial answer is that if the fading can be assumed *slow enough*, it should be possible to derive a suitable essentially noiseless phase reference for either coherent FSK or ideal PSK. Alternatively, for DPSK, the requirement is simply that the received signal phase remains approximately the same over time periods of two pulse lengths. As discussed in Chap. 8, one can also consider constructing a phase reference for each pulse by a running average over a large number of prior pulses. In Rayleigh fading, one can again hypothesize *sufficiently* slow fading that the SNR improvement due to such longer averaging in deriving the phase reference is still available in these generalized DPSK systems or in ideal

PSK or coherent FSK systems. On the other hand, in fading, there is clearly a tendency for the phase derived by such an average to become a poorer reference for the "current" pulse as the average extends longer and longer into the past; hence there must be a compromise dependent on the rate of fading. Some pertinent results are given in Chap. 11. In the remainder of this section, we explore only the simple calculations of fading effects on the assumption of "sufficiently slow fading," so that (9-5-19) and (9-5-20) can be directly averaged over Rayleigh fading. Theoretical results such as outlined in Chap. 11 and associated experimental data indicate that the simplified results based upon "slow, nonselective" fading are applicable in practice only within limitations.

Averaging (9-5-19) and (9-5-20) over the Rayleigh-fading p.d.f. gives immediately

$$P^{(1)} = \int_0^\infty \frac{1}{2} \exp(-\alpha\gamma) \frac{1}{\gamma_0} \exp\left(-\frac{\gamma}{\gamma_0}\right) d\gamma = \frac{1}{2 + 2\alpha\gamma_0} \tag{9-5-20}$$

and

$$P^{(2)} = \int_0^\infty \frac{1}{2} \operatorname{erfc} \sqrt{\alpha\gamma} \frac{1}{\gamma_0} \exp\left(-\frac{\gamma}{\gamma_0}\right) d\gamma = \frac{1}{2}\left(1 - \frac{1}{\sqrt{1 + 1/\alpha\gamma_0}}\right) \tag{9-5-21}$$

(The latter result is obtained by an obvious integration by parts.) Thus the following are the average probabilities of error in slow, nonselective Rayleigh fading:

$$P = \frac{1}{2 + \gamma_0} \qquad \text{noncoherent FSK} \tag{9-5-22}$$

$$P = \frac{1}{2}\left[1 - \frac{1}{\sqrt{1 + 2/\gamma_0}}\right] \qquad \text{coherent FSK} \tag{9-5-23}$$

$$P = \frac{1}{2}\left[1 - \frac{1}{\sqrt{1 + 1/\gamma_0}}\right] \qquad \text{ideal PSK} \tag{9-5-24}$$

$$P = \frac{1}{2 + 2\gamma_0} \qquad \text{differentially coherent PSK} \tag{9-5-25}$$

These results are shown in the curves of Fig. 9-5-7. Again, there is an exact 3-db difference in performance between coherent FSK and ideal PSK, as well as between noncoherent FSK and DPSK. These are simply a reflection of the 3-db difference in the relative performance of these systems (represented by the differences in the constant α) at *all* levels of SNR. The kind of results presented in Fig. 9-5-7 also are observed experimentally.[1]

[1] E.g., J. W. Allnatt, E. D. J. Jones, and H. B. Law, Frequency Diversity in the Reception of Selectively Fading Binary Frequency-Modulated Signals, *Proc. IEE*, vol. 104, part B, pp. 98–110, March, 1957; and E. F. Florman and R. W. Plush, Measured Statistical Characteristics and Narrow-Band Teletype Message Errors on a Single-Sideband 600-Mile-Long Ultrahigh-Frequency Tropospheric Radio Link, *J. Res. Natl. Bur. Std.*, vol. 64D, pp. 125–133, March–April, 1960.

For comparison, the noncoherent FSK and ideal PSK curves of Fig. 7-5-1 for error rate with steady signal are reproduced as the dotted curves in Fig. 9-5-7, using the same abscissa to now denote the steady SNR. The severe degradation due to fading fluctuations about the mean received

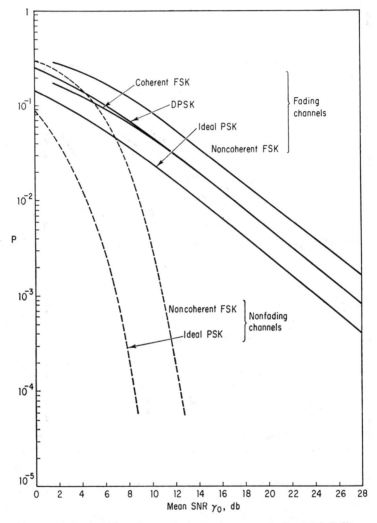

FIG. 9-5-7. Probability of error for several systems in Rayleigh fading.

signal level is obvious. For a single binary channel subject to slow, non-selective Rayleigh fading, additional system margins (mean SNR required in fading as compared with SNR required in the absence of fading) of the order of 10 db must be provided for error rates in the 0.001 to 0.01 range, with approximately an additional 10 db required for every order of magnitude (factor of 10) further decrease in allowed system error rate. Indeed, from (9-5-22) to (9-5-25) the asymptotic performance for large average SNR is given by

$$\gamma_0 \gg 1 \begin{cases} P^{(1)} \to \dfrac{1}{2\alpha\gamma_0} \begin{cases} P \to \dfrac{1}{\gamma_0} & \text{noncoherent FSK} & \text{(9-5-26)} \\[2ex] P \to \dfrac{1}{2\gamma_0} & \text{DPSK} & \text{(9-5-27)} \end{cases} \\[4ex] P^{(2)} \to \dfrac{1}{4\alpha\gamma_0} \begin{cases} P \to \dfrac{1}{2\gamma_0} & \text{coherent FSK} & \text{(9-5-28)} \\[2ex] P \to \dfrac{1}{4\gamma_0} & \text{ideal PSK} & \text{(9-5-29)} \end{cases} \end{cases}$$

Thus, at large SNR, error rate for *all* these systems is exactly inversely proportional to the mean SNR. In comparison, with steady signals changes in SNR produce *exponential* changes in error rate, whereas with Rayleigh fading, error rate changes only inversely. This is the dominant qualitative difference. It also indicates the additional design burden imposed upon systems required to operate in fading and the resulting importance of techniques (such as the diversity techniques discussed in Chaps. 10 and 11) for mitigating the effects of fading.

Qualitatively, the degradation introduced by fading is caused by the very low signal levels which occur in Rayleigh fading, during which the conditional probability of error is thus very close to 0.5. In this sense, one may view the improvement through diversity techniques (Chap. 10) to lie in modifying the p.d.f. for γ so that it tends to be very small for small γ, rather than the exponential behavior in (9-5-4) for which the p.d.f. actually peaks at $\gamma = 0$. To more quantitatively illustrate this interpretation of fading effects, one can examine the ranges of γ responsible for the errors, still under the assumption of the Rayleigh distribution. We can examine two integrals whose relation to (9-5-20) and (9-5-21) is obvious,

$$N^{(1)}(\gamma_1) = \int_0^{\gamma_1} \frac{1}{2} \exp(-\alpha\gamma) \frac{1}{\gamma_0} \exp\left(-\frac{\gamma}{\gamma_0}\right) d\gamma$$

$$= \frac{1 - \exp[-(1 + 1/\alpha\gamma_0)(\alpha\gamma_1)]}{2 + 2\alpha\gamma_0} \quad \text{(9-5-30)}$$

$$N^{(2)}(\gamma_1) = \int_0^{\gamma_1} \frac{1}{2} \operatorname{erfc}(\sqrt{\alpha\gamma}) \frac{1}{\gamma_0} \exp\left(-\frac{\gamma}{\gamma_0}\right) d\gamma$$

$$= \frac{1}{2}\left\{\left[1-\exp\left(-\frac{\alpha\gamma_1}{\alpha\gamma_0}\right)\operatorname{erfc}\sqrt{\alpha\gamma_1}\right]\right.$$

$$\left. - \frac{1}{\sqrt{1 + 1/\alpha\gamma_0}}[1-\operatorname{erfc}\sqrt{(1 + 1/\alpha\gamma_0)(\alpha\gamma_1)}]\right\} \quad \text{(9-5-31)}$$

For given values of α and γ_0, $N^{(1)}$ and $N^{(2)}$ represent the probability of error *conditional* on γ lying in the range $0 < \gamma < \gamma_1$. If we interpret probabilities of error in the large-sample sense as the average fraction of bits in error over infinitely large populations of bits, then dividing $N^{(1)}$ and $N^{(2)}$, respectively, by $P^{(1)}$ and $P^{(2)}$ from (9-5-20) and (9-5-21) will give in each case the fraction of all the errors which occur because

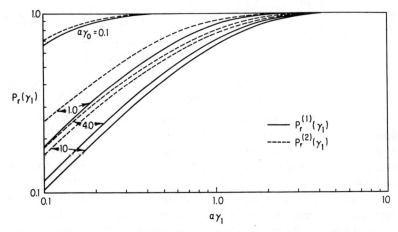

FIG. 9-5-8. Locations of SNR levels at which errors occur in Rayleigh fading.

of fading signal levels (for fixed γ_0) which are in the range $0 \leq \gamma \leq \gamma_1$. These fractions are thus

$$P_r^{(1)}(\gamma_1) = 1 - \exp\left[-\left(1 + 1/\alpha\gamma_0\right)(\alpha\gamma_1)\right] \qquad (9\text{-}5\text{-}32)$$

$$P_r^{(2)}(\gamma_1) =$$
$$1 - \frac{\exp\left(-\dfrac{\alpha\gamma_1}{\alpha\gamma_0}\right)\operatorname{erfc}\sqrt{\alpha\gamma_1} - \dfrac{1}{\sqrt{1 + 1/\alpha\gamma_0}}\operatorname{erfc}\sqrt{(1 + 1/\alpha\gamma_0)(\alpha\gamma_1)}}{1 - \dfrac{1}{\sqrt{1 + 1/\alpha\gamma_0}}}$$
$$(9\text{-}5\text{-}33)$$

They are shown plotted in Fig. 9-5-8, with $P_r^{(1)}$ and $P_r^{(2)}$ as a function of $\alpha\gamma_1$, for various values of $\alpha\gamma_0$ as parameter.[1]   In (9-5-32), it is particularly apparent that for $\alpha\gamma_0 \gg 1$ (as is necessary for any reasonably low error rate), the fraction $P_r^{(1)}(\gamma_1)$ is *independent* of γ_0.   That is, regardless of the overall average rate of errors (i.e., how small or large the total is), a certain *fraction* always occur in a range of SNR determined only by the particular fraction being considered.   This is particularly related to the exponential conditional probability of error involved in $P^{(1)}$.   However,

[1] The result (9-5-32) is taken from B. B. Barrow, Error Probabilities for Data Transmission over Fading Radio Paths, Doctoral Dissertation, Delft, 1962; the result (9-5-33) is given in terms of densities of error location in H. B. Law, The Detectability of Fading Radiotelegraph Signals in Noise, *Proc. IEE*, vol. 104, part B, pp. 130–140, March, 1957.

as shown by Fig. 9-5-8, the general behavior is characteristic also of ideal coherent-detection processes.

Again, these last results indicate that any operation which can alter the fading p.d.f. so as to reduce the relative concentration near $\gamma = 0$ can be expected to greatly reduce the error rates at a given mean fading level γ_0. As will be seen in Chap. 10, this is one useful interpretation of the manner in which diversity receiving techniques effect system improvements.

9-6. Signal Behavior in Channels with Arbitrary Selectivity and Rapidity

It was already indicated above that for many configurations, probability of error for a single pulse can be conveniently calculated by regarding the received signal, as well as the additive noise, as a complex Gaussian process. This is especially true in nonadaptive receiving systems, represented by a fixed filter or cross-correlation operation. In these cases, the generalized detection formulas derived in Chap. 8 can be directly applied, requiring first only computation of the appropriate correlations of the joint signal-plus-noise processes. Even in more general cases of adaptive reception, where primarily linear operations are used, the basic calculations involve exactly the same properties of the signal-plus-noise process. In this section, the statistical characterization of Sec. 9-2 is applied, to indicate the general nature of such correlation calculations.

When the fading-reception problem can be identified with the models of Chap. 8, it can be immediately generalized to include a specular component in the fading. The received signal is then the sum of a steady component, plus a Rayleigh-fading component described as a zero-mean complex Gaussian process.[1] For convenience, and without any major loss in generality, we shall assume that the steady component contains an undistorted signal and that any Doppler shift can be ignored.

Along with the specular and Rayleigh-fading signal components, additive bandpass zero-mean Gaussian noise is also present in the receiver. Thus, at the input to the receiver bandpass filters, we can totally identify a deterministic (nonfading) signal component, plus a complex zero-mean Gaussian process which is the sum of the receiver noise *and* the Gaussian fading part of the signal. These two latter processes are independent (since they have physically independent origins), usually with radically different intensities, power spectra, and autocorrelation functions.

The receiver filters then represent a further linear operation upon all input voltages. As earlier, the output waveforms and particularly the

[1] Note that only for a cw signal will the received signal be a *stationary* zero-mean complex Gaussian process. More generally, with modulation, the received signal will be a complex, zero-mean Gaussian process, but *nonstationary* because of changes in the modulation transmitted.

values at the sampling instant for pulse decision resulting from the *steady signal component* are deterministic and simply calculated in terms of the input waveform and the receiver filter transfer functions (or equivalent impulse responses). The remainder of the filter output voltages at the sampling instant arise from the linear filtering operations upon the complex zero-mean Gaussian fading signal and additive noise input process and hence themselves are samples from a complex zero-mean Gaussian process. In other words, at the sampling instants, the filter outputs can be totally viewed as drawn from a complex, nonzero-mean Gaussian process, in which the nonvanishing mean is identified with the specular components of the received signal.

These filter outputs are then applied to appropriate detectors and decision circuitry (as described in the models of Sec. 8-1). Finally, then, the probability of an error relates to incorrect decisions based upon the detected filter outputs The formulas derived in Chap. 8 refer to very general nonzero-mean complex Gaussian processes as the detector inputs and clearly apply directly to our present problem with no new examination of the detection problem required.[1] The additional results below supplement the detection formulas of Chap. 8 for this problem by indicating the statistical characteristics of the receiver filter outputs. Referring to the results in Sec. 9-2, the *received* signal (at the *input* to receiver filters) has the form

$$s(t) = \text{Re} \, [u(t) \exp (j2\pi f_0 t)] \tag{9-6-1}$$

where
$$u(t) = Au_0(t - t_1) + \int_{-\infty}^{\infty} \beta(t - \tau; t)u_0(\tau) \, d\tau \tag{9-6-2}$$

The first term in (9-6-2) represents the specular component, assumed to arrive with a delay t_1 relative to some nominal mean time implied in (9-6-2) and with the complex factor A describing the relative amplitude and phase of this specular component. The Rayleigh-fading component is described by the integral in (9-6-2) with $\beta(\tau; t)$ the stationary complex zero-mean Gaussian process describing the time-varying equivalent low-pass impulse response of the medium and with τ again measuring delays relative to some nominal mean value. A statement equivalent to (9-6-2) is

$$u(t) = Au_0(t - t_1) + \int_{-\infty}^{\infty} H(f;t) U_0(f) \exp (j2\pi ft) \, df \tag{9-6-3}$$

where $U_0(f)$ is the spectrum of $u_0(t)$ and $H(f;t)$ is the stationary complex zero-mean Gaussian process describing the time-varying equivalent low-pass transfer function of the medium.

We now characterize a bandpass receiving filter by its equivalent low-pass impulse response $k(t)$. With $u(t)$ describing the input, the complex

---

[1] It may be recalled that the generalized models of Chap. 8 did not include coherent FSK, so that the results here, combined with those in Chap. 8, specifically cover non-coherent FSK and generalized PSK reception, including DPSK.

envelope of the filter output is given by

$$v(t) = \int_{-\infty}^{\infty} k(t - x)u(x)\, dx \tag{9-6-4}$$

$$= A \int_{-\infty}^{\infty} k(t - x)u_0(x - t_1)\, dx$$

$$+ \iint_{-\infty}^{\infty} k(t - x)\beta(\tau;x)u_0(x - \tau)\, d\tau\, dx \tag{9-6-5}$$

On an *ensemble* basis, for a given $u_0(t)$, the first term here represents the mean value of $v(t)$,

$$\langle v(t) \rangle = A \int_{-\infty}^{\infty} k(t - x)u_0(x - t_1)\, dx$$

$$= A \int_{-\infty}^{\infty} k(t - t_1 - x)u_0(x)\, dx \tag{9-6-6}$$

The fluctuation component of $v(t)$ is the zero-mean complex Gaussian process designated by

$$\phi(t) = v(t) - \langle v(t) \rangle \tag{9-6-7}$$

$$= \iint_{-\infty}^{\infty} k(t - x)\beta(\tau;x)u_0(x - \tau)\, d\tau\, dx \tag{9-6-8}$$

Its mean-square value is

$$\tfrac{1}{2}\langle |\phi(t)|^2 \rangle = \iiiint_{-\infty}^{\infty} k^*(t - x_1)k(t - x_2)\tfrac{1}{2}\langle \beta^*(\tau_1;x_1)\beta(\tau_2;x_2) \rangle$$

$$u_0^*(x_1 - \tau_1)u_0(x_2 - \tau_2)\, d\tau_1\, dx_1\, d\tau_2\, dx_2 \tag{9-6-9}$$

Using the characterization in (9-2-38) in terms of the multipath autocovariance profile, this becomes

$$\tfrac{1}{2}\langle |\phi(t)|^2 \rangle = \iiiint_{-\infty}^{\infty} k^*(t - x_1)k(t - x_2)r_T(\tau_1; x_2 - x_1)\delta(\tau_1 - \tau_2)$$

$$u_0^*(x_1 - \tau_1)u_0(x_2 - \tau_2)\, d\tau_1\, dx_1\, d\tau_2\, dx_2$$

$$= \iiint_{-\infty}^{\infty} k^*(t - x_1)k(t - x_2)r_T(\tau; x_2 - x_1)$$

$$u_0^*(x_1 - \tau)u_0(x_2 - \tau)\, d\tau\, dx_1\, dx_2 \tag{9-6-10}$$

Furthermore, $r_T(\tau; x_2 - x_1)$ can be expressed in terms of its power spectrum, as described by (9-2-57). This leads to a result which can be written in the form

$$\tfrac{1}{2}\langle |\phi(t)|^2 \rangle = \iiiint_{-\infty}^{\infty} [k^*(t - x_1)u_0^*(x_1 - \tau)\, \exp\,(j2\pi\mu x_1)]$$

$$[k(t - x_2)u_0(x_2 - \tau)\, \exp\,(-j2\pi\mu x_2)]V_T(\tau;\mu)\, dx_1\, dx_2\, d\tau\, d\mu \tag{9-6-11}$$

$$= \iint_{-\infty}^{\infty} |w(t,\tau,\mu)|^2 V_T(\tau;\mu)\, d\tau\, d\mu \tag{9-6-12}$$

where we have conveniently defined

$$w(t,\tau,\mu) = \exp{(j2\pi\mu\tau)} \int_{-\infty}^{\infty} k(t-x)u_0(x-\tau) \exp{(-j2\pi\mu x)}\,dx \quad (9\text{-}6\text{-}13)$$

$$= \int_{-\infty}^{\infty} k(t-\tau-x)u_0(x) \exp{(-j2\pi\mu x)}\,dx \quad (9\text{-}6\text{-}14)$$

Examining (9-6-13), one observes that $w(t,\tau,\mu)$ is the *deterministic* equivalent low-pass response of the filter to the transmitted signal, arriving at a *relative delay* τ, and *shifted in frequency by an amount* μ. In effect, (9-6-12) is a weighted power averaging over all values of μ and τ, the weighting describing the effects of the medium.

Some interesting insight is obtainable from (9-6-12) into the interpretation of *slow* and *flat* (nonselective) fading. First, one may recall from (9-2-59) that for a tone transmitted, the average received power $R_S(0)$ is given by

$$R_S(0) = \int_{-\infty}^{\infty}\int_{-\infty}^{\infty} V_T(\tau;\mu)\,d\tau\,d\mu \quad (9\text{-}6\text{-}15)$$

For a fixed value of $R_S(0)$, one can then expect $\langle|\phi(t)|^2\rangle$ to be maximum if $V_T(\tau;\mu)$ is concentrated to the greatest extent possible around the values of τ, μ for which $w(t,\tau,\mu)$ is maximum. In general, one does desire $\langle|\phi(t)|^2\rangle$ to be as *large* as possible, since this represents the mean power level in the fading *signal* component. For example, in the absence of a specular component, the signal part of the filter output undergoes purely Rayleigh fading with the mean SNR proportional to $\langle|\phi(t)|^2\rangle$. Assuming the filter tuned to carrier frequency (including any mean Doppler shift), the physical interpretation of $w(t,\tau,\mu)$ implies that it will have maximum value at $\mu = 0$ and presumably also will maximize in τ at $\tau = 0$ (assuming an appropriate choice has been made of nominal propagation delay). Thus $\langle|\phi(t)|^2\rangle$ peaks if $V_T(\tau;\mu)$ is extremely narrow both in μ, *with respect to signal and filter bandwidths*, and in τ, with *respect to pulse durations and filter response times*. Narrowness in μ implies a very narrowband fading power spectrum, i.e., *fading slow with respect to signal pulse lengths*. Narrowness in τ implies a *basically nonselective* situation. From (9-6-12), when $V_T(\tau;\mu)$ is not narrow in either μ or τ, the mean SNR of the Rayleigh-fading signal components is relatively lower.

As a side comment, these results are particularly related to the model assumed in this section for the receiver, namely that it includes a *fixed, nonvarying* (nonadaptive) filter. Such a filter is characterized by a bandwidth or response time. Thus, an alternative viewpoint on the results above is that fading rapidity is represented by the range of Doppler shifts on received signal components and that when these components begin to fall outside the receiving filter bandwidth, significantly less average energy is passed by the filter. Similarly, the narrower the multipath spread represented by the range in τ, the larger the relative portion of signal adding coherently through the filter smoothing action[1] (or, if the receiver is a cross-correlator utilizing a replica of the *transmitted* signal as the reference, the larger the portion of signal which cross-correlates properly). In a very real sense, from a decision-theory viewpoint, the difficulty is that the received signal is undergoing stochastic changes without the receiver adapting to these changes. Once these changes are significant enough (because of selective fading, or fast fading, or both) so that the *shape* of the individual received pulse is different from the transmitted pulse, it is no longer possible to design a fixed receiving filter (based on knowledge of the transmitted pulse) which is even closely suboptimum for the generality of received pulse shapes. The problem of attempting to "adapt" to the stochastic changes introduced by the medium has led, for example, to considering systems involving "sounding" the channel, such as discussed in Chap. 11.

Aside from the interpretive discussion above, the important fact is that (9-6-6)-(9-6-14) describe the fading signal components in the filter output for *completely arbitrary fading rapidity and selectivity*. Such effects as signal distortion due to selectivity are completely included in that for the digital-data case, regardless of distortion, one need only be interested in the values of the filter output voltages at the sampling instants. However, one must always keep in mind that if $V_T(\tau;\mu)$ is significant at values of τ roughly of the same order of magnitude as pulse lengths, then $w(t,\tau,\mu)$ will effectively contain contributions to $\phi(t)$ due to values of $u_0(t)$ during earlier pulse intervals and hence will include some energy having the nature of intersymbol interference. In the latter case, one must be concerned with message statistics which describe the kinds of sequences described by $u_0(t)$, hence there is an additional ensemble over which effects must be averaged. Usually, however, intersymbol interference can be expected to involve no more than one or two previous pulses, and it is easiest to carry out the separate calculations for the various possibilities and average them directly with proper weighting.

We have indicated above the nature of the portion of individual filter outputs corresponds to fading signal terms. For applying the detection formulas of Chap. 8, one will have to consider the composite process composed of the sum of these signal terms and of the filtered additive receiver noise. Deriving the required covariances, including cross-covariances of the outputs of pairs of filters (for the signal terms, a generalization of the computations above), is reasonably straightforward and will not be presented here. The reader is referred to Chap. 11 for specific performance computations for signals and channels where either the slow-fading or nonselective-fading assumptions are no longer valid.

---

[1] I.e., with respect to voltages developed at the decision sampling instants.

CHAPTER 10

LINEAR DIVERSITY COMBINING TECHNIQUES

The results of the previous chapter indicate the severe performance degradation associated with Rayleigh fading, measured in tens of decibels additional mean SNR relative to performance with nonfading signal. The major additional engineering costs implied in meeting such differences by increased transmitter power, antenna size, etc. make any alternative possibilities very attractive economically. While our specific calculations have referred only to digital data transmission, it is quite obvious that the Rayleigh-fading distribution also implies severe performance degradation for any analog transmission system, i.e., an extremely high mean signal level will be needed to avoid having the signal "drop into" the noise over too large a percentage of the time.

An alternative to increased power, etc., is the utilization of special modulation and reception techniques which are less vulnerable to fading effects. Of these techniques, the best known and most widely used are the multiple-receiver combining techniques categorized as diversity. The diversity *principle* applies to both analog and digital transmission, being aimed simply towards reducing the signal fading range (especially the probability of near-zero fades, or "deep fades" as often termed). In this chapter, a lengthy discussion is presented of those diversity techniques based on *linear* combining networks and their performance.

Linear diversity combining involves relatively simple weighted linear sums of multiple received signals. As such, it is closely related to the use of signal repetition for enhancement of SNR, as discussed in Chap. 2. Linear diversity combining is the only kind generally applicable for distortionless reception of *analog transmission*. However for digital data transmissions, one may admit more general types of processing, with the goal of optimum digital decisions (just as matched-filter processing generally involves a severe distortion of signals but results in statistically optimum decisons). Such decision-oriented diversity techniques are discussed in Chap. 11.

Diversity possibilities for counteracting short-term fading effects were apparently first discovered in experiments with spaced receiving antennas at h-f.[1] It was observed that with sufficient spacing between antennas,

---

[1] E.g., A. deHaas, *Radio-Nieuws*, vol. 10, pp. 357–364, December, 1927, and vol. 11,

the (short-term) fading fluctuations of the signal received at one antenna tend to be independent of the fluctuations of the signal received on the second antenna. It then was suggested and demonstrated that a "switch" operating so as to derive the system output from the stronger of the two signals at each instant[1] will greatly reduce the depth of fading effects that would be observed with either signal alone.

Obviously there are mechanisms other than spaced receiving antennas for achieving independently fading signals. Depending on the propagation mechanism, these may include:

1. Space (spaced antenna) diversity
2. Frequency diversity
3. Angle (-of-arrival) diversity
4. Polarization diversity
5. Time (signal-repetition) diversity
6. Multipath diversity (Rake)

Of these, the last two have been primarily considered only for digital data transmission. Except for polarization diversity, there is generally also no limit to the number of diversity branches, i.e., the number of more-or-less independently fluctuating signals which can be made available to be combined, by multiplication of equipment. One is also not limited to selecting only the instantaneously stronger signal. Thus linear combining methods have been commonly identified in the recent literature as follows:

1. Selection combining
2. Maximal-ratio combining
3. Equal-gain combining

In addition, when reception involves linear demodulation, it is in principle irrelevant whether the signals are combined before or after demodulation. However, as discussed later, for nonlinear demodulation techniques (such as involved when frequency modulation has been employed), there will be a performance difference between predetection and postdetection linear combining.

10-1. Methods for Achieving Diversity Branches

We first briefly consider how "independently" fading diversity branches are achieved in practice. Later (Sec. 10-10) it will be shown that signifi-

---

pp. 80–88, February, 1928; portions translated by B. B. Barrow, *Proc. IRE*, vol. 49, pp. 367–368, January, 1961; H. H. Beverage and H. O. Peterson, Diversity Receiving System of RCA Communications, Inc., for Radiotelegraphy, *Proc. IRE*, vol. 19, pp. 531–561, April, 1931; H. O. Peterson, H. H. Beverage, and J. B. Moore, Diversity Telephone Receiving System of RCA Communications, Inc., *Proc. IRE*, vol. 19, pp. 562–584, April, 1931.

[1] Or using one output until it becomes too weak relative to some desired threshold and then automatically switching to the other if it is at that time above the threshold.

cant diversity effectiveness can still be achieved even when fairly high correlations exist among the complex Gaussian signal processes on the individual diversity branches. Hence there is a degree of imprecision associated with any specification below of the "separation" (in distance, frequency, angle, time, etc.) required to achieve satisfactory diversity.

Space Diversity. The use of spaced transmitting or receiving antennas is the most common diversity technique encountered in present practice. In simplest form, a single transmitting antenna beam "illuminates" a certain portion of the "scattering" (or "reflecting" or "refracting") medium. Viewed from a *receiving* site, this "illuminated volume" has an angular extent which is a function of the transmitting beamwidth, the distance from each terminal to the "illuminated volume,"[1] and of directional aspect factors of the "scattering" or "reflection." The energy-carrying rays arriving at the receiving point thus appear to emanate over some angular spread. The additional stochastic nature of the medium will cause observations at the receiving point to indicate a fluctuating apparent angle of arrival for incident radiation, within this angular spread.

For a simple interpretation of space diversity, one can visualize (Fig. 10-1-1) two receiving antennas of identical beamwidths, separated by a distance D in a direction perpendicular to the direction of arrival of rays from the "scattering" volume. Assume $D \ll R$, where R is the distance to the scattering volume. Then one can visualize the rays from the (nominal) extremities of the scattering volume to some point (say the phase center) of antenna 1, and from the same extremities to some similar point on antenna 2. At antenna 1, the phase difference due to the different electrical lengths L_1 and L_2 of these rays is

$$\Delta_1 = \frac{2\pi}{\lambda} (L_1 - L_2) \qquad (10\text{-}1\text{-}1)$$

and at antenna 2, with lengths L_1' and L_2', the difference is

$$\Delta_2 = \frac{2\pi}{\lambda} (L_1' - L_2') \qquad (10\text{-}1\text{-}2)$$

The difference between these quantities is

$$\Delta = \Delta_1 - \Delta_2 = \frac{2\pi}{\lambda} [(L_1 - L_1') - (L_2 - L_2')] \qquad (10\text{-}1\text{-}3)$$

Moreover, $R \gg D$, and it can also be assumed that $R \gg A$ where A is the width of the scattering volume as seen by the receiving antennas. Assum-

---

[1] The term "illuminated volume" is not particularly appropriate to the multihop character of ionospheric-skywave propagation. However, it serves as a convenient reference term for the more physically realistic situation, which the reader can readily visualize.

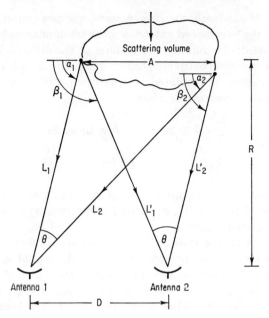

FIG. 10-1-1. Dual space-diversity reception configuration.

ing A to subtend an angle θ as seen from the receiving site,

$$\theta = \frac{A}{R} \ll 1 \text{ radian} \tag{10-1-4}$$

then in Fig. 10-1-1, to first order

$$\alpha_2 \doteq \alpha_1 \qquad \beta_2 \doteq \beta_1 \tag{10-1-5}$$

That is, to first order, the rays of length L_1 and L_2 are parallel and

$$L_2 - L_1 \doteq A \cos \alpha_1 \tag{10-1-6a}$$

Similarly $\qquad\qquad L_2' - L_1' \doteq A \cos \beta_1 \tag{10-1-6b}$

Then also to first-order, with α_1 and β_1 near $\pi/2$,

$$|\Delta| \doteq \frac{2\pi}{\lambda} A \left|\cos \alpha_1 - \cos \beta_1\right| = \frac{2\pi}{\lambda} A \left|\alpha_1 - \beta_1\right| \tag{10-1-7}$$

But $|\alpha_1 - \beta_1|$ is the angle subtended at the scattering volume by the antenna spacing D,

$$|\alpha_1 - \beta_1| \doteq \frac{D}{R} \tag{10-1-8}$$

and thus $\qquad\qquad |\Delta| \doteq \frac{2\pi}{\lambda} A \frac{D}{R} \doteq \frac{2\pi}{\lambda} D\theta \tag{10-1-9}$

Recalling now the discussion of Sec. 9-2 on Rayleigh fading originating from addition of randomly varying phasors, one can expect uncorrelated fading here at the two spaced antennas if the set of phasors being received at one is substantially different from those at the other. With (10-1-9) indicating the relation between phasors representing the extreme rays, one can thus expect uncorrelated fadings when Δ is several r-f cycles in size, i.e., in *order of magnitude* when

$$\frac{2\pi}{\lambda} D\theta \gg 2\pi \qquad \text{(a few times } 2\pi\text{)}$$

or $\qquad\qquad D \gg \frac{\lambda}{\theta} \qquad \left(\text{a few times } \frac{\lambda}{\theta}\right)$

$$(10\text{-}1\text{-}10)$$

Note again, this is only an order-of-magnitude statement, and then only as an estimate of the spacing required for obtaining complete decorrelation between spaced antennas.

In h-f skywave propagation, where angle-of-arrival fluctuations appear to be usually confined[1] to the order of 1 to 5°, this would imply a "correlation distance" between spaced antennas of the order of 40 to 200 λ. At 10 Mc, for example, this would imply a required diversity spacing of at least a kilometer. This is substantially larger than that found necessary in practice,[2] which is more of the order of a couple hundred meters at 10 Mc (possibly, as remarked earlier, because diversity can be effective even with relatively high correlations). This suggests that a better estimate than (10-1-10) might be

$$D \approx \frac{\lambda}{\theta} \qquad\qquad (10\text{-}1\text{-}11)$$

It might be added that dual space diversity is quite common in high-quality h-f circuits.

In tropospheric scatter, at relatively short ranges (below about 200 miles), the angular spread of arriving radiation is usually governed by the antenna beamwidths, commonly of the order of 1 to 2°. Accordingly a separation of the order of 100 λ is usually estimated to suffice for complete

---

[1] M. Balser and W. B. Smith, Some Statistical Properties of Pulsed Oblique HF Ionospheric Transmissions, *J. Res. Natl. Bur. Std.*, vol. 66D, pp. 721–730, November–December, 1962; E. N. Bramley, Some Aspects of the Rapid Directional Fluctuations of Short Radio Waves Reflected at the Ionosphere, *Proc. IEE*, vol. 102, part B, pp. 533–540, July, 1955.

[2] S. H. Van Wambeck and A. H. Ross, Performance of Diversity Receiving Systems, *Proc. IRE*, vol. 39, pp. 256–264, March, 1951; G. L. Grisdale, J. G. Morris, and D. S. Palmer, Fading of Long-Distance Radio Signals and a Comparison of Space- and Polarization-Diversity Reception in the 6–18 Mc/s Range, *Proc. IEE*, vol. 104, part B, pp. 39–51, January, 1957; R. E. Lacy, M. Acker, and J. L. Glaser, Performance of Space and Frequency Diversity Receiving Systems, *IRE Natl. Conv. Record*, part II, pp. 148–152, 1953; J. Grosskopf, M. Scholz, and K. Vogt, Korrelationsmessungen im Kurzwellenbereich, *NTZ*, vol. 11, pp. 91–95, February, 1958.

decorrelation, and this is roughly confirmed experimentally.[1] At longer ranges, the spread may become more controlled by geometry and aspect (i.e., resulting in smaller angular extents than the beamwidths), and relatively larger antenna spacings may then be required for decorrelation. In tropospheric scatter, dual space receiving diversity is also quite common, often coupled with a use of dual transmitting antennas to achieve a form of quadruple diversity, as described later.

The discussion above has emphasized antennas spaced crosswise to the direction of propagation. One can also achieve diversity by spacing on the ground along the direction of propagation. The angle θ is this case would measure the apparent vertical extent of the illuminated volume, rather than the lateral extent. Furthermore, if D is spacing along the ground and the elevation angle at which rays are arriving is γ, the effective antenna spacing for diversity purposes is $D \sin \gamma$, with γ usually only a few degrees. At h-f, with higher elevation angles of arrival, such an effect would be expected to be less significant than for troposcatter. In troposcatter, perhaps an order of magnitude greater spacing has been estimated to be required for diversity using longitudinal antenna spacing as compared with lateral spacing. Space-diversity systems in operation usually employ lateral spacing.

In a similar vein, receiving antennas can be spaced in height; expect for the change in aspect relationships governing the angular extent of the illuminated volume, one would expect the required spacings here to be the same as for lateral spacing on the ground.

Frequency Diversity. The discussion of selective fading in Sec. 9-2 already makes it obvious that transmission of the same signal at sufficiently spaced carrier frequencies will provide independently fading versions of the signal, thus "frequency diversity." To obtain relatively complete decorrelation, one would want a spacing an order of magnitude larger than the nominal width of the frequency-time cross-correlation function defined earlier. The bandwidths individually occupied at each carrier frequency can, of course, be narrow enough so that fading is non-selective on each individual branch.

Frequency diversity has been employed at h-f[2] and in tropospheric scatter,[3] in both cases apparently primarily for experimental purposes. (As discussed later, a hybrid form of space-frequency diversity is common on troposcatter systems.) The costs of frequency diversity appear

---

[1] E.g., J. H. Chisholm, W. E. Morrow, Jr., B. E. Nichols, J. F. Roche, and A. E. Teachman, Properties of 400 Mcps Long-Distance Tropospheric Circuits, *Proc. IRE*, vol. 50, pp. 2464–2482, December, 1962.

[2] Lacy, Acker, and Glaser, *loc. cit;* also, C. D. May, Jr., Doubling Traffic Capacity of Single-Sideband Systems, *IRE Nat. Conv. Record*, part II, pp. 145–147, 1953.

[3] N. H. Knudzton and P. E. Gudmandsen, Results from a Three-hop Tropospheric Scatter Link in Norway with Parallel Operations on 900 mc and 2200 mc, *IRE Trans. Commun. Systems*, vol. CS-8, pp. 20–26, March, 1960.

primarily to lie in the multiplied frequency allocation, the difficulties of generating several transmitted signals, and the need for combining signals received at several different frequencies.

Angle Diversity.   In using Fig. 10-1-1 to discuss space diversity, it was assumed that both receiving antennas are pointed towards the same bearing.   Hence, even when the receiving beamwidths are narrower than the inherent angular extent of the illuminated volume (as determined by transmitter beamwidth and scattering or reflection aspect relationships), the two beams are viewing the same portion of this volume.   Space diversity is obtained by the relative phasings among rays from this one portion of the volume.   Equally well, however, with sufficiently narrow receiving beams, one could employ two receiving beams, with a common phase center, but oriented towards different, or at least *partially nonoverlapping* portions of the illuminated volume.   The signals received via the two beams would then be decorrelated, to the extent that nonoverlapping portions of the volume are being viewed.   There have been two different suggestions on how the associated transmitting beam should be designed. One is that a single broad beam should be used; the other is that as many individual transmitting beams should be employed as there are receiving beams, each transmitting beam illuminating specifically that portion of the medium simultaneously being viewed by an associated receiving beam. It has not been shown conclusively that the additional costs of this latter configuration are warranted,[1] except insofar as the total transmitted power may be increased if the maximum available rating of power amplifier is involved with each transmitter and it would be inefficient to parallel a group of these together in a single transmitter.   This configuration may also be simplest when the same antennas are to be used for communication in both directions.

Angle diversity requires antenna beamwidths narrow compared with the angular extent limitations of the illuminated volume imposed by both geometric and aspect relationships.   Thus it has apparently never been seriously suggested for h-f, where required antenna sizes would be exorbitant.   On the other hand, it has been very seriously suggested and studied for tropospheric scatter[2] as a means of using more effectively the already large reflectors required to provide sufficient antenna gain as part of the system "margin."   These suggestions arose when detailed interferometer-scanning measurements in tropospheric scatter indicated that squinted antennas, each individually detecting only a narrow cone in

---

[1] R. Bolgiano, Jr., N. H. Bryant, and W. E. Gordon, Diversity Reception in Scatter Communication with Emphasis on Angle Diversity, Cornell University, Dept. of E.E., *Res. Rept.* 359, January, 1958.

[2] Bolgiano, Bryant, and Gordon, *loc. cit.;* also, J. H. Vogelman, J. L. Ryerson, and M. H. Bickelhaupt, Tropospheric Scatter System Using Angle Diversity, *Proc. IRE*, vol. 47, pp. 688–696, May, 1959.

apparent angles of arrival, could achieve significant diversity effect. The engineering advantage accrues in realizing the multiple beams by multiple feeds with a single large reflector. An alternative suggestion which has received some study is that of using a tracking feed on the receiving antenna to track on the instantaneous apparent angle of arrival.[1] It has been shown that this should be closely equivalent in performance to a high order of angle diversity utilizing the same size of reflector.

Polarization Diversity. Polarization diversity implies a single polarization at the transmitter, with depolarization in the propagation medium. Independent reception is possible with two orthogonal polarizations, and the two resulting signals do not fade in a correlated manner. This has been shown to occur for long-distance reception in the h-f band, where magnetoionic effects in the medium cause a varying elliptic polarization to be received when a linear polarization is transmitted. In fact, with crossed linearly polarized feeds, there is a reported tendency for the pair of received signals to fade in an anticorrelated manner,[2] indicative of such rotating ellipticity.[3] For practical applications, there is a limitation to only essentially dual diversity by this technique. (There are only two orthogonal polarization modes; any third polarization would yield a linear combination of the other two and hence, as we show later, cannot contribute to any diversity effectiveness.) Even dual polarization diversity might be quite useful; for example, as mentioned, more than dual diversity of any type is rarely used at h-f. For high-quality long-distance h-f circuits, it has been common to achieve high directivity with rhombic antennas; this would involve major awkwardness in constructing two highly directive, orthogonally polarized antennas in one unit, whereas if they are to be constructed separately and spaced, the spacing itself would tend to produce diversity without the additional effort of two different receiving polarizations. More recently, however, with the use of log-periodic antennas, a dual-polarized directional antenna for polarization diversity has appeared more feasible.

In tropospheric scatter, on the other hand, the dielectric nature of the inhomogeneities producing the propagation effects implies that there will

[1] S. Stein and D. E. Johansen, A Theory of Antenna Performance in Scatter-Type Reception, *IRE Trans. Antennas and Propagation*, vol. AP-9, pp. 304–311, May, 1959; D. E. Johansen, The Tracking Antenna—A Promising Concept for Scatter Communications, *Proc. 7th Natl. Commun. Symp.*, Utica, N.Y., pp. 134–149, October, 1961; also Final Report on Investigation of Antenna Systems for Scatter-Type Reception, Applied Research Laboratory, Sylvania Electronic Systems, AFCRL-742, August, 1961.

[2] Grisdale, Morris and Palmer, *loc. cit.;* Van Wambeck and Ross, *loc. cit.*

[3] Note that anticorrelated envelope fading (about the mean) must necessarily refer to specular components changing in polarization. For jointly Rayleigh-fading processes, if they are Rayleigh, the envelope correlations are necessarily positive or zero, as pointed out in Sec. 10-10 (Table 10-10-1).

be practically no change in the polarization as the wave propagates. This has been observed experimentally,[1] in tests with nominally linear transmitted polarization in which the orthogonal polarization component received was of the order of 12 to 20 db below that received in the nominal transmitted polarization.   Thus polarization diversity using a single transmitted polarization is not promising in tropospheric scatter.   Since the transmitted polarization remains unchanged, one might also visualize the possibility of achieving dual diversity by transmitting in two orthogonal polarizations and receiving each separably.   However, again the dielectric nature of the "scattering" implies that the "scattering" will not be polarization-dependent and hence that there will be a near-unity correlation on the fading observed in the two polarizations.[2]   Thus polarization diversity per se is not available in tropospheric scatter.

At this point, it is relevant to describe a hybrid frequency-space diversity, dual-polarization system which is in common use on tropospheric-scatter networks.[3]   This is a quadruple-diversity system shown schematically in Fig. 10-1-2.   Two large antenna reflectors are used at each end of the link, each with a multiple (usually concentric) feed for simultaneous transmission at one frequency and reception at two other frequencies. For one direction of communication, one antenna at the transmitting end transmits in a horizontal polarization and the other at a conveniently spaced different frequency in a *vertical* polarization.   Thus at the receiving terminal, two signals are received at *each* antenna, distinguishable both in frequency and polarization and hence readily channeled into separate receivers.   It is clear that if the transmitting antennas are spaced by the diversity distance, then (by electromagnetic reciprocity) the two signals received at each single receiving antenna are themselves in space diversity (and would be even if they were at the same frequency).   The difference in polarization and frequency then serves primarily to conveniently "tag"

[1] J. H. Chisholm, P. A. Portmann, J. T. deBettencourt, and J. F. Roche, Investigations of Angular Scattering and Multipath Properties of Tropospheric Propagation of Short Radio Waves Beyond the Horizon, *Proc. IRE*, vol. 43, pp. 1317–1335, October, 1955.

[2] Chisholm, Portmann, et al., *loc. cit.;* also, E. F. Florman and R. W. Plush, Measured Statistical Characteristics and Narrow-Band Teletype Message Errors on a Single-Sideband 600-Mile-Long Ultrahigh-Frequency Tropospheric Radio Link, *J. Res. Natl. Bur. Std.*, vol. 64D, pp. 125–133, March–April, 1960.

[3] G. L. Mellen, W. E. Morrow, Jr., A. J. Pote, W. H. Radford, and J. B. Wiesner, UHF Long-Range Communications Systems, *Proc. IRE*, vol. 43, pp. 1269–1287, October, 1955; R. A. Felsenheld, H. Havstad, J. L. Jatlow, D. J. LeVine, and L. Pollack, Wide-Band Ultrahigh-Frequency Over-the-Horizon Equipment, *AIEE Trans.*, vol. 77, part I (Communications and Electronics, no. 35), pp. 86–93, March, 1958; K. P. Stiles, F. G. Hollins, E. T. Fruhner, and W. D. Siddall, The Miami–Havana Radio System and Its Integration Into the Telephone Networks, *AIEE Trans.*, vol. 77, part I (Communications and Electronics, No. 35), pp. 94–96, March, 1958.

the signals so that they can be separated for use in a diversity combiner. However the convenient frequency spacing will itself often be sufficient for frequency diversity action so that in such operation, a two-fold mechanism may be involved in producing the diversity action.   The pair of signals at the second receiving antenna are likewise in diversity with each other.   Finally, the *receiving-antenna spacing* is sufficient for diversity between signals received at the same frequency on the two antennas. However, the antenna spacings may not alone be adequate to produce diversity between the two "crossing" paths.   In fact, experiments with a single frequency and only polarization discrimination[1] indicate a fairly

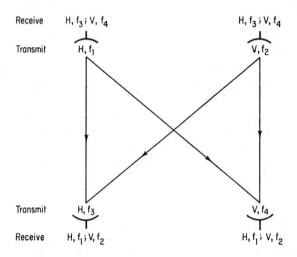

FIG. 10-1-2. Quadruple-diversity configuration.

high degree of correlation for the crossing paths.   Thus, here, the frequency-diversity action will be important in totally producing quadruple diversity with relatively large mutual independence between the fading fluctuations on the four receiving channels.

The quadruple-diversity configuration described above is also operationally important in providing a certain degree of equipment redundancy. If any single antenna or its associated transmitter and receivers goes out of operation, there is still a complete dual-diversity capability in *each* direction.

Time and Multipath Diversity.   Time diversity and multipath diversity are closely related and have been particularly applied only to digital data transmissions.   In time diversity, the same bit of information is repetitively transmitted at time intervals well separated compared with the reciprocal of the average fading rate.   The fade levels associated with the various repetitions will then be essentially independent, so that

[1] Florman and Plush, *loc. cit.*

appropriate combination of the repetitions will give a diversity performance. Unlike techniques such as space diversity, time diversity is attained without any increase in total average received power per information bit. (See also Sec. 11-4.) In space diversity, for example, such an increase occurs because of the added antenna aperture and in frequency diversity or in multiple-transmitting-beam angle diversity, increased total transmitter power is implied by the multiple transmitters (assuming there is no limitation on total primary power at the transmitting terminal).

Obviously, time diversity requires information storage both at the transmitter and receiver. Such storage, and particularly the diversity combination of the processed signal repetitions, is much simpler for digital than for analog transmissions. Thus most discussions of time diversity have been in terms of digital transmissions.

A kind of time diversity can be achieved in multipath situations when sufficiently wideband signals are transmitted that the multipath may be viewed as creating a series of echoes. If the wideband signals are designed so as to include an inherent time base indicator, then the contributions arriving via the different parts of the multipath structure can be separated in the course of reception, and combined in diversity. Such multipath diversity is one interpretation of the Rake technique, described more fully in Sec. 11-5.

10-2. General Principles of Linear Combining

Beginning with Sec. 10-4, we shall define and compare performance among several linear diversity combination techniques. Some of these involve assumptions about one's ability to estimate the state of the channel. Certain more general aspects of these models will be discussed here first.

First, from the discussion of techniques for achieving diversity branches, it should be obvious that long-term fading effects, due to general gross changes in the medium, affect all diversity channels identically, and thus *diversity operation cannot compensate for the long-term effects.*[1] Accordingly we shall here be considering only stationary short-term fading in our mathematical models of diversity performance.

Next, diversity operation presumes the availability of N *distinguishable, dissimilarly fading,* signal-transmission channels, the "diversity branches." The diversity receiving system chooses at each "instant"

[1] In a loose sense, repetition of information at extremely long intervals might be considered a form of time diversity for coping with long-term effects. However, such repetition would be accomplished practically only because of failure of messages to get through during severe long-term fading and would not involve automatic combining networks such as implied by the term "diversity."

the best of the N signals or some desirable additive combination of all. However, the system has not infinite bandwidth, so that it cannot truly function on an instant-to-instant basis. The word "instant" therefore refers to a brief time span determined by the time constants of the estimating and control circuits involved in the combiner. It is apparent that for the system to be successful in mitigating the effects of short-term fading, these combiner time constants must also be substantially shorter than the reciprocal of the fading rate mentioned earlier. At the same time, whenever the combiners derive an estimate of the signal level on each diversity branch, one would also ideally like the estimate to be as noiseless as possible, as free as possible of errors due to noise in the receiver on that branch. In most of the theoretical literature on linear diversity combiners,[1] the assumption is in fact made that completely *noisefree estimates* are available of the signals on the individual diversity branches. We shall also use this assumption throughout this chapter. It is an eminently justifiable assumption when the smoothing time in the estimating circuits can be very long compared with the reciprocal of the noise bandwidth, so that sizable SNR improvement is accomplished. As shown later (Sec. 11-3), the SNR improvement in deriving the estimate needs only be a few decibels in order for performance to be essentially that with a noiseless estimate.

The assumption of a noisefree estimate is quite appropriate, for example, for the large class of multichannel (FDM-FM or FDM-SSB) tropospheric-scatter systems, in which i-f bandwidths are typically several hundred kilocycles wide and postdetection bandwidths usually at least several tens of kilocycles wide immediately after the detector. The receiver noise at these points, correspondingly, has fluctuation times of fractions of a millisecond or even microseconds. On the other hand, the "period" of the short-term fading fluctuations is of the order of 0.1 to 10.0 sec. Thus, for these systems, the signal fading rates are slower by a factor of 10^2 to 10^4 than the rates of the noise fluctuations after detection or before detection, respectively. On this basis, one can select a smoothing interval for the estimation circuits short enough so that the fading signal remains approximately constant during each such interval, but at the same time long enough to provide extensive statistical averaging of the receiver noise. For the case cited, the time constant of the estimating circuits is typically a few milliseconds.

---

[1] E.g., F. J. Altman and W. Sichak, Simplified Diversity Communication System for Beyond-the-Horizon Links, *IRE Trans. Commun. Systems*, vol. CS-4, pp. 50–55, March, 1956; D. G. Brennan, Linear Diversity Combining Techniques, *Proc. IRE*, vol. 47, pp. 1075–1102, June, 1959; S. Stein, Clarification of Diversity Statistics in Scatter Propagation, Proc. Symposium on Statistical Methods in Radiowave Propagation (UCLA, June, 1958), Pergamon Press, New York, 1960; J. N. Pierce and S. Stein, Multiple Diversity with Non-Independent Fading, *Proc. IRE*, vol. 48, pp. 89–104, January, 1960.

At the same time, while the ability to achieve a noisefree estimate of fading state may be justified for many combinations of system parameters, it may not be appropriate to all. An example is a narrowband signal whose bandwidth is less than an order of magnitude larger than the fading rate, so that smoothing time is insufficiently long to provide a significantly higher SNR in the estimate than associated with the signal proper. In such a case the estimate may not be regarded as noisefree and one could not then expect to achieve the kind of linear combining system performance discussed immediately below. As discussed later in Chap. 11, the techniques may still be applied but with lesser performance; or one may apply other diversity combining techniques which require no estimation at all but also have lesser performance.

For the remainder of this chapter, we proceed on the basis that a noisefree estimate is available of the signal level on each diversity branch. This estimate is obtained during a brief running time interval (an "instant") during which the level of the fading r-f signal remains essentially *constant* on each diversity branch. The various linear combiners will be characterized as providing over each instant an output which is some particular weighted combination of the instantaneous signal levels on each diversity branch and a similarly weighted combination of the noises in the receivers on each branch.

To define diversity performance, one considers the statistics of fluctuation of the combiner output over longer time intervals, typically many tens of seconds, or minutes long. Such an interval is a long time with respect to the fluctuation rate of the short-term fading, long enough to include complete statistical samples of the signal fading. However, it is very short with respect to the fluctuations of the *median* of the Rayleigh fading, so that the short-term fading remains stationary over such an interval. For a given receiving system, behavior over an interval of short-term fading stationarity describes the *short-term statistics* resulting from diversity operation. Mathematically, it will be assumed (ergodicity) that completely equivalent statistics are obtained by the analytically more convenient process of averaging over the ensemble of fading on all branches.

Alternatively stated, diversity combiners will be defined on the basis of how they form an output at each instant during which some unchanging signal level is assumed to exist on each diversity branch (different on each); and then we shall discuss the statistics of the diversity combiner output over a longer interval, over which the signal levels on the several branches each change within a Rayleigh-fading law. In carrying out the latter analysis, we imagine the signal to be a section of a stationary random process defined over an infinite time base, any reasonably long section of which has the same statistics as any other.

It is apparent that throughout here we are discussing only slow fading situations. More importantly, by the implications that the diversity weighting is based upon measurement of a *single* complex parameter in each branch (envelope and r-f phase), we are also assuming nonselective fading on each branch, which can be represented as *multiplicative noise*. In Chap. 11, some results are given on diversity performance when there is selectivity in the fading or other causes of imperfect estimation.

The performance analyses will also assume that the additive noises associated with signal on the various diversity branches are independent. This is consistent with the important practical case in which the dominant additive noise is introduced in the receiver front-ends in each diversity branch. However, it will not necessarily be true, for example, with respect to antenna (atmospheric) noise in space-diversity at h-f. The portion of such noise which arrives over long distances may be in diversity, just as is the desired long-distance signal, but noise of much closer origin may not be. Likewise, external interference such as ignition noise or interfering radio transmissions may be received with fading and diversity if it arrives by the same propagation medium, but may not be in diversity if it is of more local origin. It should also be noted that once the dominant noise mechanism is not receiver noise, it may also no longer have Gaussian character; it may be impulsive in nature, or it may be narrower-band than the receiver. In either case, even if diversity is taking place, the signal-noise statistics may be radically different from those based on receiver noise. Some discussion of these effects is given in Sec. 10-12.

10-3. Diversity Improvement and Relation to System Design

The term "diversity improvement" or "diversity gain" is commonly employed to describe the effectiveness of various diversity configurations. These terms have no standard definition. One common definition is based on the significance of diversity in reducing the fraction of the time in which the signal drops to unusable levels. Thus, one defines an *outage rate* at some particular specified level, usually specified with respect to the mean output noise level of the combiner. Similar reductions in outage rates can be obtained in principle without diversity by increasing the fading median through increased transmitter powers, antenna sizes, etc. Thus, one can meaningfully compare the lesser median carrier-to-noise ratio required per radio channel (per diversity branch) using diversity, in order to stay within some specified outage rate, with the median carrier-to-noise ratio required on a single (nondiversity) channel for the same outage rate. The ratio of these medians is then termed the diversity improvement. For very low outage rates (0.1 per cent or 1 per cent), calculations of the outage rate involve the near-zero "tails" of the probability density functions. Thus outage rate is not linearly related to median signal-noise ratio, and diversity improvement as defined by outage rates is only *distantly* related to increase in average signal-noise ratio by use of diversity.   As will be seen, the latter, the fact that the *average* output SNR from a combiner is greater than that on any individual branch is *not* the most significant factor in interpretation for system design.

The outage-rate definition of diversity improvement will have a direct engineering meaning only if signal legibility is directly determined by outage rate at some particular "threshold" value specified with respect to the mean receiver noise.   In particular, the bulk of tropospheric-scatter communications systems have employed frequency-modulation, so that the concept of a threshold phenomenon, as is known to occur with such bandwidth-exchange systems, seems entirely natural at first, at least for this application.   However, recent studies[1] have indicated that even with frequency-modulation systems, the "FM quieting threshold" is not a valid criterion for such important applications as the transmission of digital data.   Therefore, although the definition of diversity improvement based on an outage rate at fixed level is mathematically simple and convenient, it should be regarded mainly as a good *qualitative* indication of diversity performance.   The real improvements in diversity can only be specified by using much more specific criteria, such as voice articulation rates or digital data error rates under fading conditions, as the standards for system performance.

To amplify the situation, let us consider the role of diversity in over-all system design.   Diversity reduces the average power required within each short-term fading interval.   However, the selection of power level must also take into account the long-term fading.   For example, typical troposcatter system design is based upon breaking down a yearly period, typically into hourly segments (periods during which the short-term fading is presumed stationary), each characterized by a median level. The usual design specification is then a requirement for *propagational reliability* or satisfactory performance for something like 99%, or 99.9%, or 99.99% of the hours of the year.   For example, a 99.9% reliability allows unsatisfactory performance during no more than 0.1% of the year, or roughly 8 hours.   This kind of specification of long-term reliability seems completely appropriate when one's primary interest is in minimizing the duration of "down" periods, lengthy periods (like an hour) when the communication link is unusable.

Any definition of satisfactory short-term performance, such as an error rate, along with the assumption of short-term Rayleigh fading, determines a required median level of signal in each diversity branch relative

[1] B. B. Barrow, Error Probabilities for Telegraph Signals Transmitted on a Fading FM Carrier, *Proc. IRE*, vol. 48, pp. 1613–1629, September, 1960; D. E. Johansen, Binary Error Rates in Fading FDM-FM Communications, *IRE Trans. Commun. Systems*, vol. CS-9, pp. 206–214, September, 1961.

to receiver noise levels. When the medians fall below this level, the "hour" will be unacceptable. With the known long-term statistics of the hourly medians and the specified long-term propagational reliability, this in turn fixes the required system margin (transmitter powers, antenna sizes, etc.). As will be shown, the median level required per diversity branch for acceptable operation tends to decrease as the order of diversity (number of branches) increases. Again, any such decrease can be immediately equated to a saving in required nondiversity system margin and hence is a more specific definition of diversity gain, referenced to the particular specification on satisfactory short-term performance.

For digital data transmission, the form of specification on short-term performance is straightforward enough: a maximum allowable error rate. Diversity improvement is then strictly a comparison of the required average or median level of short-term (Rayleigh) fading per diversity branch, versus the order of diversity. For fully linear receiving systems, this is exactly the kind of computation which we shall pursue in great detail during most of this chapter. For nonlinear receiving systems, such as the transmission of digital data over frequency-division multiplexed voice channels with the multiplexed channels transmitted by FM of a radio carrier, as is common in most existing troposcatter networks, detailed theoretical understanding is not that readily available. Computations which have been made for this case[1] have been based upon the assumption of nonselective slow fading. These have indicated that operation could still be excellent with signals well below the "FM quieting threshold" and hence achieve satisfactory performance at lower r-f signal-noise ratios than required for voice signals in equivalent channels. On the other hand, some experimental data have apparently indicated important performance degradations due to selective fading distortion (see Sec. 9-2). There appears to be little detailed experimental or theoretical understanding of multichannel FDM-FM systems by which to relate an operational error-rate requirement to required median levels.

For voice transmission, the standard technique for specifying short-term fading performance is even less satisfactory. In most cases where the troposcatter system is part of a telephone trunking network, satisfactory performance is described as "toll-quality" performance. Standard telephone practice describes this in terms of an average voice channel test tone-to-noise ratio of the order of 50 db with permissible occasional drops to the order of 27 to 30 db. In troposcatter system design, this usually appears in the definition of an acceptable hour as a requirement that the voice channel test tone-to-noise ratio exceeds, say, 28 db for at least 99% of the hour.[2] In a network, this may be a requirement on net-

---

[1] Barrow, *loc. cit.;* Johansen, *loc. cit.*

[2] In certain applications, a much lesser SNR may be adequate and will be reflected in the specifications.

work propagational reliability over several links in tandem; the qualitative problem is the same in either case. This of course allows for a direct outage-rate interpretation in design and has been the basis for most troposcatter system design calculations. Such a specification represents an extrapolation from test results on basically nonfading trunking systems; unfortunately there appear to be no direct data on articulation or intelligibility testing of voice in which the effects of Rayleigh fading (and particularly the effects on an FM signal) have been studied in detail.

Finally, before plunging into the mathematics, we present some useful intuitive conclusions about the relative effectiveness of various forms of diversity combining. First, it is apparent that any more general combining, properly done, should permit better results than selection of the instantaneously strongest branch. This follows since the combiner can, at the very least, be made capable of using the instantaneously best signal; anything added must, by definition, represent an improvement. Let us define an "acceptable" combiner output signal as corresponding to an SNR for which performance is within the design specification. Then selection will itself furnish an acceptable signal whenever any one of the available signals is acceptable, and all that a more general combiner can provide under such circumstances is "greater acceptability" through, for example, an even higher instantaneous SNR. However, for all such events, the specification is met by both arrangements. Hence the improvement possible by more general combiner operation can come only from those intervals when there is *no* acceptable signal in any one individual diversity branch, but where at least some of the signals are high enough that an effective combination can still produce an acceptable combiner output SNR. Of the two classes of events just described, it is readily visualized that for low orders of diversity such as used operationally, and for reasonably low error rates or other high-quality performance, the first class, where instantaneously some one strong branch itself provides an acceptable signal, is *very much* the larger. Therefore, for relatively low order of diversity, the *added* diversity improvement provide 1 by a more general combiner over the diversity improvement provided by a selector must be small *relative* to the diversity improvement achieved by just the selector alone. This effect will be strongly evident in the quantitative results below.

10-4. Selection Combining

We consider first selection combining, with M diversity branches. Each of the M branches is characterized by an equivalent low-pass transfer function $H_k(f;t)$, $k = 1, \ldots, M$, with the t dependence of each indexing the stochastic time variations of the channel responses. As mentioned, for most of our diversity discussions, we shall assume non-

selective fading on each diversity branch.   Recalling Sec. 9-2, this implies
that for all f in the signal spectrum, one can set

$$H_k(f;t) = H_k(0;t) \equiv g_k(t) \qquad (10\text{-}4\text{-}1)$$

where each $g_k(t)$ thus defined is, for multipath fading with no specular
component, a zero-mean complex Gaussian time process.   Recalling representations such as (9-2-23) to (9-2-26), the signals in the respective diversity branches can then be represented in the form

$$s_k(t) = \text{Re} \left[g_k(t)u(t) \exp\left(j2\pi f_0 t\right)\right] \qquad (10\text{-}4\text{-}2)$$

where f_0 is the carrier-frequency (in frequency-diversity, we can assume
for purposes of our discussion, that all signals are reduced to at least a
common i-f).   As pointed out earlier, each $g_k(t)$ thus acts as a multiplicative noise.   The (complex-valued) equivalent low-pass signal $u(t)$ containing the message information is common to all branches.   It may be
conveniently regarded normalized to unit mean-square envelope over a
typical period $2T$,

$$\frac{1}{2T}\int_{-T}^{T} |u(t)|^2 \, dt = 1 \qquad (10\text{-}4\text{-}3)$$

Actually, by our definition of each "instant" as being much longer than
the reciprocal of the receiver bandwidth and hence of the modulation
bandwidth, it is reasonable to assume that $u(t)$ is completely averaged
over any such "instant."   A stronger and more relevant statement is that
if fading is not to have a catastrophic distorting effect on the demodulated
signal, it must be regarded as changing very slowly compared with the
modulation changes in the signal.   Without calling attention to it each
time, it will therefore be implicit in our discussions below that the averaging
in (10-4-3) is complete over each "instant."   With (10-4-3), and the slow-
fading assumption for each multiplicative noise $g_k(t)$, the mean-square
value for each of the latter represents the average signal power over short-
term fading in each branch; the power level is defined at the points where
(10-4-2) is defined, say at the i-f outputs.

The complex envelope of the additive noise in the kth receiver (branch)
is $n_k(t)$, with mean intensity over each "instant," as well as over any
longer interval, given by

$$\tfrac{1}{2}\langle|n_k(t)|^2\rangle = N_k \qquad (10\text{-}4\text{-}4)$$

Usually all the N_k will be equal.   Using (10-4-3), the instantaneous signal-
noise ratio in the kth receiver (branch) can now be meaningfully defined as

$$\gamma_k = \frac{1}{2}\frac{|g_k|^2}{N_k} \qquad (10\text{-}4\text{-}5)$$

The ideal selection diversity combiner is defined as choosing for the
system output, during each "instant," the signal from that receiver which
has the largest SNR.   Assuming a monotonic detector function, the

results obtained should be the same whether selection is made at i-f, with detection occurring only on the selector output, or is made after detection in each diversity branch. That is, either approach should result in the same branch selected at each "instant," and hence the same detected output. In discussing practical bases for making the selection, it is useful to note that if all the receivers are identical in noise level, the highest value of γ_k corresponds also to the highest value of $(|g_k|^2/2) + N_k$. Accordingly, the receiver selected is that which also has the highest *total* instantaneous power. For example, if automatic gain control is used with a sufficiently rapid response that it follows the signal fading, the AGC voltage can be monitored directly to determine the branch with highest SNR. Note also that for selection, the point in each branch at which the SNR is estimated need not be the same point at which the combining action takes place.

Another selection control technique useful in systems employing wide-deviation FM is based on the prediscriminator (i-f) bandwidth being several times wider than the information bandwidth to which the discriminator output is usually filtered. Furthermore (Chap. 3) the discriminator output signal is essentially independent of i-f carrier-to-noise ratio, down to values well below the "quieting threshold," while the noise in the output has a power spectral density inversely proportional to the i-f SNR and, prior to postdiscriminator filtering, has components out to frequencies corresponding to half the i-f bandwidth. By demodulating in each branch prior to selection, it is thus feasible to select a narrow band in the discriminator output *outside* the information band, hence containing only noise, and render from its level an excellent estimate of the branch SNR. This "out-of-band" noise-monitoring technique has been the basis of a substantial number of tropospheric-scatter diversity combiners, particularly in the earlier systems.

Statistics over Short-term Fading. With the selector action now defined, we turn to determining its performance over short-term fading. Conveniently, we picture the selection as taking place at i-f and seek the statistics of the SNR at the selector *output*. First, we write the probability density function (p.d.f.) of γ_k, the instantaneous SNR in each branch defined in (10-4-5). Since the N_k can be regarded as fixed numbers, the statistics of each γ_k over branch fading are those of the associated $|g_k|^2$. In these initial discussions we shall assume all the g_k mutually independent. Then, since we are assuming Rayleigh fading, the $|g_k|^2$ are independently exponentially distributed and hence so are the γ_k. Defining Γ_k as the average of γ_k over the short-term fading,

$$\Gamma_k = \langle \gamma_k \rangle = \frac{1}{2} \frac{\langle |g_k|^2 \rangle}{N_k} \tag{10-4-6}$$

one has the individual p.d.f.'s,

$$p(\gamma_k) = \frac{1}{\Gamma_k} \exp\left(-\frac{\gamma_k}{\Gamma_k} \right) \tag{10-4-7}$$

The associated cumulative distributions are

$$\text{Prob}\,(\gamma_k < x) = 1 - \exp\left(-\frac{x}{\Gamma_k}\right) \tag{10-4-8}$$

Over short-term fading, one can now describe all those events in which the selector output signal-noise ratio γ is less than some value x, as exactly that set of events in which *each* of the branch SNR's is simultaneously below x. But since the fading is assumed independent in each of the M branches, the probability that $\gamma < x$ is the product of the independent probabilities that each $\gamma_k < x$,

$$\text{Prob}\,(\gamma < x) = \prod_{k=1}^{M} \text{Prob}\,(\gamma_k < x) = \prod_{k=1}^{M}\left[1 - \exp\left(-\frac{x}{\Gamma_k}\right)\right] \tag{10-4-9}$$

The corresponding p.d.f. for γ is

$$p(\gamma) = \frac{d}{dx}\left\{\prod_{k=1}^{M}\left[1 - \exp\left(-\frac{x}{\Gamma_k}\right)\right]\right\}_{x=\gamma} = \frac{d}{d\gamma}\left\{\prod_{k=1}^{M}\left[1 - \exp\left(-\frac{\gamma}{\Gamma_k}\right)\right]\right\} \tag{10-4-10}$$

There are two special cases of particular interest. One is when all the diversity branches have equal mean SNR over the short-term fading, i.e., all the Γ_k are equal to some value Γ,

$$\Gamma_k = \Gamma \tag{10-4-11}$$

Then

$$\text{Prob}\,(\gamma < x) = \left[1 - \exp\left(-\frac{x}{\Gamma}\right)\right]^{M} \tag{10-4-12a}$$

$$p(\gamma) = \frac{M}{\Gamma}\exp\left(-\frac{\gamma}{\Gamma}\right)\left[1 - \exp\left(-\frac{\gamma}{\Gamma}\right)\right]^{M-1} \tag{10-4-12b}$$

The other case of interest is in the form of (10-4-9) and (10-4-10) at values of γ well below the mean values of any branch,

$$\gamma \ll \Gamma_k \qquad k = 1, \ldots, M \tag{10-4-13a}$$

Then, to first-order,

$$\text{Prob}\,(\gamma < x) = x^{M}\Big/\prod_{k=1}^{M} \Gamma_k \tag{10-4-13b}$$

and

$$p(\gamma) = M\gamma^{M-1}\Big/\prod_{k=1}^{M} \Gamma_k \tag{10-4-13c}$$

Clearly, (10-4-13b) and (10-4-13c) are not valid where, say, one of the Γ_k approaches zero. The restriction (10-4-13a) clearly shows this. However, we shall often write expressions such as (10-4-13b) or (10-4-13c) where for brevity the restriction like (10-4-13a) is not repeatedly written.

In such cases, it is left to common sense to indicate that such a restriction is still implicit and that otherwise a different series approximation may be relevant. If, for example, Γ_M is so small that the SNR of interest appears to fall in a range where $\Gamma_M < \gamma \ll (\Gamma_1, \Gamma_2, \ldots, \Gamma_{M-1})$, the appropriate useful approximation to (10-4-9) would be

$$\text{Prob } (\gamma < x) = \left[1 - \exp\left(-\frac{x}{\Gamma_M} \right) \right] x^{M-1} \Bigg/ \prod_{k=1}^{M-1} \Gamma_k \qquad (10\text{-}4\text{-}14a)$$

and, if $\Gamma_M \ll x$,

$$\text{Prob } (\gamma < x) = x^{M-1} \Bigg/ \prod_{k=1}^{M-1} \Gamma_k \qquad (10\text{-}4\text{-}14b)$$

with, further, an estimate from the value $1 - \exp\left(-\dfrac{x}{\Gamma_M} \right)$ of the *multiplicative error* in using (10-4-14b) as the approximation. In (10-4-14b) one confirms the intuitive impression that there is effectively only an $(M - 1)$-fold diversity action when the mean SNR on the Mth branch is well below the SNR level of interest.

From the distributions in (10-4-9) to (10-4-13), one can calculate many statistics of the selector combiner output. In Sec. 10-8, error rates will be calculated and compared for various linear diversity combiners. At this point, we confine attention to outage rate, as described by the cumulative distributions. The set of curves of the distribution (10-4-12a) gives directly the outage rate at level x (percentage of time γ is below x), and is shown for various M in Fig. 10-4-1.[1] The plot is on arithmetic probability paper, with the SNR plotted in decibels relative to 0 db representing the median (50-percentile) point for the $M = 1$ curve. The $M = 1$ curve is of course the simple distribution for SNR in Rayleigh fading, or, alternatively, is the distribution of SNR in each diversity branch. From (10-4-8), the median value Γ_{med} for a single branch is related to the mean value Γ by

$$\Gamma_{\text{med}} = 0.693\Gamma \qquad (10\text{-}4\text{-}15)$$

that is, Γ is 1.59 db above Γ_{med}.

Figure 10-4-1 makes evident the greatly decreased range of fading introduced by diversity, as well as the observation that the *rate of the decrease* in fading range diminishes rapidly with increasing M. Another interpretation for design purposes is the diversity gain versus M, using the outage-rate criterion of diversity improvement outlined earlier. One then compares the single-branch medians required versus M to achieve some particular outage rate at some arbitrary threshold. Because the data in Fig. 10-4-1 are normalized to single-branch median, independent

[1] From Stein, *loc. cit.*

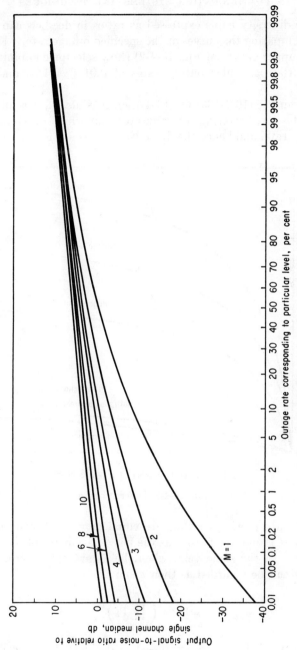

Fig. 10-4-1. Probability distribution for selector combining.

437

of M, the diversity gains expressed as ratios in decibels can be read by directly comparing the curves at the specified outage rate. For example, the three upper curves of Fig. 10-4-2[1] show selector combining diversity gains for the particular outage rates of 0.01%, 0.1%, and 1.0%, for various M.

By examining (10-4-13b) or (10-4-13c), it is also apparent that at low outage rates [or, better, at all values of γ for which (10-4-13a) is valid], the outage rate, and hence the diversity gain, is a function of the *product*

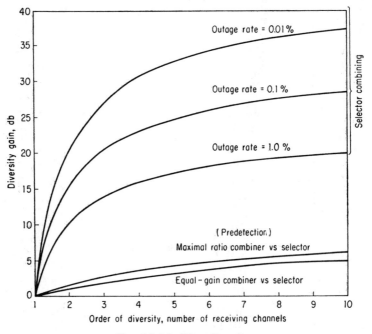

FIG. 10-4-2. Diversity gain.

of the several Γ_k, whether they are equal or not. When all are equal, so that $\Gamma_k = \Gamma$, one refers to Γ as the basic parameter of the distribution (10-4-13b). In the same vein, when the Γ_k are not all equal, the basic parameter can be regarded as their geometric mean

$$\Gamma_g = \Big(\prod_{k=1}^{M} \Gamma_k \Big)^{\frac{1}{M}} \tag{10-4-16}$$

Equivalently, if the Γ_k are expressed in decibels, Γ_g in decibels is their arithmetic mean. Examples of the overall combiner output probability distributions in cases of unequal branch SNRs are given later, in Fig. 10-5-3.

[1] From Stein, *loc. cit.*

The curves of Fig. 10-4-2 verify that selector combining provides a large amount of diversity gain with simply dual diversity and that the rate of further gain with increasing order of diversity steadily diminishes. This is another view of the rate of change of shallowness in the fading distributions in Fig. 10-4-1.

For digital data error-rate performance examined later, the important feature of the diversity distributions in Fig. 10-4-1 is the zero value and flatness of the p.d.f. of the output SNR at low values of SNR. As shown particularly in (10-4-13c), Mth-order selector diversity produces a p.d.f. which not only vanishes at $\gamma = 0$, as contrasted to the no-diversity case where the exponential p.d.f. of γ actually is maximum at $\gamma = 0$, but the

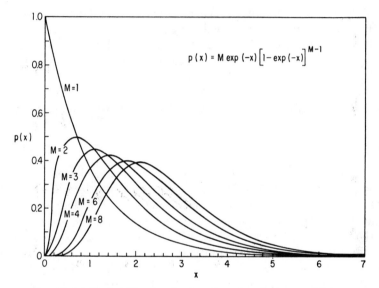

FIG. 10-4-3. Probability density functions for selector combining.

first $M - 2$ derivatives also vanish at $\gamma = 0$. This is shown more graphically in Fig. 10-4-3 by redrawing some of the data of Fig. 10-4-1 in terms of the p.d.f.'s, again for the case where all Γ_k are equal to some Γ. The significance for digital transmission can be seen by comparing with the discussion in Sec. 9-5, particularly in connection with Fig. 9-5-8.

As mentioned earlier, a slightly different selection rule sometimes can be implemented, particularly with the concept of a strict threshold uppermost in mind. In this alternative, which has sometimes been termed "scanning" diversity combining, a branch is selected which has SNR above the specified threshold, and this branch is maintained in use *until* its SNR drops below the threshold. When it does, any other branch is selected whose SNR exceeds threshold, and the combiner keeps utilizing this branch until it "fails;" and so forth. It is clear that this system has the *same outage rate* with respect to the specified threshold as the selector combiner, although the distribution of the output SNR is otherwise different. It also has the advantage in implementation of requiring fewer switchings on the average and of allowing comparison of branch signals against a preset bias rather than against each other. On the other hand, the concept of a sharp performance threshold may have little practical validity. A system employing the "scanning" technique may then suffer in overall performance if no effective nominal threshold serves as a really adequate basis for signal selection.

10-5. Maximal-ratio Combining

We now examine a more general form of combining. While the results are also applicable to combining after detection, we consider here the predetection case. Recalling (10-4-2) to (10-4-4), the total complex envelopes at i-f in the respective diversity branches are of the form

$$v_k(t) = g_k(t)u(t) + n_k(t) \tag{10-5-1}$$

The most general linear combining results in an output complex envelope

$$v(t) = \sum_{k=1}^{M} \alpha_k v_k(t) \tag{10-5-2}$$

where the α_k are complex factors which are changed from instant to instant as the branch signals change over the short-term fading. The α_k are often termed the combiner weighting factors.[1] Selector combining is then the particular case where at any instant, all the α_k are zero except for the branch with largest SNR, where it is some arbitrary constant. Selector combining involves transients due to switching (the shape of the rise in the combiner output of the newly selected branch voltages and of the decay of the old ones). Thus there are practical reasons for desiring a combiner in which the several α_k vary more gradually with signal fading so that abrupt switching is avoided.

In this section, we consider the optimal form of such a more general combiner, defining optimality for the moment as achievement of the maximum possible combiner output signal-noise ratio at *each* instant. From (10-5-1) and (10-5-2), the instantaneous combiner output has, respectively, the signal and noise complex envelopes

$$s(t) = u(t) \sum_{k=1}^{M} \alpha_k g_k \tag{10-5-3}$$

[1] Although we shall not here be concerned with actual networks, it should be noted that (10-5-2) has the form of a scattering-matrix representation for the output of a multiport network at one port in terms of inputs at all the other ports. Conservation of energy then dictates that $\Sigma|\alpha_k|^2 \leq 1$, with equality if and only if the network is lossless and matched at all input ports.

and
$$n(t) = \sum_{k=1}^{M} \alpha_k n_k(t) \qquad (10\text{-}5\text{-}4)$$

Assuming again the $n_k(t)$ are mutually independent, the instantaneous output noise power is

$$N = \tfrac{1}{2}\langle |n(t)|^2 \rangle = \sum_{k=1}^{M} |\alpha_k|^2 N_k \qquad (10\text{-}5\text{-}5)$$

Recalling the normalization in (10-4-3), the instantaneous output SNR is then

$$\gamma = \frac{1}{2} \frac{\left| \sum\limits_{k=1}^{M} \alpha_k g_k \right|^2}{\sum\limits_{k=1}^{M} |\alpha_k|^2 N_k} \qquad (10\text{-}5\text{-}6)$$

This can be maximized by standard differentiation techniques, remembering that α_k is a complex factor and hence is specified by two independent real numbers rather than one. It can also instructively be maximized[1] by applying the Schwarz Inequality for complex-valued numbers,

$$\left| \sum_{k=1}^{M} a_k^* b_k \right|^2 \le \left(\sum_{k=1}^{M} |a_k|^2 \right) \left(\sum_{k=1}^{M} |b_k|^2 \right) \qquad (10\text{-}5\text{-}7)$$

This can be interpreted as an inequality on the scalar product of two complex-valued vectors relative to their individual magnitudes. A necessary and sufficient condition for the equality to hold is that the two vectors be parallel and in phase.

$$b_k = K a_k \qquad \text{for all } k \qquad (10\text{-}5\text{-}8)$$

where K is some arbitrary complex constant. To apply the inequality to (10-5-6), we can set

$$a_k = \frac{g_k^*}{\sqrt{N_k}} \qquad b_k = \alpha_k \sqrt{N_k} \qquad (10\text{-}5\text{-}9)$$

Thus
$$\left| \sum_{k=1}^{M} \alpha_k g_k \right|^2 \le \left(\sum_{k=1}^{M} \frac{|g_k|^2}{N_k} \right) \left(\sum_{k=1}^{M} |\alpha_k|^2 N_k \right) \qquad (10\text{-}5\text{-}10)$$

Or
$$\gamma \le \frac{1}{2} \sum_{k=1}^{M} \frac{|g_k|^2}{N_k} \qquad (10\text{-}5\text{-}11)$$

with equality (maximization) holding if, and only if

$$\alpha_k = K \frac{g_k^*}{N_k} \qquad \text{for each } k \qquad (10\text{-}5\text{-}12)$$

---

[1] E.g., D. G. Brennan, Linear Diversity Combining Techniques, *Proc. IRE*, vol. 47, 1075–1102, June, 1959.

where K is any arbitrary complex constant. In words, the optimum weight for each branch has a magnitude proportional to the signal magnitude and inverse to the branch-noise power level, and has a phase canceling out the signal (channel) phase to within some identical value for all branches. The latter phase alignment allows fully coherent addition of the branch signal components. The terms on the right of (10-5-11) are just the individual instantaneous SNR's on each branch defined in (10-4-5). Thus this combiner results in an instantaneous output SNR which is the sum of the instantaneous SNR's on the individual branches,

$$\gamma = \sum_{k=1}^{M} \gamma_k \qquad (10\text{-}5\text{-}13)$$

The term "maximal-ratio combiner" has been coined[1] to describe this type of combiner. The combining rule of (10-5-12) has been long known more generally (e.g., in connection with optimum predetection integration of repeated radar pulses) as the optimum weighting for summing a set of terms when each term consists of a desired coherently additive part and a part incoherent from term to term.

To examine the tolerances required in realizing maximal-ratio combiner performance, suppose that instead of the value specified by (10-5-12), errors in estimating the signal amplitude and phase result in α_k which differ from their correct values by some magnitude factor q_k and some phase ϕ_k

$$\alpha_k = q_k \exp\left(j\phi_k\right) \frac{K g_k{}^*}{N_k} \qquad (10\text{-}5\text{-}14)$$

Using (10-5-6) directly, the resulting output SNR will then be

$$\gamma = \frac{\left| \sum_{k=1}^{M} [q_k \exp\left(j\phi_k\right)]\gamma_k \right|^2}{\sum_{k=1}^{M} q_k{}^2 \gamma_k} \qquad (10\text{-}5\text{-}15)$$

From this equation, it can readily be shown that an overall phase-lock error of 37.5° will cause no more than 1 db deterioration and 60° error will cause less than 3 db deterioration (at the 3-db level, one might want to establish the bounds more tightly). Similarly, an overall relative magnitude error of 0.5 db will cause no more than 1 db error, and 1.5 db no more than 3 db error (again, at this level, one would want to establish the bounds more tightly).

Distribution over Short-term Fading, for Equal Branch SNR's. Returning now to the ideal case, with instantaneous SNR described by (10-5-13), we determine the distribution over the short-term fading, again assuming that the several γ_k are independently distributed. The p.d.f. of

[1] Brennan, *loc. cit.*

γ, $p(\gamma)$, is then conveniently determined by first evaluating its characteristic function.   Since γ and all the γ_k are all positive real, it is convenient to consider a Laplace transform,

$$F(s) = \int_0^\infty \exp{(-s\gamma)} p(\gamma) \, d\gamma = \langle \exp{(-s\gamma)} \rangle$$

$$= \prod_{k=1}^{M} \langle \exp{(-s\gamma_k)} \rangle \qquad (10\text{-}5\text{-}16)$$

With the p.d.f.'s of (10-4-7),

$$\langle \exp{(-s\gamma_k)} \rangle = \int_0^\infty \exp{(-s\gamma_k)} \frac{1}{\Gamma_k} \exp\left(-\frac{\gamma_k}{\Gamma_k}\right) d\gamma_k$$

$$= \frac{1}{1 + s\Gamma_k} \qquad \text{Re } s \geq 0 \quad (10\text{-}5\text{-}17)$$

Thus $$F(s) = \prod_{k=1}^{M} \frac{1}{1 + s\Gamma_k} \qquad (10\text{-}5\text{-}18)$$

The inversion of (10-5-16) then gives

$$p(\gamma) = \frac{1}{2\pi j} \int_{c-j\infty}^{c+j\infty} \frac{\exp{(s\gamma)}}{\prod\limits_{k=1}^{M} (1 + s\Gamma_k)} \, ds \qquad c \geq 0 \quad (10\text{-}5\text{-}19)$$

The contour of integration can obviously be closed at ∞ in the left-half plane with only poles enclosed.   Hence the integral can be evaluated by routine residue calculations, in terms of exponentials (with polynomial multipliers for higher-order poles).   However, again we consider only two special cases.   One is when all the Γ_k are equal, $\Gamma_k = \Gamma$, giving

$$p(\gamma) = \frac{1}{\Gamma^M} \frac{1}{(M-1)!} \left[\frac{\partial^{M-1}}{\partial s^{M-1}} \exp{(s\gamma)} \right]_{s = -\frac{1}{\Gamma}}$$

$$= \frac{1}{(M-1)!} \frac{\gamma^{M-1}}{\Gamma^M} \exp\left(-\frac{\gamma}{\Gamma}\right) \qquad (10\text{-}5\text{-}20)$$

The cumulative distribution is

$$\text{Prob}\,(\gamma < x) = \int_0^x p(\gamma) \, d\gamma = 1 - \int_x^\infty p(\gamma) \, d\gamma \qquad (10\text{-}5\text{-}21)$$

With (10-5-20), the distribution can be identified with the statistical chi-square distribution of order $2M$, a fact already obvious from (10-5-13). (Each of the γ_k is the sum of the squares of two independent zero-mean Gaussian variates of equal variance.   When all the Γ_k are equal, γ is the sum of the squares of $2M$ such variates, which is the basic definition of a chi-square process.)

The outage rate defined by (10-5-21) is shown plotted for various M in Fig. 10-5-1.[1]   The superficial similarity to the curves of Fig. 10-4-1 for

[1] From Stein, *loc. cit.*

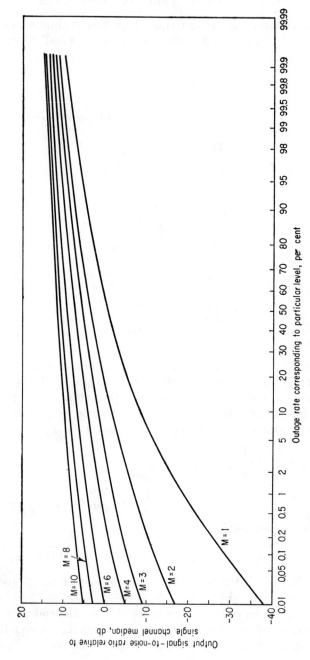

FIG. 10-5-1. Probability distribution for predetection maximal-ratio combining.

444

selector combining is quite evident.   Indeed, the values of diversity gain on an outage-rate basis are only slightly greater (regarding a few decibels as slight in this context) than for selection.   The ratio (or decibel difference) of these diversity gains at low outage rates, such as the outage rates considered earlier in Fig. 10-4-2, is a function of M but independent of outage rate.   The reason for this is obvious from examining (10-5-20) at small values of γ,

$$p(\gamma) = \frac{1}{(M-1)!} \frac{\gamma^{M-1}}{\Gamma^M} \qquad \gamma \ll \Gamma \qquad (10\text{-}5\text{-}22)$$

The corresponding approximation to (10-5-21) gives for the outage rate[1]

$$\text{Prob}\ (\gamma < x) = \int_0^x \frac{1}{(M-1)!} \frac{\gamma^{M-1}}{\Gamma^M}\, d\gamma = \frac{1}{M!}\frac{x^M}{\Gamma^M} \quad (10\text{-}5\text{-}23)$$

Comparison with the equivalent approximation (10-4-13b) for the selector, when all Γ_k are equal, shows that the maximal-ratio combiner diversity gain exceeds that for the selector by exactly a factor $^M\sqrt{M!}$!   (This is the factor by which the value x/Γ is larger in the maximal-ratio case, at which a specified outage rate is attained.)   This factor is shown plotted in decibels in Fig. 10-4-2 as the next-to-bottom curve, showing the *best* additional diversity gain (in the outage-rate sense) that can be accomplished by *any* linear combining technique, over the selection technique. The same factor can be expected to enter for *any* performance statistic which depends primarily on the p.d.f. of combiner output at low values of output SNR (e.g., see also Sec. 10-8).

A presentation of comparative combiner statistics which may be more useful for design purposes is given in Fig. 10-5-2,[2] giving separately the comparative combiner output distributions for $M = 2, 3, 4$, and 8 (the equal-gain combiner shown on these figures will be discussed in the next section).   The essentially constant ratio (decibel difference) between selection and maximal-ratio combiner, at low outage rates, is quite obvious in these graphs.

Distribution over Short-term Fading for Unequal Branch SNRs. Although a full evaluation of (10-5-19) can be given when not all the Γ_k are equal, we are particularly interested again in the probability density function at low values of γ.   Hence, we shall be satisfied with the leading terms of the power series expansion of $p(\gamma)$ for small γ.   In (10-5-19), all the singularities of $F(s)$ are confined within a finite domain in the left-half

---

[1] An exact computation using (10-5-24) gives

$$\text{Prob}\ (\gamma < x) = \frac{1}{(M-1)!}\, \gamma\left(M, \frac{x}{\Gamma}\right) = \exp\left(-\frac{x}{\Gamma}\right) \sum_{k=M}^{\infty} \frac{1}{k!}\left(\frac{x}{\Gamma}\right)^k$$

where $\gamma(a,x)$ is the incomplete gamma function.

[2] From Brennan, *loc. cit.*

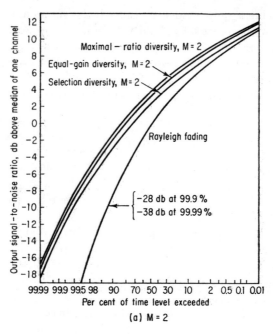

(a) M = 2

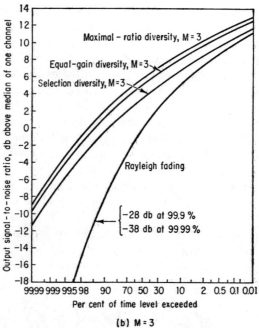

(b) M = 3

FIG. 10-5-2. Combiner probability distributions.

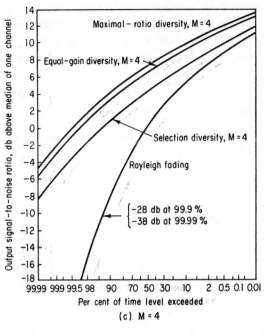

(c) M = 4

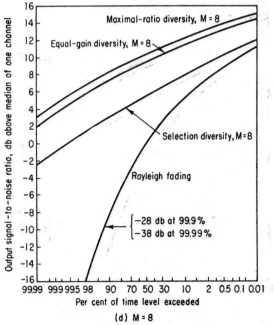

(d) M = 8

Fig. 10-5-2. (*Continued*)

s plane. The integration contour can then be closed over a semicircle of radius $R_0 \to \infty$, in the left-half plane, over which the integral vanishes. However, with all the singularities of $F(p)$ contained with this closed contour, the contour can be changed into a full circle of any radius R_0 such that

$$R_0 > |s_k|_{\max} \tag{10-5-24}$$

where $|s_k|_{\max}$ is the largest radius at which any singularity is located. Along this new path, $F(s)$ is analytic (out to ∞) and hence is expandable in an absolutely convergent Laurent series of the form

$$F(s) = \sum_{m=0}^{\infty} a_m \frac{1}{s^m} \tag{10-5-25}$$

In inverting the transform, one can interchange orders of integration and summation, the resulting series being still absolutely convergent. Thus, the p.d.f. can be written

$$p(\gamma) = \sum_{m=0}^{\infty} a_m \frac{1}{2\pi j} \oint_{R_0} \frac{\exp(s\gamma)}{s^m} \, ds \tag{10-5-26}$$

The individual integrals in (10-5-26) can be evaluated by standard residue calculations (the only singularity in each is at $s = 0$), giving finally the absolutely convergent series

$$p(\gamma) = \sum_{m=0}^{\infty} a_m \frac{\gamma^{m-1}}{(m-1)!} \tag{10-5-27}$$

For the specific $F(s)$ of (10-5-18), while the entire series can be expressed, we confine our attention to the leading nonzero term. Thus one finds

$$a_m = 0 \qquad m = 1, \dots, M-1 \tag{10-5-28a}$$

and the leading nonzero coefficient is

$$a_M = 1 \Big/ \prod_{k=1}^{M} \Gamma_k \tag{10-5-28b}$$

Accordingly, in (10-5-27), with $p(\gamma)$ approximated at low γ by its leading term,

$$p(\gamma) \doteq \frac{1}{\displaystyle\prod_{k=1}^{M} \Gamma_k} \frac{\gamma^{M-1}}{(M-1)!} \tag{10-5-29}$$

The same result could be obtained by expanding the factors in (10-5-19) and evaluating term-by-term.[1]

---

[1] Another alternative derivation for combiner output p.d.f.'s at low SNR, described by B. B. Barrow, Diversity Combination of Fading Signals with Unequal Mean

Again, whether all the Γ_k are equal or not, (10-5-29) shows that the product of the several Γ_k (or their geometric mean) is the controlling parameter for the distribution at low values of γ. The same conclusion applied to the selector combiner and the difference between selection and maximal-ratio combining maintains the same relation as already discussed in connection with Fig. 10-4-2.

Again, (10-5-29) applies only for γ in the range $\gamma \ll \Gamma_k$, for all $k = 1,$ . . . , M. Mathematically the statement is that the power-series representation for $p(\gamma)$ has a rapid convergence only when $\gamma \ll \Gamma_k$, for all k. At some larger γ, the sum in (10-5-27) converges only when a large number of terms are considered. However, as in the selection case, one expects that at values of γ larger than some of the branch mean SNR's, say K of them, the p.d.f. will behave very much like that of a lower $(M - K)$-order diversity system. For example, let us assume that these K branches all have equal mean SNR's,

$$\Gamma_k = \Gamma_M \qquad k = M - K + 1, M - K + 2, \ldots, M - 1, M \qquad (10\text{-}5\text{-}30)$$

and that we are interested in values of γ such that

$$\Gamma_M < \gamma < \Gamma_k \quad k = 1, \ldots, M - K \qquad (10\text{-}5\text{-}31)$$

Then (10-5-18) can be written as the product of two transforms

$$F(s) = F_1(s)F_2(s) \qquad (10\text{-}5\text{-}32a)$$

$$F_1(s) = \frac{1}{(1 + s\Gamma_M)^K} \qquad F_2(s) = \frac{1}{\displaystyle\prod_{k=1}^{M-K} (1 + s\Gamma_k)} \qquad (10\text{-}5\text{-}32b)$$

These have the respective inverses $f_1(\gamma)$ and $f_2(\gamma)$. Recalling (10-5-20),

$$f_1(\gamma) = \frac{1}{(K - 1)!} \frac{\gamma^{K-1}}{\Gamma_M{}^K} \exp\left(-\frac{\gamma}{\Gamma_M}\right) \qquad (10\text{-}5\text{-}33a)$$

while by (10-5-29), for γ much smaller than the remaining Γ_k,

$$f_2(\gamma) \doteq \frac{1}{\displaystyle\prod_{k=1}^{M-K} \Gamma_k} \frac{\gamma^{M-K-1}}{(M - K - 1)!} \qquad (10\text{-}5\text{-}33b)$$

By the convolution theorem, now, the inverse of (10-5-32a) can be

---

Strengths, *IRE Trans. Commun. Systems*, vol. CS-11, pp. 73–78, March, 1963, is based on directly carrying out the convolutional integration for a sum of independent random variables, using the leading term(s) of the p.d.f.'s for the individual variables. In the low SNR limit, the convolutional integration corresponds to a simple M-fold volume integration, with the differences in outage rate performance between the selector, maximal ratio, and equal-gain combiners simply related to slightly different shapes of the volume in the different cases.

written as

$$p(\gamma) = \int_0^\gamma f_2(\gamma - x) f_1(x) \, dx \qquad (10\text{-}5\text{-}34)$$

Since $f_1(x)$ effectively vanishes in this integral except in a narrow range (of width Γ_M) around $x = 0$, one can approximate

$$f_2(\gamma - x) \doteq f_2(\gamma) - x \frac{d}{d\gamma} f_2(\gamma) = f_2(\gamma) \left(1 - x \frac{M - K - 1}{\gamma} \right) \qquad (10\text{-}5\text{-}35)$$

For $\gamma \gg \Gamma_M$,

$$\int_0^\gamma f_1(x) \, dx \doteq 1 \qquad \int_0^\gamma x f_1(x) \, dx \doteq \langle x_1 \rangle = K\Gamma_M \qquad (10\text{-}5\text{-}36)$$

where $\langle x_1 \rangle$ has been recognized as the *average* SNR in the sum of the K diversity branches with individual average SNR's Γ_M. With (10-5-35) to (10-5-36), an excellent approximation to (10-5-34) is

$$p(\gamma) = f_2(\gamma) \left[1 - \frac{K\Gamma_M}{\gamma} (M - K - 1) \right] \qquad (10\text{-}5\text{-}37)$$

For $\gamma \gg K(M - K - 1)\Gamma_M$, it follows that

$$p(\gamma) \doteq f_2(\gamma) \qquad (10\text{-}5\text{-}38)$$

and there is effectively only $(M - K)$-fold diversity at this level of γ. Incidentally, at a given value of γ, the values of Γ_M at which (10-5-38) holds appears to be *much smaller* than in the analogous result for selector combining, implying that maximal-ratio combiners can make much more *effective* use in diversity of relatively weak signals than can selector combiners. This also agrees with physical intuition.

The formulas above can be illustrated with some specific examples of complete distributions calculated with unequal SNR's in the branches. Fig. 10-5-3a[1] shows complete distributions for fourfold diversity for both maximal-ratio and selection diversity, in which two of the branches are 6 db lower in average SNR than the other two. In the maximal-ratio case, this results from an exact integration of (10-5-19); in the selection case, from exact use of (10-4-9). The 0 db reference on these curves is the mean SNR on one of the strong branches. Similarly, Figs. 10-5-3b and c[2] show results for maximal-ratio combining in dual diversity and fourfold diversity, respectively, with various combinations of different branch gains. The quadruple diversity configuration in Fig. 10-5-3c is basically similar to that in a in that one pair of branches has one mean SNR and the other pair has another value. All the curves in Fig. 10-5-3 clearly show the decibel averaging at low SNR—and also show that this holds closely over the major part of the distribution, at least the lower 30 per cent and often more.

[1] From Barrow, *loc. cit.*

[2] From J. Granlund and W. Sichak, Diversity Combining for Signals of Different Medians, *IRE Trans. Commun. Systems*, vol. CS-9, pp. 138–145, June, 1961.

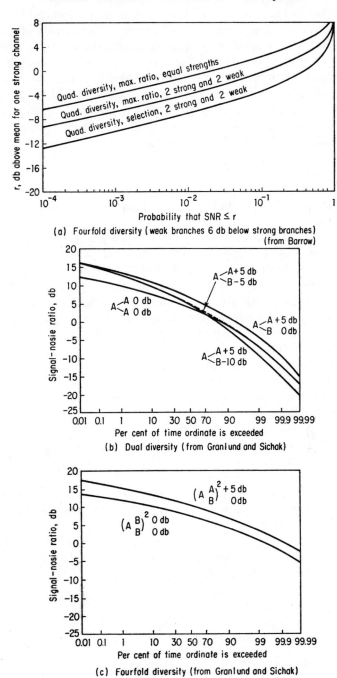

(a) Fourfold diversity (weak branches 6 db below strong branches)
(from Barrow)

(b) Dual diversity (from Granlund and Sichak)

(c) Fourfold diversity (from Granlund and Sichak)

FIG. 10-5-3. Diversity combination with unequal SNR's.

The curves in Fig. 10-5-3 were developed in both instances[1] to investigate quadruple-diversity tropospheric-scatter configurations of the type shown in Fig. 10-1-2, seeking the most favorable configuration when two of the four antennas involved are of one size and two of another. The differing diversity branch mean SNR's are then due to the different total transmitting plus receiving antenna gains associated with each branch. A symmetric configuration using one large and one small antenna at each end appears preferable, although substantial advantage appears to result only if (unlike Fig. 10-1-2) the large antenna at each end is used for transmitting *both* signals, utilizing frequency separation to achieve the fourfold diversity. This advantage would however sacrifice the equipment reliability concept discussed earlier in connection with Fig. 10-1-2 and involve the problems of diplexing two high-power transmissions in a single feed.

Additional Comments. It is relevant to ask whether it is reasonably possible to achieve the measurements required to achieve maximal-ratio combining. We have already remarked on the tolerances required in the estimates. For predetection combining, as discussed above, both phase-lock of the several signals *and* appropriate weighting are required. Within conventional systems (not including special signal design techniques to facilitate the combining), one could seek to accomplish the phase lock and the amplitude weighting separately. The amplitude weighting can be achieved readily in troposcatter f-m systems, for example, by demodulating conventionally in each branch, and calibrating the out-of-band noise in terms of i-f carrier-to-noise ratio[2] (viz., the earlier discussion on selector combining). The phase lock can also be separately achieved, pairwise (see the later discussion on equal-gain combiners). However, the equipment complexity is unattractive, especially when compared with the relative simplicity and almost equal performance of the equal-gain predetection combiner discussed in the next section. At the same time, one can also use maximal-ratio combining after detection, in which case the signal phase-lock problem no longer occurs (also see the discussion of Sec. 10-9 on postdetection maximal-ratio combining).

Even if not practical for implementation in conventional systems, the basic nature of the optimal linear combining rule here denoted as maximal-ratio combining leads to its playing an important role in a number of "nonconventional" systems, primarily in connection with digital-data transmission. One of these is the Rake system (Sec. 11-5). Another (Sec. 11-3) is the transmission of unmodulated pilot tones for the express purpose of providing combiner control information. Beyond this, there

---

[1] Barrow, *loc. cit.;* Granlund and Sichak, *loc. cit.*

[2] R. V. Locke, Jr., Experimental Comparison of Equal-Gain and Maximal-Ratio Diversity Combiners, *Proc. IRE*, vol. 48, pp. 1488–1489, August, 1960; this, however, is a discussion of postdetection combiners on an SSB system.

is considerable importance in the concept and results of maximal-ratio combining since these provide a useful theoretical upper bound on performance against which to compare any possibly simpler suboptimum linear combining technique of interest. Indeed, the results have already been applied here this way, as a reference for discussing the effectiveness of the suboptimum selector combining technique.

10-6. Equal-gain Combining

The maximal-ratio predetection combiner is an ideal in linear diversity combining technique, but requires a major effort in instrumentation to achieve the correct weighting factors. Furthermore, the additional advantages of maximal-ratio over selection combining are not so large that they cannot be lost by difficulties in achieving the proper combining. Again, we recall our earlier interpretation, that most of the diversity benefit will arise just from selection of the strongest signal at each instant. That is, so long as the combining technique uses *the strongest signal branch to advantage*, other details of the combiner operation will result in *relatively minor change in the diversity performance*.   This consideration suggests that a simple phase-locked addition of all the branches[1] would still provide incoherent addition of the noises and coherent addition of all the signals, emphasizing the largest of the latter, and accordingly providing effective diversity performance.

For this combiner, then, the weighting factors α_k in (10-5-3) to (10-5-6) all have phase opposite to that of the signal in the respective branches, but all have equal magnitude. Hence this is termed "equal-gain" combining.   In actual implementation,[2] a simple circuit is used to phase-lock two inputs (at i-f), which are then summed; for higher-order diversity, pyramiding of these is envisioned (for convenience, then, M is always a power of 2).   Using (10-5-6), the combiner output SNR with ideal equal-gain combining is just

$$\gamma = \frac{1}{2} \frac{\left[\sum_{k=1}^{M} |g_k| \right]^2}{\sum_{k=1}^{M} N_k} \qquad (10\text{-}6\text{-}1)$$

where the $|g_k|$ are the individual signal envelope factors.   The effects of imperfect phase lock can be estimated here just as they were for the maximal-ratio combiner, with essentially the same bounds on tolerances.

[1] F. J. Altman and W. Sichak, Simplified Diversity Communication System for Beyond-the-Horizon Links, *Elec. Commun.*, vol. 33, pp. 151–160, June, 1956 (reprinted with revisions from *IRE Trans. Commun. Systems*, vol. CS-4, pp. 50–55, March, 1956.)

[2] R. T. Adams and B. M. Mindes, Evaluation of IF and Baseband Diversity Combining Receivers, *IRE Trans. Commun. Systems*, vol. CS-6, pp. 8–13, June, 1958.

Note that the assumption of equal noise levels in all branches is crucial to proper operation of this equal-gain combiner, since otherwise those branches with large noise levels would dominate the output SNR even if the branch itself were weak in signal level. If various branches have unequal receiver noise (for example, because of different noise figures in frequency-diversity receivers), one way to equalize the noise levels would be to use different gains in these branches, prior to the combiner. It is not offhand clear that this would lead to the most effective operation overall; we shall further consider this question below. In the selection and maximal-ratio combiner cases, we tacitly ignored the analogous question, on the basis that the combiner weights then are chosen from an estimate of the SNR on each branch, the latter ratio being independent of the receiver gain in the branch. (Or in these cases, one can simplify the combining by indeed adjusting the gains so that the noise levels are equal in each branch. This is implicit when one proposes to use largest envelope as the criterion in selection. In the maximal-ratio case, with equal noise levels, the combiner factors could be based on estimating signal level only, where this might be achievable, for example, by a relatively long-term integration of the received signal plus noise.)

In (10-6-1), the individual fading signal envelopes $|g_k|$ are Rayleigh-distributed, so that the short-term distribution involves that of the normalized sum of M independent such variables. The basic variable can be conveniently regarded to be

$$y = \frac{1}{\sqrt{2N_T}} \sum_{k=1}^{M} |g_k| \qquad (10\text{-}6\text{-}2)$$

where

$$N_T = \sum_{k=1}^{M} N_k \qquad (10\text{-}6\text{-}3)$$

is the total noise. A simple transformation will then yield the distribution of γ,

$$\gamma = y^2 \qquad (10\text{-}6\text{-}4)$$

Unfortunately, even in the simple case where all branches have identical signal statistics, the distribution of γ cannot be expressed in simple closed form. Instead, the distribution has been determined by numerical integration of the convolutional formula for the distribution of a sum of independent variables.[1] The results, applied to our problem, are shown as the equal-gain combiner curves in Fig. 10-5-2 and redrawn as a set for the various M in Fig. 10-6-1. These assume equal mean noise powers in all branches.

It is apparent from Fig. 10-5-2 that equal-gain predetection diversity is indeed extremely effective, and that just phase-locked addition of M signals with incoherent associated noises, but without the additional

[1] Brennan, *loc. cit.*

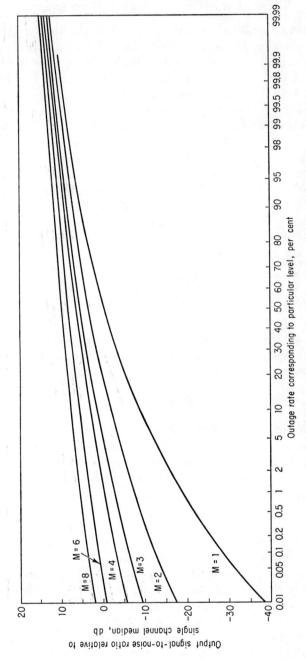

FIG. 10-6-1. Probability distribution for predetection equal-gain combining.

455

elaboration of amplitude weighting factors, is statistically extremely effective in achieving diversity results. Indeed, the near parallelism of the equal-gain and maximal-ratio distributions over their entire ranges is quite striking. Over a wide range of outage rates the difference (in decibels) between performance with equal-gain and either selection or maximal-ratio is also a function of M only and not of outage rate. This difference is shown as the lowest curve on Fig. 10-4-2. These observations indicate that the equal-gain output SNR p.d.f. at low values of γ should also have a form very similar to (10-5-29), except for a factor which changes very slowly with M. This form can be obtained by the method introduced above (for obtaining the analogous result in the maximal-ratio case when not all the Γ_k are equal) keeping in mind that the $|g_k|$ are independently Rayleigh-distributed with normalized mean-square values given in terms of the Γ_k in (10-4-6). The result for the p.d.f. of the output SNR, at low values of γ, is

$$p(\gamma) = \frac{2^{M-1}}{(2M-1)!} \frac{1}{\prod\limits_{k=1}^{M} (N_k/N_T)} \frac{\gamma^{M-1}}{\prod\limits_{k=1}^{M} \Gamma_k} \qquad (10\text{-}6\text{-}5)$$

In the expression above, the Γ_k are signal-noise ratios in the several diversity branches and are thus independent of the gains in these branches. The earlier question concerning adjustment of the branch gains when the branch statistics are not all alike enters only through the factor $\prod\limits_{k=1}^{M} (N_k/N_T)$ in (10-6-5), at least insofar as the leading term of $p(\gamma)$ is sufficient for describing outage rates or other practical performance statistics. To maximize equal-gain combiner performance, one wishes to uniformly minimize $p(\gamma)$ for small γ. This implies maximizing the denominator factor. But, with (10-6-3),

$$\sum_{k=1}^{M} \frac{N_k}{N_T} = 1 \qquad (10\text{-}6\text{-}6)$$

and hence the issue may be stated as finding the set of M factors whose product is maximum subject to the constraint that their sum is unity. It is readily determined (for example, analytically, by using Lagrange multipliers) that subject to this constraint, the factors should each be equal to $1/M$. Thus, indeed, the earlier intuition is correct, that the best performance is obtained with branch gains adjusted for equal noise levels at the combiner input, even if this results in further unequalizing signal levels on the various branches. With this now assumed,

$$\prod_{k=1}^{M} \frac{N_k}{N_T} = \left(\frac{1}{M}\right)^M \qquad (10\text{-}6\text{-}7)$$

and (10-6-5) becomes

$$p(\gamma) = \frac{2^{M-1} M^M}{(2M-1)!} \frac{\gamma^{M-1}}{\prod\limits_{k=1}^{M} \Gamma_k} \qquad (10\text{-}6\text{-}8)$$

The corresponding approximation for the outage rate can be written

$$\text{Prob } (\gamma < x) = \int_0^x p(\gamma) \, d\gamma = \frac{(2M)^M}{(2M)!} \frac{x^M}{\prod\limits_{k=1}^{M} \Gamma_k} \qquad (10\text{-}6\text{-}9)$$

To facilitate comparison with the maximal-ratio case, we can utilize a familiar gamma-function identity (written here in terms of factorials),

$$(2M)! = \frac{2^{2M}}{\sqrt{\pi}} M! (M - \tfrac{1}{2})! \qquad (10\text{-}6\text{-}10)$$

Thus $$\text{Prob } (\gamma < x) = \frac{(M/2)^M \sqrt{\pi}}{(M - \tfrac{1}{2})!} \left(\frac{1}{M!} \frac{x^M}{\prod\limits_{k=1}^{M} \Gamma_k} \right) \qquad (10\text{-}6\text{-}11)$$

The last factor in parentheses corresponds exactly to the p.d.f. for maximal-ratio combining of the same diversity branches, as displayed in (10-5-29). The difference in diversity gain shown in Fig. 10-4-2 when all the Γ_k are equal to some Γ, the ratio by which the required Γ is larger than in the maximal-ratio case, is simply then

$$q = \sqrt[M]{\frac{(M/2)^M \sqrt{\pi}}{(M - \tfrac{1}{2})!}} = \frac{M}{2} \frac{1}{\sqrt[M]{(M - \tfrac{1}{2})!/\sqrt{\pi}}} \qquad (10\text{-}6\text{-}12)$$

As seen in Fig. 10-4-2, this factor varies extremely slowly with M. Indeed, using Stirling's formula for large M,

$$M \gg 1 \qquad (M - \tfrac{1}{2})! \approx \sqrt{2\pi} \exp\left[-(M + \tfrac{1}{2})\right](M + \tfrac{1}{2})^M$$

$$q \approx \frac{e}{2} = 1.36 \qquad \text{or} \qquad 1.34 \text{ db} \qquad (10\text{-}6\text{-}13)$$

This limit is also apparent in Fig. 10-4-2.

10.7. Further Comments on Comparative Combiner Statistics

In the subsequent sections of this chapter we shall explore various ramifications of the derived combiner statistics. In some of these cases, as has already been evidenced above in analyzing output SNR statistics, analyses can be more conveniently accomplished for certain combiner types than for others. However, as shown most usefully for these purposes in Fig.

10-5-2 for the common case when all the Γ_k are equal, the output SNR p.d.f.'s are closely related. Specifically, the p.d.f.'s are all very closely parallel. Furthermore, this parallelism was shown to extend to the case when the Γ_k are unequal, especially at the low SNR end of the distributions. Thus, *any* performance statistic which depends only on the *first-order p.d.f.* of the combiner output, especially if it is strongly dependent on the form of the p.d.f. at low output SNR, can be expected to be identical for all the combiner types to within the ratios determined by the parallelism in decibel differences displayed in Fig. 10-5-2 and given by the two lower curves of Fig. 10-4-2, where diversity gain based on outage rate was the statistic being examined. Thus, one can derive performance statistics analytically by using that combiner form which is most convenient mathematically and then closely estimate the performance using other combiners by adding the effect of these ratios with respect to the statistic being examined. Note we are referring here to other measures of diversity improvement than the outage-rate diversity gain employed up to now.

We shall also examine other statistics (output SNR distribution with correlation in fading among diversity branches; effect of diversity on distributions of lengths of fades) which are, however, dependent on the branch input statistics and not obviously related solely to first-order p.d.f. for the combiner output. In each case, we can conveniently carry out a solution for only one combiner type but shall, however, again argue that the results are highly indicative for *all* combiners.

Finally, while our entire discussion above has assumed pure Rayleigh fading on each branch, it has been noted[1] that the same qualitative relationships will hold when there is also a specular component present in the fading. In this case, recalling (9-2-69), with the SNR defined by

$$\gamma = \frac{v^2}{N}$$

the fading SNR has a p.d.f.

$$p(\gamma) = \frac{1}{\Gamma_R} \exp\left(-\frac{\Gamma_0}{\Gamma_R}\right) \exp\left(-\frac{\gamma}{\Gamma_R}\right) I_0\left(\frac{2\sqrt{\gamma}\sqrt{\Gamma_0}}{\Gamma_R}\right) \quad (10\text{-}7\text{-}1)$$

where Γ_R = ratio of mean-square value of fading component to noise

Γ_0 = ratio of mean-square value of specular component to noise

One can observe that for small γ, specifically such that

$$\gamma \ll \frac{\Gamma_R^2}{4\Gamma_0} \qquad \gamma \ll \Gamma_0 \qquad\qquad (10\text{-}7\text{-}2)$$

$$p(\gamma) \doteq \frac{1}{\Gamma_R} \exp\left(-\frac{\Gamma_0}{\Gamma_R}\right) \qquad (10\text{-}7\text{-}3)$$

This leading term differs from the pure Rayleigh-fading case ($\Gamma_0 = 0$) only in the presence of the exponential factor, involving the ratio of the

[1] Barrow, *loc. cit.*

strength of specular and fading components. Aside from these (constant) factors modifying the effective value of Γ_R for each branch (indeed increasing it), one can infer that such statistics as outage rate (at outage rates of interest) for the various combiner types are basically unchanged by the presence of the specular component. Alternatively, note that for a diversity branch with SNR given by (10-7-1), the Laplace-transform characteristic function is

$$
\begin{aligned}
F(s) &= \int_0^\infty \exp\left(-s\gamma\right) \frac{1}{\Gamma_R} \exp\left(-\frac{\Gamma_0}{\Gamma_R}\right) \exp\left(-\frac{\gamma}{\Gamma_R}\right) I_0\left(\frac{2\sqrt{\Gamma_0 \gamma}}{\Gamma_R}\right) d\gamma \\
&= \frac{1}{1 + s\Gamma_R} \exp\left(-\frac{\Gamma_0}{\Gamma_R}\right) \exp\left(\frac{\Gamma_0}{\Gamma_R} \frac{1}{1 + s\Gamma_0}\right)
\end{aligned}
\tag{10-7-4}
$$

Then, the limiting behavior of $F(s)$ as $s \to \infty$, which we have seen to be crucial in describing diversity performance, is also seen to be essentially as in the pure Rayleigh-fading case ($\Gamma_0 = 0$) except for the additional exponential factor, $\exp\left(-\Gamma_0/\Gamma_R\right)$, which has the effect of increasing the effective value of Γ_R for performance involving small γ.

10-8. Digital Data Performance of Ideal Linear Combining Systems

One important statistic alternative to the outage-rate criterion of diversity performance is the error-rate performance for digital signaling in a fully linear transmission-reception mode (i.e., linear down to detector stages). These error-rate calculations will here be based on the slow, nonselective fading assumptions implicit in our preceding discussions of combiner output statistics. With the assumption of system linearity, this will be simply an extension to different SNR p.d.f.'s of the calculations of Sec. 9-5 for the slow, nonselective single (nondiversity) Rayleigh-fading signal. More general models are discussed in Chap. 11.

The models implied below do not include all digital signaling over fading channels. For example, both at h-f and in some contemplated PCM troposcatter systems, FSK systems may use linear frequency detectors rather than dual-filter, intersymbol-interference-free detection. As shown in Chap. 8, the error-rate result for the frequency detector may only approximate the simple exponential dependence on SNR that we assume below for noncoherent FSK. In addition, in many wideband applications, digital data can be sent in voice channels which in turn are transmitted by FDM-FM techniques, to which the linear reception system model does not apply (however, see also Sec. 10-9).

We shall consider FSK and PSK systems (omitting on-off systems as being primarily of academic interest in the present context). The general forms of the probability of error, conditional on the filtered combiner output SNR associated with each individual pulse decision, are those specified in (9-5-19) and (9-5-20). These are then averaged over the diversity combiner output SNR statistics derived above under the assumption of slow, nonselective independent fading among all branches.

Thus, consider first the conditional error probability

$$P_\gamma^{(1)} = \tfrac{1}{2} \exp\left(-\alpha\gamma\right) \begin{cases} \alpha = \tfrac{1}{2} & \text{noncoherent FSK} \\ \alpha = 1 & \text{differentially coherent PSK} \end{cases} \quad (10\text{-}8\text{-}1)$$

With the combiner output SNR p.d.f. given by $p(\gamma)$, $\gamma > 0$, the averaged probability of error is

$$P^{(1)} = \tfrac{1}{2} \int_0^\infty \exp\left(-\alpha\gamma\right) p(\gamma)\, d\gamma \quad (10\text{-}8\text{-}2)$$

For selector combining, one can use $p(\gamma)$ directly from (10-4-10). For maximal-ratio combining, (10-8-2) can be identified as a particular value of the Laplace-transform characteristic function for the combiner output, as given by (10-5-16) to (10-5-18). For equal-gain combining, we have in Sec. 10-6 neither a convenient formula for $p(\gamma)$ valid over the full range of γ nor a convenient representation for its characteristic function. Thus evaluation is facile for the first two combiners mentioned, with only qualitative implications drawn for the equal-gain system. However, the evaluation is only truly convenient for the maximal-ratio combiner, and most of our detailed results will be for this case.

Considering maximal-ratio combining, direct comparison of (10-8-2) with (10-5-16) and (10-5-18) gives the average error rate,

$$P_{\text{m.r.}}^{(1)} = \frac{1}{2} \prod_{k=1}^{M} \left(\frac{1}{1 + \alpha\Gamma_k}\right) \quad (10\text{-}8\text{-}3)$$

With the several Γ_k sufficiently greater than unity, and $\alpha = \tfrac{1}{2}$ or 1 as in (10-8-1), one has to excellent approximation at error rates of practical interest,

$$P_{\text{m.r.}}^{(1)} \approx \frac{1}{2} \frac{1}{\alpha^M} \frac{1}{\displaystyle\prod_{k=1}^{M} \Gamma_k} \quad (10\text{-}8\text{-}4)$$

Note for comparison that if one used the approximate p.d.f. of (10-5-29), valid for low γ but assumed for the moment to be essentially valid for all γ, (10-8-2) becomes

$$P_{\text{m.r.}}^{(1)} = \frac{1}{2} \int_0^\infty \exp\left(-\alpha\gamma\right) \frac{1}{(M-1)!} \frac{\gamma^{M-1}}{\displaystyle\prod_{k=1}^{M} \Gamma_k}\, d\gamma = \frac{1}{2} \frac{1}{\alpha^M} \frac{1}{\displaystyle\prod_{k=1}^{M} \Gamma_k} \quad (10\text{-}8\text{-}5)$$

which is exactly the same result as (10-8-4). The obvious interpretation is that the error rate depends (in this slow-fading case) only upon the probability distribution of output SNR at low γ. *From this observation*, one can immediately expect the comparative performance among the several combiners to be exactly the same as in comparing outage-rate diversity gain.   Furthermore, one can expect that the *comparative* results should also not be importantly changed when one goes over to the error-function form of error probability, characterizing coherent detection systems.   Note it is only the comparative results which are unchanged. Actual diversity gain depends on the error-rate objective, much as it depends on the specific outage rate when the latter is a criterion.

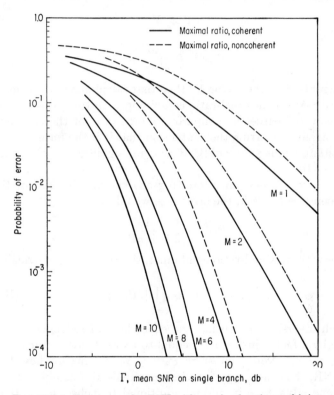

Fig. 10-8-1. Error rates for FSK with maximal-ratio combining.

The result (10-8-5) is shown in the dashed curves of Fig. 10-8-1[1] for various M in the case when all the $\Gamma_k = \Gamma$.   In line with earlier remarks, the curves apply also to the case of unequal Γ_k, when Γ is regarded as their geometric mean.

On can also evaluate $P^{(1)}$ in the selection-combiner case, using (10-4-10) in (10-8-2).   The integrals can be evaluated by successive evaluation by parts, leading in the general case to a lengthy algebraic expression, which

[1] The curves of Fig. 10-8-1 are taken from B. B. Barrow, Error Probabilities for Data Transmission Over Fading Radio Paths, Doctoral Thesis, Delft, 1962, Figs. 3-2 and 3-4.

again can be reduced to simpler form at low error rates. In the case when all the Γ_k are equal to some value Γ, the error rate has the form

$$P_{\text{sel}}^{(1)} = \frac{1}{2} \frac{M!}{\displaystyle\prod_{k=1}^{M} (k + \alpha\Gamma)} \tag{10-8-6}$$

The assumption that interest lies in low error rates, so that

$$\alpha\Gamma \gg M \tag{10-8-7}$$

implies that

$$P_{\text{sel}}^{(1)} \doteq \frac{M!}{2(\alpha\Gamma)^M} \tag{10-8-8}$$

This is larger by just the factor $M!$ than that calculated in the comparable case in (10-8-5) for maximal-ratio combining. In turn, this is the same factor discovered earlier in comparing outage rate for the two combiner methods, again supporting the contention that it is the form of the p.d.f. at low instantaneous values of SNR which is significant in the usual performance statistics.

Returning to (10-8-3) an interesting observation[1] is that for the kth branch operating *by itself*, the error rate would be

$$P_k^{(1)} = \frac{1}{2} \frac{1}{1 + \alpha\Gamma_k} \tag{10-8-9}$$

and hence with maximal-ratio combining, the resultant *error rate* is

$$P_{\text{m.r.}}^{(1)} = \tfrac{1}{2} \prod_{k=1}^{M} [2P_k^{(1)}] \tag{10-8-10}$$

Thus, each diversity branch has the effect here of reducing the overall error-rate by a factor just exactly equal to twice its own error rate when operating alone. Note that since $P_k^{(1)} \leq \frac{1}{2}$, no matter how low the branch SNR, it is clear that for *ideal* maximal-ratio combining there is always some advantage in adding additional branches, no matter how weak they are. For selection combining, the approximate equivalent result is

$$P_{\text{sel}}^{(1)} = \frac{M!}{2} \prod_{k=1}^{M} [2P_k^{(1)}] \tag{10-8-11}$$

This suggests that with *ideal* selection, the weakest branch is effective in reducing error rate by its presence only if for this branch

$$2P_k^{(1)} < \frac{1}{M} \tag{10-8-12}$$

---

[1] B. B. Barrow, Error Probabilities for Telegraph Signals Transmitted on a Fading FM Carrier, *Proc. IRE*, vol. 48, pp. 1613–1629, September, 1960.

However, (10-8-11) is a valid approximation only under the assumption (10-8-7), which is equivalent in this approximation to (10-8-12). Hence (10-8-11) provides no simple basis for any statements as to the effectiveness of additional branches. Physically, addition of another branch in ideal selection should never deteriorate the system.

The results (10-8-4) and (10-8-6) obviously can be used to calculate diversity gains as a function of required error rate. However, they also can be directly applied in any system calculation; hence we omit curves of "error-rate diversity gain." The formulas (10-8-10) and (10-8-11) can also be very useful, because of their simplicity, in rapidly estimating the effects of additional diversity on error rate during design computations.

Finally, from comparing (10-6-11) with (10-5-29), one can predict for equal-gain combining the result at low error rates,

$$P_{e.g.}^{(1)} = \frac{(M/2)^M \sqrt{\pi}}{2(M - \frac{1}{2})!} \prod_{k=1}^{M} [2P_k^{(1)}] \tag{10-8-13}$$

Again the approximation under which this holds is such that one cannot directly deduce from it judgments about the effectiveness of a particular weak branch. (The reader is, however, reminded of the discussion in Sec. 10-6.) Neither (10-8-11) nor (10-8-13) are shown on Fig. 10-8-1, since they represent approximations, at error rates of practical interest, which would represent only a shift in SNR from that shown for maximal-ratio combining.

Next, we turn to coherent-detection systems, with the conditional error probability given by (9-5-20),

$$P_\gamma^{(2)} = \frac{1}{2} \operatorname{erfc} \sqrt{\alpha\gamma} \qquad \begin{cases} \alpha = \frac{1}{2} & \text{coherent FSK} \\ \alpha = 1 & \text{ideal coherent PSK} \end{cases} \tag{10-8-14}$$

and the averaged probability of error,

$$P^{(2)} = \frac{1}{2} \int_0^\infty \operatorname{erfc} \sqrt{\alpha\gamma}\, p(\gamma)\, d\gamma \tag{10-8-15}$$

In the diversity context, the requirement for a coherent phase reference for coherent detection implies sufficient information about, or control of, the phases in the several branches that phase-locked addition can be done. This is available with either maximal-ratio or equal-gain combining in slow fading. However, selector combining does not appear meaningful in such a coherent-detection context.

No convenient closed-form solution of (10-8-15) appears available. For maximal-ratio combining with all branches equal in strength, one can develop a series solution of which the leading term represents the behavior at low error rates. The result obtained is the same as when one uses directly the approximate p.d.f. of (10-5-29), valid for low SNR. The latter evaluation is simpler and is the one presented here. With

(10-5-29) in (10-8-15),

$$P_{\text{m.r.}}^{(2)} = \frac{1}{2(M-1)!} \int_0^\infty \text{erfc} \sqrt{\alpha\gamma} \; \frac{\gamma^{M-1}}{\Gamma^M} \, d\gamma \qquad (10\text{-}8\text{-}16)$$

The substitution $y = \alpha\gamma$ and integration by parts then yields a recognizable integral,

$$P_{\text{m.r.}}^{(2)} = \frac{1}{2\sqrt{\pi}} \frac{1}{(\alpha\Gamma)^M} \frac{1}{M!} \int_0^\infty y^{M-\frac{1}{2}} \exp(-y) \, dy$$

$$= \frac{1}{2\sqrt{\pi}} \frac{1}{(\alpha\Gamma)^M} \frac{(M-\frac{1}{2})!}{M!} \qquad (10\text{-}8\text{-}17)$$

Again, if the branch mean SNR's are unequal, it will be the geometric mean of their SNR's in the formula above which will describe performance.

An exact computation of the error rate for coherent detection, using the p.d.f. of (10-5-20), yields the solid curves of Fig. 10-8-1[1] for coherent FSK ($\alpha = \frac{1}{2}$). For ideal coherent PSK ($\alpha = 1$), the same curves would be obtained at 3 db lower mean SNR. The asymptotic behavior of (10-8-17) is evident in these curves at error rates below about 10^{-2} to 10^{-3}.

One can also compare the result in (10-8-17) with that in (10-8-4), to determine analytically for a given type of combining (in this case, maximal-ratio) the relative merits of various forms of coherent and noncoherent reception as shown in Fig. 10-8-1. From (10-8-4), within the assumptions concerning slow multiplicative fading, differential phase-shift keying ($\alpha = 1$) achieves any given error rate at exactly 3 db less SNR than noncoherent FSK ($\alpha = \frac{1}{2}$), at all mean SNR's. Likewise in (10-8-17), ideal coherent PSK ($\alpha = 1$) requires exactly 3 db less SNR than ideal coherent FSK ($\alpha = \frac{1}{2}$). Finally, comparing DPSK with ideal PSK, i.e. the cases $\alpha = 1$ in (10-8-4) and (10-8-17) respectively, the latter requires a smaller SNR on each branch (or in the geometric mean), the relative factor being

$$\Delta = \left[\frac{M!(-\frac{1}{2})!}{(M-\frac{1}{2})!} \right]^{\frac{1}{M}} \qquad (10\text{-}8\text{-}18)$$

For large M, this can be approximated by Stirling's formula, to show that $\Delta \approx 1$. For smaller values, with Δ expressed in decibels we have the table[2]

M	Δ, db
1	3.0
2	2.1
3	1.7
4	1.4
8	0.9

[1] From Barrow, Error Probabilities for Data Transmission Over Fading Radio Paths, *op. cit.*

[2] Barrow, *op. cit.*, p. 43, Table III.

Thus at low error rates, DPSK is about 1 db poorer than ideal PSK in a nonfading environment (Chap. 8), about 3 db poorer in Rayleigh fading, and again only slightly over 1 db poorer for quadruple or higher-order diversity.

An interesting extension can also be obtained to the result in Sec. 9-5 on the values of instantaneous SNRs at which errors tend to occur. Conveniently, this will be specifically answered for maximal-ratio combining in systems with the noncoherent detection conditional-error probability, (10-8-1), and with all branches of equal mean SNR. Thus, in analogy to (9-5-30), we write instead of the probability of error (10-8-2), the probability of error conditional on the combiner output SNR being less than some value γ_1,

$$N^{(1)}(\gamma_1) = \frac{1}{2} \int_0^{\gamma_1} \exp\,(-\alpha\gamma)p(\gamma)\,d\gamma \qquad (10\text{-}8\text{-}19)$$

This can be evaluated by using the p.d.f. of (10-5-20) for M-fold maximal-ratio combining output,

$$\begin{aligned}
N^{(1)}(\gamma_1) &= \frac{1}{2(M-1)!} \int_0^{\gamma_1} \frac{\gamma^{M-1}}{\Gamma^M} \exp\left[-\left(\alpha\gamma + \frac{\gamma}{\Gamma}\right)\right] d\gamma \\
&= \frac{1}{2(M-1)!} \frac{1}{(1+\alpha\Gamma)^M} \int_0^{\gamma_1\left(\alpha+\frac{1}{\Gamma}\right)} x^{M-1} \exp\,(-x)\,dx
\end{aligned}$$

$$\qquad (10\text{-}8\text{-}20)$$

This computation is basically identical with that for the cumulative distribution for the output SNR in maximal-ratio combining. The exact result is directly expressible in terms of the incomplete gamma function. This result is shown plotted for the case $\alpha = \frac{1}{2}$ (noncoherent FSK) in Fig. 10-8-2,[1] for $M = 1, 2,$ and 4. Again, for large Γ, as is also evident from (10-8-20), the location of errors is *very little dependent on* Γ. It does vary more strongly with M. The case $M = 1$ is of course the result discussed earlier in (9-5-30). Figure 10-8-2 shows clearly the effect of diversity in "decreasing the occupancy of low SNR's" in the combiner output. The result is a shift towards relatively higher values of the SNRs at which the significant portion of the errors occur.

As an interesting addition, the figures across the top in Fig. 10-8-2 represent the conditional probability of an error, $\frac{1}{2}\exp\,(-\frac{1}{2}\gamma_1)$ for any given output SNR (plotted in one-to-one relation with the bottom axis on the premise that $1/\Gamma \ll \frac{1}{2}$). Thus another important interpretation of these curves[2] is that the use of diversity tends to *significantly reduce* the clustering of errors. For example, with no diversity 80 per cent of the binary errors occur at levels where the probability of error in any particular element is greater than 10 per cent, while with quadruple

[1] Barrow, *op. cit.*, Fig. 3-3.
[2] Barrow, *loc. cit.*

diversity only 10 per cent of the errors occur at such levels.   This may be of significance in estimating the effectiveness of using coding techniques in slow fading over these channels.

Data similar to that in Fig. 10-8-2, but for the case of coherent detection and expressed in terms of the density of error occurrences, have been presented in the literature.[1]   The conclusions are essentially the same as in the noncoherent case.

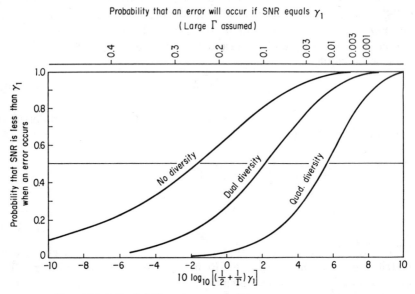

FIG. 10-8-2. Probability of error conditional on range of SNR.

10-9. Postdetection versus Predetection Combining in FM Systems; Digital Data Transmission in FDM-FM

For frequency division multiplex-FM (FDM-FM) systems, it was earlier pointed out that the first detection (from FM to multiplexed baseband) involves the nonlinear process of frequency detection for which output SNR is not generally a linear function of input SNR.   However, FDM-FM systems are common in tropospheric-scatter networks designed for over-horizon telephone trunking, so that there has been substantial interest in understanding the effects of fading and of antifade techniques such as diversity on the performance of such systems.   We will confine attention here, again, to short-term Rayleigh fading.

As mentioned earlier, in "conventional" tropospheric-scatter design, an adequate median level for short-term fading is usually defined in terms

[1] H. B. Law, The Detectability of Fading Radiotelegraph Signals in Noise, *Proc. IEE*, vol. 104, part B, pp. 130–140, March, 1957.

of a specified outage rate, i.e. that median which maintains the SNR above threshold for some percentage of time. For FDM-FM systems, the threshold is usually chosen as the "FM threshold," the "breakpoint" in the detector characteristic. In diversity, the outage rate and required median are based on diversity statistics. Thus, for predetection combining, one considers the outage rate at that i-f SNR (*combiner output*) which corresponds to the detection threshold. This is just the outage rate considered in the diversity calculations in the previous sections.

The possibility of postdetection combining was also mentioned. For FDM-FM, this implies frequency demodulation in each diversity branch *followed* by diversity combiner action. This was prominent in early troposcatter systems, but has tended to be superseded by predetection linear combiners such as the equal-gain combiner. Nevertheless, postdetection combining is still of some interest. It is clear that in selection combining, which instantaneously uses the best branch, the same choice will be made in either pre- or postdetection combining. Thus, for selection combining there is also no change from the previous outage-rate statistics. However, it will be recalled that on an outage-rate basis, the advantage of maximal-ratio combining over selection lies with those events in which each individual branch SNR is below threshold, but the sum of the SNR's is above. For postdetection maximal-ratio combining, with outage rate being calculated at the FM threshold, these additional events refer to situations in which each branch is below threshold, and an optimized (maximal-ratio weighting) sum is taken on the *postdetection* signals. Because of the nonlinear relation of output SNR to input SNR for FM demodulation below threshold, however, it is clear that postdetection maximal-ratio combining will have substantially less advantage over selection combining than in the predetection case. Below threshold, it is reasonable[1] to assume a square-law input-output relation in SNR for frequency demodulation. On this basis, for example, it can be shown[2] that for dual diversity, ideal postdetection maximal-ratio combining has only 0.5 db advantage over selection combining, compared with 2 db in the predetection case.

Of substantial additional interest is the error-rate performance of these FDM-FM systems for digital data transmitted within a voice channel of such a system. It is readily shown that when the FM threshold is chosen on the basis of voice requirements, digital errors are almost exclusively confined to the *below-threshold* region. Thus, to perform

---

[1] B. B. Barrow, Error Probabilities for Telegraph Signals Transmitted on a Fading FM Carrier, *Proc. IRE*, vol. 48, pp. 1613–1629, September, 1960; D. E. Johansen, Binary Error Rates in Fading FDM-FM Communications, *IRE Trans. Commun. Systems*, vol. CS-9, pp. 206–214, September, 1961.

[2] Stein, Clarification of Diversity Statistics in Scatter Propagation, *op. cit.*, p. 288–292.

error-rate calculations for an FDM-FM system employing some diversity combining technique, one can assume the below-threshold square-law characteristic to hold over the *entire* domain of SNR's. On this basis, extensive calculations have been carried out[1] for predetection combiners. The p.d.f.'s derived for combiner output SNR are transformed (through the one-to-one square law relation) into p.d.f.'s for voice-channel SNR, and one then averages the conditional error probability for each digital technique over the latter distribution.[2] Because the only significant portion of the p.d.f. for the combiner output SNR is that relating to low input SNR, the *relative* performance of the several combining techniques is essentially the same as noted in our earlier discussion. Since further details of the results as applied to design involve FDM-FM design characteristics, which are not our purpose here, the interested reader is referred to the cited references. One important caveat, mentioned earlier, is that all these results are premised on nonselective fading, whereas there apparently exist experimental data indicating errors to be produced by severe FM intermodulation-distortion effects, due to selectivity in the fading at low levels, at SNR's significantly higher than would be indicated by the analyses of nonselective-fading models.[3]

10-10. Effect of Correlation in Fading among Diversity Branches

All our discussion to this point has been premised on the assumption of independence between the fading on the several diversity branches. It is clear that there will be many cases in which this cannot be achieved because of insufficient antenna spacing (due to siting limitation in spaced antenna diversity), insufficient frequency spacing (because of frequency allocation or equipment design difficulties in frequency diversity), beam overlap (in angle diversity), inadequate delay (storage or delay limitations in time diversity), etc. The ensuing practical question is, to what extent is independence or decorrelation required in the fading among the several branches in order that the diversity is still effective?

Returning to an intuitive perspective for a moment, the effectiveness of diversity is based upon the *independent occurrence of deep fades* in all the diversity branches. But for the kinds of outage rates (or error rates) of practical interest, the thresholds which define these outages, or "deep fades," are usually low compared with median level (at least for low orders of diversity), and thus the deep fades represent

---

[1] Barrow, *op. cit.;* Johansen, *op. cit.*

[2] In a multiplex situation each voice channel, or telegraph sub-channel, represents a narrow-band filtering of the discriminator output. Hence the assumption in these analyses is that, while the discriminator output is non-Gaussian, it is reasonable to regard the individual channel noises as Gaussian, per the Central Limit Theorem.

[3] Johansen, *op. cit.*

relatively *rare* probabilistic events. Since it can be anticipated that even relatively high correlations need not imply anywhere near as much correspondence in the occurrence of these *rare* events, one can expect that a large portion of the diversity effectiveness will be retained even when significant correlations exist! This is indeed the result which will be shown quantitatively below.

Two useful results are available regarding the effects of correlation upon diversity. One of these, historically the first model analyzed in detail on this problem, deals with dual (two-fold) diversity and *selection* combining. It does not appear easily possible, however, to extend this analysis to higher-order selection combining. The second is a more general result for maximal-ratio combining, with arbitrary orders of diversity. Again, all results below are still premised on slow, multiplicative Rayleigh fading.

Dual-diversity Selection Combining. The dual-diversity selection combining result is presented first. The correlated multiplicative complex Gaussian processes on the two branches are assumed to be jointly Gaussian, with complex cross-covariance ρ. Note that the normalized *envelope* covariance between branches is very closely given by $|\rho|^2$ (see Table 10-10-1 at the end of this section). We may also assume the two branches to be unequal in strength. Recalling the definitions of mean SNR in (10-4-6), one can conveniently normalize the envelopes in the two branches to the rms noise levels N_k by dividing by the factor $\sqrt{2N_k}$. These normalized envelopes are denoted by R_1 and R_2. Thus, with Γ_1 and Γ_2 representing the respective mean SNR's for the two branches ($\Gamma_k = \langle R_k^2 \rangle$), the joint p.d.f. of R_1 and R_2 at any instant is just[1]

$$p(R_1,R_2) = \frac{4R_1R_2}{\Gamma_1\Gamma_2(1 - |\rho|^2)} I_0 \left[\frac{2|\rho|R_1R_2}{(1 - |\rho|^2)\sqrt{\Gamma_1\Gamma_2}} \right]$$
$$\exp\left[-\frac{1}{1 - |\rho|^2}\left(\frac{R_1^2}{\Gamma_1} + \frac{R_2^2}{\Gamma_2}\right)\right] \quad (10\text{-}10\text{-}1)$$

According to the selection combining rule, then, the probability that the instantaneous combiner output SNR γ is below some value x is just

$$\text{Prob } (\gamma < x) = \text{Prob } (R_1 < \sqrt{x}, R_2 < \sqrt{x})$$
$$= 1 - \text{Prob } (R_1 > \sqrt{x}) - \text{Prob } (R_2 > \sqrt{x})$$
$$+ \text{Prob } (R_1 > \sqrt{x}, R_2 > \sqrt{x}) \quad (10\text{-}10\text{-}2)$$

The first two probabilities here are the simple distributions for Rayleigh fading. The third probability requires determination of an integral evaluated in Appendix A. With the latter result adapted to the nota-

[1] W. B. Davenport and W. L. Root, "Introduction to Random Signals and Noise," p. 163, McGraw-Hill Book Company, New York, 1958.

tion above, the result is written in either of the two equivalent forms,

$$\text{Prob } (\gamma < x) = 1 - \exp\left(-\frac{x}{\Gamma_1}\right) Q\left(\sqrt{\frac{2x}{\Gamma_2(1 - |\rho|^2)}},\, |\rho|\sqrt{\frac{2x}{\Gamma_1(1 - |\rho|^2)}}\right)$$

$$- \exp\left(-\frac{x}{\Gamma_2}\right)\left[1 - Q\left(|\rho|\sqrt{\frac{2x}{\Gamma_2(1 - |\rho|^2)}},\right.\right.$$

$$\left.\left.\sqrt{\frac{2x}{\Gamma_1(1 - |\rho|^2)}}\right)\right] \quad (10\text{-}10\text{-}3)$$

$$= 1 - \exp\left(-\frac{x}{\Gamma_1}\right) Q\left(\sqrt{\frac{2x}{\Gamma_2(1 - |\rho|^2)}},\, |\rho|\sqrt{\frac{2x}{\Gamma_1(1 - |\rho|^2)}}\right)$$

$$- \exp\left(-\frac{x}{\Gamma_2}\right) Q\left(\sqrt{\frac{2x}{\Gamma_1(1 - |\rho|^2)}},\, |\rho|\sqrt{\frac{2x}{\Gamma_2(1 - |\rho|^2)}}\right)$$

$$+ \exp\left[-\frac{x}{1 - |\rho|^2}\left(\frac{1}{\Gamma_1} + \frac{1}{\Gamma_2}\right)\right] I_0\left[\frac{2|\rho|x}{(1 - |\rho|^2)\sqrt{\Gamma_1\Gamma_2}}\right]$$

$$(10\text{-}10\text{-}4)$$

It is readily verified that in the case $|\rho| = 0$ (independent fading), (10-10-3) or (10-10-4) reduce to the previously derived result, for $M = 2$ in (10-4-9). At the other extreme, one can regard the case of perfect correlation in the fluctuations, $|\rho| = 1$. The two branches may still be unequal in mean SNR, in which case with perfect correlation one would expect the receiver to always choose the branch with larger mean SNR. Without loss of generality, we assume $\Gamma_1 \geq \Gamma_2$. The Q-function arguments in (10-10-3) or (10-10-4) both approach infinity but with finite ratio and with differences given by

$$\left.\begin{array}{l} \sqrt{\dfrac{2x}{\Gamma_2(1 - |\rho|^2)}} - |\rho|\sqrt{\dfrac{2x}{\Gamma_1(1 - |\rho|^2)}} \\[2ex] |\rho|\sqrt{\dfrac{2x}{\Gamma_2(1 - |\rho|^2)}} - \sqrt{\dfrac{2x}{\Gamma_1(1 - |\rho|^2)}} \end{array}\right\}$$

$$= \sqrt{\frac{2x}{1 - |\rho|^2}}\left(\frac{1}{\sqrt{\Gamma_2}} - \frac{1}{\sqrt{\Gamma_1}}\right) \to +\infty \quad (10\text{-}10\text{-}5)$$

One can now apply the asymptotic formulas of Appendix A to this limiting case in (10-10-3). Recalling that $\frac{1}{2}$ erfc $(-\infty) = 1$, one then obtains the expected result,

$$\lim_{|\rho|\to 1} \text{Prob } (\gamma < x) = 1 - \exp\left(-\frac{x}{\Gamma_1}\right) \quad (10\text{-}10\text{-}6)$$

In the special case $\Gamma_1 = \Gamma_2 = \Gamma$, (10-10-3) and (10-10-4) become

$$\text{Prob } (\gamma < x) = 1 - \exp\left(-\frac{x}{\Gamma}\right)\left[1 - Q\left(|\rho|\sqrt{\frac{2x}{\Gamma(1 - |\rho|^2)}},\, \sqrt{\frac{2x}{\Gamma(1 - |\rho|^2)}}\right)\right.$$

$$\left.+ Q\left(\sqrt{\frac{2x}{\Gamma(1 - |\rho|^2)}},\, |\rho|\sqrt{\frac{2x}{\Gamma(1 - |\rho|^2)}}\right)\right] \quad (10\text{-}10\text{-}7)$$

$$= 1 - 2 \exp\left(-\frac{x}{\Gamma}\right) Q\left(\sqrt{\frac{2x}{\Gamma(1 - |\rho|^2)}}, |\rho|\sqrt{\frac{2x}{\Gamma(1 - |\rho|^2)}}\right)$$

$$+ \exp\left[-\frac{2x}{\Gamma(1 - |\rho|^2)}\right] I_0\left[\frac{2|\rho|x}{\Gamma(1 - |\rho|^2)}\right] \quad (10\text{-}10\text{-}8)$$

The result (10-10-8) for equal strength branches is essentially that derived by Staras[1] in apparently the first detailed analysis of the effects of correlation upon diversity.   Staras derived his result for dual diversity with selection combining in the form of a functional series, with computations from this series presented in the form of appropriate curves.   Such curves, for the case of equal mean SNR's in the two branches, are shown in Fig. 10-10-1a, in a form more analogous to our earlier results.[2]   Note the graph uses $|\rho|$, the magnitude of the complex cross-covariance, rather than $|\rho|^2$, which is very nearly the envelope cross-covariance (see Table 10-10-1) and has been variously employed in presenting similar results in the literature.   Moreover, the more general result in (10-10-3) and (10-10-4) can be used to demonstrate the effect of correlation on operation with unequal branch levels, as shown in Figs. 10-10-1b and c for $\Gamma_1/\Gamma_2 = 2$ and 10, respectively.   In Fig. 10-10-1a, when $\Gamma_1 = \Gamma_2$, it is clear that dual-diversity *action* holds even for $|\rho| = 0.95$ (i.e., the slope at low SNR is parallel to the $|\rho| = 0$ curve) but that there is a decreasing *diversity gain* as $|\rho|$ increases.   Comparing $|\rho| = 0.95$ to the no-diversity case ($|\rho| = 1$), there is still a diversity gain of 5.6 db at the 1 per cent outage-rate point.   At all outage rates below 1 per cent, with $|\rho| = 0.95$, the diversity gain is 4.6 db less than with uncorrelated fading ($|\rho| = 0$).   For example, recalling Fig. 10-4-2, at 0.1 per cent outage rate there is still a diversity gain with $|\rho| = 0.95$ ($|\rho|^2 = 0.9$) of slightly over 10 db!   In Figs. 10-10-1b and c, the imbalance in diversity branch strengths leads to lower overall diversity gain.   For example, recall that for $\Gamma_1 = 2\Gamma_2$, the effective equivalent equal-branch dual-diversity system has levels of $\sqrt{\Gamma_1\Gamma_2} = \Gamma_1/\sqrt{2}$, hence 1.5 db less than the no-diversity stronger branch; this is the $|\rho| = 1$ curve in Fig. 10-10-1b.   However, in b, again dual-diversity action appears to hold for $|\rho|$ as high as 0.95, with the loss in effective dual-diversity gain (compared to $|\rho| = 0$ for the same Γ_1,Γ_2) again 4.6 db.   In c, with $\Gamma_1 = 10\Gamma_2$, the potential diversity gain is now reduced by 5 db; the effective dual-diversity action at low outage rates seems to hold for $|\rho|$ as high as 0.8 to 0.9.   For $|\rho| = 0.95$ again, the loss in diversity gain at the 1 per cent point is about 4 db, but because of the lower overall potential diversity gain with $\Gamma_1 = 10\Gamma_2$, it appears that useful diversity gain requires $|\rho|$ below about 0.8.

Most of the effects noted above can be illustrated analytically by study-

[1] H. Staras, Diversity Reception with Correlated Signals, *J. Appl. Phys.*, vol. 27, pp. 93–94, January, 1956.

[2] A similar presentation is given in Brennan, *op. cit.*, p. 1091.

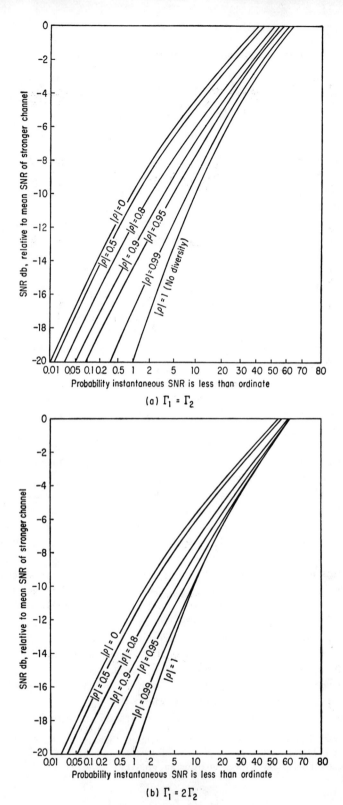

(a) $\Gamma_1 = \Gamma_2$

(b) $\Gamma_1 = 2\Gamma_2$

Fig. 10-10-1. See opposite page.

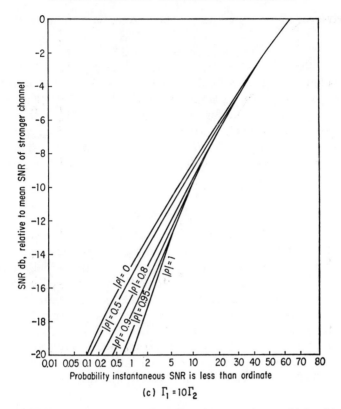

FIG. 10-10-1. Effect of correlation on dual diversity, selection combining (a) $\Gamma_1 = \Gamma_2$. (b) $\Gamma_1 = 2\Gamma_2$.   (c) $\Gamma_1 = 10\Gamma_2$.

ing the limiting behavior of (10-10-3) and (10-10-4) at low outage rates, and under the assumption $x \ll (\Gamma_1, \Gamma_2)$.   To this end, we note an expansion for the Q function when both its arguments are small.   Using its basic definition (Appendix A)

$$Q(a,b) = \int_b^{\infty} \exp\left(-\frac{a^2 + x^2}{2}\right) I_0(ax)x\, dx$$

$$= 1 - \int_0^b \exp\left(-\frac{a^2 + x^2}{2}\right) I_0(ax)x\, dx \quad (10\text{-}10\text{-}9)$$

and expanding $I_0(ax)$ and the exponential for the case in which $(a,b) \ll 1$, one obtains for the leading terms to order a^4, b^4, a^2b^2,

$$Q(a,b) = 1 - \frac{b^2}{2} + \frac{a^2b^2}{4} + \frac{b^4}{8} + \text{higher-order terms} \quad (10\text{-}10\text{-}10)$$

Thus, in (10-10-4), for x small and $1 - |\rho|^2$ reasonably nonzero ($|\rho|$ not extremely near unity), one finds as the leading term to order x^2,

$$\text{Prob } (\gamma < x) = x^2 \left[\frac{1}{\Gamma_1 \Gamma_2} \frac{1}{(1 - |\rho|^2)} \right] \tag{10-10-11}$$

Thus, for low outage rates (and therefore, as we have seen, also for low error rates with digital data transmission), and provided the covariances are not too near unity, the diversity action is very similar to the action in the absence of correlation, with a slight loss in diversity gain. This was already quite evident in the curves of Fig. 10-10-1. The specific requirement apparent from (10-10-3) or (10-10-4) is that interest lie in values of x such that

$$x \ll \begin{cases} \Gamma_1(1 - |\rho|^2) \\ \Gamma_2(1 - |\rho|^2) \end{cases} \tag{10-10-12}$$

When the levels of interest are not consistent with this relation, either because the actual level of interest is too high, or because $|\rho|$ is too near unity for (10-10-12) to hold, one can expect (as in the earlier discussions concerning unequal branch levels) the effective order of diversity to decrease. From (10-10-12), it is apparent that $|\rho|$ must *exceed* 0.95 before $1 - |\rho|^2 = 0.1$, that is, before there is an order-of-magnitude level change in the criteria on x for dual-diversity action.

It is also clear from (10-10-11) that for correlations not too near unity, it is sensible from a dual-diversity viewpoint to speak of *correlation as reducing the effective mean branch SNRs* by the relation

$$(\Gamma_k)_{\text{eff}} = \Gamma_k \sqrt{1 - |\rho|^2} \tag{10-10-13}$$

It is clear that these are exactly the factors appearing in Fig. 10-10-1. It is interesting to note that $|\rho|$ must exceed 0.85 before the loss in diversity gain reaches 3 db, whereas the basic diversity gain available from dual diversity (Fig. 10-4-2) is of course of the order of 10 to 20 db.

The simple form of the result in (10-10-11) suggests that an analysis of higher-order diversity with selection combining would also indicate some similar simple form. It seems likely that computations can be efficiently carried out if one starts out with formulas analogous to (10-10-2) as the basic formula, immediately making the specialization to interest at relatively small values of x. The specific difficulty lies in the fact that one cannot set down a simple closed formula like (10-10-1) for the joint distribution of envelopes of mutually correlated Gaussian processes when the number of envelopes is greater than two (except for the "Markov" case, when the correlations are exponential, but the resulting closed forms are still awkward for any further general analysis). While this seems unlikely to prevent making the special limiting calculation, it completely discourages any more general analysis for selection combining. Instead, we turn to an examination of the effects of correlation upon maximal-ratio combining, where a more general result for arbitrary orders of diversity can be conveniently obtained.

Maximal-ratio Combining. We consider predetection maximal-ratio combining. Results for this case were first derived for dual diversity only,[1] and were shown to be similar to the result cited earlier for dual selection combining of correlated fading signals. Subsequently, a general analysis was given for arbitrary orders of diversity.[2] In turn, the latter is a special case of a more general problem of substantial analytical interest, the distribution of a Hermitian quadratic form in jointly distributed complex Gaussian variates.

We return to the definition (10-4-5) and the result (10-5-13) for the instantaneous SNR due to predetection maximal-ratio combining in slow multiplicative fading. It is convenient to redefine the complex multiplicative process on each branch normalized to rms noise,

$$z_k = \frac{g_k}{\sqrt{N_k}} \qquad (10\text{-}10\text{-}14)$$

with the instantaneous branch SNR then given by

$$\gamma_k = \tfrac{1}{2}|z_k|^2 \qquad (10\text{-}10\text{-}15)$$

The assumption now is that for M-fold diversity, the $\{z_k\}$ are M jointly distributed Gaussian variates.

With (10-5-13), the instantaneous SNR at the maximal-ratio combiner output is

$$\gamma = \sum_{k=1}^{M} \gamma_k = \tfrac{1}{2} \sum_{k=1}^{M} |z_k|^2 = \tfrac{1}{2}\, \mathbf{z}^{T*}\mathbf{z} \qquad (10\text{-}10\text{-}16)$$

where we have introduced the column matrix $\mathbf{z}$, with elements z_k (see Appendix B). For our assumption of multiplicative, zero-mean (nonspecular component) Rayleigh fading, the $\{z_k\}$ comprise over the short-term fading a joint, zero-mean complex Gaussian process. The variate γ as defined by (10-10-16) is then a special case of a Hermitian quadratic form in complex Gaussian variates, treated in Appendix B. For our results here, we have the special case where the matrix of the quadratic form $\mathbf{F}$ is simply half the identity matrix,

$$\mathbf{F} = \tfrac{1}{2}\mathbf{I} \qquad (10\text{-}10\text{-}17)$$

and where we are assuming zero-mean processes

$$\langle \mathbf{z} \rangle = 0 \qquad (10\text{-}10\text{-}18)$$

[1] K. S. Packard, Effect of Correlation on Combiner Diversity, *Proc. IRE*, vol. 46, pp. 362–363, January, 1958. Similar results, in a radar context, were earlier given in M. Schwartz, Effects of Signal Fluctuation on the Detection of Pulse Signals in Noise, *IRE Trans. Inform. Theory*, vol. IT-2, pp. 66–71, June, 1956.

[2] J. N. Pierce and S. Stein, Multiple Diversity with Non-Independent Fading, *Proc. IRE*, vol. 48, pp. 89–104, January, 1960.

We also have a variate γ which is positive real, so that in describing its p.d.f. by a characteristic function below, it is convenient to use a Laplace-transform definition,

$$G_\gamma(s) = \int_0^\infty \exp{(-s\gamma)}p(\gamma)\,d\gamma = \langle\exp{(-s\gamma)}\rangle \quad (10\text{-}10\text{-}19)$$

We then have immediately from Appendix B the result for this case,

$$G_\gamma(s) = \frac{1}{\det{(\mathbf{I} + s\mathbf{R}^*)}} = \frac{1}{\displaystyle\prod_{k=1}^{M}(1 + s\lambda_k)} \quad (10\text{-}10\text{-}20)$$

where $\mathbf{R}$ is the (Hermitian positive semidefinite) covariance matrix of the $\{z_k\}$, and the λ_k are its (nonnegative real) eigenvalues. Note that since $\mathbf{R}^*$ and $\mathbf{R}$ have the same eigenvalues, (10-10-20) can equally well be written as

$$G_\gamma(s) = \frac{1}{\det{(\mathbf{I} + s\mathbf{R})}} = \frac{1}{\displaystyle\prod_{k=1}^{M}(1 + s\lambda_k)} \quad (10\text{-}10\text{-}21)$$

The inversion of (10-10-20) is

$$p(\gamma) = \frac{1}{2\pi j}\int_{c-j\infty}^{c+j\infty}\exp{(s\gamma)}G_\gamma(s)\,ds$$

$$= \frac{1}{2\pi j}\int_{c-j\infty}^{c+j\infty}\frac{\exp{(s\gamma)}}{\displaystyle\prod_{k=1}^{M}(1 + s\lambda_k)}\,ds \quad \text{Re } c > 0 \quad (10\text{-}10\text{-}22)$$

(Note that although the results of Appendix B were derived on the basis of $\mathbf{R}$ being positive definite, hence with all $\lambda_k > 0$, we have asserted from (10-10-20), on the basis of analytic continuation, that the result continues to apply in the limit of *infinitesmally* small λ_k, hence when some of the λ_k may be zero and accordingly $\mathbf{R}$ is positive semidefinite.)

We can now interpret (10-10-21) and (10-10-22) by direct comparison with the general result presented in (10-5-18) and (10-5-19) for maximal-ratio combining with independently fading branches. The forms are identical, with each of the λ_k above playing the role of a power level for an *independently fading* diversity branch. In other words, recalling our earlier discussion on the implications of unequal branch power levels for diversity effectiveness, the *effective* order of diversity in our correlated fading case with maximal-ratio combining is determined by the number of eigenvalues of $\mathbf{R}$ which are essentially above the threshold to which the diversity performance is being referred. This role of the eigenvalues of $\mathbf{R}$ should not really be surprising. It is well known that a set of uncorrelated variables can be formed from a set of correlated variables, in a metric-preserving transformation, such that the eigenvalues of the original covariance matrix represent the intensities of the newly created uncorrelated variables. Since, moreover, the maximal-ratio combining rule can be viewed as defining a distance in the space of the $2M$ real variates, its operation is independent of metric-preserving transformations in defining the variates and hence can be viewed as operating on the uncorrelated variates whose intensities are defined by the λ_k.

Note that with respect to other combining rules, we have no rigorous reason for believing that the eigenvalues of the covariance matrix are again totally descriptive of the diversity effectiveness. However, we can conjecture that the *differences* in performance between various types of combiners are again (despite the correlations) relatively small compared to the diversity gain for *any* one type. Also the maximal-ratio result above is the *best* performance that one can achieve with the set of correlated fadings.

Returning to (10-10-21) and (10-10-22), the complete result is portrayed here in terms of matrix eigenvalues. Unfortunately there is no general "formula-type" solution to matrix eigenvalue problems, except for certain special forms. In many cases, e.g., in a uniformly spaced antenna diversity array (an analogous problem occurs in the optimal summing of uniformly spaced time samples from a stationary process), the elements of **R** when the matrix is properly ordered are functions only of separation, i.e.,

$$R_{kj} = f(k - j)$$

The resulting $M \times M$ matrix is known mathematically as a Toeplitz form, specifically a finite Toeplitz matrix; it has only M independent (complex) values describing fully the set of M^2 elements. Even then, the general eigenvalue problem is solvable only in two closely related cases:[1]

$$R_{kj} = \begin{cases} Aq^{|k-j|} & k \geq j \\ A(q^*)^{|k-j|} & k < j \end{cases} \qquad (10\text{-}10\text{-}23)$$

(In the uniformly spaced time sample problem, A real, q arbitrary complex, this covariance matrix represents the Gaussian Markov process, that is, RC-filtered white Gaussian noise.)

$$R_{kj} = \begin{cases} A & k = j \\ Aq & k = j + 1 \\ Aq^* & k = j - 1 \\ 0 & |k - j| > 1 \end{cases} \qquad (10\text{-}10\text{-}24)$$

There is a connection between the two cases in that the second covariance matrix is intimately related to the inverse of the first. Physically, the results for the second case would be useful when one has designed for nearly independent fading and expects residual cross-correlation only between "adjacent" branches.

[1] J. N. Pierce and S. Stein, *op. cit.*, Appendixes III and IV; also U. Grenander and G. Szegö, "Toeplitz Forms and Their Applications," chap. 5, University of California Press, Berkeley, Calif., 1958.

A third solvable general matrix arises when there is circular symmetry in the diversity array; e.g., this might arise in a circularly disposed angle-diversity feed system, or in a triangularly disposed spaced-antenna diversity array. In this case

$$R_{kj} = f(k - j, \text{modulo } M) \tag{10-10-25}$$

e.g. $R_{13} = R_{24} = R_{35} = R_{46} = \ldots = R_{M-2,M} = R_{M-1,1} = R_{M,2}$

(and the matrix is still Hermitian, with $R_{kj} = R_{jk}{}^*$). Such a matrix, also characterized by only M values, is known as a circulant, and has a well-known general eigenvalue solution.[1]

Aside from referencing these solvable eigenvalue problems within the class of interest, we shall not present the detailed results here. For most of our diversity interest, it appears that the desired information may often be derived directly from algebraic operations on the covariance matrix $\mathbf{R}$. Our first statement is that, assuming for the moment that none of the λ_k are too small and hence that there is Mth-order effective diversity, (10-5-29) and the results in Appendix B indicate that the important parameter in determining diversity effectiveness at low outage rates is

$$\prod_{k=1}^{M} \lambda_k = \det \mathbf{R} \tag{10-10-26}$$

If one recalls the basis on which this parameter was established as the criterion, using (10-5-29), it is clear that the similar result above can also be directly inferred from (10-10-20). Again, to determine the *effective order* of diversity, however, one must also be able to establish that the lowest eigenvalue of $\mathbf{R}$ is reasonably large (for Mth-order diversity).

We may also note the dual-diversity case, to compare against the earlier solution obtained for selection combining. For the variables z_1, z_2 of (10-10-14), whose joint envelope p.d.f. is given by (10-10-1), the covariance matrix is

$$\mathbf{R} = \begin{pmatrix} \Gamma_1 & \rho \sqrt{\Gamma_1 \Gamma_2} \\ \rho^* \sqrt{\Gamma_1 \Gamma_2} & \Gamma_2 \end{pmatrix} \tag{10-10-27}$$

Accordingly $\det \mathbf{R} = \Gamma_1 \Gamma_2 (1 - |\rho|^2)$ (10-10-28)

and the eigenvalues are the solution to

$$\begin{vmatrix} \Gamma_1 - \lambda & \rho \sqrt{\Gamma_1 \Gamma_2} \\ \rho^* \sqrt{\Gamma_1 \Gamma_2} & \Gamma_2 - \lambda \end{vmatrix} = 0 \tag{10-10-29}$$

i.e. $\lambda_1 = \frac{1}{2}[\Gamma_1 + \Gamma_2 - \sqrt{(\Gamma_1 + \Gamma_2)^2 - 4\Gamma_1 \Gamma_2 (1 - |\rho|^2)}]$ (10-10-30a)

$\lambda_2 = \frac{1}{2}[\Gamma_1 + \Gamma_2 + \sqrt{(\Gamma_1 + \Gamma_2)^2 - 4\Gamma_1 \Gamma_2 (1 - |\rho|^2)}]$ (10-10-30b)

[1] E.g., R. Bellman, "Introduction to Matrix Analysis," p. 234, McGraw-Hill Book Company, New York, 1960.

TABLE 10-10-1. ENVELOPE CROSS-CORRELATION VS. SQUARED MAGNITUDE
OF COMPLEX CROSS-CORRELATION

$|\rho|$ = magnitude of normalized complex cross-covariance of complex Gaussian processes

ρ_{env} = magnitude of normalized cross-covariance of envelopes (referred to mean value)

$|\rho|^2$	ρ_{env}	$|\rho|^2$	ρ_{env}	$|\rho|^2$	ρ_{env}
0.00	0.0000	0.40	0.376	0.80	0.780
0.01	0.0092	0.41	0.386	0.81	0.791
0.02	0.0183	0.42	0.396	0.82	0.801
0.03	0.0275	0.43	0.405	0.83	0.812
0.04	0.0367	0.44	0.415	0.84	0.823
0.05	0.0459	0.45	0.425	0.85	0.833
0.06	0.0551	0.46	0.435	0.86	0.844
0.07	0.0643	0.47	0.445	0.87	0.855
0.08	0.0736	0.48	0.454	0.88	0.866
0.09	0.0828	0.49	0.464	0.89	0.877
0.10	0.0921	0.50	0.474	0.90	0.888
0.11	0.101	0.51	0.484	0.91	0.899
0.12	0.111	0.52	0.494	0.92	0.910
0.13	0.120	0.53	0.504	0.93	0.921
0.14	0.129	0.54	0.514	0.94	0.932
0.15	0.138	0.55	0.524	0.95	0.943
0.16	0.148	0.56	0.534	0.96	0.954
0.17	0.157	0.57	0.544	0.97	0.966
0.18	0.167	0.58	0.554	0.98	0.977
0.19	0.176	0.59	0.564	0.99	0.988
0.20	0.185	0.60	0.574	1.00	1.00
0.21	0.195	0.61	0.584		
0.22	0.204	0.62	0.594		
0.23	0.214	0.63	0.604		
0.24	0.223	0.64	0.614		
0.25	0.233	0.65	0.624		
0.26	0.242	0.66	0.635		
0.27	0.252	0.67	0.645		
0.28	0.261	0.68	0.655		
0.29	0.271	0.69	0.665		
0.30	0.280	0.70	0.676		
0.31	0.290	0.71	0.686		
0.32	0.299	0.72	0.696		
0.33	0.309	0.73	0.707		
0.34	0.318	0.74	0.717		
0.35	0.328	0.75	0.727		
0.36	0.338	0.76	0.738		
0.37	0.347	0.77	0.748		
0.38	0.357	0.78	0.759		
0.39	0.367	0.79	0.769		

SOURCE: J. N. Pierce; see J. N. Pierce and S. Stein, Multiple Diversity with Non-Independent Fading, *Proc. IRE*, vol. 48, pp. 89–104, Appendix V, January, 1960.

The smaller root λ_1 approaches zero when $|\rho|^2 \to 1$. However, as long as $|\rho|^2$ is reasonably less than unity, λ_1 is of the same order as λ_2, and dual-diversity effectiveness holds. Thus, for $|\rho|^2 \ll 1$, we can use (10-10-28) to state that we have effective maximal-ratio dual diversity, with an equivalent (independent fading model) SNR for each branch given *exactly* as in (10-10-13)

$$(\Gamma_k)_{\text{eff}} = \Gamma_k \sqrt{1 - |\rho|^2} \tag{10-10-31}$$

Thus, in the dual-diversity case, the effective SNR's in the two branches are identical for both selection and maximal-ratio combining, and the difference in performance between the two combiners is exactly that noted earlier in the case of independent fading. Note that these *effective SNR's* which describe behavior at low SNR's are a notational convenience. They are not the same as the λ_k's, but rather describe their geometric mean, which is actually the parameter describing performance.

One is therefore strongly tempted to conjecture that similar comparative behavior among combiner types will continue to hold for higher-order diversity. Since the calculation in a correlated fading case can always be made for maximal-ratio combining, the conjecture is that any other combining will be poorer (at low outage rates of interest) by exactly the differences discussed in connection with independently fading branches, at the order of diversity being effectively obtained.

Before leaving this topic of correlated fading, we may remind the reader again of the paucity of accurate data concerning the normalized *complex* cross-correlations ρ between the joint Gaussian processes describing nonindependently fading diversity branches. Rather, most of the data has concerned the normalized cross-covariance of *envelopes*, which as noted earlier, is very closely related to $|\rho|^2$, the squared *magnitude* of the complex cross-correlation of the Gaussian processes. This closeness is shown in detail in Table 10-10-1, where the normalized envelope cross-covariance ρ_{env} is tabulated as a function of $|\rho|^2$.

10-11. Effect of Diversity on Distributions of Lengths of Fades

In Sec. 9-4, experimental fade-duration statistics in tropospheric scatter were described for the single Rayleigh-fading (nondiversity) channel. The statistics of the durations of fades at various levels were given, as a function of the level. Although there are no completely sharp system thresholds, nevertheless many applications are characterized by a relatively narrow critical range in instantaneous SNR's which divides a region of nearly perfect behavior from one of "failure." For example, one may recall from Fig. 10-8-2 the relative narrowness of the region within which "instantaneous" digital data performance degrades from no errors to a very high probability of error. The system can often be viewed in terms of a threshold level lying in the middle of the critical range, with at least qualitative properties judged then from fade-duration statistics. Our purpose in this section therefore will be to understand how diversity affects such statistics.

There are three parameters in describing fade statistics: (1) The average rate of occurrence of fades, i.e., how often the fading signal passes through the reference level. (2) The distribution of the durations of the fades below reference level. (3) The distribution of the intervals between successive fades.

For many applications, such as the effect of clustering of errors upon the performance of error-control coding over fading channels, it is clear that the distribution of fade durations is particularly relevant. However, neither in this case nor in other applications do there appear to exist detailed data from which to interpret such distributions with respect to system performance. Hence, we shall confine our remarks in this section merely to discussing the duration distributions for their own sake.

In this problem of diversity fade-duration statistics, the solution has been found for the case of *selection* combining and *independent* fading among diversity branches, again assuming multiplicative fading.[1] These results do not aim at deriving the fade-duration statistics for a single channel but only at determining the effects of diversity when the individual channel statistics are assumed already known (as in the data of Sec. 9-4).

The results can be presented in terms of the following two parameters:

μ_k, the probability, or fraction of total time that a fade below the reference level is in process on the kth branch. For pure Rayleigh fading

$$\mu_k = 1 - \exp\left(-\frac{L_k}{\Gamma_k}\right) \qquad (10\text{-}11\text{-}1)$$

where L_k is half the square of the reference level, normalized to mean-square noise in the branch, and Γ_k is the mean SNR in the branch (averaged over fading).

$Q_k(\tau)$, the expected number of fades per unit time with duration exceeding τ, in the kth branch.

To describe the effects of diversity, one defines similar quantities $\mu^{(M)}$ and $Q^{(M)}(\tau)$, analogous to μ_k and $Q_k(\tau)$, for the selection combiner output when there are M independently fading branches.

The quantity $\mu^{(M)}$, the total fraction of time that a fade is in process in the output, is given by the law governing the probability of simul-

[1] S. Stein and D. E. Johansen, A Statistical Description of Coincidences Among Random Pulse Trains, *Proc. IRE*, vol. 46, pp. 827–830, May, 1958. Subsequently, it has become apparent that this problem can be solved routinely by the modern methods of queuing theory.

taneous occurrence of random events,

$$\mu^{(M)} = \prod_{k=1}^{M} \mu_k \tag{10-11-2}$$

This is simply in another form the result expressed earlier in (10-4-9) for the distribution of the selection combiner output. For $Q^{(M)}(\tau)$, one obtains

$$Q^{(M)}(\tau) = -\frac{d}{d\tau} \prod_{k=1}^{M} \int_{\tau}^{\infty} Q_k(\theta) \, d\theta \tag{10-11-3}$$

This is also readily seen to be identical to the form

$$Q^{(M)}(\tau) = \left[\prod_{k=1}^{M} \int_{\tau}^{\infty} Q_k(\theta) \, d\theta \right] \sum_{k=1}^{M} \frac{Q_k(\tau)}{\int_{\tau}^{\infty} Q_k(\theta) \, d\theta} \tag{10-11-4}$$

This solution is not difficult to use for computational purposes, even if the Q_k can only be integrated numerically. For the relatively common case where the input branches have identical statistics, $Q_k(\tau) \equiv Q(\tau)$,

$$Q^{(M)}(\tau) = MQ(\tau) \left[\int_{\tau}^{\infty} Q(\theta) \, d\theta \right]^{M-1} \tag{10-11-5}$$

The average duration $\langle \tau^{(M)} \rangle$ of the fades in the combiner output is given by

$$\frac{1}{\langle \tau^{(M)} \rangle} = \sum_{k=1}^{M} \frac{1}{\langle \tau_k \rangle} \tag{10-11-6}$$

In the case of all branches being statistically identical, with $\langle \tau \rangle$ the average fade duration on each branch,

$$\langle \tau^{(M)} \rangle = \frac{\langle \tau \rangle}{M} \tag{10-11-7}$$

Thus at the reference level, in Mth-order diversity with all branches statistically alike, the average fade duration is reduced in length by exactly a factor of M.

We shall illustrate the results above by examining experimental data in Rayleigh fading on tropospheric scatter such as also described in Sec. 9-4. One set of these data[1] is shown in Fig. 10-11-1. In our notation, the solid curves of Figs. 10-11-1a and b present direct experimental measurements of $Q(\tau)$ for a single branch, and $Q^{(2)}(\tau)$ for dual diversity, respectively. That is, the latter is a measured result for dual diversity in which the two input branches are presumably identical with the statistics of Fig. 10-11-1a. The branches are described as essentially uncorre-

[1] Wright and Cole, *loc. cit.*

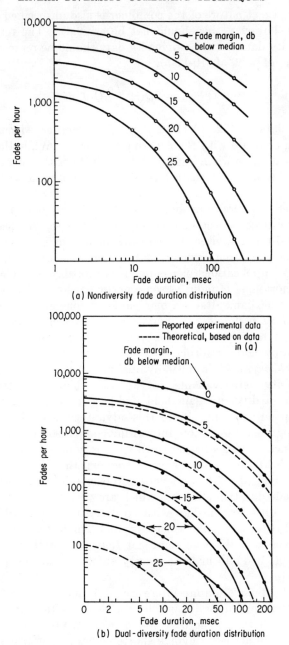

(a) Nondiversity fade duration distribution

(b) Dual-diversity fade duration distribution

FIG. 10-11-1. Troposcatter fade data, including dual diversity.

lated. The exact nature of the combiner is also unspecified (as we comment later, however, this should not be critical). The relation of the dual-diversity data to the no-diversity data should be represented by the special case, $M = 2$, of (10-11-5),

$$Q^{(2)}(\tau) = 2Q(\tau) \int_\tau^\infty Q(\theta)\, d\theta \qquad (10\text{-}11\text{-}8)$$

Using the data of Fig. 10-11-1a then gives the dashed curves of Fig. 10-11-1b to compare with the experimental data. While the agreement is poor,[1] the data shown in Fig. 10-11-1 appear to be the only experimental data available upon which to base such a comparison with theoretical results.

The effect of diversity in shortening the fades at some particular level taken with respect to the no-diversity median is shown clearly between Figs. 10-11-1a and b, either in the experimental or the theoretical data. However, in comparing diversity performance with no-diversity performance from an applications viewpoint, it is probably not realistic to consider the shortening of fades at some particular level with respect to the no-diversity median. Rather, one wants to compare effects in systems with *equivalent performance*. For example, as seen earlier, if one uses total outage rate as a criterion there is a diversity gain available, in that equivalent performance is achieved with a diversity system having *much lower levels* in the individual branches than would be required if no diversity were available. It was also shown that essentially the same kinds of diversity gain hold if digital error rate is the criterion rather than outage rate. Since this advantage is used as part of the system design margin, a more interesting comparison takes into account the difference in single-branch medians for equivalent performance in actual applications. For example, the experimental curve for dual diversity in Fig. 10-11-1b at a level 10 db below the single-branch median indicates fade-duration statistics which are very closely similar to those at 20 to 25 db below median with no diversity in Fig. 10-11-1a. But with a 15-db diversity gain (which Fig. 10-4-2 indicates to be very typical of dual diversity), these do represent *equivalent* systems. The −5-db curve in Fig. 10-11-1b likewise is very similar to the −15-db curve in Fig. 10-11-1a.

The implications are quite interesting. Namely, it is not really clear that an operational design using diversity (and with lower power levels on each branch than if no diversity or a lesser order of diversity were being used) will actually involve shorter fades at performance levels of

---

[1] The corollary data presented by Wright and Cole, *loc. cit.*, suggests that the statistics may have been taken over periods too long to represent stationary Rayleigh fading, or that other disturbances were present at least part of the time in a nonstationary manner.

interest than an equivalent system based on a lower order of diversity. Indeed our rudimentary comparison suggests that, depending on the diversity gain involved *and* upon the levels of performance of interest, the fade-duration statistics may be closely similar in the two cases, or, if they differ, that the differences may lie in *either* direction.

In view of the possible importance of this conclusion and the paucity of general experimental fade-duration data, we shall illustrate this remark with respect to *average* fade duration, as an indicative statistic.   To this end, we can use the data of Fig. 10-11-1a to derive average rate of fade at each level.   This is shown as the second column of Table 10-11-1a. From the basic Rayleigh-fading statistics in Fig. 10-4-1 ($M = 1$), we also have the quantity μ of (10-11-1) for each level, as given in the third column of Table 10-11-1a.   Then one obtains the average fade duration at each level, as given in the fourth column.   Now suppose one is interested in 0.1 per cent outage rate.   From Fig. 10-4-1, with selection combining, the threshold level of interest can be determined in each case with respect to the single-branch median.   This is shown in the second column of Table 10-11-1b.   Then, using (10-11-7), and estimating $\langle \tau \rangle$ for each level by an estimation (rough interpolation) from the results for $\langle \tau \rangle$ in Table 10-11-1a, one can derive the anticipated average fade duration at the level of interest, appropriate to each order of diversity.   The results are shown as the third column of Table 10-11-1b.   Note the very low value for no diversity and the very large increase when any diversity is added— this is clearly related to the much-flattened probability distribution in Fig. 10-4-1 due to diversity.   It is also seen that with further increase in order of diversity, the average fade duration *increases* and then starts to decrease. This behavior is clearly related to the increasingly flattened distributions of Fig. 10-4-1 such that there is a very slow rate of additional flattening beyond a moderate order of diversity.

This simple computation points out again a warning on interpreting diversity statistics for system design.   If fade durations are important to performance with a particular type of modulation (for example, if long fades are more destructive than short ones) one might have to reevaluate the entire question of diversity effectiveness.   At this time, the question must remain open because there is not sufficient data on the effect of fading rapidity on various kinds of signaling (including coding) and because the sharp threshold assumption is not as completely justifiable a model for any system performance as one would like.

Earlier, it was emphasized that along with the sharp-threshold assumption, the discussion above assumes selection combining and independently fading branches.   For other types of combining, but retaining the assumption of independence between branches, it can be recalled that *at least at those levels represented by low outage rates*, our earlier results indicated very similar performance for all combiner types.   The interpretation was that most of the time in diversity, the combiner output represents one branch significantly larger than any of the others, hence the combiner details are not essential. Similarly, one can qualitatively extrapolate here to the intuitive opinion that the fade-duration results for selection combining diversity should very closely represent those for all types of combining.

One can further stretch the above argument to cases of correlated fading in the diversity branches. Again, so long as the correlation is not

TABLE 10-11-1. EFFECT OF DIVERSITY ON AVERAGE FADE DURATION

(a) Average Fade Duration at Various Levels

Level below no-diversity median	Average fade rate across level, $N = Q(0)$	Fraction of time below level, μ	Average fade duration, $\langle \tau \rangle = \mu/N$
0 db	(estimated) 18,000/hr = 5/sec	0.50	100 msec
5 db	8,200/hr = 2.3/sec	0.21	91 msec
10 db	5,000/hr = 1.4/sec	0.07	50 msec
15 db	3,200/hr = 0.89/sec	0.022	25 msec
20 db	1,800/hr = 0.5/sec	0.007	14 msec
25 db	1,200/hr = 0.33/sec	0.002	6 msec

(b) Average Fade Duration with Varying Diversity, at 0.1% Outage Rate

Order of diversity	Level below single-branch median	Estimate $\langle \tau^{(M)} \rangle = \langle \tau \rangle/M$
1	28.0 db	4 msec (est.)
2	13.5 db	$3\frac{2}{2} = 16$ msec (est.)
3	8.0 db	$6\frac{5}{3} = 22$ msec
4	5.5 db	$8\frac{5}{4} = 21$ msec
6	2.5 db	$9\frac{5}{6} = 16$ msec
8	1.0 db	$9\frac{8}{8} = 12$ msec

unreasonably high, say of the order of 0.6 or less, it was observed that there was relatively little change from the independent-fading case. Qualitatively, again, this was attributed to the fact that a reasonably small correlation results in negligibly significant correlation among the "rare events," the deep fades. This again suggests that there is little reason to expect the fade-duration results to differ markedly from those for selection combining with independent branch fading.

Finally, it was mentioned earlier that there might be substantial interest (someday) in the distributions of the intervals *between* fades. There are at this time no statistical data on the distribution of such intervals for the single Rayleigh-fading channel. However, the problem of extending such data (were it available) to the diversity context has been formally solved within the realm of queuing theory. It may be of interest to point out that, mathematically, the diversity fade-duration problem is identical to the duration of intervals *between failures* for a series connection (say a communications relay system) when these intervals are known statistically for each individual link; while the problem of the intervals *between* fades in diversity is identical to that of the durations of *outage times* for the series connection. In fact, diversity is equivalent to a parallel or redundant network, and our statements are those of the duality between parallel and series connections. At least one treatment of both aspects of the problem has been given in terms of the reliability of such series connections.[1]

10-12. Effect of External Noise or Interference

The entire discussion on diversity in this chapter has referred to the additive noise as having the characteristics of front-end receiver noise, namely that it is stationary and independent between diversity branches. In some important applications, however, the noise significant to system performance may arise from sources external to the receiving system. For example, in the lower portion of the h-f band, the important noise may be atmospheric noise propagated from long distances by propagation mechanisms similar to those used for the signal. In this case, the noise may be fading just as the signal does. That is, the noise on each branch may be Gaussian with a time-varying intensity, the time variations being characteristic of the short-term fading (and on a longer time scale, of the long-term fading) characteristic of the channel. A more common occurrence at h-f may simply be the presence of an interfering signal propagated from long distances. In either case, the interference may also itself tend to be fading independently at spaced diversity antennas, for example.

In cases such as this, one likely needs to carry out calculations specific to each particular problem. However, some important general observations can be made which are quite relevant in many such cases.[2] Consider the case of fading noise. The SNR on one branch is then the ratio of the instantaneous intensities of two independently fading Rayleigh processes. If the instantaneous signal power is designated μ_S and the instantaneous noise power is μ_N, these quantities fluctuate with the p.d.f.'s

$$p(\mu_S) = \frac{1}{\mu_{OS}} \exp\left(-\frac{\mu_S}{\mu_{OS}} \right) \tag{10-12-1}$$

$$p(\mu_N) = \frac{1}{\mu_{ON}} \exp\left(-\frac{\mu_N}{\mu_{ON}} \right) \tag{10-12-2}$$

[1] D. S. Palmer, A Theoretical Study of the Statistics of Working Spells and Periods of Breakdown for a Number of Radio Links in Series, *Proc. Symp. on Statistical Methods in Radiowave Propagation*, UCLA, June, 1958, Pergamon Press, New York, 1960.

[2] F. E. Bond and H. F. Meyer, The Effect of Fading on Communication Circuits Subject to Interference, *Proc. IRE*, vol. 45, pp. 636–642, May, 1957.

where μ_{OS} and μ_{ON} are the respective mean values over the short-term fading. The instantaneous SNR is

$$\gamma = \frac{\mu_S}{\mu_N} \qquad (10\text{-}12\text{-}3)$$

The p.d.f. of γ is then given by

$$p(\gamma) = \int_0^\infty \left[\frac{1}{\mu_{ON}} \exp\left(-\frac{\mu_N}{\mu_{ON}} \right) \right] \left[\frac{\mu_N}{\mu_{OS}} \exp\left(-\frac{\gamma \mu_N}{\mu_{OS}} \right) \right] d\mu_N$$

$$= \frac{1}{\mu_{ON}\mu_{OS}} \frac{1}{(1/\mu_{ON} + \gamma/\mu_{OS})^2} = \frac{1}{(\sqrt{K} + \gamma/\sqrt{K})^2} \qquad (10\text{-}12\text{-}4)$$

where K is the ratio of the two intensities,

$$K = \frac{\mu_{OS}}{\mu_{ON}} \qquad (10\text{-}12\text{-}5)$$

The probability that γ exceeds some value γ_0 is

$$\text{Prob } (\gamma > \gamma_0) = \int_{\gamma_0}^\infty \frac{1}{(\sqrt{K} + \gamma/\sqrt{K})^2} \, d\gamma = \frac{1}{1 + \gamma_0/K} \qquad (10\text{-}12\text{-}6)$$

The interesting point now is that for $\gamma_0 \ll K$, that is, for instantaneous SNR's low compared with the ratio of mean signal to mean noise power,

$$\text{Prob } (\gamma > \gamma_0) \doteq 1 - \frac{\gamma_0}{K} + 0\left(\frac{\gamma_0}{K}\right)^2 \qquad (10\text{-}12\text{-}7)$$

In this leading term, then, the p.d.f. is identical to what it is for the distribution

$$\text{Prob } (\gamma > \gamma_0) = \exp\left(-\frac{\gamma_0}{K} \right) \qquad (10\text{-}12\text{-}8)$$

the latter being the distribution for the case of a fading signal, but *non-fading* noise. Thus, to the extent to which a diversity operation can still be performed on the basis of somehow identifying separately the signal and the noise levels on each branch, *all the earlier results on diversity performance will continue to hold essentially without change.* The implication of the equivalence between (10-12-6) and (10-12-8) is simply that, probabilistically, low SNR occurs most of the time because of the signal fading to low levels, rather than the noise level becoming high.

It is not always clear in a case of fading interference that a distinction can always be made for combiner control purposes between the signal and the interference. In such a case one can visualize a selection diversity operation based, for example, on choosing at each instant the branch with the highest total intensity (signal plus interference). It has been shown[1] that for dual-diversity the reduction in diversity gain is about 1.5 db.

[1] Bond and Meyer, *loc. cit.*

Another kind of external noise of importance might arise locally, e.g., ignition noise of nearby origin in troposcatter or h-f reception or locally generated atmospherics in h-f reception.   In this case, the noise will not be fading, but it *may be identical*, i.e., perfectly correlated, in all diversity branches.   Then some of our previous analysis in this chapter, particularly that relating to the maximal-ratio combiner, no longer holds.   In any summation of signals from the several branches, the noises will add just as coherently as the signals.   In such an event, it becomes clear that the optimum combiner is a selection combiner (choice of that branch with the instantaneously highest SNR).   Further, with a selector combiner, diversity gain performance does not depend upon whether the noises in the several branches are independent or correlated.   Thus, one should be able to perform as well as indicated in the earlier results for selection combining; moreover, any attempt at a weighting combiner may actually lead to poorer performance (this has interesting cautionary implications for system design).   The use of a selection combiner, or a combiner which under the occurrence of such external noise performs equivalently to a selection combiner, leads then to a performance such as described in detail in Sec. 10-4—almost as good as when the noises are independent in the branches and maximal-ratio combining can be gainfully applied.

CHAPTER 11

DECISION-ORIENTED DIVERSITY FOR
DIGITAL TRANSMISSION

Digital transmission with linear diversity combining was examined in Chap. 10 to illustrate the performance achieved by linear combining techniques. However, it was emphasized that the latter apply under slow, nonselective fading, when accurate measurement of the channel states is available. Under these circumstances, the output of a linear combining network is itself a multiplicative-fading, but otherwise undistorted, version of the transmitted signal, with a much-reduced dynamic range of fading. Hence, when applicable, linear diversity combining generally can be used with any form of analog or digital signaling. Consequently, the emphasis in Chap. 10 was largely on the instantaneous fluctuations of SNR at the combiner output, with interpretations such as outage rate and digital error rate subsequently deduced from it.

To achieve from the received signal an accurate measure of each channel state, as required for useful linear combining, implies sufficient smoothing time that estimation errors due to the additive receiver noise can be rendered negligible. However, there was no analysis in Chap. 10 to determine how accurate a channel estimate is needed, or is available, when one takes the fading statistics into account. One problem here is that within the realm of analog signals (i.e., with signal fidelity as the reception goal), it is at best argumentative as to what are appropriate usable mathematical criteria for judging performance. However, with digital signaling and error-rate as the performance criterion, one can become substantially more specific about many of these questions. Thus, within the context of digital signaling over fading channels, this chapter will generalize the results of Chap. 10. The emphasis will be on reexamining the entire diversity combining concept, when one abandons signal fidelity as an irrelevance, and instead establishes minimum error rate as the sole goal.

11-1. Optimum Combining for Digital Signaling in Slow, Nonselective Fading

Significant general guidelines can be established by extending to the diversity situation the maximum-likelihood decision-theoretic considerations of Chap. 2. In M-fold diversity reception, M different waveforms are simultaneously available for processing, all bearing the *same* message information, and variously contaminated by additive receiver noise. Each of the M waveforms is drawn from a statistical ensemble, in accordance with the fading statistics for the corresponding diversity channel. Most generally, we shall assume Rayleigh fading with a possible specular component, so that each channel is representable as a randomly time-varying linear filter whose impulse response is a complex nonzero-mean Gaussian process. There may be nonvanishing cross-correlations in the fading fluctuations among the several diversity channels.

The minimum probability of error decision is made by calculating from the M observed waveforms the posterior probability of each possible message sequence and then selecting that sequence which has the highest posterior probability, or maximum likelihood. The optimum diversity receiver, by definition, automatically performs the essential portions of this decision calculation, including both the processing of the waveform received in each diversity branch, and the method of combining these processed voltages.

Related Results. The literature bearing upon this problem appears to begin with the work of Price[1] on the optimum reception of digital signals passed through a fading channel of the type defined above. These results have been generalized by Kailath.[2] Their physical interpretation has been primarily concerned with elucidating the principles underlying the Rake technique (Sec. 11-5) as a generalized correlation detector. However, with only minor changes in interpretation, the results clearly also apply to diversity systems in general. For example, Rake can be viewed as a kind of multipath diversity system. Turin also analyzed this kind of channel, assuming a priori the resolvability of the multipath into individual nonselectively fading paths[3] and later generaliz-

[1] R. Price, The Detection of Signals Perturbed by Scatter and Noise, *IRE Trans. Inform. Theory*, vol. PGIT-4, pp. 163–170, September, 1954; and Optimum Detection of Random Signals in Noise, with Application to Scatter-Multipath Communication, *IRE Trans. Inform. Theory*, vol. IT-2, pp. 125–135, December, 1956.

[2] T. Kailath, Optimum Receivers for Randomly Varying Channels, *Proc. 4th London Symp. Inform. Theory*, 1960, Butterworth Scientific Publications, London, 1961; T. Kailath, Correlation Detection of Signals Perturbed by a Random Channel, *IRE Trans. Inform. Theory*, vol. IT-6, pp. 361–366, June, 1960; J. M. Wozencraft, "Sequential Reception of Time-Variant Dispersive Transmissions," in E. J. Baghdady (ed.), "Lectures on Communication System Theory," McGraw-Hill Book Company, New York, 1961, Chap. 12; T. Kailath, Adaptive Matched Filters, *Symposium on Mathematical Optimization Techniques*, Santa Monica, Calif., October, 1960, in R. Bellman (ed.), "Mathematical Optimization Techniques," University of California Press, Berkeley, Calif., 1963, Chap. 6.

[3] G. L. Turin, Communication through Noisy, Random-Multipath Channels, *IRE Nat. Conv. Record*, part. 4, pp. 154–166, March, 1956.

ing the analysis to the broader diversity situation.[1]   An important insight into the limiting cases of zero knowledge and perfect knowledge of the channel states, and comparison of performances, was provided by Pierce.[2] Results by Turin and Pierce on performance of optimum and suboptimum receivers are referenced later.

It is beyond our purpose here to outline the complete scope of this work. Specifically, in this first section, we determine the optimum diversity receiver only under conditions where the fading diversity channels can be assumed to be fading nonselectively and to be changing slowly over durations corresponding to at least a few information pulses.   This simplifies the presentation.   At the same time, it will be seen to contain the major qualitative interpretations of the broader situations.   The remaining sections of this chapter will deal with performance analysis of both optimum and related suboptimum receivers.

One assumption inherent in most of the decision-theoretic formulations in the literature cited is that if the transmitted waveforms corresponding to a message symbol are confined to some interval of length T, then the optimum receiver bases the associated decision *solely* upon the voltages available during the corresponding interval of length T at the receiver, say taken as the interval $(0,T)$.   This implies that no information useful to the decision is available from signals received outside $(0,T)$.   Nevertheless, some of the resulting optimum receiver processing during $(0,T)$ has then been interpreted as channel estimation.   Clearly, this is a severely restricted form of channel estimation if it is based solely on the $(0,T)$ span.   It is also clearly inconsistent with the intuition underlying the diversity concept for the slowly fading channel.   Namely, if the channel varies slowly enough, its state can be measured relatively noiselessly and used to effect useful diversity combining.   For example, one technique for monitoring the channel state in a digital signaling system would be to transmit a pilot tone (unmodulated tone) along with the information-bearing waveforms.[3]

We will examine here a model typified by the pilot-tone concept.   In slow fading, smoothing of a pilot tone to reduce additive noise effects may

[1] G. L. Turin, On Optimal Diversity Reception, *IRE Trans. Inform. Theory*, vol. IT-7, pp. 154–166, July, 1961.

[2] J. N. Pierce, Theoretical Diversity Improvement in Frequency-Shift Keying, *Proc. IRE*, vol. 46, pp. 903–910, May, 1958.

[3] There seems to be a line of thought that using some of the available transmitter power solely for channel estimation is undesirable because all the available energy ought to be employed to enhance discriminability among the information symbols themselves.   Yet even within this point of view, there remains the possibility of basing a channel estimate upon those receiver-processed prior waveforms which are indicated *by the associated digital decisions* to most likely have represented the actual signal.   The principles involved have been touched upon by Wozencraft, *loc. cit.*, and by Kailath, "Adaptive Matched Filters," 1960, *op. cit.*

be extended over many tens of information pulse lengths.   A satisfactorily high SNR for diversity combining and detection would then require assigning to the pilot tone only a relatively small fraction of the transmitted energy (see also the performance calculations of Sec. 11-2).   Alternatively, one may be able to take advantage of the signal structure.   For example, for binary DPSK, one may "wipe out" the information content (0, π phase shifts) by using a squaring or frequency-doubling circuit, thereby avoiding the need for a separate pilot tone.   We shall assume that the

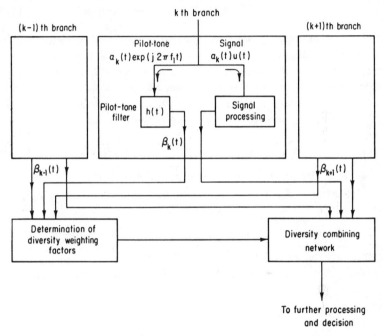

FIG. 11-1-1. Use of filtered pilot tone for diversity combining.

performance of all such systems can be at least qualitatively inferred from studying a straightforward pilot-tone model.

Channel Estimation by Pilot-tone Measurement.   It is assumed that each diversity branch is a nonselective Rayleigh-fading channel, possibly including a specular component.   The effect of the kth channel upon any signal is then described by a multiplicative nonzero-mean stationary Gaussian process, $\alpha_k(t)$.   The latter can be directly observed as the multiplicative fading factor on a pilot tone transmitted over this channel but contaminated by additive zero-mean complex Gaussian noise in the receiver.   Thus, one is limited to forming a continuous best estimate of $\alpha_k(t)$ from observation of the received pilot tone plus noise over the interval $(-\infty, t)$.   We shall assume here (Fig. 11-1-1) that the receiver processing for this purpose consists of a bandpass filter in each diversity branch centered on the pilot-tone frequency, with equivalent low-pass impulse response $h(t)$ and equivalent low-pass transfer function $H(f)$. Optimally, the time constant of this smoothing will be chosen to remove additive noise to the greatest extent possible, without including such distant prehistory that a false estimate of $\alpha_k(t)$ results.

With $\{n_k(t)\}$ as the complex envelopes of the additive noises, the complex envelope of the pilot-tone filter output in the kth receiver at time t is given by

$$\beta_k(t) = \int_{-\infty}^{\infty} h(t - \tau) \left[\alpha_k(\tau) + n_k(\tau)\right] d\tau \qquad (11\text{-}1\text{-}1)$$

where for convenience we assume identical filters in every branch. Since the $\{\alpha_k(\tau)\}$ are nonzero-mean stationary complex Gaussian, so are the $\{\beta_k(t)\}$. For later performance calculations, we will require the joint statistics of the $\{\alpha_k(t)\}$ and $\{\beta_k(t)\}$, especially as to the extent to which each $\beta_k(t)$ is a measure of the corresponding $\alpha_k(t)$.

On an ensemble basis, their means are related by

$$\langle\beta_k\rangle = \langle\alpha_k\rangle \int_{-\infty}^{\infty} h(t - \tau)\, d\tau = \langle\alpha_k\rangle H(0) \qquad (11\text{-}1\text{-}2)$$

where $H(0)$ is the equivalent low-pass transfer function of the filter, at center frequency. Assuming correlated fading on the several branches, the covariances of the $\{\alpha_k(t)\}$ will be defined as

$$a_{kj}(\tau) = \tfrac{1}{2}\langle[\alpha_k(t) - \langle\alpha_k\rangle]^*[\alpha_j(t + \tau) - \langle\alpha_j\rangle]\rangle \qquad (11\text{-}1\text{-}3)$$

Then the covariances of the $\{\beta_k(t)\}$, taken only at zero time-lag (interest will lie only in simultaneous estimates of the channels) are defined as

$$g_{kj} = \tfrac{1}{2}\langle(\beta_k - \langle\beta_k\rangle)^*(\beta_j - \langle\beta_j\rangle)\rangle \qquad (11\text{-}1\text{-}4a)$$

$$= \iint_{-\infty}^{\infty} h^*(t - \tau_1)h(t - \tau_2)[a_{kj}(\tau_2 - \tau_1) \\ + \delta_{kj}b_k(\tau_2 - \tau_1)]\, d\tau_1\, d\tau_2 \qquad (11\text{-}1\text{-}4b)$$

where δ_{kj} is the Kronecker delta symbol, we have assumed the additive noises to be mutually independent of each other and of the channel fading, and $b_k(\tau)$ is the autocovariance of the additive noise on the kth branch. Let $H(f)$ be the filter transfer function corresponding to $h(t)$, $A_{kj}(f)$ the cross-power density spectrum corresponding to $a_{kj}(\tau)$, and $B_k(f)$ the power density spectrum corresponding to $b_k(\tau)$. Then

$$A_{kj}(f) = \int_{-\infty}^{\infty} \exp\left(-j2\pi f\tau\right)a_{kj}(\tau)\, d\tau \qquad (11\text{-}1\text{-}5a)$$

$$B_k(f) = \int_{-\infty}^{\infty} \exp\left(-j2\pi f\tau\right)b_k(\tau)\, d\tau \qquad (11\text{-}1\text{-}5b)$$

and

$$g_{kj} = \int_{-\infty}^{\infty} |H(f)|^2[A_{kj}(f) + \delta_{kj}B_k(f)]\, df \qquad (11\text{-}1\text{-}6)$$

Similarly the cross-covariances of the $\{\alpha_k(t)\}$ with the estimation variates

$\{\beta_k(t)\}$ are

$$c_{kj} = \tfrac{1}{2}\langle[\alpha_k(t) - \langle\alpha_k\rangle]^*[\beta_j(t) - \langle\beta_j\rangle]\rangle \qquad (11\text{-}1\text{-}7a)$$

$$= \int_{-\infty}^{\infty} h(t - \tau)a_{kj}{}^*(t - \tau)\,d\tau = \int_{-\infty}^{\infty} H(f)A_{kj}(f)\,df \quad (11\text{-}1\text{-}7b)$$

The joint distribution of the $\{\alpha_k(t)\}$ and $\{\beta_k(t)\}$, taken at a common instant of time, can then be defined as follows: Define the partitioned $2M \times 1$ column matrix of their joint values,

$$\phi = \left(\frac{\alpha}{\beta}\right) \qquad (11\text{-}1\text{-}8)$$

where α and β are the column matrices of the α_k and β_k, respectively (the common t variable now being suppressed). Then the covariance matrix for the components of ϕ is

$$\Phi = \tfrac{1}{2}\langle(\phi - \langle\phi\rangle)^*(\phi - \langle\phi\rangle)^T\rangle \qquad (11\text{-}1\text{-}9)$$

where the T superscript indicates the transposed matrix. If we define $\mathbf{a}$ as the matrix with components $a_{ij}(0)$ defined by (11-1-3), and $\mathbf{g}$ and $\mathbf{c}$ as the Hermitian matrices defined by (11-1-4) and (11-1-7), then Φ has the partitioned form

$$\Phi = \begin{pmatrix} \mathbf{a} & \mathbf{c} \\ \mathbf{c}^{T*} & \mathbf{g} \end{pmatrix} \qquad (11\text{-}1\text{-}10)$$

The joint p.d.f. of the components of ϕ, which is hence the joint p.d.f. of the components of α and β, is

$$p(\phi) = p(\alpha,\beta) = \frac{1}{(2\pi)^M \det \Phi} \exp\left[-\tfrac{1}{2}(\phi - \langle\phi\rangle)^T \Phi^{-1}(\phi - \langle\phi\rangle)^*\right] \quad (11\text{-}1\text{-}11)$$

One can now regard the knowledge of α imparted by the measurements β to be completely described by the *conditional p.d.f.* of α, conditional on the observed values of β,

$$p_\beta(\alpha) = \frac{p(\alpha,\beta)}{p(\beta)} \qquad (11\text{-}1\text{-}12)$$

where, using the earlier definition of $\mathbf{g}$,

$$p(\beta) = \frac{1}{(2\pi)^M \det \mathbf{g}} \exp\left[-\tfrac{1}{2}(\beta - \langle\beta\rangle)^T \mathbf{g}^{-1}(\beta - \langle\beta\rangle)^*\right] \quad (11\text{-}1\text{-}13)$$

It is also readily shown that the partitioned matrix Φ in (11-1-10) has the partitioned inverse,[1]

$$\Phi^{-1} = \begin{pmatrix} (\mathbf{a} - \mathbf{c}\mathbf{g}^{-1}\mathbf{c}^{T*})^{-1} & (\mathbf{c}^{T*} - \mathbf{g}\mathbf{c}^{-1}\mathbf{a})^{-1} \\ (\mathbf{c} - \mathbf{a}\mathbf{c}^{-1T*}\mathbf{g})^{-1} & (\mathbf{g} - \mathbf{c}^{T*}\mathbf{a}^{-1}\mathbf{c})^{-1} \end{pmatrix} \qquad (11\text{-}1\text{-}14)$$

Then the exponential in (11-1-11) can be written in terms of quadratic

---

[1] This is a form of Schur's Identity, e.g., M. Marcus, Basic Theorems in Matrix Theory, *Natl. Bur. Std.*, *(U.S.) Appl. Math. Ser.*, no. 57, January, 1960.

forms in α and β. With this and (11-1-13) then substituted into (11-1-12), one can show that the resulting conditional p.d.f. has the form

$$p_\beta(\alpha) = \frac{1}{(2\pi)^M \det \mathbf{R}} \exp\left[-\frac{1}{2}(\alpha - \hat{\alpha})^T \mathbf{R}^{-1}(\alpha - \hat{\alpha})^*\right] \quad (11\text{-}1\text{-}15)$$

where

$$\mathbf{R} = \mathbf{a} - \mathbf{cg}^{-1}\mathbf{c}^{T*} \quad (11\text{-}1\text{-}16a)$$

and

$$\hat{\alpha} = \langle\alpha\rangle + \mathbf{c}^*(\mathbf{g}^{-1})^*(\beta - \langle\beta\rangle) \quad (11\text{-}1\text{-}16b)$$

This distribution, then, represents the knowledge of the channel states imparted by the measurement β, including such effects as the presence of a specular component implied by the value $\langle\alpha\rangle$. The most likely value of the elements $\{\alpha_k\}$ is given by the corresponding estimates $\{\hat{\alpha}_k\}$, with the covariance matrix $\mathbf{R}$ representing the residual uncertainties in the knowledge of the channel states.

When all channels are fading independently, one has

$$g_{kj} = g_k \delta_{kj} \qquad c_{kj} = c_k \delta_{kj} \qquad a_{kj} = a_k \delta_{kj} \quad (11\text{-}1\text{-}17)$$

Furthermore one may identify

$$a_k = \sigma_k^2 \quad (11\text{-}1\text{-}18)$$

as the a priori variance of the $\{\alpha_k\}$, and define a set of normalized covariances $\{\rho_k\}$ by

$$c_k = \rho_k \sqrt{a_k g_k} \quad (11\text{-}1\text{-}19)$$

Then for independent fading, the forms in (11-1-16) become

$$R_{kj} = \sigma_k^2(1 - |\rho_k|^2)\,\delta_{kj} \quad (11\text{-}1\text{-}20a)$$

$$\hat{\alpha}_k = \langle\alpha_k\rangle + \sqrt{\frac{a_k}{g_k}}\,\rho_k^*(\beta_k - \langle\beta_k\rangle) \quad (11\text{-}1\text{-}20b)$$

In turn, (11-1-15) then becomes

$$p_\beta(\alpha) = \prod_{k=1}^{M} p_{\beta_k}(\alpha_k) = \prod_{k=1}^{M} \frac{1}{2\pi\hat{\sigma}_k^2} \exp\left(-\frac{1}{2}\frac{|\alpha_k - \hat{\alpha}_k|^2}{\hat{\sigma}_k^2}\right) \quad (11\text{-}1\text{-}21a)$$

where

$$\hat{\sigma}_k^2 = \sigma_k^2(1 - |\rho_k|^2) \quad (11\text{-}1\text{-}21b)$$

It is interesting to note the limiting cases here. Whenever for some k, $\rho_k = 0$ so that the measurement β_k gives no knowledge of the corresponding channel state, the conditional p.d.f. of α_k is only that given by the known long-term channel statistics. At the other extreme, if $\rho_k = 1$, implying a perfect measurement of the channel, then $\hat{\sigma}_k^2 \to 0$ and $\alpha_k = \hat{\alpha}_k = \langle\alpha_k\rangle + \sqrt{a_k/g_k}\,(\beta_k - \langle\beta_k\rangle)$ precisely. That is, the p.d.f. for α_k in (11-1-12) becomes a representation for $\delta(\alpha_k - \hat{\alpha}_k)$ as $\hat{\sigma}_k^2 \to 0$, as expected for a nonzero-mean Gaussian process as its fluctuation component decreases to zero intensity. Note again that the fluctuation in (11-1-21a) refers to the uncertainty in the estimate, not to the channel itself.   Thus $\beta_k - \langle \beta_k \rangle$ is an estimate of the instantaneous value of the fluctuation component of the kth channel, the factor $\sqrt{a_k/g_k}$ serves to reflect this measurement into the scale of α_k, and the addition of this product to $\langle \alpha_k \rangle$ gives the estimate of the present value of α_k.

The important general result here is (11-1-15).   The conditional p.d.f. for $\boldsymbol{\alpha}$ during any span $(0,T)$ is that of a complex *nonzero*-mean Gaussian process, *whether or not* there is a specular component.   The optimum receiver for pure Rayleigh fading will thus be the same *in form* as for a zero-memory channel (one for which no estimate is available) with a specular component.   The difference is that for the latter, the receiver structure is based upon $\langle \boldsymbol{\alpha} \rangle$ and remains fixed, whereas for the pilot-tone case, $\hat{\boldsymbol{\alpha}}$ will vary and the optimum receiver structure will vary with it ("adaptively") as shown below.

Maximum-likelihood Processors for Diversity Reception.   We shall consider a binary communications signal being received by M diversity branches.   We assume that the interval $(0,T)$ defines the time of arrival of signal voltages corresponding to a particular information element, in all the diversity branches.[1]   Over this time interval, let $\{z_k(t)\}$, $k = 1$, $\ldots$, M represent the complex envelopes of signal plus additive noise voltages available in the receivers in the several branches.   Then (Chap. 2) the optimum processor measures the posterior probabilities of each possible transmitted digital waveform (there are only two in the binary case) and chooses the most probable as its decision.   In the diversity-reception case, these probabilities are derived from the *totality* of available waveforms: signal-plus-noise waveforms over $(0,T)$, plus the information derived from pilot tones.   We shall indicate this calculation below for the binary case, in a form which immediately generalizes to any higher-order signaling.

Over $(0,T)$, let $s^{(1)}(t;\phi_1)$ and $s^{(2)}(t;\phi_2)$ be the complex envelopes of the signals which would be transmitted to represent the respective binary states.   In addition to the time dependence, a phase dependence has been explicitly indicated in these waveforms.   This phase is taken to be a *constant* over the duration of the waveform.   For coherent signaling and detection, the phases are assumed completely known *at the receivers* to within the phase introduced by each diversity channel.[2]   On the other hand, for a noncoherent signaling system, such as noncoherent FSK, the possible transmitted symbols are regarded to have a completely random associated phase factor, constant over each symbol but random from one symbol to the next.   In determining the optimum processing

---

[1] For differential PSK, as we have discussed, the time interval $(0,T)$ would have to correspond to that occupied by the two successive pulses which determine a message bit.

[2] I.e., the transmitted phases are fixed relative to phases transmitted during prior intervals.

of the received waveforms, an assumed lack of phase knowledge of the transmitted signal is different from lack of phase knowledge of the diversity channels. The difference is that when the channel states are known but the signal phase is unknown, the unknown phase is still identical on all the diversity channels, and the processed outputs of the several branches can be added *coherently* even though the final detection-decision process is necessarily *noncoherent*. On the other hand, when the diversity channel phases are unknown, coherent addition is not possible, even if both transmitter and receiver are completely stable in frequency.

The probabilities to be computed and compared are the posterior probabilities, conditional on the observed $\{z_k(t)\}$ and on whatever information is available concerning the channel, that binary states 1 or 2 were transmitted. These conditional probabilities are denoted by

$$f_j = P(j|\{z_k\}) \qquad (11\text{-}1\text{-}22a)$$

where f_j = probability that the jth state was received during $(0,T)$, given the observed waveforms $\{z_k(t)\}$ over $(0,T)$; in the binary case, $j = 1$ or 2. Using Bayes' rule,

$$f_j = P(j|\{z_k\}) = \frac{p_j(\{z_k\})P(j)}{p(\{z_k\})} \qquad (11\text{-}1\text{-}22b)$$

where $p(\{z_k\})$ is the unconditional probability density function that the set of waveforms $\{z_k\}$ will occur;[1] $p_j(\{z_k\})$ is the same p.d.f. *conditional* on the transmission of the jth symbol; and $P(j)$ is the probability that the message symbol transmitted during $(0,T)$ is the jth symbol. We can assume all possible elements in the message sequence to be equiprobable; in our binary case,

$$P(1) = P(2) = \tfrac{1}{2} \qquad (11\text{-}1\text{-}23a)$$

In addition, since the denominator in (11-1-2b) is independent of j, one can rewrite (11-1-2b) as

$$f_j = Cp_j(\{z_k\}) \qquad (11\text{-}1\text{-}23b)$$

where C is some number common to all the f_j.

For $s^{(j)}(t;\phi_j)$ transmitted ($j = 1$ or 2) over $(0,T)$, and the assumption of slow, nonselective-fading channels, the $\{z_k(t)\}$ have the forms

$$z_k(t) = \alpha_k s^{(j)}(t;\phi_j) + n_k(t) \qquad k = 1, \ldots, M \qquad (11\text{-}1\text{-}24)$$

where α_k is the complex gain of the kth transmission channel (kth diversity branch), assumed constant over $(0,T)$ but varying statistically over longer times; and $n_k(t)$ is the complex envelope of the additive noise in the kth branch. We also assume the receiver noises in the several diver-

---

[1] Recall that the notation $p(z)$, where z is complex, is strictly a shorthand notation for the joint p.d.f. of the real and imaginary parts of z. The notation $p(z)\,dz$ is to be taken in the same sense.

sity branches to be mutually independent and spectrally flat over the receiver bandwidths,[1] with the same one-sided power spectral density n_0. Then one can write the p.d.f. for a typical one of the complex envelopes $n_k(t)$ over $(0,T)$ in the form[2]

$$p[n_k(t)] = K \exp \left\{ - \frac{\int_0^T |n_k(t)|^2 \, dt}{2n_0} \right\} \qquad (11\text{-}1\text{-}25)$$

where K is a proportionality factor. Thus, *conditional* on the value α_k and on $s^{(j)}(t;\phi_j)$, each z_k has the p.d.f.

$$p[z_k(t)|\alpha_k, s^{(j)}(t;\phi_j)] = K \exp \left\{ - \frac{\int_0^T |z_k(t) - \alpha_k s^{(j)}(t;\phi_j)|^2 \, dt}{2n_0} \right\} \qquad (11\text{-}1\text{-}26)$$

Lumping K into the constant C, one can now write (11-1-23) as

$$f_j = C \int \cdots \int \prod_{k=1}^M \left\{ \exp \left[- \frac{\int_0^T |z_k(t) - \alpha_k s^{(j)}(t;\phi_j)|^2 \, dt}{2n_0} \right] \right\}$$
$$p(\phi_j)p(\alpha_1, \ldots, \alpha_M) \, d\alpha_1 \ldots d\alpha_M \, d\phi_j \qquad (11\text{-}1\text{-}27)$$

where $p(\alpha_1, \ldots, \alpha_M)$ is the joint p.d.f.[3] of the $\{\alpha_k\}$ and $p(\phi_j)$ is the p.d.f. of the signal phase. Note we can consider $p(\phi_j) = \delta(\phi_j - \phi_0^{(j)})$ for coherent signaling and detection, where $\phi_0^{(j)}$ is some constant; and $p(\phi_j) = \dfrac{1}{2\pi}$ for noncoherent signaling.

We assume all the $s^{(j)}(t;\phi_k)$ to have the same energy factor; normalized to n_0, this is represented by

$$\gamma_0 = \int_0^T \frac{1}{n_0} |s^{(j)}(t;\phi_j)|^2 \, dt \qquad (11\text{-}1\text{-}28a)$$

Over short-term fading, the actual average ratio of signal energy to noise power density in the kth diversity branch is then

$$\Gamma_k = \tfrac{1}{2}\langle |\alpha_k|^2 \rangle \gamma_0 \qquad (11\text{-}1\text{-}28b)$$

If the integral in the exponentials of (11-1-27) is now expanded and all factors common to all the f_j are absorbed into the number C, the decision

---

[1] A generalization of the derivation to the case where noises are not equal in all channels is straightforward, essentially by redefining gain constants in the several branches.   A generalization to the case where the noises are not spectrally flat is given by Turin, 1961, *loc. cit.*, or Kailath, 1960, *loc. cit.*, where it is shown that the first operation desired in each receiver is in fact a "noise-whitening" filter.

[2] E.g., this is implied in Sec. 2-5; or see Turin, 1956, *loc. cit.* The notation (11-1-25) is actually justified only by virtue of its later use in ratio-type comparisons.

[3] As explained already, this p.d.f. will be a conditional p.d.f. based upon whatever information is available concerning the channel states during $(0,T)$.

parameters can be rewritten as

$$f_j = C \int \cdots \int \prod_{k=1}^{M} \exp \left\{ -\tfrac{1}{2}|\alpha_k|^2 \gamma_0 + \mathrm{Re}\frac{\left[\alpha_k{}^* \int_0^T z_k(t) s^{(j)*}(t;\phi_j)\, dt \right]}{n_0} \right\}$$
$$p(\phi_j)p(\alpha_1, \ldots, \alpha_M)\, d\alpha_1 \ldots d\alpha_M\, d\phi_j \quad (11\text{-}1\text{-}29)$$

In (11-1-29), the indicated operation to be performed in each branch on the observed waveform $z_k(t)$ is cross-correlation against the possible transmitted states, forming in each branch the measurements

$$w_k{}^{(j)}(\phi_j) = \frac{1}{n_0} \int_0^T z_k(t) s^{(j)*}(t;\phi_j)\, dt \quad (11\text{-}1\text{-}30)$$

This integral is the usual cross-correlation or matched-filter operation,[1] its value conveniently normalized to n_0. Since we assumed here that each channel remains steady in some state during $(0,T)$, it is not surprising to find this as the optimum operation within each branch. Recalling the discussion of Sec. 7-7, it should also be recognized that certain suboptimum operations in each branch receiver may perform almost as well as the matched filter, in that almost as much signal-noise discrimination would be achieved in the resulting filter outputs. With (11-1-30),

$$f_j = C \int \cdots \int \exp \left[-\sum_{k=1}^{M} \{ \tfrac{1}{2}|\alpha_k|^2 \gamma_0 + \mathrm{Re}\, [\alpha_k{}^* w_k{}^{(j)}(\phi_j)] \} \right]$$
$$p(\phi_j)p(\alpha_1, \ldots, \alpha_M)\, d\alpha_1 \ldots d\alpha_M\, d\phi_j \quad (11\text{-}1\text{-}31)$$

It now remains to seek the combining structure implied by these forms for the decision variable. Note it is already clear here that optimization of reception in slow, multiplicative fading involves two separate procedures, one being optimization of the filtering process in each receiver to provide a specific parameter (the filter output in each receiver at the decision instant) and the other an optimum zero-memory combining of these parameters from the several receivers. Thus, the optimum-combiner rule to be determined from (11-1-31) will still be the optimum combiner even if the $\{w_k{}^{(j)}(\phi_j)\}$ are obtained in each receiver by other than the optimum filtering.

To obtain the optimum-combiner rule, it remains now to introduce the joint p.d.f. $p(\alpha_1, \ldots, \alpha_M)$ representing the degree of knowledge of the states of the several channels *during the interval* $(0,T)$, based upon measurements made over prior intervals.

---

[1] Note, in the case of coherent signaling, this operation implies a full cross-correlation which includes a coherent detection aspect in that the signal phase is used in defining the correlator. While, as discussed in Chap. 7, the cross-correlation can be performed as a bandpass operation, and the coherent detection deferred to a final operation, our mathematical discussion below will assume the full cross-correlation contained in the $w_k{}^{(j)}$.

Perfect Knowledge of the Channel States.   One extreme case is when the prior measurements allow a perfect estimate of each channel.   If the latter set of complex values is denoted $\{a_k\}$, then during the interval in question, the joint p.d.f. of the $\{\alpha_k\}$ is

$$p(\alpha_1, \ldots, \alpha_M) = \prod_{k=1}^{M} \delta(\alpha_k - a_k) \qquad (11\text{-}1\text{-}32)$$

In this case, the decision parameters of (11-1-31) become simply

$$f_j = C \exp\left(-\gamma_0 \sum_{k=1}^{M} \tfrac{1}{2}|a_k|^2\right) \int \exp\left[\operatorname{Re} \sum_{i=1}^{M} a_k{}^* w_k{}^{(j)}(\phi_j)\right] p(\phi_j)\, d\phi_j$$

$$(11\text{-}1\text{-}33)$$

This shows immediately that when the channel states are known perfectly, the optimum-combining rule for either coherent or noncoherent signaling involves forming the linear sums

$$b^{(j)}(\phi_j) = \sum_{k=1}^{M} a_k{}^* w_k{}^{(j)}(\phi_j) \qquad (11\text{-}1\text{-}34)$$

That is, the processed voltages from each branch are weighted according to the amplitude of the channel gain, with a phase factor in each channel compensating for that introduced by the channel.   This can be put into more familiar form by recalling that each of the $w_k{}^{(j)}(\phi_j)$ is a linear functional on the corresponding $z_k(t)$.   Since (11-1-34) is a linear sum, the order of performing these linear operations can clearly be reversed. Thus one could equally well form first the linear combination

$$\beta(t) = \sum_{k=1}^{M} a_k{}^* z_k(t) \qquad (11\text{-}1\text{-}35)$$

and then filter this to form the $b^{(j)}(\phi_j)$, using the matched filters indicated in (11-1-30) or any reasonable suboptimum filtering.   Clearly, (11-1-35) is exactly the maximal-ratio combining rule of Chap. 10, for the case where all receiver noises are identical.   (Inspection of the preceding derivation also shows that if the receiver noises had been assumed to be of different intensity, the more general maximal-ratio combining rule of Chap. 10 would have resulted.)

Finally, as explained earlier, for coherent signaling $p(\phi_j)$ is to be regarded as a delta function, hence according to (11-1-33) the binary decision is made according to the value of k for which $\operatorname{Re}\{b^{(j)}\}$ is a maximum.   This last operation is merely the remaining mathematical statement specifying a synchronous detection operation.   Likewise, for noncoherent signaling, the assumption is that $p(\phi_j) = 1/2\pi$, and hence

(Chap. 2) the decision parameters are given in terms of the modified Bessel function $I_0(|b^{(j)}|)$, and the decision is made according to the value of j for which $|b^{(j)}|$ is a maximum. It also follows from the above discussion that the binary probability-of-error calculations of Chap. 10, assuming maximal-ratio combining, apply directly as the performance for the optimum diversity receiving structures in the case of perfect knowledge of the channel states.

Partial Knowledge of the Channel States. Next, we discuss the case where the channel states are partially known. As described earlier, for Rayleigh fading with a specular component, the complex channel gain on each diversity branch is a complex nonzero-mean Gaussian process. Following the earlier detailed discussion of channel estimates derived by linear smoothing of a pilot tone plus receiver noise, the partial knowledge of the channel states is reflected in a joint Gaussian p.d.f. for the channel states as given in (11-1-15),

$$p(\alpha_1, \ldots, \alpha_m) = \frac{1}{(2\pi)^M \det \mathbf{R}} \exp\left[-\tfrac{1}{2}(\boldsymbol{\alpha} - \hat{\boldsymbol{\alpha}})^T \mathbf{R}^{-1} (\boldsymbol{\alpha} - \hat{\boldsymbol{\alpha}})^*\right] \quad (11\text{-}1\text{-}36)$$

Again, $\boldsymbol{\alpha}$ is the column matrix with complex components α_k, $\hat{\boldsymbol{\alpha}}$ is the column matrix of the conditional means (the estimates of the channel state) and $\mathbf{R}$ is the covariance matrix reflecting the statistical uncertainty in these channel estimates.

In this general case, the average over the $\{\alpha_k\}$ in (11-1-31) can be performed as a special case of the results in Appendix B for the characteristic function of a Hermitian quadratic form in complex Gaussian variates. One can rewrite (11-1-31) by introducing the column vector $\mathbf{w}^{(j)}$ with components $w_k^{(j)}(\phi_j)$. Then, recalling the Hermitian nature of $\mathbf{R}(\mathbf{R}^T = \mathbf{R}^*)$, (11-1-31) can be usefully rewritten as

$$f_j = C \int p(\phi_j) \exp\left\{\tfrac{1}{2}[\mathbf{w}^{(j)T}\hat{\boldsymbol{\alpha}}^* + \hat{\boldsymbol{\alpha}}^T\mathbf{w}^{(j)*}] + \tfrac{1}{2}\mathbf{w}^{(j)T}\mathbf{R}\mathbf{w}^{(j)*}\right\} d\phi_j$$

$$\int \cdots \int \frac{\exp\left(-\tfrac{1}{2}\gamma_0\boldsymbol{\alpha}^T\boldsymbol{\alpha}^*\right)}{(2\pi)^M \det \mathbf{R}} \exp\left\{-\tfrac{1}{2}[\boldsymbol{\alpha} - \hat{\boldsymbol{\alpha}} - \mathbf{R}^T\mathbf{w}^{(j)}]^T\right.$$

$$\left. \mathbf{R}^{-1}[\boldsymbol{\alpha} - \hat{\boldsymbol{\alpha}} - \mathbf{R}^T\mathbf{w}^{(j)}]^*\right\} d\alpha_1 \ldots d\alpha_M \quad (11\text{-}1\text{-}37)$$

The multiple inner integral is now recognizable as a particular value of the Laplace-transform characteristic function of the Hermitian quadratic form $\boldsymbol{\alpha}^T\boldsymbol{\alpha}^*$, where $\boldsymbol{\alpha}$ is a complex Gaussian process with mean $\hat{\boldsymbol{\alpha}} + \mathbf{R}^T\mathbf{w}^{(j)}$ and covariance matrix $\mathbf{R}$. From the results of Appendix B, one obtains for the decision parameters

$$f_j = C \int p(\phi_j) \frac{1}{\det(\mathbf{I} + \gamma_0\mathbf{R}^*)} \exp\left\{\tfrac{1}{2}\mathbf{w}^{(j)T}\mathbf{R}\mathbf{w}^{(j)*} + \tfrac{1}{2}[\mathbf{w}^{(j)T}\hat{\boldsymbol{\alpha}}^* + \hat{\boldsymbol{\alpha}}^T\mathbf{w}^{(j)*}]\right\}$$

$$\exp\left\{-\tfrac{1}{2}\gamma_0[\hat{\boldsymbol{\alpha}} + \mathbf{R}^T\mathbf{w}^{(j)}]^T{}^*(\mathbf{I} + \gamma_0\mathbf{R}^*)^{-1}[\hat{\boldsymbol{\alpha}} + \mathbf{R}^T\mathbf{w}^{(j)}]\right\} d\phi_j \quad (11\text{-}1\text{-}38)$$

This can be written more compactly by noting that the order of multiplication is unimportant in a scalar product, for example $\mathbf{w}^{(j)T}\hat{\boldsymbol{\alpha}}^* = \hat{\boldsymbol{\alpha}}^{T*}\mathbf{w}^{(j)}$; that from the Hermitian nature of $\mathbf{R}$, $\mathbf{w}^{(j)T}\mathbf{R}\mathbf{w}^{(j)*} = \mathbf{w}^{(j)T*}\mathbf{R}^*\mathbf{w}^{(j)}$; and, as is easily proved, that

$$(\mathbf{I} + \gamma_0\mathbf{R}^*)^{-1}\mathbf{R}^T = \mathbf{R}^T(\mathbf{I} + \gamma_0\mathbf{R}^*)^{-1} \qquad (11\text{-}1\text{-}39)$$

Then after some algebra, and lumping into C a factor

$$\exp\left[-\tfrac{1}{2}\hat{\boldsymbol{\alpha}}^{T*}(\mathbf{R}^*)^{-1}\hat{\boldsymbol{\alpha}}\right]/\det(\mathbf{I} + \gamma_0\mathbf{R}^*)$$

(independent of j), (11-1-38) can be rewritten in either of two simply related alternative forms

$$f_j = C\int p(\phi_j)\exp\{\tfrac{1}{2}[\mathbf{w}^{(j)} + (\mathbf{R}^*)^{-1}\hat{\boldsymbol{\alpha}}]^{T*}[(\mathbf{R}^*)^{-1} + \gamma_0\mathbf{I}]^{-1}$$
$$[\mathbf{w}^{(j)} + (\mathbf{R}^*)^{-1}\hat{\boldsymbol{\alpha}}]\}\,d\phi_j, \qquad (11\text{-}1\text{-}40a)$$

$$= C\int p(\phi_j)\exp\{\tfrac{1}{2}[\mathbf{R}^*\mathbf{w}^{(j)} + \hat{\boldsymbol{\alpha}}]^{T*}[(\mathbf{R}^*)^{-1}(\mathbf{I} + \gamma_0\mathbf{R}^*)^{-1}]$$
$$[\mathbf{R}^*\mathbf{w}^{(j)} + \hat{\boldsymbol{\alpha}}]\}\,d\phi_j \qquad (11\text{-}1\text{-}40b)$$

In the case of coherent operation $[p(\phi_j) = \delta(\phi_j - \phi_0^{(j)})]$, the decision parameter in (11-1-40) is simply the integrand (with $\phi_j = \phi_0^{(j)}$). Since the value of an exponential varies monotonically with its argument, it is then sufficient to regard the latter as the decision parameters. Still using the notation f_j for these decision parameters (operationally equivalent to, but no longer identical with, the quantities f_j above), it follows from (11-1-40) that they can be written in the following equivalent forms:

$$f_j = [\mathbf{w}^{(j)} + (\mathbf{R}^*)^{-1}\hat{\boldsymbol{\alpha}}]^{T*}[(\mathbf{R}^*)^{-1} + \gamma_0\mathbf{I}]^{-1}[\mathbf{w}^{(j)} + (\mathbf{R}^*)^{-1}\hat{\boldsymbol{\alpha}}] \qquad (11\text{-}1\text{-}41)$$

$$= [\mathbf{R}^*\mathbf{w}^{(j)} + \hat{\boldsymbol{\alpha}}]^{T*}[(\mathbf{R}^*)^{-1}(\mathbf{I} + \gamma_0\mathbf{R}^*)^{-1}][\mathbf{R}^*\mathbf{w}^{(j)} + \hat{\boldsymbol{\alpha}}] \qquad (11\text{-}1\text{-}42)$$

Two additional equivalent forms, which differ from each other trivially, are

$$f_j = \mathbf{w}^{(j)T*}[(\mathbf{R}^*)^{-1} + \gamma_0\mathbf{I}]^{-1}\mathbf{w}^{(j)}$$
$$+ 2\mathrm{Re}\{\mathbf{w}^{(j)T*}[(\mathbf{R}^*)^{-1} + \gamma_0\mathbf{I}]^{-1}(\mathbf{R}^*)^{-1}\hat{\boldsymbol{\alpha}}\} \qquad (11\text{-}1\text{-}43)$$

$$= \mathbf{w}^{(j)T*}(\mathbf{I} + \gamma_0\mathbf{R}^*)^{-1}\mathbf{R}^*\mathbf{w}^{(j)} + 2\mathrm{Re}\{\mathbf{w}^{(j)T*}(\mathbf{I} + \gamma_0\mathbf{R}^*)^{-1}\hat{\boldsymbol{\alpha}}\} \qquad (11\text{-}1\text{-}44)$$

These are derived from the first and second respectively by dropping in each case the j-independent quadratic form in $\hat{\boldsymbol{\alpha}}$.

The receiving structures implied by these forms are typified in Fig. 11-1-2, corresponding to (11-1-41). Operations are shown only in terms of complex envelopes, indicating amplitude and phase weighting networks and multiplication operations.[1] In each diversity branch, a term involving the channel estimate is added to one involving each of the filter outputs ($j = 1, 2$ in the binary case). Then for each j, these terms are combined as indicated by the quadratic form. The form (11-1-43) is easily

---

[1] Note that if α_1, α_2 are complex envelopes, the complex envelope $\alpha_1^*\alpha_2$ can be obtained by having the carriers for α_1 and α_2 at two different frequencies f_1 and f_2 and then multiplying (mixing) the two waveforms, with extraction of the difference frequency components. The resulting complex envelope at frequency $f_1 - f_2$ is $\alpha_1^*\alpha_2$.

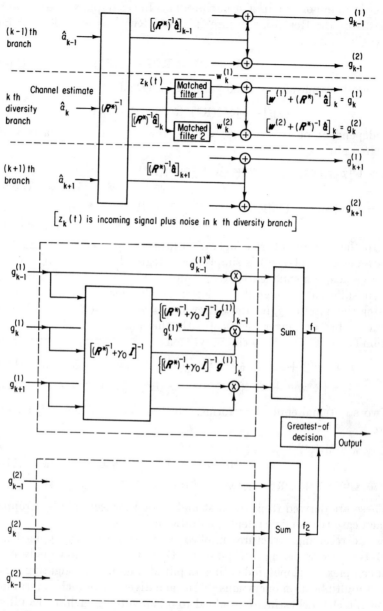

FIG. 11-1-2. Optimum decision structure for coherent operation, illustrated for binary case.

put into a closely similar form by recognizing that the first term is a quadratic Hermitian form, hence real; thus (11-1-43) can alternatively be written as

$$f_j = \text{Re} \{\mathbf{w}^{(j)T*}[(\mathbf{R}^*)^{-1} + \gamma_0\mathbf{I}]^{-1}[\mathbf{w}^{(j)} + 2(\mathbf{R}^*)^{-1}\hat{\mathbf{a}}]\} \quad (11\text{-}1\text{-}43a)$$

The Re { } operation here indicates a final explicit coherent-detection operation, against a reference at the appropriate frequency with phase based on the known stability of the signal phase. For other purposes (discussed later) it is more useful to regard (11-1-43) as the sum of two separate operations, the general structure of the receiver being obvious by comparison with Fig. 11-1-2. It is perhaps also fascinating to note that (11-1-41) and (11-1-42) do not involve any explicit coherent-detection operation such as in (11-1-43) or (11-1-43a). Rather the coherent nature of the signaling is implicit in the addition of the $\mathbf{w}^{(j)}$ components to the channel estimates [recall that each $\mathbf{w}^{(j)}$ already contains the result of an explicit cross-correlation against the jth of the waveform set[1]].

In the case of noncoherent operation, every component of $\mathbf{w}^{(j)}$ in (11-1-40a) or (11-1-40b) contains the identical factor $\exp(j\phi_j)$, with $p(\phi_j) = 1/2\pi$. To carry out the averaging then indicated in these equations, one can write specifically

$$\mathbf{w}^{(j)} = \mathbf{y}^{(j)} \exp(j\phi_j) \quad (11\text{-}1\text{-}45)$$

Thus the components of $\mathbf{y}^{(j)}$ include the channel phase, but the common signal phase has been written explicitly as a separate scalar factor. The form of the resulting integration is straightforward. Absorbing j-independent exponential factors into the constant C, the resulting decision parameters for noncoherent signaling can be written as

$$f_j = C \exp \{\tfrac{1}{2}[\mathbf{y}^{(j)T*}(\mathbf{I} + \gamma_0\mathbf{R}^*)^{-1}\mathbf{R}^*\mathbf{y}^{(j)}]\} I_0[|\mathbf{y}^{(j)T*}(\mathbf{I} + \gamma_0\mathbf{R})^{-1}\hat{\mathbf{a}}|] \quad (11\text{-}1\text{-}46)$$

Then, using (11-1-45) to return the form to one involving the filter outputs, one finds

$$f_j = C \exp \{\tfrac{1}{2}[\mathbf{w}^{(j)T*}(\mathbf{I} + \gamma_0\mathbf{R}^*)^{-1}\mathbf{R}^*\mathbf{w}^{(j)}]\}$$
$$I_0[|\mathbf{w}^{(j)T*}(\mathbf{I} + \gamma_0\mathbf{R}^*)^{-1}\hat{\mathbf{a}}|] \quad (11\text{-}1\text{-}47)$$

The nature of the decision parameters for noncoherent operation is now obvious. Unlike the coherent case, one must not only form certain quadratic forms and scalar products, but must in general perform functional operations upon these to determine the decision parameters. One extremely interesting comparison, however, is to compare (11-1-47) against (11-1-44). Exactly the same quadratic form and scalar product enter, the major difference in operation being that an envelope detector and functional operation is required in (11-1-47) where a coherent detection is implied in (11-1-44).

---

[1] See footnote in connection with Eq. (11-1-30).

We have just noted that the same two basic *combining* operations can be regarded to be involved on the $\mathbf{w}^{(j)}$ for either coherent or noncoherent system operation. One basic combining operation is independent of $\hat{\alpha}$ and merely depends on the *known* statistics of the process. This is a quadratic form in the $\mathbf{w}^{(j)}$ only, which is hence formed with a fixed network, no matter the states of the Rayleigh-fading channels.

The other operation is a scalar product between the $\mathbf{w}^{(j)}$ and a linear matrix operation on $\hat{\alpha}$, formed the same way but then detected differently for coherent versus noncoherent operation. Since the estimates $\hat{\alpha}$ will vary as the channels change instantaneous state, the nature of the weights on the components $w_k^{(j)}$ will also vary. The circuitry determining and controlling these varying weights, and forming the sum, is thus an "adaptive" network, very similar in sense to the diversity combiners discussed in Chap. 10. It is through this second operation that the total-diversity receiver is "adaptive" to changes in the channel. The nature of the optimum-diversity receiver structures are perhaps made more evident by examining below some limiting cases, which are also extremely relevant in practical applications.

Independently Fading Diversity Branches. In this case, the covariance matrix $\mathbf{R}$ is purely diagonal

$$(\mathbf{R})_{kj} = \lambda_k \, \delta_{kj} \tag{11-1-48}$$

with λ_k then representing the variance for the uncertainty in the estimate $\hat{\alpha}_k$ on the kth diversity branch. Then

$$(\mathbf{R}^{*-1})_{kj} = \frac{1}{\lambda_k} \, \delta_{kj} \tag{11-1-49}$$

and
$$[(\mathbf{R}^*)^{-1} + \gamma_0 \mathbf{I}]_{kj}^{-1} = \left(\frac{1}{\lambda_k} + \gamma_0\right)^{-1} \delta_{kj} \tag{11-1-50}$$

Thus the basic combining operations reduce in this case[1] to

$$\mathbf{w}^{(j)T*}[(\mathbf{R}^*)^{-1} + \gamma_0 \mathbf{I}]^{-1} \mathbf{w}^{(j)} = \sum_{k=1}^{M} \frac{|w_k^{(j)}|^2}{\gamma_0 + (1/\lambda_k)}$$

$$= \sum_{k=1}^{M} \frac{\lambda_k}{1 + \gamma_0 \lambda_k} |w_k^{(j)}|^2 \tag{11-1-51}$$

and
$$\mathbf{w}^{(j)T*}(\mathbf{I} + \gamma_0 \mathbf{R}^*)^{-1} \hat{\alpha} = \sum_{k=1}^{M} \frac{\hat{\alpha}_k w_k^{(j)*}}{1 + \gamma_0 \lambda_k} \tag{11-1-52}$$

Thus with independently fading branches the squared magnitudes of the individual diversity branch filter outputs are used in the fixed-weighted sums; and separately, each filter output is mixed against its channel estimate and the results added in another weighted sum based

[1] E.g., Turin, 1956, *loc. cit.*

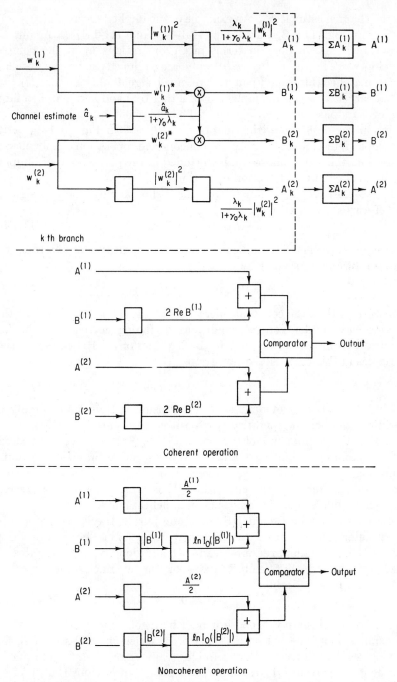

FIG. 11-1-3. Optimum diversity receiver for independently fading branches.

on the channel estimates.   An example of the implied receiver structure is shown in Fig. 11-1-3, based on (11-1-44) and (11-1-47).   Again, the structure is shown only in terms of the operations upon the complex envelopes.   The quantities $w_k{}^{(1)}$, $w_k{}^{(2)}$ are assumed to be the result of exact matched filtering upon the received signal plus noise $z_k(t)$.   As noted earlier, this can be implemented either by bandpass matched filtering or bandpass cross-correlation.   This does not affect the quadratic forms in the $w_k{}^{(1)}$, $w_k{}^{(2)}$ [the quantities $A^{(1)}$, $A^{(2)}$ in Fig. 11-1-3], or the envelope detection operations in noncoherent operation.   In coherent operation, the signal phase can be included in the phase reference implied in the final coherent detection operation.

Phase-shift Keying.   For binary phase-shift keying, the two signaled waveforms are related by

$$s^{(1)}(t;\phi_1) = -s^{(2)}(t;\phi_2) \qquad (11\text{-}1\text{-}53)$$

Consequently, (11-1-30) indicates that the quantities of interest after initial filtering are related by

$$w_k{}^{(1)}(\phi_1) = -w_k{}^{(2)}(\phi_2) \qquad (11\text{-}1\text{-}54)$$

Considering then the coherent-operation case in (11-1-44), it is clear that in this case, under general conditions of fading correlation, the first quadratic form in f_j is the same for both values of j.   Hence the decision variables in this case reduce simply to

$$f_j = \text{Re} \left[\mathbf{w}^{(j)T*}(\mathbf{I} + \gamma_0\mathbf{R}^*)^{-1}\hat{\boldsymbol{\alpha}} \right] \qquad (11\text{-}1\text{-}55)$$

With (11-1-54), it is evident that the decision is thus made simply by deciding whether the quantity f_1 is positive or negative.   It is also evident that the components of the vector $(\mathbf{I} + \gamma_0\mathbf{R}^*)^{-1}\hat{\boldsymbol{\alpha}}$ serve as maximal-ratio combining weighting factors in the respective branches, including canceling out channel phase.   It is clear, therefore, that with some reasonable estimate of the channel, PSK is possible; also, that PSK is impossible unless there is some such channel estimate.

Zero Estimate of Channel State.   For purely Rayleigh fading with no specular component on any diversity channel, the Gaussian multiplicative channel gains are zero-mean.   If additionally, no estimates are made of the "instantaneous" states of the channels, then recalling (11-1-16b), in our formulas

$$\hat{\boldsymbol{\alpha}} \equiv \mathbf{0} \qquad (11\text{-}1\text{-}56)$$

This may occur simply because it may be inconvenient or too costly to transmit a pilot tone or to use a signal from which channel-state information is readily derived.   For example, while channel-state information can be derived from DPSK signals, it is not at all obvious that information could equivalently be derived from noncoherent FSK signals.   Or, fading, while still "slow," may be suspected to vary too rapidly to allow long enough smoothing times for worthwhile operation. Above all, it will be seen in the next section that the performance differences between having a channel estimate available and having none available but using the appropriate optimum combining for that case, are sufficiently small to make quite relevant the possibility of not using any channel estimates.

With $\hat{\alpha} = 0$ and $I_0(0) = 1$, the decision parameters for *both* the coherent and noncoherent signaling cases, in (11-1-44) and (11-1-47), respectively, are the *identical* fixed-weighted sum, namely (again keeping the notation f_j for the decision parameters),

$$f_j = \mathbf{w}^{(j)T*}(\mathbf{I} + \gamma_0 \mathbf{R}^*)^{-1}\mathbf{R}^*\mathbf{w}^{(j)} \tag{11-1-57}$$

Here, as shown by (11-1-16a) with $\mathbf{c} = \mathbf{0}$, $\mathbf{R}$ will now be the a priori covariance matrix for the fading on the several channels. The form (11-1-57) is not surprising, in that $\hat{\alpha} = 0$ implies that the individual diversity channel phases are completely unknown. Hence coherent combining is essentially impossible. As implied in discussing phase-shift keying above, detection based on signal phase is also impossible. Indeed, in (11-1-57) the factor $\exp(j\phi_j)$ associated with all the components of $\mathbf{w}^{(j)}$ does not enter at all into the decision parameter f_j since both $\mathbf{w}^{(j)}$ and $\mathbf{w}^{(j)*}$ appear in the quadratic form. Hence the alternative symbols of the signaling alphabet must not in any way depend on phase for distinguishability. Regardless of whether the transmitted waveforms are phase-stable, only noncoherent detection will have any meaning in this case of unknown channel phases. For maximum distinguishability in binary signaling the symbols should then be orthogonal; e.g., in binary signaling, this statistically maximizes the difference between the two decision parameters.[1]

If the Rayleigh-fading channels are also fading independently, (11-1-51) shows that the decision parameter of (11-1-57) reduces simply to the fixed-weighted sum,

$$f_j = \sum_{k=1}^{M} \frac{\lambda_k}{1 + \gamma_0 \lambda_k} |w_k^{(j)}|^2 = \sum_{k=1}^{M} \frac{P_k}{1 + \gamma_0 P_k} |w_k^{(j)}|^2 \tag{11-1-58}$$

Since there is no estimate of the channels, and since they are fading independently, we have made the obvious connection,

$$\lambda_k = P_k \tag{11-1-59}$$

where P_k is the average signal power level on the kth channel. Finally, if all diversity branches are of equal intensity, the decision parameter becomes simply

$$f_j = \sum_{k=1}^{M} |w_k^{(j)}|^2 \tag{11-1-60}$$

---

[1] Note, with phase-stable transmission, DPSK is an allowed form involving noncoherent detection. As will be seen, the requisite combining operation follows strictly this point of view, rather than a phase-detection concept.

This is the square-law combiner originally described by Pierce.[1] The simple generalization represented by (11-1-57) and (11-1-58) can be termed generalized quadratic combining. It should be recognized that (11-1-41) and (11-1-42) indicate that for *coherent* operation, for more arbitrary fading conditions, the optimum receiver can also be structured as a generalized quadratic combiner.

As pointed out by Pierce, the optimum combiner and noncoherent operation described above represents the *minimum* capability which should be achievable over the slow, multiplicative-fading channel, when the channel statistics are Rayleigh and known but there is no accompanying knowledge of the instantaneous states of the channels. The maximum capability occurs when there is an exact knowledge of the channel states, in which case we earlier showed that maximal-ratio combining should be used, with best performance achieved by using coherent PSK signaling. In Sec. 11-2, we shall compare performance in these two limiting cases, as well as in intermediate situations.

Additional Comments. From these results on optimal-diversity reception in slow, multiplicative fading, we shall later qualitatively infer the nature of optimum receivers when the slow- or nonselective-fading assumptions are removed. In effect, as explained in Sec. 11-4, analyses for *selective fading* fall back upon the principles inferred from the slow, multiplicative-fading assumption by regarding the channel multipath structure to be composed of nonselective-fading segments (e.g., as described earlier in Sec. 9-2). As for rapidity of fading, this limits the signal coherence, and its effects on optimum receiving rules can be directly inferred from the square-law combining principle.[2]

However, defining optimum receiver structures as we have done in this section is only a first step. Knowledge of these structures is useful only insofar as it leads to determination of upper bounds on performance, and design concepts for practical diversity receivers, either optimum or suboptimum. For suboptimum receivers as well, the picture is not complete unless their performance can be analyzed.

Consequently, the remainder of this chapter is devoted to selected performance results and related aspects of both suboptimum and optimum receivers. These are chosen to indicate the nature of the theoretical analysis problem and the practical principles to be used for engineering intuition in designing for fading channels. It may help in reading to keep in mind the essential limiting cases under slow, multiplicative fading. On the one hand, maximal-ratio combining with coherent PSK operation represents an ultimate in performance, achieved on the assumption of perfect instantaneous knowledge of the channels. On the other hand,

---

[1] Pierce, *loc. cit.*

[2] The interested reader should also refer to the works of Kailath and Turin, referenced earlier; see also Sec. 11-4.

with knowledge of the transmitted signals but no knowledge of the channel states, one should have to fare no more poorly than square-law combining (including such nonessential modifications as occur when some channels are on the average weaker than others, fading nonindependently, or at times more rapidly than the slow-fading assumption used in the derivations above).

11.2. Performance of Quadratic Combiner Systems in Slow, Multiplicative Fading

In Chap. 10, we have already evaluated digital performance with maximal-ratio combining, the optimum operation when channel states are perfectly known. Here, we shall further evaluate the performance of certain diversity receivers optimum under less ideal conditions. The models for which detailed analysis is available are limited and involve various restrictions, which will be introduced at appropriate points. We start by outlining a general analysis for a quadratic combiner, as already observed to enter in many of these receiver structures.

General Character of the Quadratic Combiner Analysis. Specifically, consider a binary signaling, M-fold-diversity receiver based upon the decision parameter described by (11-1-41). To recapitulate, this diversity receiver makes its decisions by determining the larger of a pair of decision parameters f_1 and f_2, expressed by quadratic forms as follows:

$$f_1 = [\mathbf{w}^{(1)} + (\mathbf{R}^*)^{-1}\hat{\boldsymbol{\alpha}}]^{T*}[(\mathbf{R}^*)^{-1} + \gamma_0\mathbf{I}]^{-1}[\mathbf{w}^{(1)} + (\mathbf{R}^*)^{-1}\hat{\boldsymbol{\alpha}}] \quad (11\text{-}2\text{-}1)$$
$$f_2 = [\mathbf{w}^{(2)} + (\mathbf{R}^*)^{-1}\hat{\boldsymbol{\alpha}}]^{T*}[(\mathbf{R}^*)^{-1} + \gamma_0\mathbf{I}]^{-1}[\mathbf{w}^{(2)} + (\mathbf{R}^*)^{-1}\hat{\boldsymbol{\alpha}}] \quad (11\text{-}2\text{-}2)$$

The $M \times 1$ matrix $\hat{\boldsymbol{\alpha}}$ comprises the set of estimates of the states of the M diversity channels derived from measurements on the channels; $\mathbf{R}$ is the $M \times M$ covariance matrix of the statistical uncertainties of the channel states about these estimates; and γ_0 is a normalized ratio of symbol energy to the power spectral density of the receiver noise,

$$\gamma_0 = \frac{\int_0^T |s^{(1)}(t)|^2 \, dt}{n_0} = \frac{\int_0^T |s^{(2)}(t)|^2 \, dt}{n_0} \quad (11\text{-}2\text{-}3)$$

The signal phase parameter employed in our earlier notation has been suppressed here, since its significance has been fully explored in deriving the various combining rules. Thus $s^{(1)}(t)$ and $s^{(2)}(t)$ here represent the signaling waveforms, assumed to be of equal energy. The average SNR on each diversity channel is given by γ_0 multiplied by the mean-square magnitude of the channel gain.

Within a convenient normalization, the components of the $M \times 1$ matrices $\mathbf{w}^{(1)}$ and $\mathbf{w}^{(2)}$ are the results of filtering the signal and noise in the several branches, with filters designed to respond to $s^{(1)}(t)$ and $s^{(2)}(t)$, respectively. Optimally, these may be matched filters (or equivalent cross-correlators), but more generally, as discussed following (11-1-30), they may be suboptimum filters. With $z_k(t)$ representing the received signal pulse plus noise over $(0,T)$ in the kth branch and with similar filters assumed used in all diversity branches, the components of $\mathbf{w}^{(1)}$ and $\mathbf{w}^{(2)}$ are given by

$$w_k{}^{(j)} = \frac{1}{n_0} \int_0^T h^{(j)}(T - \tau) z_k(\tau) \, d\tau \qquad (11\text{-}2\text{-}4)$$

where $h^{(1)}(\tau)$, $h^{(2)}(\tau)$ are the pair of filter responses.[1] In turn, with α_k the complex channel gain on the kth branch during $(0,T)$,

$$z_k(t) = \alpha_k s(t) + n_k(t) \qquad (11\text{-}2\text{-}5)$$

where $s(t)$ is either $s^{(1)}(t)$ or $s^{(2)}(t)$, according to whichever binary state is being signaled, and $n_k(t)$ is the additive noise on the kth branch.

Specifically, we assume $s^{(1)}(t)$ to be signaled. Then the probability of error is

$$P_e = \text{Prob} \, (f_1 < f_2) \qquad (11\text{-}2\text{-}6)$$

It is readily shown that the same probability of an error is obtained when $s^{(2)}(t)$ is signaled. Examining (11-2-4), the signals will enter into the decision through the parameters

$$h_{11} = \frac{1}{n_0} \int_0^T h^{(1)}(T - \tau) s^{(1)}(\tau) \, d\tau \qquad h_{12} = \frac{1}{n_0} \int_0^T h^{(2)}(T - \tau) s^{(1)}(\tau) \, d\tau$$

$$(11\text{-}2\text{-}7)$$

and the noises through the parameters

$$n_k{}^{(1)} = \frac{1}{n_0} \int_0^T h^{(1)}(T - \tau) n_k(\tau) \, d\tau \qquad n_k{}^{(2)} = \frac{1}{n_0} \int_0^T h^{(2)}(T - \tau) n_k(\tau) \, d\tau$$

$$(11\text{-}2\text{-}8)$$

Then in (11-2-4),

$$\mathbf{w}^{(1)} = h_{11}\boldsymbol{\alpha} + \mathbf{n}^{(1)} \qquad \mathbf{w}^{(2)} = h_{12}\boldsymbol{\alpha} + \mathbf{n}^{(2)} \qquad (11\text{-}2\text{-}9)$$

where $\boldsymbol{\alpha}$ is the $M \times 1$ matrix of the channel states $\{\alpha_k\}$.

The basic variables in the decision functionals of (11-2-1) and (11-2-2) are defined by the $M \times 1$ column matrices $\boldsymbol{\xi}^{(1)}$ and $\boldsymbol{\xi}^{(2)}$,

$$\boldsymbol{\xi}^{(1)} = \mathbf{w}^{(1)} + (\mathbf{R}^*)^{-1}\hat{\boldsymbol{\alpha}} = h_{11}\boldsymbol{\alpha} + (\mathbf{R}^*)^{-1}\hat{\boldsymbol{\alpha}} + \mathbf{n}^{(1)} \qquad (11\text{-}2\text{-}10a)$$
$$\boldsymbol{\xi}^{(2)} = \mathbf{w}^{(2)} + (\mathbf{R}^*)^{-1}\hat{\boldsymbol{\alpha}} = h_{12}\boldsymbol{\alpha} + (\mathbf{R}^*)^{-1}\hat{\boldsymbol{\alpha}} + \mathbf{n}^{(2)} \qquad (11\text{-}2\text{-}10b)$$

Since $\boldsymbol{\alpha}, \hat{\boldsymbol{\alpha}}, \mathbf{n}^{(1)}$, and $\mathbf{n}^{(2)}$ are all complex Gaussian variates, so are $\boldsymbol{\xi}^{(1)}$ and $\boldsymbol{\xi}^{(2)}$. To condense the notation further, define a $2M \times 1$ column matrix

---

[1] In coherent PSK, there may be physically only one signal filter in each diversity branch, its sign providing the basis for decision. In our formulation, this would correspond to $h^{(1)}(t) = -h^{(2)}(t)$. For mathematical convenience in treating the more general case, the analysis here will assume each branch receiver provides two quantities (differing only by sign in the case cited), loosely referring to these as being two filter outputs in each diversity branch.

ξ, with $\xi^{(1)}$ and $\xi^{(2)}$ as $M \times 1$ partitions,

$$\xi = \begin{pmatrix} \xi^{(1)} \\ \hline \xi^{(2)} \end{pmatrix} \tag{11-2-11}$$

We also define a partitioned $2M \times 2M$ matrix $\mathbf{Q}$,

$$\mathbf{Q} = \begin{pmatrix} [(\mathbf{R}^*)^{-1} + \gamma_0\mathbf{I}]^{-1} & 0 \\ \hline 0 & -[(\mathbf{R}^*)^{-1} + \gamma_0\mathbf{I}]^{-1} \end{pmatrix} \tag{11-2-12}$$

Then one can write

$$f_1 - f_2 = \xi^{T*}\mathbf{Q}\xi \tag{11-2-13}$$

In terms of this quadratic form, the probability of error becomes

$$P_e = \text{Prob }(f_1 - f_2 < 0) = \text{Prob }(\xi^{T*}\mathbf{Q}\xi < 0) \tag{11-2-14}$$

Thus one is again faced with a problem in the distribution of a Hermitian quadratic form in complex Gaussian variates. The variates themselves have statistics defined by their means

$$\langle\xi\rangle = \begin{pmatrix} h_{11}\langle\alpha\rangle + (\mathbf{R}^*)^{-1}\langle\hat{\alpha}\rangle \\ \hline h_{12}\langle\alpha\rangle + (\mathbf{R}^*)^{-1}\langle\hat{\alpha}\rangle \end{pmatrix} \tag{11-2-15}$$

and by their covariance matrix

$$\mathbf{L} = \tfrac{1}{2}\langle(\xi - \langle\xi\rangle)^*(\xi - \langle\xi\rangle)^T\rangle = \begin{pmatrix} \mathbf{A}_{11} & \mathbf{A}_{12} \\ \mathbf{A}_{12}{}^{T*} & \mathbf{A}_{22} \end{pmatrix} \tag{11-2-16a}$$

where

$$\mathbf{A}_{kj} = \tfrac{1}{2}\langle[\xi^{(k)} - \langle\xi^{(k)}\rangle]^*[\xi^{(j)} - \langle\xi^{(j)}\rangle]^T\rangle \tag{11-2-16b}$$

We recall that the additive noises are assumed to be independent of the multiplicative noises, mutually independent between the diversity branches, and spectrally flat over the receiver bandwidths with equal (one-sided) noise power density n_0 in all branches.[1] Thus,

$$\tfrac{1}{2}\langle n_k{}^*(t)n_j(t + \tau)\rangle = \delta_{kj}n_0\,\delta(\tau) \tag{11-2-17}$$

Hence for the quantities $n_k^{(1)}$ and $n_k^{(2)}$,

$$\tfrac{1}{2}\langle n_k^{(1)*}n_j^{(1)}\rangle = N_{11}\delta_{kj} \qquad N_{11} = \frac{1}{n_0}\int_0^T |h^{(1)}(x)|^2\,dx$$

$$= \frac{1}{n_0}\int_{-\infty}^{\infty} |H^{(1)}(f)|^2\,df \tag{11-2-18}$$

$$\tfrac{1}{2}\langle n_k^{(2)*}n_j^{(2)}\rangle = N_{22}\delta_{kj} \qquad N_{22} = \frac{1}{n_0}\int_0^T |h^{(2)}(x)|^2\,dx$$

$$= \frac{1}{n_0}\int_{-\infty}^{\infty} |H^{(2)}(f)|^2\,df \tag{11-2-19}$$

$$\tfrac{1}{2}\langle n_k^{(1)*}n_j^{(2)}\rangle = N_{12}\delta_{kj} \qquad N_{12} = \frac{1}{n_0}\int_0^T h^{(1)*}(x)h^{(2)}(x)\,dx$$

$$= \frac{1}{n_0}\int_{-\infty}^{\infty} H^{(1)*}(f)H^{(2)}(f)\,df \tag{11-2-20}$$

[1] Again, recall that if the noise levels are not equal in all branches, the gain constants in the branches can be redefined to make them so, with corresponding changes in the signal levels.

Here $H^{(k)}(f)$ is the transfer function corresponding to $h^{(k)}(t)$, on the assumption that the latter vanishes outside of $(0,T)$.

The matrix of Gaussian variates $\hat{\alpha}$ is precisely defined from (11-1-16b) as

$$\hat{\alpha} = \langle \alpha \rangle + \mathbf{c}^*(\mathbf{g}^{-1})^*(\boldsymbol{\beta} - \langle \boldsymbol{\beta} \rangle) \qquad (11\text{-}2\text{-}21)$$

and $\mathbf{R}$ from (11-1-16a) as

$$\mathbf{R} = \mathbf{a} - \mathbf{cg}^{-1}\mathbf{c}^{T*} \qquad (11\text{-}2\text{-}22)$$

where $\boldsymbol{\beta}$ represents the actual measurements on the pilot tones and the other matrices are covariances in α and $\boldsymbol{\beta}$, defined in writing (11-1-10). Using these definitions, (11-2-15) becomes

$$\langle \xi \rangle = \begin{pmatrix} [h_{11}\mathbf{I} + (\mathbf{R}^*)^{-1}]\langle \alpha \rangle \\ [h_{12}\mathbf{I} + (\mathbf{R}^*)^{-1}]\langle \alpha \rangle \end{pmatrix} \qquad (11\text{-}2\text{-}23)$$

and the elements of $\mathbf{L}$ in (11-2-16) have the form

$$\mathbf{A}_{kj} = (h_{1k}{}^*\mathbf{I} + \mathbf{R}^{-1})(\mathbf{a} - \mathbf{R})(h_{1j}\mathbf{I} + \mathbf{R}^{-1}) + h_{1k}{}^*h_{1j}\mathbf{R} + N_{kj}\mathbf{I}$$
$$(11\text{-}2\text{-}24)$$

where $\quad \mathbf{a} - \mathbf{R} = \mathbf{cg}^{-1}\mathbf{c}^{T*} \qquad (11\text{-}2\text{-}25)$

These forms describe the statistics of ξ. The problem, in (11-2-14), is to determine the probability that the Hermitian quadratic form

$$q = \xi^{T*}\mathbf{Q}\xi^* \qquad (11\text{-}2\text{-}26)$$

is negative, with $\mathbf{Q}$ defined by (11-2-12). In Chap. 8 and Appendix A, a complete solution is given to this mathematical problem for the non-diversity case when ξ has only two components. A generalization of this general closed-form result to greater dimensionality of ξ is not presently available. Instead, following Turin's calculations,[1] the results of Appendix B can be used to characterize $p(q)$, the p.d.f. of q, and then to portray some properties of the general solution.

Referring to Appendix B, one can immediately write the characteristic function of the p.d.f. $p(q)$ as

$$F_q(\eta) = \int_{-\infty}^{\infty} \exp(j\eta q)p(q)\,dq \qquad (11\text{-}2\text{-}27)$$

$$= \frac{\exp[j\eta\langle\xi\rangle^{T*}(\mathbf{Q}^{-1} - 2j\eta\mathbf{L}^*)^{-1}\langle\xi\rangle]}{\det(\mathbf{I} - 2j\eta\mathbf{L}^*\mathbf{Q})} \qquad (11\text{-}2\text{-}28)$$

Expressing $p(q)$ as the inverse transform of $F_q(\eta)$, the probability required

---

[1] Results derived by Turin, referenced in Chap. 8 and Appendix A, were based on this alternative approach even in the two-component case. Turin's important general results on performance of the quadratic combiner are contained in G. L. Turin, On Optimal Diversity Reception, II, *IRE Trans. Commun. Systems*, vol. CS-10, pp. 22–31, March, 1962.

in (11-2-14) can be expressed as

$$P_e = \text{Prob } (q < 0) = \int_{-\infty}^{0} p(q) \, dq = \frac{1}{2\pi} \int_{-\infty}^{0} \int_{-\infty}^{\infty} \exp \, (-j\eta q) F_q(\eta) \, d\eta \, dq$$

$$= \frac{1}{2\pi} \int_{-\infty+jc}^{\infty+jc} \frac{F_q(\eta)}{-j\eta} \, d\eta \tag{11-2-29}$$

with $c > 0$ for convergence of the evaluated q integral.

In view of the complicated form in (11-2-28), the calculation indicated in (11-2-29) is not readily performed. Instead, to obtain useful results, we shall have to confine ourselves to certain cases of special interest.

Pure Rayleigh Fading. Purely Rayleigh fading, with zero specular component, is defined by $\langle \alpha \rangle = \mathbf{0}$. Then in (11-2-23),

$$\langle \xi \rangle = \mathbf{0} \tag{11-2-30}$$

The form in (11-2-28) then simplifies considerably, to

$$F_q(\eta) = \frac{1}{\det \, (\mathbf{I} - 2j\eta \mathbf{L}^* \mathbf{Q})} \tag{11-2-31}$$

The denominator here is a $2M$th order polynomial in η. Hence, *in principle*, the integration in (11-2-29) can now be carried out via residue calculations. The form is more readily discerned by identifying $\{\sigma_k\}$, $k = 1, \ldots, 2M$, as the set of $2M$ eigenvalues of the matrix $\mathbf{L}^* \mathbf{Q}$. Then (e.g., see Appendix B), (11-2-31) can be rewritten as

$$F_q(\eta) = \frac{1}{\displaystyle\prod_{k=1}^{2M} (1 - 2j\eta\sigma_k)} \tag{11-2-32}$$

Although the matrix product $\mathbf{L}^* \mathbf{Q}$ is not in itself generally Hermitian (unless $\mathbf{L}^*$ and $\mathbf{Q}$ happen to commute), it can be shown (and is already implied by the derivation in Appendix B) that the eigenvalues are real. Since $\mathbf{L}$ is positive semidefinite, all its eigenvalues are positive or zero; on the other hand, from the form of $\mathbf{Q}$ in (11-2-12), it is apparent that half its eigenvalues are positive and the other half negative. It can then be shown that of the nonzero eigenvalues of $\mathbf{L}^* \mathbf{Q}$, half are also positive and half negative.[1] Then in evaluating (11-2-32) by residue calculations, there are at most a total of M poles involved in the residue calculation, all located on the imaginary axis.

Unfortunately, even in this Rayleigh-fading case, one cannot make useful general statements concerning performance without further specialization.

---

[1] This property follows from the invariance of the "signature" of a matrix under such transformations.

Signaling without Pilot Tone.[1] One special limiting case is that when no pilot tone is used. As noted earlier, with slow, multiplicative, purely Rayleigh fading still assumed, the optimum receiver becomes a quadratic combiner employing noncoherent detection in each branch. When all branches are of equal strength and fading independently, the combiner reduces to a square-law combiner.

When there is zero pilot tone, the cross-covariance matrix c is identically zero, so that in (11-2-24) and (11-2-25),

$$cg^{-1}c^{T*} = 0 \tag{11-2-33}$$

and in (11-2-16),

$$L = \begin{pmatrix} |h_{11}|^2 R + N_{11}I & h_{11}{}^*h_{12}R + N_{12}I \\ h_{11}h_{12}{}^*R + N_{12}{}^*I & |h_{12}|^2 R + N_{22}I \end{pmatrix} \tag{11-2-34}$$

Then the matrix product L^*Q has the form

$$L^*Q = \begin{pmatrix} (|h_{11}|^2 R^* + N_{11}I)[(R^*)^{-1} + \gamma_0 I]^{-1} & -(h_{11}h_{12}{}^*R^* + N_{12}{}^*I)[(R^*)^{-1} + \gamma_0 I]^{-1} \\ (h_{11}{}^*h_{12}R^* + N_{12}I)[(R^*)^{-1} + \gamma_0 I]^{-1} & -(|h_{12}|^2 R^* + N_{22}I)[(R^*)^{-1} + \gamma_0 I]^{-1} \end{pmatrix} \tag{11-2-35}$$

In this form, the partitions are all functions of only the matrix R^*, hence the eigenvalues of L^*Q can be shown to be directly related to those of R^*. Since all the partitions are functions only of R^*, they commute. Moreover, the determinant of a partitioned form where the partitions commute can be written as[2]

$$\det \begin{pmatrix} A & B \\ C & D \end{pmatrix} = \det (AD - BC) \tag{11-2-36}$$

The eigenvalues of the matrix in (11-2-35) are the $2M$ solutions σ to the polynomial (determinantal) equation

$$\det (L^*Q - \sigma I) = 0 \tag{11-2-37}$$

With (11-2-36) this reduces to evaluating an $M \times M$ determinant involving only a matrix function of R^*. In turn, this is readily solved by recalling that if $f(R)$ is a matrix function of R, its eigenvalues are given by

$$F_k = f(\lambda_k) \tag{11-2-38}$$

where λ_k are the successive eigenvalues of R. From (11-2-35) to (11-2-37), one finds two eigenvalues of L^*Q for each of the λ_k, given by

$$\left. \begin{matrix} \sigma_k{}^{(1)} \\ \sigma_k{}^{(2)} \end{matrix} \right\} = \frac{1}{2} \frac{1}{(1/\lambda_k) + \gamma_0} \{ (|h_{11}|^2 - |h_{12}|^2)\lambda_k + (N_{11} - N_{22})$$

$$\pm \sqrt{[(|h_{11}|^2 + |h_{12}|^2)\lambda_k + (N_{11} + N_{22})]^2 - 4|h_{11}h_{12}{}^*\lambda_k + N_{12}{}^*|^2} \} \tag{11-2-39}$$

---

[1] The analyses in this subsection closely follow Turin, 1961, *loc. cit.*, except for not assuming matched-filter receivers in each branch at the outset.

[2] F. R. Gantmacher, "Theory of Matrices," vol. 1, p. 46, Chelsea Publishing Company, New York, 1959.

Since $\mathbf{R}$ is positive semidefinite, the λ_k are all positive or zero; then it can be shown that of each pair of eigenvalues in (11-2-39), the first $[\sigma_k{}^{(1)}]$ is positive and the second $[\sigma_k{}^{(2)}]$ is negative. In general the second is also smaller in magnitude.

Simpler forms result, as derived directly by Turin, when the receiver filters are assumed to be matched to the pair of signaling waveforms. Then in (11-2-7),

$$h^{(j)}(T - \tau) = s^{(j)*}(\tau) \tag{11-2-40}$$

Recalling the definition of γ_0 in (11-2-3) and defining

$$\mu = \frac{1}{\gamma_0} \int_0^T \frac{s^{(1)}(\tau)s^{(2)*}(\tau) \, d\tau}{n_0} \tag{11-2-41}$$

as the measure of nonorthogonality between the two signal states, the parameters in (11-2-7) and (11-2-18) to (11-2-20) become

$$\begin{aligned} h_{11} = N_{11} = N_{22} &= \gamma_0 \\ h_{12} = N_{12} &= \gamma_0\mu \end{aligned} \tag{11-2-42}$$

Then, with some algebra, the result (11-2-39) reduces to

$$\left.\begin{array}{c} \sigma_k{}^{(1)} \\ \sigma_k{}^{(2)} \end{array}\right\} = \frac{\gamma_0\lambda_k}{1 + \gamma_0\lambda_k} \left\{ \frac{\gamma_0\lambda_k}{2}(1 - |\mu|^2) \pm \sqrt{\left[\frac{\gamma_0\lambda_k}{2}(1 - |\mu|^2) + 1\right]^2 - |\mu|^2} \right\} \tag{11-2-43}$$

or, in the form closely like that written by Turin (where $\gamma_0\lambda_k$ represented normalized eigenvalues),

$$\left.\begin{array}{c} \sigma_k{}^{(1)} \\ \sigma_k{}^{(2)} \end{array}\right\} = \frac{1}{2}\frac{\gamma_0{}^2\lambda_k{}^2(1 - |\mu|^2)}{1 + \gamma_0\lambda_k} \left[1 \pm \sqrt{1 + 4\frac{1 + \gamma_0\lambda_k}{\gamma_0{}^2\lambda_k{}^2(1 - |\mu|^2)}} \right] \tag{11-2-44}$$

In (11-2-43) or (11-2-44), it is readily shown that if one denotes each $\sigma_k{}^{(1)}$ by μ_k,

$$\mu_k = \sigma_k{}^{(1)} \tag{11-2-45a}$$

then

$$\sigma_k{}^{(2)} = -\frac{\mu_k}{1 + \mu_k} \tag{11-2-45b}$$

Note that γ_0 and λ_k enter these equations always through the product $\gamma_0\lambda_k$, as expected from the original definition of γ_0 and the interpretation that the λ_k, the eigenvalues of $\mathbf{R}$, represent the average signal intensities of the (statistically) independent multiplicative fading components of the M diversity branches in this non-pilot-tone case.

Referring now to (11-2-32) and (11-2-29), and using (11-2-45) to write half the eigenvalues in terms of the other half, the probability of error for matched filtering in slow Rayleigh fading, with no pilot-tone estimates, becomes

$$P_e = \frac{j}{2\pi}\left[\prod_{k=1}^{M}\left(\frac{1+\mu_k}{4\mu_k^2}\right)\right]\int_{-\infty+jc}^{\infty+jc}\frac{d\eta}{\eta\left[\prod_{k=1}^{M}\left(\eta+\frac{j}{2\mu_k}\right)\right]\left[\prod_{k=1}^{M}\left(\eta-j\frac{1+\mu_k}{2\mu_k}\right)\right]}$$

(11-2-46)

where c is a small positive real number.

Before discussing evaluations of this integral, we note another important specialization when the pair of signal states are sufficiently different (remember, in the absence of pilot tone, we are discussing noncoherent reception where the binary states should optimally be orthogonal), so that the pair of filters are orthogonal both in their response to the opposing signals and in having zero cross-correlation of their noise outputs (however, not necessarily matched filters). Then in (11-2-7) and (11-2-20),

$$h_{12} = N_{12} = 0 \tag{11-2-47}$$

We may also assume the filters basically identical in form; thus in (11-2-18) and (11-2-19),

$$N_{11} = N_{22} = N \tag{11-2-48}$$

Then the eigenvalues in (11-2-39) reduce to

$$\sigma_k^{(1)} = \frac{|h_{11}|^2\lambda_k + N}{(1/\lambda_k) + \gamma_0} \qquad \sigma_k^{(2)} = -\frac{N}{(1/\lambda_k) + \gamma_0} \tag{11-2-49}$$

In the special case of matched filters, these assumptions correspond simply to $\mu = 0$ in (11-2-41), giving for the eigenvalues

$$\mu_k = \sigma_k^{(1)} = \gamma_0\lambda_k \qquad \sigma_k^{(2)} = -\frac{\mu_k}{1+\mu_k} \tag{11-2-50}$$

We now proceed to specific results of interest.

Square-law Combiner: Independent Fading, No Pilot Tone, Equal Branches. The case of independent slow, multiplicative fading, with no pilot tone, and with all branches equal in strength leads to the square-law combiner as the optimum receiver, as seen earlier in (11-1-60). In this case, $\mathbf{R}$ is diagonal with all its elements (eigenvalues) equal,

$$\lambda_k = P \tag{11-2-51}$$

where P is the average signal power on each channel. As defined in (11-1-28b),

$$\Gamma = P\gamma_0 \tag{11-2-52}$$

is the average symbol SNR on each channel (averaged over fading).

We consider first the simplest case, of orthogonal signals and matched filters in each branch. Then, in (11-2-50),

$$\mu_k = \gamma_0 P = \Gamma \qquad \text{for all } k \tag{11-2-53}$$

and the probability of error is given by (11-2-46) as

$$
P_e = \frac{j}{2\pi}\left(\frac{1+\Gamma}{4\Gamma^2}\right)^M \int_{-\infty+jc}^{\infty+jc} \frac{d\eta}{\eta(\eta+j/2\Gamma)^M[\eta-j(1+\Gamma)/2\Gamma]^M} \qquad c > 0
$$

$$(11\text{-}2\text{-}54)$$

This is evaluable by a straightforward residue calculation, with the result in two equivalent forms,

$$
P_e = \frac{1}{(M-1)!}\frac{(1+\Gamma)^M}{(2+\Gamma)^{2M}}\sum_{k=0}^{M-1}\frac{(2M-2-k)!}{(M-1-k)!}\left(\frac{2+\Gamma}{1+\Gamma}\right)^{k+1} \qquad (11\text{-}2\text{-}55a)
$$

$$
= \frac{1}{(2+\Gamma)^M}\sum_{m=0}^{M-1}\binom{M-1+m}{M-1}\left(\frac{1+\Gamma}{2+\Gamma}\right)^m \qquad (11\text{-}2\text{-}55b)
$$

This is the basic result originally derived by Pierce[1] for the square-law combiner (using a somewhat different analysis). Pierce noted that the formula can be put into another useful form by writing

$$
\frac{(1+\Gamma)}{(2+\Gamma)} = 1 - \frac{1}{(2+\Gamma)} \qquad,
$$

expanding the factor in the sum by the binomial theorem, and invoking appropriate combinatorial identities. This alternative form,

$$
P_e = \sum_{k=0}^{M-1}\frac{(2M-1)!}{(M-1)!}\frac{(-)^k}{k!(M-k-1)!(M+k)}\frac{1}{(2+\Gamma)^{M+k}} \qquad (11\text{-}2\text{-}55c)
$$

is convenient in that its leading term provides a useful asymptotic result for large Γ. An equally useful alternative form which can be derived from (11-2-55a) is

$$
P_e = \frac{1}{[(M-1)!]^2}\sum_{k=0}^{\infty}\frac{(-)^k(2M+k-1)!}{k!(M+k)}\frac{1}{(1+\Gamma)^{M+k}} \qquad (11\text{-}2\text{-}55d)
$$

In a later publication (see Sec. 11-4), Pierce developed another useful form for the result,

$$
P_e = \frac{1}{2}\frac{\Gamma}{2+\Gamma}\sum_{k=M}^{\infty}\binom{2k}{k}\left[\frac{1+\Gamma}{(2+\Gamma)^2}\right]^k \qquad (11\text{-}2\text{-}55e)
$$

From either (11-2-55c), (11-2-55d), or (11-2-55e), the asymptotic result for large Γ is obtained as the leading term,

$$
P_e \approx \frac{(2M-1)!}{M!(M-1)!}\frac{1}{\Gamma^M} = \frac{1}{2}\frac{(M-\frac{1}{2})!\,2^{2M}}{\sqrt{\pi}\,M!}\frac{1}{\Gamma^M} \qquad (11\text{-}2\text{-}56)
$$

For more general signaling and arbitrary filtering, but still with independently fading branches of equal mean SNR, one can employ (11-2-51)

---

[1] J. N. Pierce, Theoretical Diversity Improvement in Frequency-Shift Keying, *Proc. IRE*, vol. 46, pp. 903–910, May, 1958.

in (11-2-39) and obtain series results similar to (11-2-55). The general parameter in these results (for equal-intensity branches) is an effective mean SNR given [recall that $\sigma_k^{(2)}$ is negative and less in magnitude than $\sigma_k^{(1)}$] by

$$\Gamma_0 = -\frac{\sigma^{(1)}}{\sigma^{(2)}} - 1 \tag{11-2-57}$$

where $\sigma_k^{(1)} = \sigma^{(1)}$ and $\sigma_k^{(2)} = \sigma^{(2)}$ for all k, in this model. While no

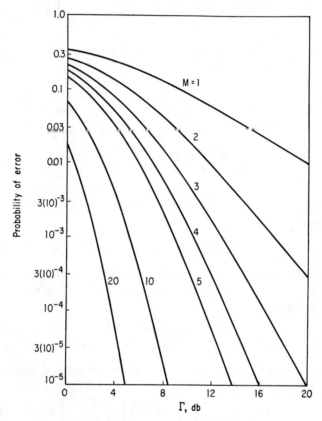

FIG. 11-2-1. Square-law combining with noncoherent FSK.

further general calculations are presented here, the formulas of (11-2-56) and (11-2-57) underlie the results discussed in Sec. 11-3.

Figure 11-2-1[1] shows numerical calculations of the exact result (11-2-55b) for various values of M. (As noted above, this figure applies to the general case, when Γ is replaced by the effective mean SNR Γ_0.) This may be compared with the results in Sec. 10-8 for digital data performance in ideal maximal-ratio combining. One such comparison is shown in

[1] From Pierce, *loc. cit.*

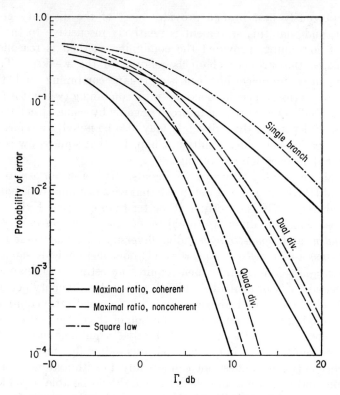

FIG. 11-2-2. Square-law versus maximal-ratio combining for binary FSK.

Fig. 11-2-2[1] for $M = 1, 2$, and 4, comparing square-law diversity combining for noncoherent FSK, with maximal-ratio combining for both noncoherent and coherent FSK, as displayed earlier in Fig. 10-8-1. The asymptotic forms (10-8-4), (10-8-17), and (11-2-56) are interesting to compare:

$$P_e \approx \frac{1}{2} \frac{(M - \frac{1}{2})!}{\sqrt{\pi}\, M!} \frac{2^M}{\Gamma^M} \qquad \text{maximal-ratio coherent FSK} \qquad (11\text{-}2\text{-}58a)$$

$$P_e \approx \frac{1}{2} \frac{2^M}{\Gamma^M} \qquad \text{maximal-ratio noncoherent FSK} \qquad (11\text{-}2\text{-}58b)$$

$$P_e \approx \frac{1}{2} \frac{(M - \frac{1}{2})!}{\sqrt{\pi}\, M!} \frac{2^{2M}}{\Gamma^M} \qquad \text{square-law noncoherent FSK} \qquad (11\text{-}2\text{-}58c)$$

Thus at low probabilities of error, there is exactly 3 db poorer performance in the last of these as compared with the first, with the maximal-ratio noncoherent FSK case in between.

On recognizes again here the remarks in Chap. 10 that use of the

[1] From B. B. Barrow, Error Probabilities for Data Transmission over Fading Radio Paths, *loc. cit.*

instantaneously best branch provides most of the diversity combining benefit, and that this statement is relatively insensitive to the detailed form of combining, provided the combining method is reasonable and emphasizes the stronger channels relative to the weaker. Thus, the performance difference between square-law combining and the best achievable performance, by maximal-ratio combining (when it is feasible), is quite small relative to the impressive gains by using either technique, as compared with no diversity. It may also be noted, by referring back to the selection-combiner results in Chap. 10, that square-law combining is better than selection combining.

The above results apply to FSK signals. It is appropriate to consider PSK and DPSK, as well. First, recall that with maximal-ratio combining, ideal coherent PSK is exactly 3 db better than coherent FSK. Thus in the most common diversity problem of *slow, multiplicative, mutually independent* and *equal-strength* fading diversity channels, there is (at low error rates) a 6-*db difference* between (1) noncoherent FSK signaling and the square-law combining, which requires no estimate of channel states and no adaptivity or control circuits to achieve the diversity performance, and (2) ideal coherent PSK signaling with maximal-ratio combining, the latter implying perfect noiseless estimation of the channel states (e.g., by use of pilot tones) and associated "adaptive" combiner control circuitry. As Pierce and later Turin emphasized, this 6-db difference represents the difference between the best one can possibly do within known concepts of signaling and reception, and the least one should be able to achieve over such circuits, so long as fading is slow enough that there is coherence of the received signal over durations corresponding to individual received pulses.

The gap becomes even narrower when one considers differential phase-shift keying. It will be recalled (Secs. 7-6 and 8-5) that DPSK can be interpreted as a form of orthogonal signaling involving successive pairs of signal pulses. Combining of the outputs of the corresponding matched filters is exactly in the class of results discussed above. The result in each channel is a "scalar product" of form $x_1x_2 + y_1y_2$. As shown earlier, the scalar product is equivalent to a difference of squares of envelopes,

$$x_1x_2 + y_1y_2 = (u_1{}^2 + v_1{}^2) - (u_2{}^2 + v_2{}^2) = |w_1|^2 - |w_2|^2 \quad (11\text{-}2\text{-}59)$$

Hence, when fading is slow enough that channel states remain essentially constant over successive pulse pairs and all diversity channels are fading independently and with equal strength, it is a direct consequence of our previous results on square-law combining that the optimum combining for DPSK in the absence of any additional pilot tone is to form the sum

$$f = \sum_{k=1}^{M} (x_{1k}x_{2k} + y_{1k}y_{2k}) \quad (11\text{-}2\text{-}60)$$

This decision variable is then fully equivalent to the difference

$$f = \sum_{k=1}^{M} |w_{1k}|^2 - \sum_{k=1}^{M} |w_{2k}|^2 \qquad (11\text{-}2\text{-}61)$$

It further follows immediately that within these models, DPSK with "square-law combining" as represented by (11-2-60) will perform precisely 3 db better at that same signal power than the noncoherent FSK results pictured in Figs. 11-2-1 and 11-2-2.   Thus, so long as slow, multiplicative fading is a reasonable assumption, there is only a *3-db* gap between the *best* that can be achieved, by pilot tones and maximal-ratio combining, and the least achievable, by "noncoherent" signaling of the DPSK variety and no pilot tone.   (One may also view DPSK as a one-pulse pilot-tone operation in a particularly simple implementation.   The above merely confirms the result noted in Chap. 8 in comparing DPSK with ideal coherent PSK: At SNRs and low error rates of interest, there is relatively little improvement between a noiseless reference signal for coherent detection and one which at least has no poorer SNR associated with it than the signal being detected.)

These statements, and the performance curves of Figs. 11-2-1 and 11-2-2, are perhaps the major results of this entire section.   Even within the scope of quadratic combining, we have discussed only a very specialized no-pilot-tone case, and compared the result with that for the other extreme of maximal-ratio combining.   The constraints upon applicability of the results, because no physical multipath fading channel can perfectly satisfy the slow, multiplicative-fading assumption, will be discussed in Sec. 11-3.   For the remainder of this section, we explore further the significance of correlations in the fading on the several channels, of unequal channel intensities, of signal nonorthogonality, and of the implications of the use of pilot tones.   This exploration will be undertaken in the context of a general asymptotic result for the probability of error defined by (11-2-14).[1]

Asymptotic Result for No-pilot-tone Case.   The useful form of asymptotic result, noted by Turin,[2] is closely related to the observation above that low P_e implies a high SNR on each branch.   It was observed in Chap. 10, in the case of correlated fadings on the several diversity branches, that the eigenvalues $\{\lambda_k\}$ of the covariance matrix $\mathbf{R}$ retain significance as the effective strengths of the independently fading components contained among the several diversity branches.   It was then

---

[1] For the quadratic combiner in slow, nonselective fading, with matched-filter reception in each branch, some simple and quite tight upper and lower bounds have been pointed out in J. N. Pierce, Approximate Error Probabilities for Optimal Diversity Combining, *IEEE Trans. Commun. Systems*, vol. CS-11, pp. 352–354, September, 1963.

[2] Turin, Optimal Diversity Reception, II, *loc. cit.*

also noted that if M diversity branches are to provide M-fold diversity action, even when fadings are mutually correlated, all these eigenvalues must be relatively high. We confine our remarks now to the no-pilot-tone quadratic-combiner case using matched filters in each diversity branch. The eigenvalues were given in (11-2-43) to (11-2-45). Making the approximations $\lambda_k \gamma_0 \gg 1$ for all k, these become, respectively,

$$\sigma_k^{(1)} = \mu_k \doteq \gamma_0 \lambda_k (1 - |\mu|^2) \qquad (11\text{-}2\text{-}62a)$$

$$\sigma_k^{(2)} \doteq -1 \qquad (11\text{-}2\text{-}62b)$$

Then the characteristic function in (11-2-32) becomes

$$F_q(\eta) \doteq \frac{1}{(1 + 2j\eta)^M} \frac{1}{\displaystyle\prod_{k=1}^{M} (1 - 2j\eta\mu_k)} \qquad (11\text{-}2\text{-}63)$$

In the latter, the μ_k are extremely large, hence we assume that for all η of interest, one can further approximate

$$F_q(\eta) \doteq \frac{1}{(1 + 2j\eta)^M} \frac{1}{(-2j\eta)^M} \frac{1}{\displaystyle\prod_{k=1}^{M} \mu_k} \qquad (11\text{-}2\text{-}64)$$

With (11-2-62a), and recalling that since λ_k are the eigenvalues of $\mathbf{R}$, their product is $\det \mathbf{R}$,

$$\prod_{k=1}^{M} \mu_k = [\gamma_0 (1 - |\mu|^2)]^M \det \mathbf{R} \qquad (11\text{-}2\text{-}65)$$

With (11-2-64) used in (11-2-29), a straightforward residue calculation then leads to the result for the matched-filter case,

$$P_e \doteq \frac{1}{[\gamma_0 (1 - |\mu|^2)]^M} \binom{2M - 1}{M} \frac{1}{\det \mathbf{R}} \qquad (11\text{-}2\text{-}66)$$

Recall that in the case of orthogonal signals ($\mu = 0$), with equal strength independently fading branches, the definition (11-2-52) gives

$$\gamma_0^M \det \mathbf{R} = \Gamma^M \qquad (11\text{-}2\text{-}67)$$

Thus it is clear that (11-2-66) is exactly identical with the earlier asymptotic result cited for that case in (11-2-56), as derived directly from the exact result.[1]

The form in which $\det \mathbf{R}$ enters into (11-2-66) is *exactly the same form* in which it entered in the analysis of correlation effects on maximal-ratio combining, as indicated in (10-5-29) with (10-10-26). Thus in slow, non-

[1] Turin, *loc. cit.*, also examines in rigorous detail, the exact solution for a covariance matrix of so-called exponential form, for which the eigenvalues can be determined exactly by formula. (This form was cited in the related discussion in Chap. 10.)

selective fading, the relative effects at low error rates of *mutual correlations* or of *unequal average-signal levels* among the fadings on the several branches *are substantially the same as for maximal-ratio combining.*

The effect of nonorthogonality of the possible waveforms, or in the receiver filtering, is also apparent in these equations. Particularly, it is clear that P_e is minimal when $\mu = 0$ and that the effect of $\mu \neq 0$ is to diminish the effective mean SNR on each branch[1] by the factor $1 - |\mu|^2$.

Asymptotic Result for Specular Component in No-pilot-tone Case. The success of the asymptotic calculation above, in which the basic integral is modified directly, points to a similar calculation in which the effects of specular components can be assessed. Thus, rather than use the characteristic function for purely Rayleigh fading, as in (11-2-31) and (11-2-32), we use the more general form in (11-2-28), noting from Appendix B that this can also be written in terms of the eigenvalues of $\mathbf{L}^*\mathbf{Q}$. Again making the approximation that $\lambda_k \gamma_0 \gg 1$ for all k, this immediately indicates that at low error rates the effect of a specular component is to multiply the error probability by an exponential factor, of form

$$\exp\left(-\tfrac{1}{2} \sum_{k=1}^{2M} |\langle \eta_k \rangle|^2\right) = \exp\left(-\tfrac{1}{2}\langle \mathbf{n} \rangle^{T*}\langle \mathbf{n} \rangle\right) \qquad (11\text{-}2\text{-}68)$$

Here the column vector $\langle \mathbf{n} \rangle$ describes the strength of the specular component. Its squared mean value is given (see Appendix B) by

$$\langle \mathbf{n} \rangle^{T*}\langle \mathbf{n} \rangle = \langle \boldsymbol{\xi} \rangle^{T*}(\mathbf{L}^{-1})^*\langle \boldsymbol{\xi} \rangle \qquad (11\text{-}2\text{-}69)$$

where $\mathbf{L}$ is the covariance matrix of (11-2-34). Thus, with additional specular components in each branch described by the matrix $\langle \boldsymbol{\xi} \rangle$ of (11-2-15), the asymptotic error probability given in (11-2-66) above is modified to the form

$$P_e = \frac{1}{[\gamma_0(1 - |\mu|^2)]^M} \binom{2M - 1}{M} \frac{\exp\left[-\tfrac{1}{2}\langle \boldsymbol{\xi} \rangle^{T*}(\mathbf{L}^{-1})^*\langle \boldsymbol{\xi} \rangle\right]}{\det \mathbf{R}} \qquad (11\text{-}2\text{-}70)$$

For example, consider statistically identical, independently fading channels with matched filter receivers, and orthogonal signals. Then from (11-2-51),

$$\mathbf{R} = P\mathbf{I} \qquad (11\text{-}2\text{-}71)$$

where P is the average signal power on each channel in the *fluctuation*

---

[1] This has been shown exactly in the dual-diversity case by both Pierce, *loc. cit.*, and Turin, *loc. cit.* Detailed calculations of the effect of nonorthogonality in the non-diversity, slow, nonselective fading case, including the effect of a specular component, are given in G. L. Turin, Error Probabilities for Binary Symmetric Ideal Reception through Nonselective Slow Fading and Noise, *Proc. IRE*, vol. 46, pp. 1603–1619, September, 1958.

component. From (11-2-34) and (11-2-42),

$$L = \begin{pmatrix} \gamma_0{}^2 R + \gamma_0 I & 0 \\ 0 & \gamma_0 I \end{pmatrix} = \begin{pmatrix} \gamma_0(\gamma_0 P + 1)I & 0 \\ 0 & \gamma_0 I \end{pmatrix} \quad (11\text{-}2\text{-}71)$$

$$L^{-1} = \begin{pmatrix} \dfrac{1}{\gamma_0(1 + \gamma_0 P)} I & 0 \\ 0 & \dfrac{1}{\gamma_0} I \end{pmatrix} \quad (11\text{-}2\text{-}72)$$

Similarly, from (11-2-23), with $\langle \boldsymbol{\alpha} \rangle$ the set of mean values of signal on the M branches,

$$\langle \xi \rangle = \begin{pmatrix} \left(\gamma_0 + \dfrac{1}{P} \right) \langle \boldsymbol{\alpha} \rangle \\ \dfrac{1}{P} \langle \boldsymbol{\alpha} \rangle \end{pmatrix}$$

Thus, with $\gamma_0 P = \Gamma$ as the mean SNR on each branch due to the signal fluctuation component,

$$P_e = \binom{2M-1}{M} \frac{1}{\Gamma^M} \exp \left[-\frac{1}{2} \left(\frac{2+\Gamma}{\Gamma} \right) \frac{2P_s}{P} \right] \quad (11\text{-}2\text{-}74)$$

where

$$P_s = \tfrac{1}{2} \langle \boldsymbol{\alpha} \rangle^{T*} \langle \boldsymbol{\alpha} \rangle \quad (11\text{-}2\text{-}75)$$

is the total mean power in the specular components on all channels. Note, if all M components of $\langle \boldsymbol{\alpha} \rangle$ are equal to some value v,

$$P_s = \frac{M}{2} |v|^2 \quad (11\text{-}2\text{-}76)$$

Thus, if there are specular components, they decrease the error rate exponentially at a rate determined by their level relative to the fluctuation component and in proportion to the order of diversity.

The Pilot Tone in Independent Purely Rayleigh-fading Channels. We have already indicated the limits in performance which can be expected from use of a pilot tone (by maximal-ratio combining). However, the preceding analyses can be readily extended to indicate the conditions under which the limit is approached for quadratic-combiner diversity. In the presence of pilot tone, this implies use of coherent operation. The additional features to be taken into account now are the statistics of the pilot-tone signal and its relation to the information-bearing signal as described by the matrices $\mathbf{g}$ and $\mathbf{c}$ defined earlier in (11-1-4) and (11-1-7) and the modification of $\mathbf{R}$ in (11-2-22).

We shall not present the detailed analysis but only cite the result, confined for simplicity to the case of independent, Rayleigh-fading channels (no specular components), with matched-filter reception in each branch. We assume orthogonal signaling with coherent operation (e.g., coherent FSK). We now use $\{\lambda_k\}$ to denote the eigenvalues of $\mathbf{a}$, rather than $\mathbf{R}$, so that the $\{\lambda_k\}$ still refer to the mean power on each branch. One then finds that the basic eigenvalues of (11-2-43), for $\mu = 0$, are now modified to the forms

$$
\left.\begin{matrix} \sigma_k{}^{(1)} \\ \sigma_k{}^{(2)} \end{matrix}\right\} = \frac{\lambda_k\gamma_0}{\lambda_k\gamma_0 + \dfrac{1}{1 - |\rho_k|^2}} \left\{ \frac{|\rho_k{}^2|}{1 - |\rho_k|^2} + \frac{\lambda_k\gamma_0}{2} \right.
$$

$$
\left. \pm \sqrt{\left(\frac{\lambda_k\gamma_0}{2} + 1\right)^2 + 2\left(\frac{\lambda_k\gamma_0}{2} + 1\right)\left(\frac{|\rho_k|^2}{1 - |\rho_k|^2}\right)\left[\frac{1}{\lambda_k\gamma_0(1 - |\rho_k|^2)} + 1\right]} \right\}
$$

$$(11\text{-}2\text{-}77)$$

where the $\{\rho_k\}$ are the *normalized* complex covariance coefficients corresponding to the components of **c** as defined in (11-1-19), where each c_k is the cross-covariance between the measurements on the pilot tones and the complex channel gain.

In this result, if one assumes high SNR, specifically that

$$
\begin{cases} \lambda_k\gamma_0 \gg 1 & (11\text{-}2\text{-}78a) \\[2mm] \lambda_k\gamma_0 \gg \dfrac{|\rho_k|^2}{1 - |\rho_k|^2} & (11\text{-}2\text{-}78b) \end{cases}
$$

then to excellent approximation the eigenvalues are given by

$$
\begin{aligned} \sigma_k{}^{(1)} &\approx \lambda_k\gamma_0 \\ \sigma_k{}^{(2)} &\approx -1 \end{aligned} \qquad (11\text{-}2\text{-}79)
$$

These are directly equivalent to the eigenvalues for the no-pilot-tone case, in (11-2-62). Thus, in this limit, the pilot tone introduces essentially no change in performance.

On the other hand, let us assume that the $\{|\rho_k|\}$ are sufficiently near unity that instead of (11-2-78), one has

$$
\frac{1}{1 - |\rho_k|^2} \gg \lambda_k\gamma_0 \gg 1 \qquad (11\text{-}2\text{-}80)
$$

Then one finds

$$
\sigma_k{}^{(1)} \doteq \lambda_k\gamma_0\left(1 + \sqrt{1 + \frac{2}{\lambda_k\gamma_0}}\right) \doteq 2\lambda_k\gamma_0 \qquad (11\text{-}2\text{-}81a)
$$

$$
\sigma_k{}^{(2)} \doteq \lambda_k\gamma_0\left(1 - \sqrt{1 + \frac{2}{\lambda_k\gamma_0}}\right) \doteq -1 \qquad (11\text{-}2\text{-}81b)
$$

Hence, as compared with (11-2-62), we see that in this case described by (11-2-80), the effective SNR on each branch has been increased by *exactly* a factor of 2. This is exactly the 3-db difference mentioned earlier between square-law combining with noncoherent FSK (no pilot tone) and the best achievable with coherent FSK, by maximal-ratio combining (pilot tone, in limit $|\rho_k| = 1$). Our remarks here are limited to FSK only in assuming orthogonal signals for convenience in the comparison.

It is intriguing to compare the two differing asymptotic results implied by (11-2-79) and (11-2-81). The conclusion is that the pilot tone will provide an advantage only when the covariance is so near unity that the factors $1/(1 - |\rho_k|^2)$ exceed the SNR level at which the desired error-rate performance is achieved. In this case, the additional (up to 6 db) advantages of coherent signaling and use of the pilot tone can be realized. When the normalized covariance is below this, one cannot do better than noncoherent signaling with quadratic combining. Clearly there is also a "transition region," which we are not describing in detail.

One should note that decorrelation effects occur in the normalized complex covariance ρ_k between the pilot-tone estimate and the channel gain both because of additive noise in the pilot-tone channel and because of fluctuations in the channel itself. With respect to the *useful* portion of the pilot-tone estimate, the quantity $|\rho_k|^2/(1 - |\rho_k|^2)$ is the effective pilot tone SNR. It may be recalled that the generalized DPSK analysis in Chap. 8 indicated that to obtain good performance the SNR on the reference channel should be larger than that associated with the signal pulse and that once the SNR on the reference channel exceeds that on the signal pulse by a significant amount, the performance is very close to that with an ideal noiseless reference. Essentially the same observations appear qualitatively above.

11-3. Performance of Suboptimal Systems

In Sec. 11-1, optimum-diversity combiners were derived for minimum probability of error in digital transmission, under the assumption of slow, multiplicative fading. In Sec. 11-2, we discussed the performance under these conditions of the quadratic-diversity combiner, largely for noncoherent operation in the absence of pilot tone, but with additional results presented for coherent operation with pilot tone used, and for the maximal-ratio combiner as the limiting case when the pilot tone provides perfect measurement of the channels.

As indicated in Sec. 11.1 (Fig. 11-1-3), when the several diversity branches are fading independently and with equal strengths, the quadratic combiner reduces to a square-law combiner. The latter, involving summing the squares of appropriately defined envelopes on the several branches, is particularly simple to implement. When the fadings are not independent, or are of unequal strength, the optimum-combiner weightings in the quadratic form (Fig. 11-1-2) involve detailed knowledge of the complex covariance matrix relating the short-term fading fluctuations on the several channels. However, the stationary short-term statistics typically change ("long-term fading") over periods of the order of minutes to an hour, so that a continuous (and perhaps impractical) measurement of the covariance matrix would then be required. On the other hand, we can appeal again to our strongly established intuition that the really significant aspect of any successful diversity-combiner operation lies in assuring that it always emphasizes the momentarily largest signal available from the several diversity branches. On this basis, there is *every reason to expect the square-law combiner to continue to function well*, even when a more general quadratic combiner is known to be optimum. This will be demonstrated in this section. Note that "square-law combiner" should be taken throughout here to imply for DPSK signaling the equivalent sum-of-scalar-products combining, as discussed earlier.

One also recognizes that since channel fading is a dynamic process and involves a nonvanishing multipath spread, the slow, multiplicative-fading assumption cannot ever be rigorously true. This leads to study of the extent to which the receiver principles derived above will still lead to high-quality performance for channels for which slow, multiplicative fading appears to be at least a good working approximation. A useful parameter characterizing the degree of approximation to slow, multiplicative fading is the *spread factor* introduced earlier, in Chap. 9. For information pulse lengths T, fading is essentially nonselective (and intersymbol interference due to multipath is small) if the multipath spread T_M satisfies

$$T_M \ll T \tag{11-3-1}$$

Likewise, if the Doppler spread (width of the received power spectrum when an unmodulated carrier is transmitted) is B_D, the requirement for essentially slow fading is

$$T \ll \frac{1}{B_D} \tag{11-3-2}$$

Thus, slow, multiplicative fading will be a good first-order approximation for values of T which satisfy both (11-3-1) and (11-3-2). This implies that the spread factor defined by

$$L = B_D T_M \tag{11-3-3}$$

must be such that

$$L \ll 1 \tag{11-3-4}$$

In addition, on the assumption that loss of signal coherence due to rapidity of fading is "equally as bad" as the distortion due to selective fading, one expects from (11-3-1) and (11-3-2) that the slow, multiplicative model will be most closely applicable for values of T near the value T_0 given by

$$B_D T_0 = \frac{T_M}{T_0} \quad \text{or} \quad T_0 = \sqrt{\frac{T_M}{B_D}} \tag{11-3-5}$$

However, from (11-3-1) and (11-3-2), one may expect the assumption to hold well for values of T in the range

$$T_0 \sqrt{L} \ll T \ll \frac{T_0}{\sqrt{L}} \tag{11-3-6}$$

Indeed, all known channels but the orbiting dipole belt do have very low spread factors. For long-distance h-f skywave transmission, with typical values $T_M = 2$ msec and $B_D = 0.3$ cps, L is $6(10)^{-4}$, and an estimate for T_0 is 80 msec. The 10 to 20 msec pulse length commonly used in such transmissions is close to this value in the sense of (11-3-6). Similarly, for microwave troposcatter (at about 200 miles range), typical values are $T_M = 0.4$ μsec and $B_D = 5$ cps. Then $L = 10^{-5}$, again much below unity, and $T_0 = 0.3$ msec. With (11-3-6), however, serial keying rates up to about 100 kilobits/sec can be expected to conform to slow, multiplicative fading.

As might be expected, the validity of the approximations just described depends on the error rate, since at lower error rates, "statistical tails" become more important. Some results reviewed further in this section indicate when the approximations fail and what the resulting effects on performance are.

A final comment is in order about the combiner models to be examined below. At the end of Sec. 11-2, it was pointed out that the utility of pilot-tone information depends upon whether a sufficiently high fraction of its total energy is well correlated with the signal fading. This was defined in terms of an effective SNR, with the statement that when this effective SNR for the pilot tone significantly exceeds the signal SNR, the performance is close to that of maximal-ratio combining, while when the reverse is true, the pilot-tone information is essentially useless towards improving performance. Thus, we are led to restrict consideration of suboptimal receivers to two models:

1. Square-law combining, with no pilot-tone.
2. Maximal-ratio combining, operating as if the pilot-tone estimates are perfect estimates of the channel.

Square-law Combining without Pilot Tone, in Slow Multiplicative Fading.[1] The difference between this combiner and the more general quadratic combiner analyzed in Sec. 11-2 lies strictly in the decision functional operating on the filter outputs in each branch. Regardless of the form of $\mathbf{R}$, the decision functional is now described by the $2M \times 2M$ partitioned matrix, $\mathbf{Q}$, conveniently written in the form analogous to the earlier (11-2-12) as

$$\mathbf{Q} = \begin{pmatrix} \dfrac{1}{\gamma_0}\mathbf{I} & \vdots & \mathbf{0} \\ \cdots & \cdots & \cdots \\ \mathbf{0} & \vdots & -\dfrac{1}{\gamma_0}\mathbf{I} \end{pmatrix} \tag{11-3-7}$$

Paralleling the calculations in (11-2-35) to (11-2-43) for the eigenvalues

[1] See G. L. Turin, On Optimal Diversity Reception, II, *IRE Trans. Commun. Systems*, vol. CS-10, pp. 22–31, March, 1962; or J. N. Pierce and S. Stein, Multiple Diversity with Non-independent Fading, *Proc. IRE*, vol. 48, pp. 89–104, January, 1960, and J. N. Pierce, same title, *Proc. IRE*, vol. 49, pp. 363–364, January, 1961.

of the matrix $\mathbf{L^*Q}$, the only change from the results in (11-2-39) or (11-2-43) is seen to be replacing the initial factor $1/[(1/\lambda_k) + \gamma_0]$ by simply $1/\gamma_0$. Corresponding to (11-2-43) for the matched-filter case, with λ_k, γ_0, and μ defined as earlier, one now finds for the eigenvalues

$$\left.\begin{matrix} \sigma_k{}^{(1)} \\ \sigma_k{}^{(2)} \end{matrix}\right\} = \gamma_0 \left\{ \frac{\gamma_0\lambda_k}{2}(1 - |\mu|^2) \pm \sqrt{\left[\frac{\gamma_0\lambda_k}{2}(1 - |\mu|^2) + 1\right]^2 - |\mu|^2} \right. \qquad (11\text{-}3\text{-}8)$$

However, as noted in Sec. 11-2, all asymptotic error-rate results correspond to the condition of high SNR, expressed by

$$\lambda_k\gamma_0 \gg 1 \qquad \text{for all } k \qquad (11\text{-}3\text{-}9)$$

Under these conditions, the eigenvalues above become *identical* with those described by (11-2-43). Hence, indeed, at low error rates, and under the assumptions of the model, the square-law combiner will deliver the same performance under conditions of correlated fading, unequal strengths in the various branches, etc., as will a more nearly optimum quadratic combiner based upon more detailed knowledge of the covariance matrix of the fading on the several branches.

To recapitulate, the assumed lack of pilot tone implies noncoherent operation and the result above indicates that square-law combining then represents an excellent engineering choice for digital reception. In addition, as noted earlier, the analysis also applies directly to DPSK signaling (a sum-of-scalar-products combiner), which is then within 3 db of the performance available in slow, nonselective fading with coherent PSK and maximal-ratio combining with perfect pilot-tone estimation.

Matched-filter Receiver with Square-law Combining without Pilot Tone, in Rapid or Selective Fading. Assuming slow, multiplicative fading, we observed in Sec. 11-1 that the first step in reception optimally employs filters matched to the *transmitted* waveform, or suboptimally employs filters which closely approach the matched filters in SNR performance. This is a manageable requirement, since the transmitted waveforms are certainly known at the receiver and the synchronization required is readily achieved.

On the other hand, we have already observed (e.g., Chap. 9) that even if channel fading can be regarded as slow and nonselective most of the time, distortion will occur during some small percentage of the time. When the fraction of pulses distorted becomes large compared with the required error rate, signal distortion rather than additive Gaussian noise can become the limiting factor in performance. Because of distortion, there will be a nonvanishing error rate even when the mean SNR is infinitely large. This has sometimes been termed a "bottoming effect" in error rate. It appears to have been initially noticed in tests over long-distance h-f links, comparing multichannel (frequency-division multiplex) noncoherent FSK signaling with multichannel (frequency-division multiplex) DPSK signaling.[1]   While the theoretical results in Sec. 11-2 for slow, multiplicative fading (or in Chap. 7 for no fading) indicate an exact 3-db advantage for DPSK when all other conditions are equivalent, these field test results indicated that under certain fading conditions and/or at very low error-rate requirements, the noncoherent FSK would out-perform DPSK.   The bottoming effects were also indicated: At very high SNR, further increases in SNR would no longer produce significant corre-sponding reductions in error rate.   Suspicion immediately pointed to the assumptions of slow, multiplicative fading in the theoretical results and indicated these would have to be revised in order to be useful for design.

Under conditions where fading distortion is the limiting factor on per-formance, receiving system design and signal structure should be based upon the ensemble of received waveforms rather than the transmitted waveforms.   Unfortunately there appear to exist no major results to cite in this area.   The related question for which some results have been obtained, motivated by the desire to interpret the test results cited above, is to determine the channel and signaling parameters under which one may safely continue to base design upon the simplifying assumptions of slow, multiplicative fading.   The relevant analyses,[2] as discussed below, basically investigate the performance of diversity receivers matched to the *transmitted* signal, for general models of fading rapidity and selectivity. Initially, we discuss performance with square-law combining.

The basic formalism of the analysis is that already applied in Sec. 11-2. For square-law combining, the decision functional Q of (11-3-7) applies. The filter outputs, $w^{(1)}$ and $w^{(2)}$, are still related to the $\{z_k(t)\}$, the sum of received signals and additive noise on the respective branches, through (11-2-4).   However, the difference now is that the received signals are no longer related to the transmitted waveforms by multiplicative noise as in (11-2-5).   Instead, using the characterization introduced in Chap. 9, the total input to each receiver filter is now given by a form

$$z_k(t) = \int_{-\infty}^{\infty} h_k(t - \tau; t)s(\tau) \, d\tau + n_k(t) \qquad (11\text{-}3\text{-}10)$$

[1] A. T. Brennan, B. Goldberg, and A. Eckstein, Comparison of Multichannel Radio-teletype Systems over a 5000-Mile Ionospheric Path, *IRE Nat. Conv. Record*, part 8, pp. 254–260, 1958; B. Goldberg, HF Radio Data Transmission, *IRE Trans. Commun. Systems*, vol. CS-9, pp. 21–28, March, 1961.

[2] H. B. Voelcker, Phase-Shift Keying in Fading Channels, *Proc. IEE*, pt. B, vol. 107, pp. 31–38, January, 1960; P. A. Bello and B. D. Nelin, The Influence of Fading Spec-trum on the Binary Error Probabilities of Incoherent and Differentially Coherent Matched Filter Receivers, *IRE Trans. Commun. Systems*, vol. CS-10, pp. 160–168, June, 1962; P. A. Bello and B. D. Nelin, The Effect of Frequency Selective Fading on the Binary Error Probabilities of Incoherent and Differentially Coherent Matched Filter Receivers, *IEEE Trans. Commun. Systems*, vol. CS-11, pp. 170–186, June, 1963; corrections in *IEEE Trans. Comm. Tech.*, vol. COM-12, pp. 230–231, Decem-ber, 1964.

where $h_k(\tau;t)$ is the time-varying equivalent low-pass impulse response of the kth diversity channel.

Thus, one can parallel the analysis of Sec. 11-2, introducing the column matrix ξ as in (11-2-10) and (11-2-11). In Rayleigh fading, with no specular component, its mean $\langle \xi \rangle$ will be zero. However, its covariance matrix $\mathbf{L}$, as defined in (11-2-16), will now be modified in accordance with the Gaussian statistics of the $h_k(\tau;t)$. The kind of calculation involved is that discussed at some length in Sec. 9-6. The details are thus essentially computational and interpretive rather than involving new theory. We shall therefore only indicate the approach and discuss the results.

To parallel the analysis in Sec. 11-2, one again organizes the partitions of ξ that is,

$$\xi = \begin{pmatrix} \xi^{(1)} \\ \xi^{(2)} \end{pmatrix}$$

so that $\xi^{(1)}$ again refers to the filter outputs in the M branches which are meant to respond to the signaled symbol, and $\xi^{(2)}$ to those which should primarily contain only noise. For FSK analysis, these correspond to the usual tone filters [matched filters, over a pulse-length interval $(0,T)$ in the discussion below]. For DPSK analysis, we shall again refer to the equivalent noncoherent-detection case, in terms of orthogonal filters operating over some $(0,2T)$ interval. In the examples previously discussed, symmetric situations were always considered where the same probability of error is obtained with either binary state signaled. This may no longer be true in some of the fading cases (although it is in the computations described below); in this case, the two probabilities would have to be calculated separately (and then usually averaged).

In all the computations cited below, diversity performance has been based on *independently* fading, *equal-intensity*, purely Rayleigh-fading diversity channels. (As in our previous analyses, independence and equal strength are convenient but not necessary restrictions.) Thus the matrix $\mathbf{L}^*\mathbf{Q}$ will again have only two distinct eigenvalues, each M-fold degenerate. Denoting these as $\sigma^{(1)}$ and $\sigma^{(2)}$, the positive semidefinite nature of a covariance matrix such as $\mathbf{L}$, and the structure of the decision matrix $\mathbf{Q}$ leads again to the statement $\sigma^{(1)} > 0$, $\sigma^{(2)} < 0$. Furthermore, the probability of error as defined is then given directly in terms of these eigenvalues, as in (11-2-55) and (11-2-56) earlier. As noted in (11-2-57), the formulas of (11-2-55) and (11-2-56) apply directly if one defines an effective mean SNR in each branch by

$$\Gamma_0 = \frac{\sigma^{(1)}}{-\sigma^{(2)}} - 1 \tag{11-3-11}$$

In these terms, citing particularly the form of (11-2-55b), the probability of error is given by

$$P_e = \frac{1}{(2 + \Gamma_0)^M} \sum_{m=0}^{M-1} \binom{M - 1 + m}{M - 1} \left(\frac{1 + \Gamma_0}{2 + \Gamma_0}\right)^m \quad (11\text{-}3\text{-}12)$$

and, from (11-2-56), asymptotically has the form

$$P_e = \binom{2M - 1}{M} \frac{1}{\Gamma_0{}^M} \quad (11\text{-}3\text{-}13)$$

It is then just the computation of the effective mean SNR, through computation of the eigenvalues described above, which leads to describing the effects of rapid or selective fading.

The first analysis, due to Voelcker,[1] dealt with DPSK in terms of the two successive filter *outputs* in the normal phase-detector implementation of DPSK. Again, because of assumed Rayleigh fading, these signal terms are zero-mean complex Gaussian processes. For slow, multiplicative fading, this normalized cross-correlation would be unity (if the signal contains no phase reversal; -1 if a phase reversal is involved), and it is the deviation below unity due to rapidity of fading whose effect Voelcker studied. He presented results for binary DPSK, asymptotic error probabilities (i.e., with receiver noise negligible) for four-phase DPSK, and also a result for the error-rate improvement due to an additional specular component (essentially as implied in the corresponding asymptotic analysis in Sec. 11-2). He showed indeed that at high mean SNR, there is a limiting value of *effective* mean SNR Γ_0 which is a function only of the normalized cross-correlation in the filter outputs, and hence corresponds to a limiting error rate due to fading effects even in the absence of receiver noise.

However, Voelcker's results are limited in that the discussion is couched in terms of correlations of successive filter *outputs* for DPSK. This still leaves undetermined the smoothing effects of the receiver filter upon the channel characteristics; e.g., how does the correlation just mentioned relate to the ratio of nominal channel fade rate to the signal keying speed? Indeed, in FSK, the important loss of coherence is within a single pulse duration, not over two. Thus a total analysis must include the filter effects. The procedure is just as outlined earlier—obtain by (11-3-10) the filter output statistics and then calculate the eigenvalues leading to determining the effective mean SNR in (11-3-12). As stated, the calculation is mainly a bookkeeping process of determining the appropriate covariances and subsequently the appropriate matrix eigenvalues. It is precisely this calculational effort which has been presented in the papers by Bello and Nelin,[2] the results of which we shall cite in detail (omitting, however, the laborious details of the computations).

---

[1] Voelcker, *loc. cit.*
[2] Bello and Nelin, *loc. cit.*

These papers specifically assume receiver filters matched to the transmitted waveforms, independently fading diversity channels with identical statistics, and square-law diversity combining. The results cover both FSK and DPSK, largely for two extremes of fading on a low-spread-factor channel. One extreme assumes nonselective fading in which only fading rapidity is examined, and the second assumes slow fading but selectivity over the signal bandwidth.

Rapid, Nonselective Fading.[1]   With reference to (11-3-10) nonselective fading implies that for a transmitted signal with complex envelope $s(t)$, the received signal on the kth diversity channel will have the form

$$u(t) = h_k(t)s(t) \qquad (11\text{-}3\text{-}14)$$

For purely Rayleigh fading, each $h_k(t)$ is zero-mean complex Gaussian; they are assumed independent from channel to channel. The fading is thus completely characterized by the complex autocovariance function for each $h_k(\tau)$, this autocovariance being the same for all channels,

$$R(\tau) = \tfrac{1}{2}\langle h_k{}^*(t)h_k(t + \tau)\rangle \qquad (11\text{-}3\text{-}15)$$

The corresponding power spectrum describes the Doppler spread for the channel (Chap. 9).

Calculations were made by Bello and Nelin for two different complex covariance functions taken as typical, possible models describing the channel fading process. One is an exponential form,

$$R_e(\tau) = S \exp\left(-2\pi B|\tau|\right) \qquad (11\text{-}3\text{-}16)$$

The other is a Gaussian shape,

$$R_g(\tau) = S \exp\left(-\frac{\pi^2 B^2 \tau^2}{\ln 2}\right) \qquad (11\text{-}3\text{-}17)$$

(The exponential form is not strictly possible physically, since it implies, for example, an infinite mean-square value for the rate of change of fading envelope. Nevertheless, it is mathematically convenient for examining the effects of a relatively long "tail" on the covariance function.)   In each form, B represents the (one-sided) half-power bandwidth (cps) of the corresponding equivalent low-pass fading power spectrum. As might be expected, B enters in relation to the keying rate; for pulse lengths T, it is convenient to define a normalized fading bandwidth

$$b = BT \qquad (11\text{-}3\text{-}18)$$

For FSK, computations were based upon rectangular tone pulses of length T, and tone spacing n/T (cps), where n is an integer. For values $b \ll 1$, that is channels which closely approximate what we have termed

---

[1] Bello and Nelin, "Influence of Fading Spectrum, etc.," 1962, *loc. cit.*

slow fading, the effective SNR's are respectively found to be

$$(\Gamma_0)_e = \frac{\Gamma\left[1 - \frac{2\pi b}{3}\left(\frac{1}{3} + \frac{1}{n^2\pi^2}\right)\right]}{1 + \left[\frac{2b}{n^2\pi}\right]\Gamma} \qquad (11\text{-}3\text{-}18a)$$

$$(\Gamma_0)_g = \frac{\Gamma\left[1 - \frac{\pi^2 b^2}{2\ln 2}\left(\frac{1}{3} + \frac{1}{n^2\pi^2}\right)\right]}{1 + \left[\frac{\pi^2 b^2}{2\ln 2(n^2\pi^2)}\right]\Gamma} \qquad (11\text{-}3\text{-}18b)$$

The ratio of the value of Γ required to achieve a value of Γ_0 to that value of Γ_0 can be termed the SNR degradation at that performance level due to

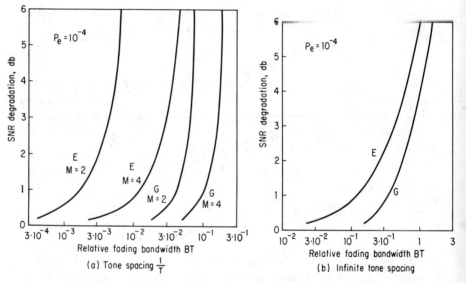

FIG. 11-3-1. SNR degradation for noncoherent FSK in rapid, nonselective fading.

fading distortion. Each value Γ_0 corresponds to a certain probability of error and the SNR degradation is thus the factor by which Γ must be increased because of the additional fading distortion effects, in order to achieve a certain error rate. Figure 11-3-1a[1] shows curves for the SNR degradation at 10^{-4} error rate, with tone spacing $1/T$ ($n = 1$), and for second- and fourth-order diversity (the effective Γ_0 required is a function of the order of diversity). Note in all the cases shown, there is a value BT above which it becomes impossible to achieve 10^{-4} error rate ("the degradation becomes infinite"). Higher-order diversity is more tolerant of the distortion, apparently because of the higher *individual* error rate

[1] Bello and Nelin, *op. cit.*, Fig. 3.

allowed per channel (lower mean SNR) with increasing diversity. For $n = \infty$, Γ_0 becomes directly proportional to Γ, and the degradation becomes a constant independent of Γ and of the order of diversity; this is shown in Fig. 11-3-1b.[1] In the case $n = \infty$, degradation is caused only by loss of coherence over the pulse length; in the case $n = 1$, there is the

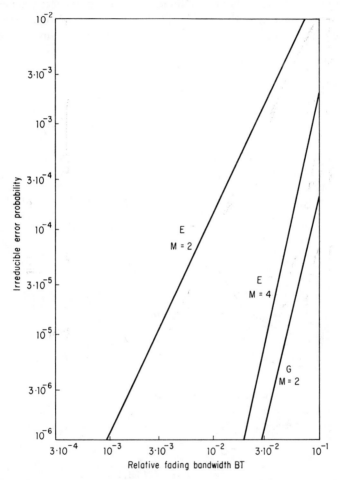

FIG. 11-3-2. Irreducible error rates for noncoherent FSK in rapid, nonselective fading.

additional effect of crosstalk produced by the fading distortions (energy spillover into the other filter).   Comparison shows that the latter accounts for a significant portion of the degradation and hence that wide tone spacings should be beneficial in such cases.   Alternatively, there may be major benefits to employing signal spectrum shaping which confines the sideband structure of the transmitted pulse waveforms.

[1] Bello and Nelin, *op. cit.*, Fig. 4.

In the limit as $\Gamma \to \infty$, Γ_0 in (11-3-18a) approaches finite values independent of Γ. The resulting irreducible error rates due to fading (i.e., for $\Gamma \to \infty$) are shown in Fig. 11-3-2[1] for several cases, at $1/T$ tone spacing, as a function of $b = BT$. For $n \to \infty$, there is no corresponding irreducible error rate.

For binary DPSK, Bello and Nelin describe a slightly more generalized signaling, for which it is shown that error rates may not be the same for Mark signaled as for Space. However, symmetry occurs for the common

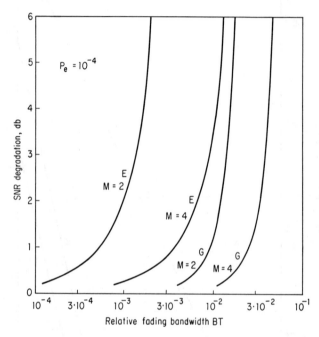

FIG. 11-3-3. SNR degradation for DPSK in rapid, nonselective fading.

phase-reversal binary DPSK. In this case, when $b \ll 1$, one obtains the effective SNRs,

$$(\Gamma_0)_e = \frac{2\Gamma}{1 + (4\pi b/3)\Gamma} \tag{11-3-19a}$$

for the exponential covariance function, and

$$(\Gamma_0)_g = \frac{2\Gamma}{1 + (\pi^2 b^2/\ln 2)\Gamma} \tag{11-3-19b}$$

for the Gaussian covariance function. Curves of SNR degradation at 10^{-4} error rate are shown in Fig. 11-3-3,[2] with essentially the same general

[1] Bello and Nelin, *op. cit.*, Fig. 5.
[2] Bello and Nelin, *op. cit.*, Fig. 8.

comments applicable as given for FSK.   The irreducible error rates corresponding to the limiting values for Γ_0, as $\Gamma \to \infty$ in (11-3-19), are shown in Fig. 11-3-4.[1]

Comparison of Fig. 11-3-3 with 11-3-1 indicates that DPSK degrades faster than FSK with rapidity of fading (as expected intuitively, since

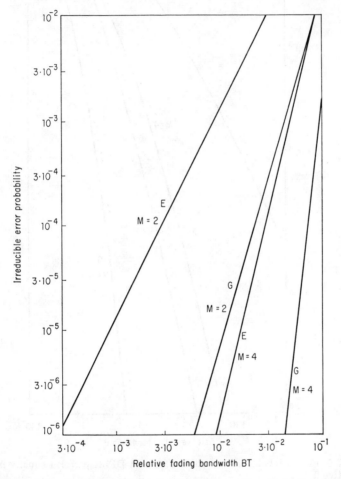

FIG. 11-3-4. Irreducible error rates for DPSK in rapid, nonselective fading.

DPSK requires coherence over an interval of $2T$ rather than just T). Thus DPSK performs better than FSK in the limit of slow, multiplicative fading, but may perform worse under rapid-fading conditions.   Figure 11-3-5[2] indicates as a function of fading rapidity the theoretical "break-

[1] Bello and Nelin, *op. cit.*, Fig. 9.
[2] Bello and Nelin, *op. cit.*, Fig. 10.

even" error probability at which the two require identical SNRs for equal performances.

Slow, Selective Fading.[1] At the other extreme of fading distortion is the assumption of slow, but selective, fading, where the channel transfer

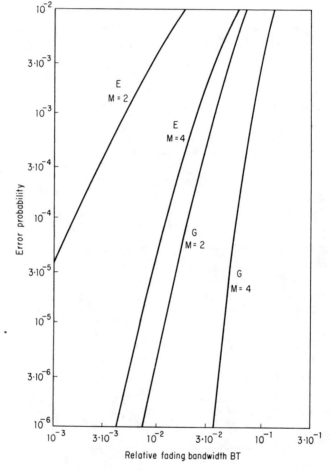

Fɪɢ. 11-3-5. Error probabilities at which FSK and DPSK perform equally in rapid, nonselective fading.

function implied by (11-3-10) is assumed not to change in form over the duration of any single message waveform, but where its spectrum will exhibit variation over the band occupied by $s(t)$. In the spectral equivalent of (11-3-10), one may write

$$U(f) = H_k(f)S(f) \tag{11-3-20}$$

[1] Bello and Nelin, "The Effect of Frequency-Selective Fading, etc.," 1963, *op. cit*

where for a Rayleigh-fading channel each $H_k(f)$ is a zero-mean complex Gaussian process *as a function of f.* It is thus completely described by a complex covariance function (the spaced frequency cross-correlation), identical for each channel,

$$R(\nu) = \tfrac{1}{2}\langle H_k^*(f)H_k(f + \nu)\rangle \tag{11-3-21}$$

As will be recalled, the transform of this $R(\nu)$ describes the intensity distribution of multipath time delays (the multipath intensity profile defined in Chap. 9).

Again, Bello and Nelin assume filters matched to the transmitted pulse and perfect synchronization. The latter is taken in the sense of matching perfectly to the average delay in the channel, so that in the absence of selective fading each $H_k(f)$ would be a constant with zero phase shift over the band. Particularly, in their computational model, the multipath is assumed to be symmetrically distributed about some center value,[1] which is then a well-defined average delay.

In view of the close relationship between selective fading and multipath spread, proper evaluation of error rate must not only include the distortion of single pulses by selective fading but also the intersymbol interference produced by the time dispersion of pulse energy. Because of multipath, a pulse whose energy is nominally confined to an interval $(0,T)$ will now have associated energy appearing over an interval described roughly by $(-T_M/2, T + T_M/2)$ where T_M is the extent of the multipath spread. The additional spreading can produce intersymbol interference with respect both to the following pulse nominally occupying the interval $(T,2T)$ and also to the preceding pulse nominally occupying $(-T,0)$. Thus in calculating probability of error for a particular symbol waveform, one has to take account of the preceding and following waveforms. These are in turn determined by the message content. Hence one has to solve for probability of error per symbol by averaging over the probabilities of error associated with all possible message sequences containing that symbol. On the basis that any very-extensive multipath or selective fading will lead to very poor performance, Bello and Nelin limited their computations to cases of small multipath spread, when only the single preceding and single following information symbol need be taken into account in considering intersymbol interference.

One must be careful in interpreting the model above. For example, when intersymbol interference becomes significant at both leading and trailing edges of a symbol waveform, a very useful palliative may be to discard a portion of the energy near both edges and to confine processing to an interior fraction of the nominal interval occupied by the waveform. While the computation could easily be modified accordingly (the receiver

[1] However, note (Chap. 9) that symmetry of the multipath profile may be physically unlikely.

filter would no longer be "matched" to the transmitted pulse) such calculations are not presently available[1], so we confine our discussion to Bello and Nelin's "matched-filter" results.

In FSK transmission of rectangular pulses the possibility exists of an apparent phase discontinuity at a Mark-Space transition if Mark and Space are generated by gating two independent oscillators. If, on the other hand, a single frequency-modulated oscillator with step changes in frequency is used, no such phase discontinuity occurs. Bello and Nelin have considered two extreme cases: one, where there is zero phase discontinuity at transitions (apparently the best case for performance); the other, a phase discontinuity of π at each transition (apparently the worst case). These should then bound the performance.

For the covariance function of the channel $R(\nu)$ only a Gaussian-shaped function was assumed, given in our notation by

$$R(\nu) = S \exp\left(-\frac{4\nu^2}{B_c^2}\right) \tag{11-3-22}$$

where S represents the relative average power received for a CW tone transmitted and $B_c/2$ is the frequency spacing at which the normalized complex correlation between spaced tones drops to $1/e$. The multipath intensity profile, the Fourier transform of (11-3-22), is just

$$r(\tau) = SB_c \frac{\sqrt{\pi}}{2} \exp\left[-\left(\frac{\pi B_c \tau}{2}\right)^2\right] \tag{11-3-23}$$

The relation of data rate to selectivity is defined by a normalized data rate,

$$d = \frac{1}{TB_c} \tag{11-3-24}$$

In order for intersymbol interference effects to be within the bounds described earlier, it appears sufficient that an inequality of order

$$d < \frac{\pi}{4} \tag{11-3-25}$$

be satisfied. When $d = \pi/4$, 99.5 per cent of the area under $r(\tau)$ is confined to the interval $|\tau| < T$.

For noncoherent FSK, calculations of the effective SNR were made, assuming small d. For rectangular keying, probability of error is symmetric for Mark or Space. Assuming Mark or binary "1," the effective SNR is calculated separately for the four possible three-element message sequences containing "1" as the middle element, 111, 010, 011, and 110

---

[1] Subsequent to this writing, some results have appeared, described as the use of "time-guard bands." The effect is directly a reduction in the effective multipath spread, insofar as the latter parameter enters performance calculations, along with a small reduction in SNR.

(the latter two cases being equivalent through symmetry).   Tone spacings of $1/T$ and of ∞ were considered.   For spacing $1/T$, different results are obtained depending upon whether or not phase discontinuities occur at Mark-Space transitions.   In terms of Γ, the mean SNR on each diversity branch, these effective SNR's are as follows, for the various sequences:

Spacing $\dfrac{1}{T}$

$d^2 \ll 1$

Phase discontinuity $= 0$

$$
\left\{
\begin{aligned}
(\Gamma_0)_{111} &= \Gamma \\[2mm]
(\Gamma_0)_{010} &= \Gamma \frac{\left[1 - \left(\dfrac{32}{3}\right)\dfrac{d^3}{\pi\sqrt{\pi}}\right]}{1 + \Gamma\dfrac{12d^4}{\pi^2}} \\[4mm]
(\Gamma_0)_{110} &= (\Gamma_0)_{011} \\[2mm]
&= \Gamma \frac{\left[1 - \left(\dfrac{16}{3}\right)\dfrac{d^3}{\pi\sqrt{\pi}}\right]}{1 + \Gamma\dfrac{d^4}{\pi^2}\left[6 - \dfrac{\Gamma}{(\Gamma+2)}\right]}
\end{aligned}
\right.
$$

(11-3-26)

Spacing $\dfrac{1}{T}$

$d^2 \ll 1$

Phase discontinuity $= \pi$

$$
\left\{
\begin{aligned}
(\Gamma_0)_{111} &= \Gamma \\[2mm]
(\Gamma_0)_{010} &= \frac{\Gamma\left[1 - \dfrac{8d}{\pi\sqrt{\pi}}\right]}{1 + \dfrac{8d^2}{\pi^2}\left[1 - \dfrac{2\Gamma}{\pi(2+\Gamma)}\right]} \\[4mm]
(\Gamma_0)_{110} &= (\Gamma_0)_{011} \\[2mm]
&= \frac{\Gamma\left(1 - \dfrac{4d}{\pi\sqrt{\pi}}\right)}{1 + \Gamma\dfrac{4d^2}{\pi^2}\left[1 - \dfrac{\Gamma}{\pi(2+\Gamma)}\right]}
\end{aligned}
\right.
$$

(11-3-27)

For an infinite tone-spacing, the results are:

Infinite tone spacing

$d < \dfrac{\pi}{4}$

$$
\left\{
\begin{aligned}
(\Gamma_0)_{111} &= \Gamma \\[2mm]
(\Gamma_0)_{010} &= \frac{\Gamma\left(1 - \dfrac{4d}{\pi\sqrt{\pi}}\right)}{1 + \Gamma\dfrac{2d^2}{\pi^2}} \\[4mm]
(\Gamma_0)_{110} &= (\Gamma_0)_{011} = \frac{\Gamma\left(1 - \dfrac{2d}{\pi\sqrt{\pi}}\right)}{1 + \Gamma\dfrac{d^2}{\pi^2}}
\end{aligned}
\right.
$$

(11-3-28)

In these results, only $(\Gamma_0)_{111} \to \infty$ as $\Gamma \to \infty$. The other effective SNR's approach finite values. Since one must average the error probabilities over all possible sequences, there is again an irreducible error

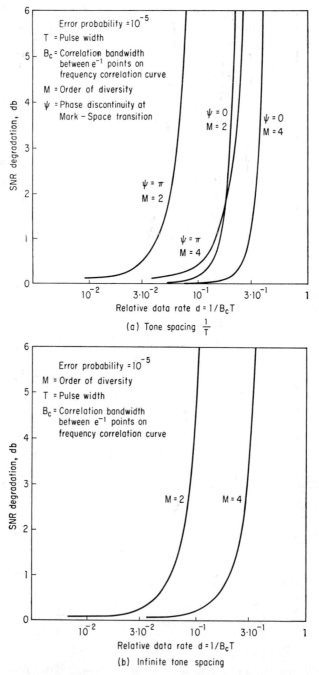

FIG. 11-3-6. SNR degradation for noncoherent FSK in slow, selective fading.

rate.   It is also apparent that the phase-discontinuous case at $1/T$ tone spacing suffers poorer performance than the phase-continuous case. Curves of the SNR degradation at a typical error rate, 10^{-5}, and for second- and fourth-order diversity are shown in Fig. 11-3-6.[1]   The other

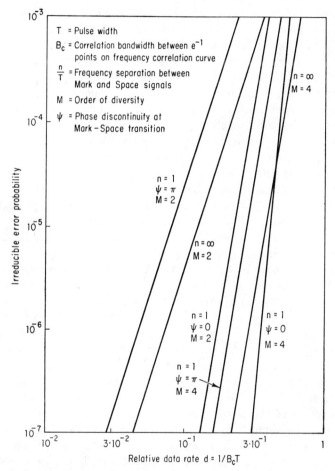

T = Pulse width

B_c = Correlation bandwidth between e^{-1} points on frequency correlation curve

$\frac{n}{T}$ = Frequency separation between Mark and Space signals

M = Order of diversity

ψ = Phase discontinuity at Mark – Space transition

Fig. 11-3-7. Irreducible error rates for noncoherent FSK in slow, selective fading.

aspect of interest, the irreducible average error rate as $\Gamma \to \infty$, is presented in the curves of Fig. 11-3-7.[1]

It is curious to note that better performance is obtained in the $1/T$ spacing, phase-continuous case than with infinite tone spacing.   Several effects appear to combine to produce this result.   First, in all cases when there is a continuous Mark sequence, the receiver Mark and Space filters, integrating over just the interval $(0,T)$, both see *continuous* Mark tones

---

[1] Bello and Nelin, *op. cit.*, Figs. 3, 4, and 5.

arriving over *all* the multipaths. Thus, at either spacing $1/T$ or with infinite spacing the Mark filter signal output realizes the average channel signal power (on the average), while the Space filter output is identically zero because of the orthogonality of Mark and Space tone pulses, at either spacing $1/T$ or infinite spacing.

Next, at infinite tone spacing, over the ensemble of sequences defined by Spaces adjacent to the Mark on either one or both sides, there will be a slight loss in the average signal output of the Mark filter integrating over $(0,T)$. However, this would not cause an irreducible error rate and can be ignored. At the same time, because of multipath, some signaled Space energy from these adjacent pulses appears in the Space filter as it integrates over $(0,T)$. Since both the Mark and Space filter outputs are fading, there is some finite probability even in the absence of additive noise that the Space filter output will exceed the Mark filter output. Indeed, it is clear from the results that in the limit, the irreducible error rate when Space occurs on both sides is just double that when Space occurs on one side only. Turning to the phase-*continuous* case at spacing $1/T$, one observes in (11-3-26) that instead of the $1/d^2$ behavior in (11-3-28) as $\Gamma \to \infty$, the limiting SNR's here are much higher, varying as $1/d^4$ (recall $d^2 \ll 1$). Since the limiting SNR effects here must still be due to signal appearing in the Space filter over $(0,T)$, when Mark is signaled, it appears that the close tone spacing somehow ameliorates these effects. The answer lies in the crosstalk which normally would occur at the $1/T$ tone spacing, when energy arrives by an "off-center" path. Because of such a path, the Space filter integrating over $(0,T)$ sees Mark over *part* of the interval and the adjacent Space over the rest of the interval. But the $1/T$ tone spacing is such that over an interval T, there is only a net 2π difference in the total phase change in a Mark versus Space waveform. Thus, the phase-continuity condition implies that the Space portion observed in the Space filter over $(0,T)$ can look very little different from a *continuation* of the Mark signal. In effect, the Space portion almost cancels out the signal which would otherwise appear due to the Mark covering less than the full T interval. This is further corroborated by noting that in the third case, of a phase discontinuity of π, the Space portion would now appear with *opposite* sign, and instead of cancellation, one would expect that this would reinforce the residual output in the Space filter. The voltage outputs in the Space filter should then be close to double those observed in the infinite spacing case, varying also as $1/d^2$. This indeed is observed from the limiting forms of (11-3-27).

Turning to binary DPSK, Bello and Nelin again apply their detailed computations to rectangular pulses with phase-reversal keying and assume that it is sufficient to take into account only the adjacent information symbol on each side of the one of interest. Because of the nature of DPSK, a total of four pulses of length T are now involved. Also, in a major difference from the FSK calculations, it must be realized that a pulse-pair without a phase reversal has a *different* spectral shape from a pulse pair which includes a phase reversal. Hence the effects of selective fading will be different for Marks and Spaces. Each probability of error must be computed separately, as averaged over all possible message sequences, and these in turn averaged together to determine net average error rate. Again the assumption of small d and matched filtering with

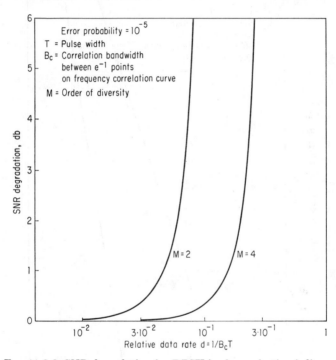

FIG. 11-3-8. SNR degradation for DPSK in slow, selective fading.

perfect synchronization is made, in the sense defined earlier. With subscripts 1 and 0 representing pulses with 0 or π phase, respectively, the effective SNR's (with respect to probability of error for the symbol defined by the two central pulses) are determined, for d small, as follows:

$$(\Gamma_0)_{1111} = 2\Gamma \tag{11-3-29a}$$

$$(\Gamma_0)_{0101} = 2\Gamma \left(1 - \frac{8d}{\pi\sqrt{\pi}} + \frac{8d^2}{\pi^2}\right)^2 \tag{11-3-29b}$$

$$(\Gamma_0)_{0110} = (\Gamma_0)_{1100} = 2\Gamma \frac{\left(1 - \dfrac{4d}{\pi\sqrt{\pi}}\right)^2}{1 + \Gamma\dfrac{8d^2}{\pi^2}} \tag{11-3-29c}$$

$$(\Gamma_0)_{0111} = (\Gamma_0)_{0100} = 2\Gamma \frac{\left(1 - \dfrac{6d}{\pi\sqrt{\pi}} + \dfrac{4d^2}{\pi^2}\right)^2}{1 + \Gamma \dfrac{4d^2}{\pi^2}\left(1 - \dfrac{1}{\pi}\right)} \qquad (11\text{-}3\text{-}29d)$$

For all other possible sequences, the effective SNR's can be determined

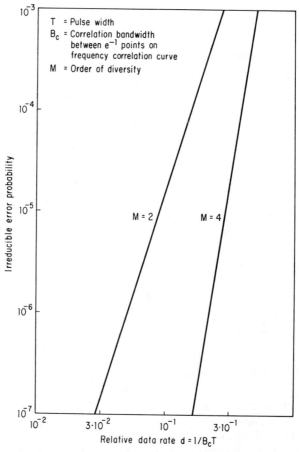

T = Pulse width
B_c = Correlation bandwidth between e^{-1} points on frequency correlation curve
M = Order of diversity

Irreducible error probability

M = 2   M = 4

Relative data rate $d = 1/B_c T$

FIG. 11-3-9. Irreducible error rates for DPSK in slow, selective fading.

by noting from physical symmetries that the same result is obtained with 1's and 0's interchanged, and/or the sequence taken in reverse order. Note that the limiting SNR again varies as $1/d^2$.

Figure 11-3-8[1] indicates the SNR degradation at an average error rate of 10^{-5}, for second- and fourth-order diversity, and Fig. 11-3-9[1] corre-

Fig. 11-3-8[1] indicates the SNR degradation at an average error rate of 10^{-5}, for second- and fourth-order diversity, and Fig. 11-3-9 corresponding curves of the irreducible error rate. Comparing Fig. 11-3-8

[1] From Bello and Nelin, op. cit., Figs. 8 and 9.

with Fig. 11-3-6, it is again observed that FSK appears generally less sensitive in the limit to these selective fading distortions, and (since contrariwise DPSK is better under slow, nonselective fading) there is some crossover point in normalized data rate beyond which FSK is better than DPSK. Values of the data rate at which crossover occurs, for an error rate of 10^{-5}, are shown in Table 11-3-1:

TABLE 11-3-1. DATA RATES FOR EQUIVALENT DPSK-FSK PERFORMANCE, AT 10^{-5} ERROR RATE

FSK case	Order of diversity	Relative data rate, $d = \dfrac{1}{B_c T}$
Tone spacing $1/T$ Phase continuous	2	0.068
	4	0.22
Tone spacing $1/T$ Phase discontinuous by π	2	0.082
	4	0.26
Tone spacing infinite	2	0.078
	4	0.24

SOURCE: P. A. Bello and B. D. Nelin, The Effect of Frequency Selective Fading on the Binary Error Probabilities of Incoherent and Differentially Coherent Matched Filter Receivers *loc. cit.*, table I.

Comparison with Figs. 11-3-8 and 11-3-9 shows that at these data rates DPSK is already operating at very close to an irreducible error rate of 10^{-5}. The implication appears to be that, in this case at least, it is only when requirements are such that the channel distortion renders DPSK almost useless for meeting the error-rate requirement that noncoherent FSK is better.

Predetection Maximal-ratio Combining with Imperfect Channel Estimates (Selectively Fading Channel with Pilot Tones). At the other extreme from the no-pilot tone, square-law diversity combining systems, one is interested in pilot-tone systems which use maximal-ratio combining even though the pilot tone provides only an imperfect estimate of the signal fading. The detailed results to be discussed are again from Bello and Nelin.[1] Their specific model assumes that maximal-ratio combining is achieved by deriving a complex combiner weighting factor in each diversity channel from a pilot tone transmitted at some spacing F from the center of the signal spectrum. It is also assumed that the fading is slow and *non*selective with respect to the signal bandwidth, but that because of the spacing F there is some decorrelation between the fading

[1] P. Bello and B. D. Nelin, Predetection Diversity Combining with Selectively Fading Channels, *IRE Trans. Commun. Systems*, vol. CS-10, pp. 32–42, March, 1962.

on the pilot tone and that on the signal. All channels are assumed to fade independently, with identical statistics and with spectrally flat additive Gaussian noise in each. In each channel, the pilot-tone component plus associated noise is mixed against the signal term (after any necessary preliminary frequency translation), as described earlier for maximal-ratio combining. The sum over all channels is then processed through appropriate matched-filter detectors. Consistent with the assumed slowness of fading, the channel is assumed to remain constant over each information pulse length, and the noise associated with the filtered pilot tone is also assumed very narrowband compared with signal bandwidth and hence constant over a signal pulse. The mixing operation thus only multiplies each signal pulse by a complex constant, changing over many pulses. (Hence one can interchange the order in which diversity summation and matched filtering are carried out.) For a signal pulse $s(t)$, the diversity summation therefore produces a complex envelope waveform at the difference frequency, of form

$$w(t) = Zs(t) + N(t) \qquad (11\text{-}3\text{-}30)$$

where the signal component $s(t)$ is multiplied by the complex number

$$Z = \exp(j\theta) \sum_{k=1}^{M} h_k^* \alpha_k \qquad (11\text{-}3\text{-}31)$$

and the noise waveform $N(t)$ comprises a sum of individual channel noises,

$$N(t) = \sum_{k=1}^{M} h_k^* \eta_k(t) \qquad (11\text{-}3\text{-}32)$$

Here the complex values h_k are the complex envelopes of the filtered pilot tones plus associated additive noises; $\eta_k(t)$ is the complex envelope of the additive noise associated with the signal pulse; α_k is the complex multiplicative fading process associated with the signal pulse; and the phase factor $\exp(j\theta)$ is a net phase associated with the difference-frequency operation (i.e., the difference of phase factors at the signal and pilot-tone frequencies). All the factors, h_k, α_k, and $\eta_k(t)$ are zero-mean complex Gaussian. The decorrelation in the fading between the pilot tone and signal is expressed by the magnitude of the normalized covariance between each α_k and h_k, assumed the same on all branches,

$$\rho = \frac{\tfrac{1}{2}\langle \alpha h^* \rangle}{[\tfrac{1}{2}\langle |\alpha|^2 \rangle \tfrac{1}{2}\langle |h|^2 \rangle]^{1/2}} \qquad |\rho| \le 1 \qquad (11\text{-}3\text{-}33)$$

Our interest will lie in ρ very near unity. The signal and pilot-tone fluctuations are assumed independent of the additive noises, and the two noises are assumed independent of each other. It can be readily shown that if Γ_p is the SNR associated with the pilot-tone measurement, and r

is the actual normalized covariance between pilot tone and signal multiplicative fluctuations, then

$$\rho = \frac{r}{\sqrt{1 + (1/\Gamma_p)}} \qquad (11\text{-}3\text{-}34)$$

If the waveform $w(t)$ in (11-3-30) is processed through filters matched to $s(t)$, one can use the basic matched-filter result to express the probability of error, conditional on the values of α_k, g_k, and ξ_k. For noncoherent FSK, which we consider in detail, this conditional probability of error is readily shown to be

$$P(\{\alpha_k\}, \{h_k\}) = \exp\left(-\frac{\Gamma}{2} \frac{\left|\sum_{k=1}^{M} \alpha_k h_k^*\right|^2}{\langle|\alpha|^2\rangle \sum_{k=1}^{M} |h_k|^2}\right) \qquad (11\text{-}3\text{-}35)$$

where the mean matched-filter output SNR in each diversity channel for the signal pulse has again been defined by Γ. The probability of error is now obtained as the average of (11-3-35) over the joint statistics of $\{\alpha_k\}$ and $\{h_k\}$.

One convenient method (different from that used by Bello and Nelin) is to recognize that for each k, α_k and h_k are joint Gaussian variates, independent of any other α_j or h_j. Hence, their joint distribution can be written in the form

$$p(\alpha_k, h_k) = p(h_k)p_{h_k}(\alpha_k) \qquad (11\text{-}3\text{-}36)$$

where $p_{h_k}(\alpha_k)$, the conditional p.d.f. of α_k when h_k is given, is also Gaussian. Thus, *conditional* on the set of variates $\{h_k\}$, the quantity $\Sigma \alpha_k h_k^*$ is a linear sum of Gaussian variates, hence itself a complex non-zero-mean Gaussian variate. Hence, conditional on the $\{h_k\}$, the conditional average of (11-3-35) is readily shown (e.g., the integrals of Appendix B) to be given by

$$P(\{h_k\}) = \frac{\exp\left[-\frac{|\rho|^2}{\langle|h|\rangle^2} \frac{\Gamma}{2 + \Gamma(1 - |\rho|^2)} \sum_{k=1}^{M} |h_k|^2\right]}{1 + (1 - |\rho|^2)\Gamma/2} \qquad (11\text{-}3\text{-}37)$$

Recalling that the several h_k are mutually independent and identically distributed zero-mean Gaussian variates, the remaining average on (11-3-37) can now be straightforwardly obtained, as

$$P_e = \frac{1}{2} \frac{[1 + (1 - |\rho|^2)\Gamma/2]^{M-1}}{(1 + \Gamma/2)^M} \qquad (11\text{-}3\text{-}38)$$

This is the desired result.

Recall now, the perfect combiner case occurs when $\rho = 1$; then (11-3-38) reduces to the earlier result (Chap. 10) for maximal-ratio combining of noncoherent FSK,

$$P_e = \frac{1}{2} \frac{1}{(1 + \Gamma/2)^M} = \frac{2^{M-1}}{(2 + \Gamma)^M} \qquad (11\text{-}3\text{-}39)$$

When $|\rho| < 1$, this result continues to hold effectively so long as

$$\Gamma \ll \frac{1}{1 - |\rho|^2} \qquad (11\text{-}3\text{-}40)$$

In effect, as observed earlier, the decorrelation evidenced by $|\rho| < 1$,

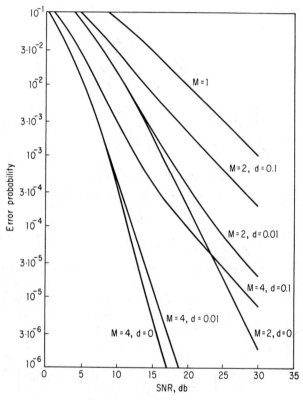

FIG. 11-3-10. Error rate versus single channel SNR for predetection combining, non-coherent FSK.

due to the combination of selective fading and of additive noise in the pilot-tone channel, is expressed by a limiting effective SNR, $1/(1 - |\rho|^2)$. So long as receiver noises *added to the signal* are the performance limitation, under the conditions of (11-3-40), performance is as if $|\rho| = 1$. However, at the other extreme, when the signal SNR is even larger, such that

$$\Gamma \gg \frac{1}{1 - |\rho|^2} \qquad (11\text{-}3\text{-}41)$$

one finds the other extreme,

$$P_e = \frac{1}{\Gamma} (1 - |\rho|^2)^{M-1} \qquad (11\text{-}3\text{-}42)$$

In this event, P_e varies only inversely as $1/\Gamma$ despite the diversity combining. However there is also evidenced in (11-3-42) a diversity behavior of order $M - 1$ with respect to the decorrelation effects; i.e., for given Γ and ρ, error rate still decreases inversely with $[1/(1 - |\rho|^2)]^{M-1}$.

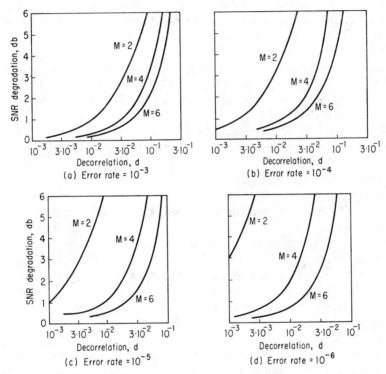

FIG. 11-3-11. SNR degradation for predetection combining, noncoherent FSK, at various error rates.

The detailed results of (11-3-38) are portrayed in the curves of Figs. 11-3-10 and 11-3-11,[1] drawn for several orders of diversity, in terms of a decorrelation parameter

$$d = \frac{1 - |\rho|^2}{2} \qquad (11\text{-}3\text{-}43)$$

In Fig. 11-3-10, the nondiversity case and the ideal-diversity results $(d = 0)$ for $M = 2$ and 4 are shown for comparison. For $M = 2$, and $d = 0.01$, diversity behavior tends to fail for error rates below 10^{-3}; for

[1] From Bello and Nelin, *loc. cit.*

lower error rates, error rate is inverse with SNR, although still with about 15 db improvement over no diversity. When d increases to 0.1, with $M = 2$, there is a 7-db improvement over no diversity, but now at all levels the error rate falls off only inversely as SNR, as in the no-diversity case. Therefore, in these cases, there is an improvement over no diversity, but (unlike the $d = 0$ case) it is not an improvement which increases as the error rate of interest becomes lower. Similarly for $M = 4$, ideal behavior holds (at least down to 10^{-6} error rate) for $d = 0.01$, but for $d = 0.1$ no-diversity behavior occurs below 10^{-3} error rate, although with 20 db better performance than with no diversity. The same data are portrayed in the curves of Fig. 11-3-11 where SNR degradation is plotted versus d, comparing at the same order of diversity the mean SNR required on each channel to achieve the indicated error rate as compared with the $d = 0$ case. Note, however, these latter curves tend to mask the significant improvement still available over the no-diversity case, as indicated in Fig. 11-3-10.

The results above for noncoherent FSK will apply directly also to DPSK, in a similar use of pilot tones, with the usual additional increase of 3 db in effective SNR. This is based on the continuing assumption of slow, multiplicative fading on each signal channel. The equivalence is most easily recognized by considering DPSK at information rate $1/T$ in terms of noncoherent matched-filter detection of orthogonal waveforms of length $2T$.

Similar derivations to those above were also carried out[1] for "exact" coherent detection with either FSK or phase reversal keying, a model in which it is assumed that coherent matched-filter detection is available on the combined signal. This implies that an exact phase reference can be maintained with respect to the *signal* component in the combiner *output*. If fading is slow enough on each channel, it is not completely unreasonable to assume that such an accurate time-varying reference can be maintained at the combiner output. The performance loss in this system is then simply the result of imperfect combining, the fact that all the available signal energy is not passed on through the combiner because of misalignment in phase in the signal components added. The latter in turn is the result of the decorrelation effects between the signal in each data channel and the associated pilot tone, which is supposed to provide exact compensation for the channel fluctuations. The most relevant feature of the result is its asymptotic behavior, a form just like (11-3-42), except for the expected 3-db SNR advantage for coherent FSK over noncoherent FSK. As in our earlier results, it follows that a similar form applies for coherent PSK, at precisely 3 db additional SNR advantage over coherent FSK.

Bello and Nelin also examined a form of coherent detection which

[1] Bello and Nelin, *op. cit.*

utilizes a *fixed* receiver reference signal.   This is based on the observation that the combiner output has a nonzero-mean value for any particular signal.   This mean arises because the pilot tones are at least partially successful in cancelling out the channel phase fluctuations.   Hence one has the possibility of a direct coherent detection of the combiner output. The problem mathematically involves the distribution of a Hermitian quadratic form in zero-mean complex Gaussian variates.   Hence the result has a form like (11-2-55), with the effective mean SNR Γ_0 given by

$$\Gamma_0 = \frac{2 \sqrt{|\rho|^2/(1 + 2/\Gamma)}}{1 - \sqrt{|\rho|^2/(1 + 2/\Gamma)}} \qquad (11\text{-}3\text{-}44)$$

Again as in the results of preceding sections, as $\Gamma \to \infty$, Γ_0 approaches a finite value.   If both $|\rho|^2$ is near unity, and $\Gamma \ll 1$, the SNR is closely given by

$$\Gamma_0 \to \frac{2}{(1 - |\rho|^2) + 1/\Gamma} \qquad (11\text{-}3\text{-}45)$$

As constrasted to (11-3-42), where P_e continued to decrease as $1/\Gamma$ no matter how large Γ becomes, the behavior implied by (11-3-45) is that of a limiting performance imposed by fading distortions, when a *fixed* (nonadaptive) phase reference is attempted in coherent operation. There is no limiting error rate in (11-3-42) because the assumption of slow, multiplicative fading precludes waveform distortion effects.   Thus, while decorrelated pilot tones degrade the combiner output SNR in that case, the envelope-detection operation continually gains contrast against noise as SNR in the data channel increases.

11-4. Diversity Operation Involving Energy Sharing and Energy Detection

The Effect of Energy Sharing in Diversity Operation.[1]   We have thus far considered communication performance in diversity reception in terms of the average received signal power on each diversity branch. However, when one recalls the various techniques for achieving diversity, it becomes clear that from a *system* design viewpoint, one ought to distinguish two different aspects of improvement due to diversity in these calculations:

1. As a primary effect, that of reducing the range of fading fluctuations through intelligent combining of several dissimilarly fading versions of the communications signal.

[1] The results here are from J. N. Pierce, Theoretical Limitations on Frequency and Time Diversity for Fading Binary Transmissions, *IEEE Trans. Commun. Systems*, vol. CS-11, pp. 186–187, June, 1963.   This material, plus detailed derivations, is also contained in Air Force Cambridge Research Laboratory Report ERD-TR-60-169 (same title), July, 1960.

2. A secondary effect, that the total available average power is the total of the average powers on each diversity channel.

However, this secondary effect may not actually be realized in a practical system design. It is literally true when diversity is achieved by spaced receiving antennas that with no power increase at the transmitting end, the average power extracted from the received field is proportional to the order of diversity, and this additional *average* power accounts in part for the performance improvement. On the other hand, in frequency diversity as an example, power must be radiated separately at the two frequencies, and the total available received power in diversity is proportional to the total power radiated to produce the diversity. In many such systems applications it may be highly relevant to consider *total primary power* to be fixed in comparing performance with various orders of diversity. In this case, Mth-order frequency diversity implies that $1/M$ of the total primary power is applied to each diversity branch. Accordingly, when one considers increasing values of M under this constraint, the average received power per branch decreases and the total average *available* power in reception remains constant. The issue then arises of how efficiently the diversity combiner uses the available power. As observed earlier, as M increases, there is a rapidly diminishing rate of diversity improvement in reducing the fluctuation effects. This is caused by the increasingly shallow range of fading in the combiner output at each higher order of diversity. Thus at some M, performance loss due to decrease in average power per channel for any further increase in M may outweigh the additional improvement due to further reduction in fluctuation effects. Thus, there may in fact be an optimum M for performance. It is this effect which we examine here.

For the discussion of energy-sharing diversity, we assume that in the no-diversity ($M = 1$) case, the *mean* SNR after filtering (i.e., at the detector input) is some value $\hat{\Gamma}$. Then, for M-fold diversity, the corresponding mean SNR in each branch after filtering will be

$$\Gamma = \frac{\hat{\Gamma}}{M} \qquad (11\text{-}4\text{-}1)$$

We confine our remarks here to noncoherent FSK transmission, under the simplifying assumptions of slow, multiplicative fading. We shall also assume all channels to be mutually independently fading and of equal strength. In the case of unequal branch strengths (or, for correlated fadings, the equivalent situation with unequal eigenvalues for the fading covariance matrix), the formulas are more complicated for calculation but presumably will lead qualitatively to the same effects as demonstrated below.

For ideal predetection maximal-ratio combining in which the phase corrections provided by the diversity weighting allow coherent addition of signal components on the several diversity branches, maximum use is made of the available received power.   From (10-8-3), with (11-4-1), the error rate for noncoherent FSK with maximal-ratio combining is then given by

$$P_e(M) = \frac{1}{2} \frac{1}{(1 + \Gamma/2)^M} = \frac{1}{2} \frac{1}{(1 + \frac{1}{2}\hat{\Gamma}/M)^M} \tag{11-4-2}$$

In this case, it can be shown that

$$\frac{\partial P_e(M)}{\partial M} < 0 \qquad \text{for all } M \tag{11-4-3}$$

although the rate of decrease of P_e with M becomes smaller as M increases and $\hat{\Gamma}/(2M) \to 0$.   The minimum error rate for energy-sharing diversity with maximal-ratio combining is thus given by the limit of (11-4-3) as $M \to \infty$,

$$\lim_{M \to \infty} P_e(M) = \frac{1}{2} \exp\left(-\frac{\hat{\Gamma}}{2}\right) \tag{11-4-4}$$

This is identical with the *nonfading, no-diversity* result for the same total mean power.   This is not unexpected physically since maximal-ratio combining does use *all* the available energy, while because of the infinite diversity, the combiner output fading range is at the same time reduced to zero about the average value $\hat{\Gamma}$.

On the other hand, consider the "minimum" and, from a practical viewpoint, the least demanding form of combining, namely square-law combining.   The error-rate dependence is given from (11-2-55) in various forms.   Pierce[1] utilized (11-2-55e), combined with (11-4-1),

$$P_e(M) = \frac{1}{2} \frac{\hat{\Gamma}/M}{[2 + \hat{\Gamma}/M]} \sum_{m=M}^{\infty} \binom{2m}{m} \left[\frac{1 + \hat{\Gamma}/M}{(2 + \hat{\Gamma}/M)^2}\right]^m \tag{11-4-5}$$

From this he showed that for square-law combining, there is indeed an optimum value of M, for which he derived analytical estimates.   He found that asymptotically (large M), error rate at optimum M is given by the formula

$$P_e \sim \frac{0.82}{\sqrt{\hat{\Gamma}}} \exp(-0.1488\hat{\Gamma}) \tag{11-4-6}$$

In this limit, square-law combining (with optimum order of diversity) thus has a performance poorer by about 5.3 db (the ratio 0.5/0.1488) than the infinite-order ideal maximal-ratio combining.

More generally, the properties of (11-4-6) can be usefully portrayed by detailed calculations from the exact formula.   This is shown in Fig. 11-4-1,[2] a plot of error rate versus $\Gamma = \hat{\Gamma}/M$, where Γ is accordingly the SNR per diversity channel.   Curves of constant $\hat{\Gamma}$ are also shown.   One

---

[1] Pierce, *loc. cit.*

[2] Presentation of the curves in this form originated with R. R. Reed, as presented in a panel discussion on modulation techniques, *Proc. Navy Rand D Clinic*, Raton, Calif., September, 1961.

significant feature is that for square-law combining, the best performance for fixed Γ is obtained for that order of diversity such that Γ is about 3 (5 db); this statement is largely independent of $\hat{\Gamma}$ for all error rates of practical interest. For the curves shown (for $\hat{\Gamma}$ in the 13 to 23-db range), the optimum order of diversity varies correspondingly from about 7 to about 70. It should also be noted in Fig. 11-4-1 that the performance for each $\hat{\Gamma}$ is essentially unchanged over a wide range of values of M or of Γ on either side of the optimum. This is particularly true for values of M above the optimum.

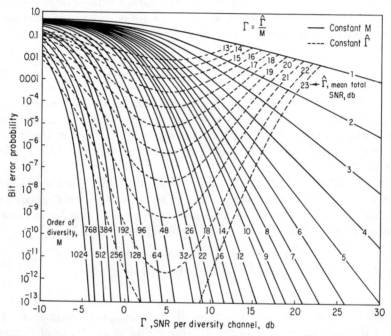

Fig. 11-4-1. Error rate for energy-sharing diversity with square-law combining, noncoherent FSK.

Energy Detection for Communication Signals Severely Distorted by Fading. The discussion above leads intuitively to an insight into methods for reception of signals severely distorted by fading. We shall discuss this subject qualitatively and briefly, only highlighting the features.

As emphasized earlier, either rapid fading within the duration of individual signal pulses or selective fading across the spectrum of such pulses results in a loss of coherence over the time or frequency structure of the signal. Assuming that under these circumstances the specific distortions due to fading are unpredictable on any specific pulse, it is then impossible to coherently extract all the available signal energy. If one continues in these situations to use receivers constructed with filters matched to the transmitted waveform, then (as discussed in Sec. 11-3) performance will be limited even when the distortions are relatively minor, but the performance will still likely be satisfactory for many applications.   However, when the distortions become major, performance will be even more severely degraded, to the point of becoming useless. The distortion problems have therefore attracted particular attention with respect to channels with a high spread factor, either a significant fraction of unity, or even an overspread channel.   It is largely in connection with such channels that the concepts to be described below originally were realized.[1]

In these cases of high spread factor, when it becomes impossible to select a pulse duration which will reasonably satisfy both the small-distortion criteria (11-3-1) and (11-3-2), the preferable choice appears to lie in selecting a relatively long pulse length.   This minimizes the problems of selective fading and intersymbol interference due to multipath elongation, but results in a significant amount of fading over each received pulse length T.   We shall use this simple model to explain energy detection (or radiometric detection, as it is sometimes termed).

In a case of rapid fading, including phase fluctuations within each pulse, it becomes clear that noncoherent signaling-detection operation should be employed.   A natural signaling technique is spaced-tone FSK, with spacing chosen sufficiently large to avoid crosstalk in the face of the spectral widening.   Note that simple DPSK cannot be used effectively in this situation, even though we have earlier emphasized its equivalence to noncoherent systems.   The point here is that while the detection process in simple DPSK *ignores* the long-term coherence (or lack thereof) in the signal, short-term coherence over a full $2T$ interval is essential for distinguishing Mark from Space.   In spaced-tone FSK, on the other hand, spectral *energy* in the vicinity of the nominal Mark frequency can be identified with Mark signals and *energy* around the Space frequency similarly identified with Space.   The recognition is on a basis of *frequency content*, a factor which is not appreciably altered (within limits, of course) by the destruction of coherence over the pulse; whereas for simple DPSK, the symbol orthogonality is strongly based upon preservation of phase coherence over each $2T$ interval.

Consider, then, noncoherent FSK with multiplicative (nonselective) fading on each pulse, occurring at a rate comparable to, or faster than

[1] R. Price and P. E. Green, Jr., Signal Processing in Radar Astronomy—Communication via Fluctuating Multipath Media, MIT Lincoln Lab, Tech. Rept. 234, October, 1960; R. S. Kennedy and I. L. Lebow, Signal Design for Dispersive Channels, *IEEE Spectrum*, vol. 1, pp. 231–237, March, 1964; I. L. Lebow, P. R. Drouilhet, N. L. Daggett, J. N. Harris, and F. Nagy, Jr., The West Ford Belt as a Communications Medium, *Proc. IEEE*, vol. 52, pp. 543–563, May, 1964.

the keying rate. The rapidity of fading is described by the normalized autocovariance function of the complex Gaussian fading process. If the nominal width of this autocovariance (down to the 0.5 or 0.3 level, say) is T_a, then over each symbol duration, there are *roughly*

$$M = \frac{T}{T_a} \tag{11-4-7}$$

independent fading states occurring. If one smooths for a duration T_a, the signal components will tend to add coherently within such an interval, but if the smoothing is extended over any longer interval, the additional signal components will tend to add incoherently with those already smoothed. Thus, consider that the fading tone signal plus additive noise is processed through a filter with nominal response time roughly T_a centered on the nominal tone frequency. Then over the course of a pulse of duration T, the filter outputs at M successive instants spaced by T_a are voltage samples which are (in the ensemble) complex zero-mean Gaussian variates and are roughly *independent*. Each will contain a signal-and-noise component at a level corresponding roughly to a mean SNR,

$$\Gamma = \frac{ST_a}{n_0} \tag{11-4-8}$$

where S is the mean signal level and n_0 is the (one-sided) power spectral density of the additive noise (assumed spectrally flat at the filter input).

The M voltage outputs of the filter over the duration T now have all the qualities needed for *diversity operation*, using a diversity combining which requires no knowledge of the fading states. Thus if one such filter is centered at the Mark tone and one at the Space tone, the M outputs on each should be square-law combined, and the decision should be based on the larger of the combiner outputs. The effect will be precisely that explored in the previous subsection, with the total "available mean SNR" entering into each decision given by

$$\hat{\Gamma} = M\Gamma = \frac{SMT_a}{n_0} = \frac{ST}{n_0} \tag{11-4-9}$$

That is, $\hat{\Gamma}$ is the usual mean E/n_0 ratio for the signaled symbol under the conditions of fading. The performance, with (11-4-8) and (11-4-9), is given by the formula of (11-4-5) or the equivalent forms in Sec. 11-2, and described by the curves of Fig. 11-4-1. While the value of T_a, and hence of $M = T/T_a$ is only roughly specified above, it will be recalled also that performance will not be sensitive to the specific value of M, so long as it is roughly correct.

One aspect relating to implementation is noteworthy. If the pre-combiner filter operates continuously (e.g., an RLC circuit), its envelope output presumably has limited bandwidth. As such, the samples regularly taken of its output, for square-law combining, can be taken to represent the continuous output envelope by a sampling-theorem argument. As is well known, because the sampling theorem involves an orthonormal representation, the integral of the square of a waveform is equal to the sum of the squares of the sampled values. Thus the square-law combining can then also be effected by square-law detection of the precombiner filter output along with postdetection integration over the $(0,T)$ interval. The net diversity effect depends only upon the number of independently fading samples contained within the interval. Note that the square-law-detected waveform is closely a measure of the instantaneous *energy* in the received signal (plus noise) and that integration over $(0,T)$ thus is a form of *energy-detection* receiver. It is not surprising that the assumed lack of phase coherence over the received signal leads one to fall back on this one parameter still distinguishing the symbol waveforms, the distinction described by the difference in concentration of *energy* about the two nominal tone frequencies.

While the curves of Fig. 11-4-1 do not indicate any bottoming effect at high SNR, this is clearly because our discussion has assumed phase coherence *always* being obtained within a correlation interval of the fading. Just as clearly, this is sometimes not true statistically and will indeed lead to a bottoming effect just as in the analyses in Sec. 11-3. Such an analysis is not available.

The remarks above can also be extended qualitatively to selectively fading situations or to combined effects of fading selectivity and rapidity within individual pulses.

11-5. Wideband Antimultipath Systems (Rake)

The Matched-filter Adaptive Receiver. In this last section, we describe the use of wideband signaling and reception as an antimultipath measure over fading channels. This is most familiar as the Rake technique.[1] The general principles will be discussed here in the context of matched-filter and diversity reception.

We recall the representations in Sec. 9-2 for a signal received over a fading multipath channel. Let $u_0(t)$ be the complex envelope of the transmitted waveform and $u(t)$ be the corresponding complex envelope of the received waveform, with the nominal propagation delay t_0 deleted from the representation. Then

$$u(t) = \int_{-\infty}^{\infty} \beta(t - \tau; t)u_0(\tau) \, d\tau = \int_{-\infty}^{\infty} \beta(\tau;t)u_0(t - \tau) \, d\tau \quad (11\text{-}5\text{-}1)$$

where $\beta(\tau;t)$ is the time-varying equivalent low-pass impulse response of

[1] R. Price and P. E. Green, Jr., A Communication Technique for Multipath Channels, *Proc. IRE*, vol. 46, pp. 555–570, March, 1958.

the channel. Suppose now $u_0(t)$ represents one waveform member of a symbol alphabet $\{u_{0k}(t); k = 1, \ldots, N\}$. Suppose also the time variations of $\beta(\tau;t)$, as indexed by its second argument (t), are slow enough that its functional dependence upon τ can be accurately monitored, for example by sounding signals (examples are described later). Then in the face of additive Gaussian receiver noise, the optimal receiver is immediately obvious from matched-filter considerations. It is an *adaptive* receiver in which the knowledge of $\beta(\tau;t)$ is used to determine the set of possible *received* signal waveforms, $\{u_k(t); k = 1, \ldots, N\}$, and these are then used as a basis for matched-filter or equivalent cross-correlation reception of the received signal plus noise. With $\hat{\beta}(\tau;t)$ as the estimate of $\beta(\tau;t)$ at time t, the estimates for the received waveforms are

$$\hat{u}_k(t) = \int_{-\infty}^{\infty} \hat{\beta}(t - \tau; t)u_{0k}(\tau)\, d\tau = \int_{-\infty}^{\infty} u_{0k}(t - \tau)\hat{\beta}(\tau;t)\, d\tau \quad (11\text{-}5\text{-}2)$$

The matched-filter receiver determines which symbol was transmitted by determining from the received signal $u(t)$, plus additive noise $n(t)$, the largest of the values

$$\Lambda_k = \int_{-\infty}^{\infty} \hat{u}_k{}^*(t)[u(t) + n(t)]\, dt \quad (11\text{-}5\text{-}3)$$

where $\hat{u}_k{}^*(t)$ is the complex conjugate of $\hat{u}_k(t)$. The integration is again implied to be on a "one-shot" basis, with the estimate $\hat{u}_k(t)$ confined to the nominal symbol duration T (or to $T + T_M$, where T_M is the multipath spread). For the time being, we ignore intersymbol interference and confine ourselves to this simple one-shot model.

For another interpretation, assume that $\hat{\beta}(\tau;t)$ is constant over the duration of the signal pulse at, say, the value $\hat{\beta}(\tau;0)$, where $t = 0$ is a nominal time instant during reception of the pulse. This slow variation has already been implied as part of the ability to estimate the channel. With this assumption, one can combine the two forms (11-5-2) and (11-5-3) and interchange the orders of integration, with the result

$$\Lambda_k = \int_{-\infty}^{\infty} \hat{\beta}^*(\tau;0)\rho_k(\tau)\, d\tau \quad (11\text{-}5\text{-}4a)$$

where
$$\rho_k(\tau) = \int_{-\infty}^{\infty} u_{0k}{}^*(t - \tau)[u(t) + n(t)]\, dt \quad (11\text{-}5\text{-}4b)$$

This suggests now a different receiver form, basically a *diversity receiver*, adaptive in the sense in which any diversity receiver is adaptive. The received signal, plus noise, is cross-correlated against a replica of each possible *transmitted* waveform, at every possible delay, and the results summed with maximal-ratio combiner weighting using the estimate of the channel at that relative delay. This equivalence of adaptive matched-filter operation to diversity operation underlies the Rakè technique and the many closely related systems. The equivalence actually continues to hold under more general channel variations, with a correspondingly generalized form of diversity within the pulse.[1]   From these equivalences, one can draw upon either "matched filter" or "diversity" principles to derive qualitative (or quantitative) estimates of the effects of various factors upon performance.   The detailed mathematics will of course be identical from either viewpoint.

The model above indicates that to achieve diversity improvement, the resolution of the multipath should be much smaller than the multipath spread T_M.   In turn this implies the use of a signal bandwidth W which is large compared to $1/T_M$.   This size of W will be implicit in the description below as the range of ultimate interest.

Tapped-delay-line Representation for the Channel and Adaptive Receiver.   The mathematics above implies a receiver based upon estimates of the channel impulse response $\beta(\tau;t)$ over the *continuum* of values of τ for which $\beta(\tau;t)$ is nonvanishing.   Working with such a continuum is infeasible practically.   Furthermore, one expects that the detail required in estimating $\beta(\tau;t)$ should not need to be significantly finer than the reciprocal of the signaling bandwidth.   That this is indeed the case is most readily shown by demonstrating a sampling-theorem representation of the channel response.[2]   For the moment, we set aside the manner in which information is conveyed within the signal, and emphasize only the channel representation/measurement problem.

Thus, assume that the transmitted signal spectrum is strictly limited to some bandwidth W cps, or that its complex envelope $u_0(t)$ has a two-sided spectrum strictly limited to

$$-\frac{W}{2} \leq f \leq \frac{W}{2} \tag{11-5-5}$$

Then it follows from the sampling theorem that $u_0(t)$ can be represented in the form

$$u_0(t) = \sum_{m=-\infty}^{\infty} u_0\left(\frac{m}{W}\right) \frac{\sin \pi W(t - m/W)}{\pi W(t - m/W)} \tag{11-5-6}$$

If $k(t)$ is the complex envelope of any other function, not necessarily band-limited, (11-5-6) gives

$$\int_{-\infty}^{\infty} u_0(t)k(t)\,dt = \frac{1}{W} \sum_{m=-\infty}^{\infty} u_0\left(\frac{m}{W}\right) k_1\left(\frac{m}{W}\right) \tag{11-5-7}$$

where the values $k_1(m/W)$ are sampled values of the function $k_1(t)$ defined

---

[1] For example, see the work of Kailath cited in Sec. 11-1.

[2] Such a model was utilized by Price and Green, *loc. cit.*, for a heuristic explanation of Rake.   It has also been the basis for the related theoretical studies of Kailath, cited in Sec. 11-1, and for representation of the orbital dipole belt, including detailed discussion of the statistical properties of such a model, in P. A. Bello, Correlation Functions in a Tapped Delay Line Model of the Orbital Dipole Channel, *IEEE Trans. Inform. Theory*, vol. IT-9, pp. 2–11, January, 1963.

by

$$k_1(t) = \int_{-\infty}^{\infty} \frac{\sin \pi W(t-x)}{\pi(t-x)} k(x)\, dx \qquad (11\text{-}5\text{-}8)$$

It is readily shown that in fact $k_1(t)$ is the function corresponding to that portion of $k(t)$ whose spectrum lies within $(-W/2, W/2)$. That is, if $K(f)$ is the spectrum of $k(t)$, the spectrum of $k_1(t)$ is

$$K_1(f) = \begin{cases} K(f) & -\dfrac{W}{2} \le f \le \dfrac{W}{2} \\ 0 & |f| \ge \dfrac{W}{2} \end{cases} \qquad (11\text{-}5\text{-}9)$$

Particularly, it follows that (11-5-1) can be written rigorously in the form

$$u(t) = \frac{1}{W} \sum_{m=-\infty}^{\infty} \beta_1\left(\frac{m}{W}; t\right) u_0\left(t - \frac{m}{W}\right) \qquad (11\text{-}5\text{-}10)$$

where $\beta_1(\tau;t)$ is an equivalent low-pass time-varying impulse response for the channel, corresponding *only* to its low-pass transfer function over the band $-W/2 \le f \le W/2$. That is,

$$\beta_1(\tau;t) = \int_{-\infty}^{\infty} \frac{\sin \pi W(\tau-x)}{\pi(\tau-x)} \beta(x;t)\, dx \qquad (11\text{-}5\text{-}11)$$

and the corresponding transfer function is given by

$$H_1(f;t) = \begin{cases} H(f;t) & |f| < \dfrac{W}{2} \\ 0 & |f| > \dfrac{W}{2} \end{cases} \qquad (11\text{-}5\text{-}12)$$

where $H(f;t)$ is the transfer function corresponding to $\beta(\tau;t)$. The implication is not in itself surprising: If the transmitted signal is confined to $|f| < W/2$ relative to carrier frequency, only the portion of the transfer function covering that band is relevant to determining the form of the received signal, *and only* that portion of the transfer function or the channel response can be inferred from measurements on the received signal.

The channel model implied by (11-5-10) is shown in Fig. 11-5-1. For all signals limited to a bandwidth W, it suffices to estimate the behavior of the channel in terms of its effective impulse response $\beta_1(\tau;t)$, at intervals spaced $1/W$ apart in τ,[1] the first (delay) variable. We define these values as

$$b_m(t) = \beta_1\left(\frac{m}{W}; t\right) \qquad (11\text{-}5\text{-}13)$$

[1] Indeed, it is the tapped-delay-line model of the channel, and the corresponding form of the receivers as discussed later, which led to the "Rake" description for the original system of this type.

or simply write b_m for short when the stochastic variations indexed by t are not at issue. In these terms, the received waveform is just

$$u(t) = \frac{1}{W} \sum_{m=-\infty}^{\infty} b_m(t)u_0\left(t - \frac{m}{W}\right) \tag{11-5-14}$$

Estimation of the channel for adaptive reception is now defined in terms of estimating the $\{b_m(t)\}$. Defining these estimates as $\{\hat{b}_m(t)\}$, the kth reference waveform in (11-5-2) required for the adaptive receiver can be written in the form

$$\hat{u}_k(t) = \frac{1}{W} \sum_{m=-\infty}^{\infty} \hat{b}_m(t)u_{0k}\left(t - \frac{m}{W}\right) \tag{11-5-15}$$

Likewise, the kth correlation process on the received signal plus noise in

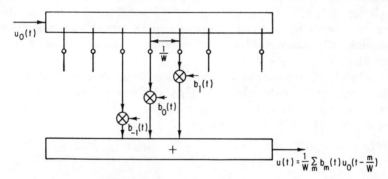

FIG. 11-5-1. Tapped-delay-line model of a multipath fading channel.

(11-5-3) or (11-5-4) can be written in the respective equivalent forms

$$\Lambda_k = \frac{1}{W} \sum_{p=-\infty}^{\infty} \hat{u}_k^*\left(\frac{p}{W}\right)\left[u\left(\frac{p}{W}\right) + n\left(\frac{p}{W}\right)\right] \tag{11-5-16}$$

$$= \frac{1}{W} \sum_{m=-\infty}^{\infty} \hat{b}_m^* \left\{\frac{1}{W} \sum_{p=-\infty}^{\infty} u_{0k}^*\left(\frac{p}{W} - \frac{m}{W}\right)\left[u\left(\frac{p}{W}\right) + n\left(\frac{p}{W}\right)\right]\right\} \tag{11-5-17}$$

In writing the second form above the assumption again is that $\hat{b}_m$ is constant over all values $t = p/W$ involved in nonvanishing terms in the inner sum over the duration of the pulse being examined. Again, the first form above implies the adaptive matched filter, while the second form represents the diversity interpretation.

The relation between the $\{b_m(t)\}$ and $\beta(\tau;t)$ is defined by (11-5-11) and (11-5-13),

$$b_m(t) = \int_{-\infty}^{\infty} \frac{\sin \pi W(m/W - x)}{\pi(m/W - x)} \beta(x;t)\, dx \tag{11-5-18}$$

Since $\beta(x;t)$ is a complex Gaussian process, so are the $\{b_m(t)\}$. The "window function"

$$\frac{\sin \pi W(\tau - x)}{\pi(\tau - x)}$$

is readily shown to approach $\delta(\tau - x)$ in the limit $W \to \infty$.[1] Thus, in this limit, indeed $b_m(t) \to \beta(m/W;t)$. For finite values of W, however, $b_m(t)$ represents a "smoothed" version of $\beta(\tau;t)$ over a range of values of τ centered around the value $\tau = m/W$. The window properties of the function

$$\frac{\sin \pi W(\tau - x)}{\pi(\tau - x)}$$

namely that its nulls fall at $|\tau - x| = 1/W$ and its half-power width is approximately $1/W$, imply that the smoothing is over a "delay shell" (recall Sec. 9-2) of width roughly $1/W$. Hence if $\beta(\tau;t)$ is nonvanishing in τ only over a range defined by the multipath spread T_M, the $b_m(t)$ will be significantly nonvanishing over a range of values of m/W given approximately by $T_M + 1/W$.

Also, while it was argued on physical grounds (Sec. 9-2) that $\beta(\tau;t)$ could be regarded to fade independently at different values of τ, it is easily shown that the same is no longer strictly true of the set of smoothed versions, $\{b_m(t)\}$. However, because

$$\frac{\sin \pi W(m/W - x)}{\pi(m/W - x)} \quad \text{and} \quad \frac{\sin \pi W(n/W - x)}{\pi(n/W - x)}$$

are orthogonal for $m \neq n$, it can also be shown that there will be a strong tendency for the $\{b_m(t)\}$ to be statistically independent if the multipath autocorrelation profile (Sec. 9-2) of $\beta(\tau;t)$ is slowly varying in τ, changing slowly when τ varies by a few times $1/W$. This is reasonably consistent with the requirement for diversity performance that $1/W \ll T_M$.

Hence, while the exact details of correlations among the $\{b_m(t)\}$ can be discussed more quantitatively, it suffices for the remainder of our discussion to assume that the tap cross-covariances are small enough to be regarded as essentially zero. The performance discussions to which this assumption will be relevant essentially cover diversity operations, so that the following additional comments apply: (1) We have already observed that relatively large covariances in fading among diversity branches diminish diversity performance in only a minor way; and (2) the previous chapters and sections have indicated how to use covariances (such as can be calculated from the formulas above), when the detailed

---

[1] I.e., for any continuous function $f(x)$,

$$\lim_{W \to \infty} \int_{-\infty}^{\infty} \frac{\sin \pi W(\tau - x)}{\pi(\tau - x)} f(x)\, dx = f(\tau)$$

multipath characteristics are known and it is desired to determine these changes in performance.   Finally, since the effective order of diversity in (11-5-17) is essentially the number of values of m at which $\langle|b_m|^2\rangle$ is significantly nonzero, one can now roughly estimate the effective order of diversity as

$$M \approx \frac{T_M + 1/W}{1/W} = T_m W + 1 \tag{11-5-19}$$

Wideband Pulse Signaling.   We can now use (11-5-10), (11-5-16) and (11-5-17) to establish the main concepts underlying Rake operation for

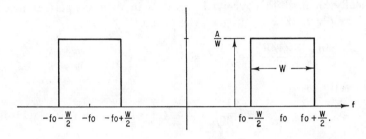

(a) Spectrum

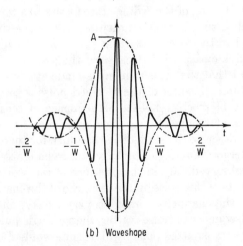

(b) Waveshape

Fig. 11-5-2. Band-limited impulse.

information transmission.   This initial discussion will consider a simple signal of bandwidth W, a "band-limited impulse."   By this is meant (Fig. 11-5-2) a band-limited pulse at carrier frequency with the normalized transmitted complex envelope

$$u_0(t) = A \frac{\sin \pi W t}{\pi t} \tag{11-5-20}$$

This results, for example, when an impulse is passed through a rectangular bandpass filter of width W centered on the carrier frequency. This is a simpler signal than usually associated with Rake operation and is more suited for illustrative purposes.

For a single pulse transmitted, centered on $t = 0$ as in (11-5-20), and with the nominal average propagation delay ignored, the received complex envelope can be represented by (11-5-14) as

$$u(t) = \frac{A}{W} \sum_{m=-\infty}^{\infty} b_m(t) \frac{\sin \pi W(t - m/W)}{\pi(t - m/W)} \tag{11-5-21}$$

Specifically then, if this received signal is in turn *sampled* at instants defined by $t = k/W (k = \text{integer})$, the property

$$\frac{\sin \pi W(m/W - k/W)}{\pi(m/W - k/W)} = W\delta_{mk} = \begin{cases} W & m = k \\ 0 & m \neq k \end{cases} \tag{11-5-22}$$

leads directly to

$$u\left(\frac{k}{W}\right) = Ab_k(t) \Big|_{t = \frac{k}{W}} \tag{11-5-23}$$

Thus, $u(m/W)$ is a direct measure of the apparent channel response at relative delay m/W (i.e., of the fading state at the mth tap in the tapped-delay-line model of the channel), measured at relative time m/W. We have emphasized in the form of writing (11-5-23) that it is the mth tap parameter which is measured. Because of the assumed slowness of fading the statement that the measurement is made at some time $t = m/W$ relative to the nominal center of the received pulse is secondary.

In the absence of receiver noise, the sequence of measured sampled values of the complex envelope received for a *single* transmitted pulse would *completely* describe the state of the channel, for that interval before the channel undergoes any significant dynamic changes. However, $u(t)$ actually can be observed only in the presence of receiver noise $n(t)$. To minimize the effects of this noise on the estimate of the channel, within the assumption that the channel is changing very slowly, one can base the estimate upon a sequence of pulses rather than a single pulse. The spacing between these transmitted pulses will be some value T_0, exceeding T_M in order to avoid ambiguities in measurements.[1] The sum of the successive values associated with the multipath delay m/W (the receiver is assumed to have sufficiently accurate timing to identify these instants properly) provides an *estimate* of the effective channel response at this propagation delay at a time t now identified only as generally indicative of the period covered by the series of measurements. In practice, a continuous monitoring of the channel can be maintained by using a filter

[1] Note the assumption here of an "underspread" channel, one whose rate of dynamic change is very slow compared with the reciprocal of the multipath spread.

to achieve the running sum, for example by feeding all samples referring to, say, the mth tap as amplitudes of conveniently shaped pulses, into an appropriate filter.   If the filter has a time constant approximately NT_0 (with the *assumption* that NT_0 is short compared with the reciprocal of the channel fading rate), the effective SNR associated with the estimate is N times that of a single measurement.

A rectangular bandpass filter of width W in the receiver front end can be assumed to minimize the additive noise, while leaving the signal undistorted.   Assuming the noise is spectrally flat with (one-sided) power density spectrum n_0, the signal-noise ratio associated with a single measurement would be

$$\gamma_1 = \frac{S}{n_0 W} \tag{11-5-24}$$

where S is the peak power observed at the mth sampling point, for each received pulse during the interval under consideration.   From (11-5-23), this is simply

$$S = \frac{1}{2}|Ab_m|^2 = \frac{A^2}{2}|b_m|^2 \tag{11-5-25}$$

$$\gamma_1 = \frac{|b_m|^2}{2}\frac{A^2}{n_0 W} \tag{11-5-26}$$

Since b_m is a Gaussian variable, S will also vary.   Over stationary short-term fading, it will be described by an exponential p.d.f.   While noise will perturb the estimate during intervals when S is small, the total contribution of this tap through the diversity combining operation will then also be relatively small, hence total performance will be little affected (recall Sec. 11-3, on pilot tones in maximal-ratio combining).   The important factor (Sec. 11-3) is that effective maximal-ratio combining can be achieved whenever the channel estimate for each diversity branch has a much higher *mean* SNR than associated with individual signal elements.

A system using the wideband signaling and estimation capability described above is now outlined in Fig. 11-5-3.   (This figure ignores many details of an operational system, including synchronization circuits, frequency translations, amplifiers, etc.)   In the system shown, *information* is transmitted by phase-reversal keying of a serial stream.   However, every Kth pulse transmitted is always a Mark, used for channel estimation; in Fig. 11-5-3, $K = 6$.   If pulses are transmitted at intervals of T sec, the average *information* rate is

$$R = \frac{K-1}{K}\frac{1}{T} \tag{11-5-27}$$

If information is accepted from the source at a uniform rate R, it must enter the system through a buffer storage, from which $K - 1$ bits are read out at the rate $1/T = [K/(K - 1)]R$, with the carrier modulated by phase reversal keying.   After each such block of $K - 1$ bits, a Kth "sounding" bit is inserted as a Mark.

In the receiver, after filtering to the signal bandwidth, the signal plus noise is passed into a delay line with $M = T_M W + 1$ or slightly more

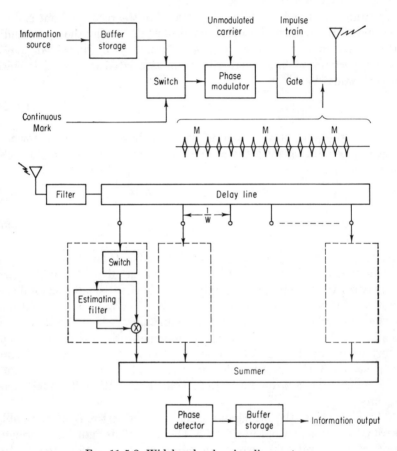

FIG. 11-5-3. Wideband pulse signaling system.

taps.   At the appropriate instant once during each interval T, the contents of the delay line are sampled at all taps, thereby simultaneously obtaining the desired set of $1/W$ spaced samples of the signal plus noise corresponding to a transmitted pulse.   Every Kth transmitted pulse, when the sounding Mark is transmitted, the delay line contents are passed into corresponding estimating filters at each tap, where a relatively noiseless estimate of the channel state is derived by smoothing over several such sounding pulses.   For example, in tropospheric scatter, one can well assume the channel to certainly change slowly over a time period of 10 msec.   Thus, if information is sent serially at a rate of 20 kilobits/ sec and one sounding pulse is utilized for every 10 information pulses ($K = 11$), a 10-msec smoothing on the sounding pulses corresponds to smoothing over $N = 20$ such pulses; hence the estimate will be derived with 13 db higher SNR than the individual information pulses.   At the other extreme, note that at 50 bits/sec, even one sounding pulse for every five information pulses would provide smoothing over only $N - 3$ pulses in a period of 0.3 sec.   While the resulting SNR margin of 5 db is probably adequate, 0.3 sec may be overly long for typical rates of change in h-f or troposcatter systems, and one may seek a more effective concept for deriving channel state (as discussed further below).

As shown in Fig. 11-5-3, at each tap the output of the estimating filter is continuously mixed against the delay-line signal-plus-noise output (usually with an additional frequency translation of the estimator output, so that the mixer output is at a convenient difference frequency).   To the extent that the channel estimate is effectively noiseless, the mixer output then represents an appropriately weighted version of the signal-plus-noise for maximal-ratio combining.   That is, the channel phase has been cancelled out and an amplitude factor applied proportional to the amplitude of each multipath component.[1]   Thus, these are summed and the output detected at the appropriate instant once per information pulse T.   Figure 11-5-3 indicates the latter operation to be coherent detection, against a phase reference (not shown) derived from the summer output, with tracking of phase required only to compensate for relative drift between basic oscillators in the transmitter and receiver, but not for channel variations.   Differential phase-shift keying and corresponding detection also can be used.   Although the ability to derive a channel estimate to enable maximal-ratio combining implies the *availability* of slightly better performance, the use of differential encoding is often viewed as avoiding possible errors due to 180° ambiguities sometimes present in a derived phase reference.

Alternative Means of Channel Estimation for Phase-reversal Systems. Now suppose one is interested in a low-information-rate system such that, as in the second example cited earlier, an unappetizingly large proportion

---

[1] Because of the finite SNR associated with deriving channel estimates, there is a danger in maximal-ratio combining of assigning nonzero weighting to diversity branches which actually contain only noise.   For example, the original Rake (described later) was designed for h-f, with $W = 10$ kc and $M = 50$ taps, to cover a potential multipath spread of $T_M = 5$ msec.   However (recall Sec. 9-3) in long-distance h-f transmission, it is unlikely that more than perhaps 10 of the taps will be actually contributing useful signal at any one time.   Unless the other taps are excluded from the combiner, for example by some kind of threshold sensing, the amount of excess noise presented to the detector may become formidable, even though each tap in itself contributes little.   Unfortunately, there is no detailed analysis available upon which to gauge the design parameters for such operation.

of the signaling capacity would have to be allocated just to sounding pulses in the system of Fig. 11-5-3. Several variants are possible; we shall discuss some typical possibilities.

First, consider particularly DPSK, in the context of applying detection to successive pulse pairs at each tap. It will be recalled (Secs. 11-1 and 11-2) that this can be processed using a form of square-law combining wherein at each tap the complex envelopes corresponding to two successive pulses, taken at the appropriate instants, are multiplied in the familiar complex scalar-product form. Summing these scalar products over all taps, and detecting the sign of the resultant, then gives the decision once per information pulse. In this DPSK "square-law combining" approach, the channel estimate is effectively limited to a one-pulse history with the same SNR as the pulse being detected (if one views the system as employing coherent detection) or to *no* channel estimate at all (if one views it as involving two-pulse orthogonal matched filters). For a slow-fading channel,[1] the difference in performance between DPSK with square-law combining and with maximal-ratio combining is of the order of 3 db, as discussed at length in Sec. 11-2. In the present context, the diversity does not involve independent equal-intensity channels. As shown in Secs. 11-2 and 11-3, one can supply weighting concomitant with the intensity variations across the multipath profile, but the difference in performance is not substantial. Of greater importance may be the effect of the correlations in fading at the various taps, which, as noted earlier, has not been explored in numerical detail with respect to square-law combining operation. On the basis that these correlations are relatively small, as also discussed qualitatively above, one can likely safely assume the performance to be very close to that with independently fading channels.

In one view, the DPSK system just described involves a stratagem by which signal energy is used for channel estimation as well as for communicating intelligence, rather than having any energy specifically dedicated to sounding. To more closely approach maximal-ratio combining by a longer channel estimate, when there is no "room" for sounding pulses, a similar stratagem is required. The general problem with phase-reversal-keyed systems in this regard is that any attempt to average directly over several information pulses will lead to an average value of zero (assuming equal occurrence of Marks and Spaces), and any nonzero result from such a finite interval average will tend to have a 180° phase ambiguity because its sign will depend upon the particular imbalance between Marks and Spaces occurring during that interval. Another possibility is frequency doubling to remove the information content, but this still leaves the 180° ambiguity in the derived reference. This requires differential encoding

---

[1] Note that the nature of the diversity operation here, in subdividing the multipath, is such that there is no selective-fading distortion in the individual diversity branches (in a sense, by definition).

of information so that such an ambiguity is nonessential in the information decision. It can also create a problem in diversity in that the 180° ambiguity occurs independently in the several diversity channels so that combining may lead to destructive, rather than constructive, summation.

Another proposal for achieving a longer estimate in a phase-reversal system is so-called decision-directed channel measurement.[1] The concept here is to delay the addition of any new pulse information to the channel-estimating filter until after a decision has been made as to its information content, i.e, the phase of its signal component. This decision indicates a *best* guess as to whether the signal component is more likely aligned in phase with the available derived reference, or is in opposite phase. In the first instance, the additional voltage is supplied directly to the input of the estimating filter; in the second instance, it is supplied through an additional phase inversion. While decision errors will introduce subtractive signal components into the estimate, these would be rare occurrences at error rates of practical interest.

Still within the context of phase-reversal keying with wideband pulses, one can also consider sending a "pilot tone" in addition to the communications signal. This is conveniently available in the case of binary phase-reversal keying by using a quadrature carrier component, pulsed in synchronism with the message-bearing component. If the latter has the complex envelope $u_0(t)$ defined in (11-5-20), the "pilot tone" would have the complex envelope

$$u_p(t) = \alpha u_0(t) \exp\left(j\frac{\pi}{2}\right) \qquad (11\text{-}5\text{-}28)$$

where α is a real factor, and $\alpha^2/(1 + \alpha^2)$ represents the fraction of total transmitted energy allocated to the sounding tone. Alternately, with (11-5-20), the total transmitted waveform during each T-length interval will have the complex envelope

$$u_T(t) = A(\pm 1 + j\alpha)\frac{\sin \pi W t}{\pi t} \qquad (11\text{-}5\text{-}29)$$

where the ± 1 denotes the alternate message states. From this point of view, with $\alpha \ll 1$, one is using phase-shift keying with phase positions less than 180° apart. A filter at carrier frequency averaging over a sufficiently long time to guarantee equal occurrences of both phase positions will average the message bearing component to zero and extract only the quadrature "pilot-tone" component, containing also the channel phase. A decision-directed procedure can also be used. The estimate is unambiguously derived in each diversity channel, hence it can be used for the complex weighting factor in maximal-ratio combining and (if an

[1] J. G. Proakis, P. R. Drouilhet, Jr., and R. Price, Performance of Coherent Detection Systems Using Decision-Directed Channel Measurement, *IEEE Trans. Commun. Systems*, vol. CS-12, pp. 54–63, March, 1964.

additional 90° phase shift is conveniently added) for achieving synchronous detection at the same time.

Alternative Means of Reception of the Wideband Pulse Signal.
Reception of the wideband pulse in Fig. 11-5-3 utilizes filtering matched to the transmitted waveform, followed by a delay line with tap spacings $1/W$, such that once each transmitted pulse interval T, the desired samples appear *simultaneously* at the taps. Note the particularly strategic choice of a sin x/x shaped pulse with zeros at all integer multiples of $1/W$ from the pulse peak. This enables the sample values at the taps to be unambiguously identified on a one-to-one basis with the $b_m(t)$ of the channel representation. Such a "tagging" property in the signal structure, with respect to "resolving the multipath," provides a basis for diversity operation with nearly independent fading in the combiner inputs. As a prelude to considering other signals with similar properties, we examine some alternative receivers for the wideband pulse waveform signaling, equivalent to that described already but introducing useful additional perspectives.

First, note that the only purpose of the delay line in Fig. 11-5-3 is to enable all the desired samples to be obtained simultaneously. One could as well simply sample the rectangular bandpass filter output at intervals $1/W$ and obtain the desired samples *sequentially*. The samples thus obtained would have to be commutated among the set of estimating filters shown in Fig. 11-5-3. However, since the samples arrive sequentially, the weighted values become available then at the summer (combiner) input sequentially. To obtain proper summing, these values now must be delayed relative to each other, to achieve alignment. This can be achieved by feeding them into successive $1/W$ spaced taps of a delay line, with the properly summed output appearing at the end of the line, or by some equivalent appropriate "stretching" of the waveform values so that there is an instant at which all can be added.

The additional interesting and important alternative to the pair of receiving systems outlined in Fig. 11-5-3 and above, respectively, occurs by replacing the rectangular bandpass filter by its equivalent cross-correlation operation. However, while the filter could be continuously operating, and hence smooth simultaneously over voltages which contribute to more than one sample, this is no longer possible with the cross-correlation operation. To demonstrate the equivalent correlation receiver, recognize in Fig. 11-5-3 that a separate matched filter could be placed at each delay-line tap output, instead of the single filter before the delay line. The delay line then must accommodate a wider bandwidth of signal plus noise. With this positioning of the matched filters, they can be replaced by cross-correlators; for the system using sounding pulses, this leads directly from Fig. 11-5-3 to the receiving system of Fig. 11-5-4. Since the incoming signal is passing down the delay line, the correlations at the tap outputs are performed simultaneously.   Hence as shown in Fig. 11-5-4, only one correlation reference signal need be generated, for example by impulse excitation at the proper instant of a rectangular bandpass filter of width W.   Since the desired signals from the various taps are all aligned in time, they can be passed directly into a summer, as shown.   Indeed, aside from the correlators, the system pictured is in all essentials identical with that discussed in connection with Fig. 11-5-3.   All the discussions of alternate sounding procedures apply as well.

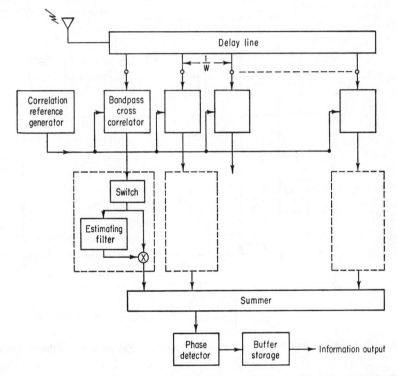

FIG. 11-5-4. Delayed signal correlation receiving system for wideband pulse signaling.

A system alternative to that in Fig. 11-5-3 was also described above, in which the delay line was removed, and samples were processed sequentially at the matched-filter output.   The cross-correlation equivalent for this system involves a *sequence* of cross-correlations against the received signal plus noise.   One convenient means for providing the references for the *sequence* of cross-correlations is to generate the desired correlation reference once per interval T and pass *it* down a delay line.   This is the system pictured in Fig. 11-5-5.   The additional delays before combining, discussed earlier for the corresponding matched-filter system, are also shown.   Otherwise, again, all prior comments apply directly.

Comparing Figs. 11-5-4 and 11-5-5, even ignoring the delay line in the latter just prior to diversity combining, there is in each case a delay line involved prior to correlation processing. The distinction in this delay-line function in the two cases has led to specifically terming them "delayed-signal" and "delayed-reference" systems, respectively, according to whether it is the received signal or the locally generated correlation reference which is passed through a delay line.

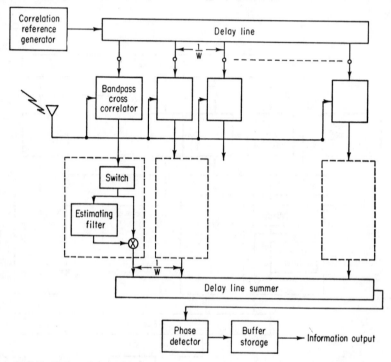

FIG. 11-5-5. Delayed-reference correlation receiving system for wideband pulse signaling.

Wideband Noiselike Signaling. It is often desirable in digital communications to transmit on a continuous, rather than on a pulsed, basis. One continuous-signal structure useful for antimultipath signaling, and allowing receiving systems very similar to those discussed, is a wide-band-pass noiselike waveform. Specifically, if the waveform is a random process with rectangular power spectral density of width W, its autocorrelation has the $\sin x/x$ shape already shown to be so useful for these systems.

For correlation reception, the use of a signal waveform with noiselike properties implies that an exact replica is available as a cross-correlation reference. The common technique is to employ binary pulse sequences

with useful "randomness" properties, generated by appropriately connected shift-registers.[1] Particularly, it is possible to design M-stage
feedback-connected shift registers which, from an arbitrary start position, generate a cyclic binary sequence with period $2^M - 1$. Such
so-called maximal-length or M sequences have an autocorrelation with a
peak value of $2^M - 1$ at zero time lag, and of the order of zero or unity
at lags of one or more elements. This property, analogous to the correlation property of white noise, has led to terming such sequences pseudorandom. When 2^M is very large, a moderately long segment of such a
sequence will exhibit autocorrelation properties similar to those of the
repetitive sequence. The sequence is usually generated as a rectangular
waveform. If the sequence rate is W_E, filtering to a bandwidth much
smaller than W_E can result in an output which, by the central limit
theorem[2], approaches stationary Gaussian character with correlation
properties determined by the filter bandwidth. Either using the sequence
directly or in a derived Gaussian form, synchronized operation of like-
connected shift-register sequence generators at the two communication
terminals will generate identical pseudorandom waveforms, precisely as
needed for communications operation.

Note that it is the correlation property of the pseudonoise which is
important. Whether its statistics are Gaussian or have some other convenient property is very little relevant for our purposes. For example,
it may be more convenient to generate a Gaussian bandpass noise and
then to limit it to constant envelope for convenience in transmission, so
that the pseudorandomness remains only in the phase structure. So
long as such operations retain the essential desired correlation properties,
they are useful for wideband signaling. For example, limited bandpass
"noise" such as described above was employed in the original Rake
system.[3]

Consider now a continuous zero-mean noiselike waveform $\xi(t)$ available
at both transmitter and receiver to be used as the complex envelope for
signaling with cross-correlation reception. Assume that its power
spectral density is rectangular in shape, over bandwidth W, and with
unity power spectral density. Thus its autocorrelation is given by

$$\rho(\tau) = \lim_{\lambda \to \infty} \frac{1}{2\lambda} \int_{-\lambda}^{\lambda} \xi^*(t)\xi(t + \tau)\, dt = \frac{\sin \pi W \tau}{\pi \tau} \qquad (11\text{-}5\text{-}30)$$

[1] E.g., S. Golomb (ed.), "Digital Communications with Space Applications,"
Prentice-Hall Inc., Englewood Cliffs, N.J., 1964.

[2] E.g., P. A. Bello, On the Approach of a Filtered Pulse Train to a Stationary
Gaussian Process, *IRE Trans. Inform. Theory*, vol. IT-7, pp. 144–149, July, 1961.
As noted therein, there are certain frequencies at which filtering will not result in a
stationary Gaussian character, others at which there is a most rapid approach to such
statistical character.

[3] Price and Green, *loc. cit.*

Now visualize that a segment of length T of this process is utilized as a message symbol over the interval $0 < t \leq T(T \gg 1/W)$. Since the signal is still essentially band-limited to W, the previous sampling representations can still be used. Thus, with (11-5-14), the received signal can be represented in the form

$$u(t) = \frac{1}{W} \sum_{m=-\infty}^{\infty} b_m(t) \xi\left(t - \frac{m}{W}\right) \qquad 0 < t \leq T \qquad (11\text{-}5\text{-}31)$$

Extracting from the replica process available at the receiver the identical T-length segment, delaying it by an amount k/W, and cross-correlating it against the received signal, the result will be

$$\zeta_k = \int_{\frac{k}{W}}^{T+\frac{k}{W}} \xi^*\left(t - \frac{k}{W}\right) u(t)\, dt$$

$$= \frac{1}{W} \sum_{m=-\infty}^{\infty} b_m \int_{\frac{k}{W}}^{T+\frac{k}{W}} \xi^*\left(t - \frac{k}{W}\right) \xi\left(t - \frac{m}{W}\right) dt \qquad (11\text{-}5\text{-}32)$$

where $b_m(t)$ is again assumed to remain constant over the message symbol. Now this is a *finite*-length integral, not the infinite-length integral (or equivalently an integral over a full period of the pseudorandom process) described in (11-5-30). Nevertheless, if $T \gg 1/W$ (say $TW \sim$ 100 to 1000), it appears to be a reasonable assumption that the finite-length integral can be well approximated by its average[1] over the ensemble of all possible T-length segments of $\xi(t)$,

$$\frac{1}{T} \int_0^T \xi^*(t)\xi(t + \tau)\, dt = \rho(\tau) \qquad (11\text{-}5\text{-}33)$$

With this approximation and (11-5-30), (11-5-32) reduces to

$$\zeta_k = \frac{T}{W} \sum_{m=-\infty}^{\infty} b_m \rho\left(\frac{k}{W} - \frac{m}{W}\right) = Tb_k$$

Thus this correlation, with the reference relatively delayed by k/W, selects only that part of the arriving signal energy represented by the kth tap in the tapped-delay-line model of the channel. Note that "self-noise" introduced by other portions of the multipath, due to the short-term correlation effect mentioned above, is of relative power level $1/TW$ when TW is large.

With this result, one can immediately portray the elements of a system. Indeed, if signaling is by phase-reversal of the $\xi(t)$ process, and if occasional symbols are dedicated to sounding (or any of the other equivalents discussed earlier), one has *exactly* the systems diagramed in Figs. 11-5-4

---

[1] The fluctuation appears to be of the order $1/\sqrt{TW}$ relative to the correlation peak.

and 11-5-5, in delayed-signal and delayed-reference versions. The distinction now is that the transmitted symbols are each of length T and form a continuous transmission, assuming the symbol rate to be $1/T$. With perfect synchronism in the receiver, each correlator restarts on the next symbol just as soon as it reaches the end of the last one. The delay operations in the receivers realign all multipath contributions so that, nevertheless, there is no intersymbol interference despite the multipath.

Correlation on a constant-amplitude waveform of length T implies a linear buildup of voltage in the correlator. Thus, as long as proper synchronism is maintained, little will be lost if integration is over slightly less than the full length T. In this sense, with the statement that T greatly exceeds the multipath spread T_M, it is possible in the delayed-reference system to eliminate the additional delay-line summer. Negligible loss in performance will result from a direct summing of the several weighted diversity signals without further aligning them in delay (with such fixed phase corrections as may be appropriate).

With one further variation, one arrives at the original delayed-signal Rake system. This is the recognition that with the continuous noiselike waveforms, it is very easy to construct sets of orthogonal waveforms. For example, for binary orthogonal signaling, one can generate a noise waveform as described above, and another which is just a frequency-shifted version of it, shifted by (say) the orthogonal spacing $1/T$, corresponding to the symbol length T. Except for the pseudorandom structure internal to the symbol, which is removed by the cross-correlation, the result is an FSK system. An alternative method of deriving a waveform orthogonal to a pseudorandom binary sequence of $+1$s and -1s is to complement every second bit in the sequence (i.e., multiply by an alternating $+1$, -1 sequence). It can be easily shown that if the same filtering is separately applied both to a rectangular waveform based on the original pseudorandom sequence and to one constructed from the orthogonal sequence, the filter outputs are also orthogonal in the sense of zero cross-correlation at all time lags. Thus, information can be conveyed by selecting one of a pair of orthogonal sequences at the transmitter for filtering and transmission and cross-correlating in the receiver on the *same* frequency for both possibilities.

To derive channel estimates in the latter signaling system, one can *add* the outputs of the two correlators at each tap, knowing that one comprises signal plus noise and the other comprises noise alone; and one can *coherently* integrate this combined output over a duration corresponding to N message symbols, resulting in an SNR which is $N/2$ times that associated with any single symbol decision (the factor $\frac{1}{2}$ arising from adding the noise outputs of both correlators). Here then is a system which can efficiently derive a high-quality channel estimate for maximal-ratio combining, in a relatively short time as compared with the use of intermittent sounding pulses. The cost is that even after maximal-ratio combining, the performance is that of an orthogonal-waveform system, roughly 3 db poorer (at low error rates) than can be available with phase-reversal keying. Note that the signaling coherence implied in the ability to derive channel estimates implies that the orthogonal systems can be

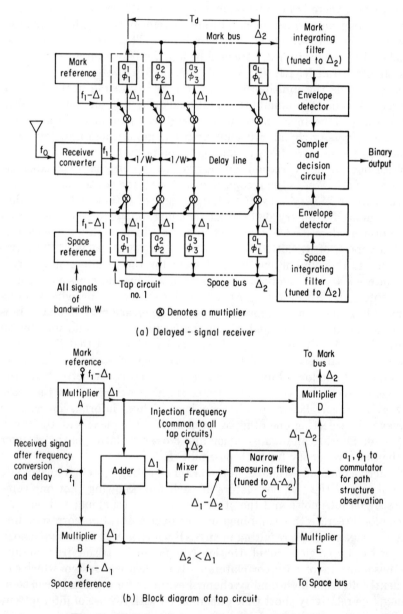

(a) Delayed - signal receiver

(b) Block diagram of tap circuit

Fig. 11-5-6. Rake receiver with orthogonal signaling.

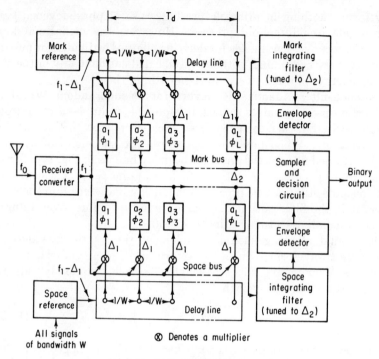

(c) Delayed reference receiver

FIG. 11-5-6. (*Continued*)

detected coherently (performance generically that of coherent FSK) if desired. The advantage over noncoherent (envelope) detection, it will be recalled, is only about 1 db at low error rates.

With this in mind, Fig. 11-5-6a shows a simplified block diagram of the original Rake receiver,[1] based on noncoherent detection. This is just a modification for orthogonal-waveform signaling of the delayed-signal correlation receiver of Fig. 11-5-4. Some practical considerations involving frequency translations are indicated. The a_k, ϕ_k are the estimates of channel amplitude and phase at each tap, multiplied onto the signal. The circuit for deriving these estimates from the communications signal, along the lines outlined above, is shown in Fig. 11-5-6b. Although noncoherent detection is shown in Fig. 11-5-6a and was used, it is known that laboratory tests verified coherent detection of the orthogonal waveforms to be possible, with the anticipated slight improvement in performance. The corresponding delayed-reference receiver is diagramed in Fig. 11-5-6c. Note, along the lines of an earlier comment, that it omits the additional delays prior to adding the weighted diversity components.

Again, while the original Rake system used orthogonal pseudorandom

[1] Fig. 11-5-6 is taken from Price and Green, *op. cit.*, Figs. 2, 3, and 6.

waveforms, nothing in principle precludes use of phase-reversal keying of a single pseudorandom process. However, the orthogonal keying does offer a convenient means for deriving channel estimates for maximal-ratio diversity combining, without specific dedication of any of the transmitted energy, in a relatively short smoothing time.

Matched-filter Adaptive Receivers for Pseudorandom Waveforms. For certain pseudorandom signals, it is possible to implement continuous matched filters rather than bandpass cross-correlators within the Rake-type receiver. When possible, this allows the simplicity of utilizing a single matched filter at the input to the delay line, as in Fig. 11-5-3, rather than requiring a cross-correlator at each delay-line tap. The continuous-filter outputs still must be processed in a delay line, since for each symbol interval T, the filter output may have significant values over a duration T_M corresponding to the multipath spread.

One signal allowing such an implementation is the pseudorandom rectangular waveform. Such a waveform, used as a symbol of length T, comprises N successive pulses of length T_E each "randomly" identified with a $+1$ or -1 and such that

$$NT_E = T \tag{11-5-35}$$

A method of generating such a waveform by using a tapped delay line is shown in Fig. 11-5-7a. There are N taps, spaced T_E apart, each connected to a common output bus through a switch set for $+1$ or -1, according to the sequence desired. Once during each interval T, a rectangular pulse of length T_E is injected into the line. The output bus will then provide precisely the desired pseudorandom rectangular waveform of length T. Note that whether this, or a shift-register method of generation is used, the transmitted waveform is identical (for the same sequence). Thus for example, even if the signal is generated as in Fig. 11-5-7a, the receiver can be a correlation receiver such as discussed heretofore. On the other hand, independent of the method of generation, one can also demonstrate a matched filter for use in the receiver (Fig. 11-5-7b). It is basically the same delay line as in Fig. 11-5-7a, except that the ± 1 switches are connected in reverse order, and it is followed by a continuous filter with time constant T_E. It is clear that if a received rectangular waveform of length T is inserted as input, the output after the additional filter contains a peak signal when the input waveform precisely fills the delay line. The output of the following filter will be roughly triangular in shape about this peak, with base length approximately $2T_E$. At all other times during the interval T, the output will be near zero, to the extent that the rectangular waveform has zero short-time autocorrelation for time lags exceeding T_E. Note the output is analogous to the wideband signaling pulse discussed initially in this section. In the multipath case, the output may, again, have many peaks over an interval corresponding to the multipath spread.   This delay-line matched filter must then be followed by the rest of the Rake receiver, as in the delayed-signal system of Fig. 11-5-3.

A quite different matched-filter system with pseudorandom transmitted waveforms has been based on an ingenious filter design.[1]   Here an all-pass filter (i.e., one with phase variations but constant gain over the band) of

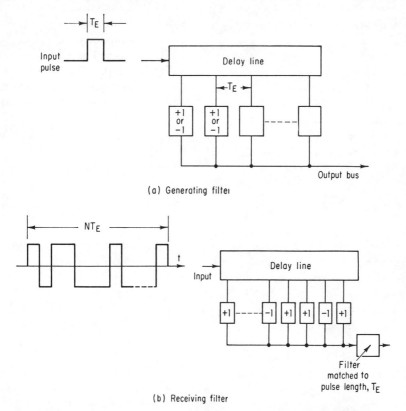

(a) Generating filter

(b) Receiving filter

Fig. 11-5-7. Delay-line filters for pseudorandom rectangular waveforms.

bandwidth W is designed as a cascade of N sections.   Each section is designed to have its phase variation occur as essentially a group delay confined to a particular band of width W/N, a different band for each section.   The total cascade is then just a rectangular bandpass filter of width W with the stated group delay.   If this cascade were excited by an impulse, the output would be a $\sin \pi W t/\pi t$ shaped pulse, much like that discussed in this section.   However, in the system cited, approximately half the sections are selected (more or less at random, but with some

[1] S. M. Sussman, A Matched Filter Communication System for Multipath Channels, *IRE Trans. Inform. Theory*, vol. IT-6, pp. 367–373, June, 1960.

ingenuity) to comprise a filter cascade which is impulse-excited to form the transmitted waveform. The cascade of the remaining sections are then readily shown to be an appropriate matched filter for this transmitted waveform. The receiver filter output is just a $\sin x/x$ pulse, for a single transmission path. The transmitted waveform, due to selective "random" dispersion of various frequency components, has the appearance of a noiselike signal of bandwidth W.

THE Q FUNCTION AND RELATED INTEGRALS[1]

1. Basic Definitions and Elementary Properties

$$Q(a,b) = \int_b^\infty \exp\left(-\frac{a^2 + x^2}{2}\right) I_0(ax)x\, dx \qquad \text{(A-1-1)}$$

$$Q(\sqrt{2a}, \sqrt{2b}) = \int_b^\infty \exp\left[-(a + y)\right]I_0(2\sqrt{ay})\, dy \qquad \text{(A-1-2)}$$

$$Q(0,b) = \exp\left(-\frac{b^2}{2}\right)$$
$$Q(a,0) = 1 \qquad \text{(A-1-3)}$$

Asymptotic relations: ($|z| \gg 1$, or roughly $|z| > 3$)

$$I_0(z) = \frac{\exp z}{\sqrt{2\pi z}}\left[1 + 0\left(\frac{1}{z}\right)\right] \qquad \text{(A-1-5)}$$

Note also erfc $(-x) = 2 - \text{erfc } (x)$

$b \gg 1, b \gg b - a$:

$$Q(a,b) \sim \frac{1}{2} \text{erfc}\left(\frac{b - a}{\sqrt{2}}\right) \qquad \text{(A-1-7)}$$

2. Transform Representations

$$I_0(z) = \frac{1}{2\pi}\int_0^{2\pi} \exp\left(z \cos \theta\right) d\theta \qquad \text{(A-2-1)}$$

$$= \frac{1}{2\pi j} \oint_C \frac{1}{p} \exp\left[\frac{z}{2}\left(p + \frac{1}{p}\right)\right] dp \qquad C = \text{unit circle} \qquad \text{(A-2-2)}$$

Re $z > 0$:

$$I_0(z) = \frac{1}{2\pi j}\int_{c-j\infty}^{c+j\infty} \frac{1}{p} \exp\left[\frac{z}{2}\left(p + \frac{1}{p}\right)\right] dp \qquad c > 0 \qquad \text{(A-2-3)}$$

[1] This Appendix is largely adapted from S. Stein, The Q-Function and Related Integrals, Research Report 467, Applied Research Laboratory, Sylvania Electronic Systems, July, 1965.

The Q function was introduced in: J. I. Marcum, A Statistical Theory of Target Detection by Pulsed Radar, *IRE Trans. Inform. Theory*, vol. IT-6, pp. 59–267, April, 1960; earlier Rand Corp. Res. Memos RM-753, July, 1948 and RM-754, December, 1947; J. I. Marcum, "Tables of the Q-function," Rand Corp. Res. Memo RM-399, January, 1950.

Examples of literature on machine computation of the Q function are: A. R. DiDonato and M. P. Jarnagin, A Method for Computing the Circular Coverage Function, *Mathematics of Computation*, vol. 16, pp. 347–355, July, 1962; D. E. Johansen, New Techniques for Machine Computation of the Q-functions, Truncated Normal Deviates, and Matrix Eigenvalues, Applied Research Laboratory, Sylvania Electronic Systems, AFCRL-556, July, 1961.

$a > 0, b > 0$:

$$I_0(ab) = \frac{1}{2\pi j} \int_{c-j\infty}^{c+j\infty} \frac{1}{p} \exp\left[\frac{ab}{2}\left(p + \frac{1}{p}\right)\right] dp \qquad c > 0 \qquad \text{(A-2-4)}$$

$$= \frac{1}{2\pi j} \int_{c-j\infty}^{c+j\infty} \frac{1}{s} \exp\left[\frac{a^2}{2} s + \frac{b^2}{2}\frac{1}{s}\right] ds \qquad c > 0 \qquad \text{(A-2-5)}$$

$$I_0(2\sqrt{ab}) = \frac{1}{2\pi j} \int_{c-j\infty}^{c+j\infty} \frac{1}{p} \exp\left(ap + \frac{b}{p}\right) dp \qquad c > 0 \qquad \text{(A-2-6)}$$

$$Q(a,b) = \exp\left(-\frac{a^2 + b^2}{2}\right) \frac{1}{2\pi j} \int_{c-j\infty}^{c+j\infty} \frac{\exp\left[(a^2/2)p + (b^2/2p)\right]}{p - 1} dp \qquad c > 1 \quad \text{(A-2-7)}$$

$$Q(\sqrt{2a}, \sqrt{2b}) = \exp\left[-(a + b)\right] \frac{1}{2\pi j} \int_{c-j\infty}^{c+j\infty} \frac{\exp\left(ap + b/p\right)}{p - 1} dp$$
$$c > 1 \quad \text{(A-2-8)}$$

Alternative form

$$Q(a,b) = -\exp\left(-\frac{a^2 + b^2}{2}\right) \frac{1}{2\pi j} \int_{c-j\infty}^{c+j\infty} \frac{\exp\left[(a^2/2p) + (b^2/2)p\right]}{p(p - 1)} dp$$
$$0 < c < 1 \quad \text{(A-2-9)}$$

3. Symmetry and Antisymmetry Relations

$$Q(a,b) + Q(b,a) = 1 + \exp\left(-\frac{a^2 + b^2}{2}\right) I_0(ab) \qquad \text{(A-3-1)}$$

$$Q(a,a) = \tfrac{1}{2}[1 + \exp\left(-a^2\right)I_0(a^2)] \qquad \text{(A-3-2)}$$

$$1 + Q(a,b) - Q(b,a) = \frac{b^2 - a^2}{b^2 + a^2} \int_{\frac{a^2+b^2}{2}}^{\infty} \exp\left(-y\right)I_0\left(\frac{2aby}{a^2 + b^2}\right) dy \qquad b > a > 0$$
$$\text{(A-3-3)}$$

Asymptotically, when $b \gg 1$, $a \gg 1$, $b \gg b - a > 0$:

$$1 + Q(a,b) - Q(b,a) \approx \text{erfc}\left(\frac{b - a}{\sqrt{2}}\right) \qquad \text{(A-3-4)}$$

Also

$$Q(a,b) + Q(b,a) - 1 \approx \frac{\exp\left[-(b - a)^2/2\right]}{\sqrt{2\pi ab}} \qquad \text{(A-3-5)}$$

$$Q(a,b) \approx \frac{1}{2}\left\{\text{erfc}\left(\frac{b - a}{\sqrt{2}}\right) + \frac{\exp\left[-(b - a)^2/2\right]}{\sqrt{2\pi ab}}\right\} \qquad \text{(A-3-6)}$$

4. Series Representations[1]

$$I_n(z) = \frac{1}{2\pi} \int_0^{2\pi} \exp\left(\pm jn\theta\right) \exp\left(z \cos \theta\right) d\theta \qquad \text{(A-4-1)}$$

$$I_n(z) = \begin{cases} \dfrac{1}{2\pi j} \oint_C \dfrac{1}{p^{n+1}} \exp\left[\dfrac{z}{2}\left(p + \dfrac{1}{p}\right)\right] dp & \text{(A-4-2)} \\[4mm] \dfrac{1}{2\pi j} \oint_C p^{n-1} \exp\left[\dfrac{z}{2}\left(p + \dfrac{1}{p}\right)\right] dp & \text{(A-4-3)} \end{cases} \qquad C = \text{unit circle}$$

a,b real:

$$I_n(ab) = \begin{cases} \dfrac{1}{2\pi j}\left(\dfrac{b}{a}\right)^n \oint_C \dfrac{1}{s^{n+1}} \exp\left(\dfrac{a^2}{2} s + \dfrac{b^2}{2}\dfrac{1}{s}\right) ds & \text{(A-4-4a)} \\[4mm] \dfrac{1}{2\pi j}\left(\dfrac{a}{b}\right)^n \oint_C s^{n-1} \exp\left(\dfrac{a^2}{2} s + \dfrac{b^2}{2}\dfrac{1}{s}\right) ds & \text{(A-4-4b)} \end{cases}$$

[1] See Marcum, *loc. cit.* Also see L. C. Maximon, On the Representation of Indefinite Integrals Containing Bessel Functions by Simple Neumann Series, *Proc. Am. Math. Soc.*, vol. 7, pp. 1054–1062, 1956.

$$Q(a,b) = \exp\left(-\frac{a^2 + b^2}{2}\right) \sum_{m=0}^{\infty} \frac{1}{2\pi j} \int_C p^{m-1} \exp\left(\frac{a^2}{2} p + \frac{b^2}{2}\frac{1}{p}\right) dp \quad \text{(A-4-5)}$$

$$= \exp\left(-\frac{a^2 + b^2}{2}\right) \sum_{m=0}^{\infty} \left(\frac{a}{b}\right)^m I_m(ab) \quad \text{(A-4-6)}$$

Alternatively,

$$Q(a,b) = 1 - \exp\left(-\frac{a^2 + b^2}{2}\right) \sum_{m=1}^{\infty} \left(\frac{b}{a}\right)^m I_m(ab) \quad \text{(A-4-7)}$$

5. Probability That One Rice Variate Exceeds Another[1]

The distribution of the envelope of a sine wave plus additive bandpass Gaussian noise (Sec. 1-4) is often termed the Rice (or sometimes, Nakagami-Rice) distribution. A pair of statistically independent Rice variates have the probability density functions

$$p(R_k) = \frac{R_k}{\sigma_k^2} \exp\left(-\frac{a_k^2 + R_k^2}{2\sigma_k^2}\right) I_0\left(\frac{a_k R_k}{\sigma_k^2}\right) \qquad 0 < a_k < \infty \qquad 0 < R_k < \infty$$
$$k = 1,2 \quad \text{(A-5-1)}$$

The probability that one of these exceeds the other[2]

$$P = \text{Prob } (R_2 > R_1) \quad \text{(A-5-2)}$$

is given by any of the following equivalent forms:

$$P = Q(\sqrt{a}, \sqrt{b}) - \frac{\nu^2}{1 + \nu^2} \exp\left(-\frac{a + b}{2}\right) I_0(\sqrt{ab}) \quad \text{(A-5-3)}$$

where
$$a = \frac{a_2^2}{\sigma_1^2 + \sigma_2^2} \qquad b = \frac{a_1^2}{\sigma_1^2 + \sigma_2^2} \qquad \nu = \frac{\sigma_1}{\sigma_2} \quad \text{(A-5-4)}$$

$$P = \frac{\nu^2}{1 + \nu^2} [1 - Q(\sqrt{b}, \sqrt{a})] + \frac{1}{1 + \nu^2} Q(\sqrt{a}, \sqrt{b}) \quad \text{(A-5-5)}$$

$$P = \frac{1}{2} [1 - Q(\sqrt{b}, \sqrt{a}) + Q(\sqrt{a}, \sqrt{b})] - \frac{1}{2} \frac{\nu^2 - 1}{\nu^2 + 1} \exp\left(-\frac{a + b}{2}\right) I_0(\sqrt{ab})$$
$$\text{(A-5-6)}$$

6. The Joint Distribution of Two Correlated Rayleigh Variates

The envelopes of two correlated complex Gaussian processes are each a Rayleigh variate with a joint distribution (Sec. 10-10)

$$p(R_1,R_2) = \frac{R_1 R_2}{\sigma_1^2 \sigma_2^2 (1 - \rho^2)} I_0\left[\frac{\rho R_1 R_2}{(1 - \rho^2)\sigma_1\sigma_2}\right] \exp\left[-\frac{1}{2(1 - \rho^2)}\left(\frac{R_1^2}{\sigma_1^2} + \frac{R_2^2}{\sigma_2^2}\right)\right]$$
$$0 < (R_1,R_2) < \infty \quad \text{(A-7-1)}$$

where
$$2\sigma_1^2 = \langle R_1^2 \rangle \qquad 2\sigma_2^2 = \langle R_2^2 \rangle$$

and ρ is the magnitude of the normalized complex cross-correlation between the two complex Gaussian processes whose envelopes are represented by R_1, R_2. The cumulative distribution is

$$P = \text{Prob } (R_1 > a_1, R_2 > a_2) \quad \text{(A-7-2)}$$

[1] See S. Stein, Unified Analysis of Certain Coherent and Non-Coherent Binary Communications Systems, *IEEE Trans. Inform. Theory*, vol. IT-10, pp. 43–51, January, 1964.

[2] The analysis of Chap. 8, incidentally, shows that the similar problem for a pair of correlated Rice variates reduces to having only to solve this case of two independent variates.

We define the parameters

$$b_1 = \frac{a_1}{\sigma_1 \sqrt{1 - \rho^2}} \qquad b_2 = \frac{a_2}{\sigma_2 \sqrt{1 - \rho^2}} \qquad \text{(A-7-3)}$$

Then P is given by either of the following alternative forms:

$$P = \exp\left[-\frac{b_1^2(1 - \rho^2)}{2} \right] [1 - Q(b_2, \rho b_1)] + \exp\left[-\frac{b_2^2(1 - \rho^2)}{2} \right] Q(\rho b_2, b_1) \quad \text{(A-7-4)}$$

$$P = \exp\left[-\frac{b_1^2(1 - \rho^2)}{2} \right] Q(\rho b_1, b_2) + \exp\left[-\frac{b_2^2(1 - \rho^2)}{2} \right] Q(\rho b_2, b_1)$$

$$- \exp\left[-\frac{b_1^2 + b_2^2}{2} \right] I_0(\rho b_1 b_2) \quad \text{(A-7-5)}$$

7. Additional Integrals

The transform representations used to evaluate the integrals described above may be readily applied to similar related forms. The evaluation in Sec. 5 applies to the general integral form

$$\int_0^\infty x \exp\left(-\frac{\lambda^2 + x^2}{2} \right) I_0(\lambda x) Q(\mu, \nu x) \, dx \qquad \text{(A-8-1)}$$

and that in Sec. 6 to the integral form

$$\int_\gamma^\infty x \exp\left[-\frac{x^2(1 - \rho^2)}{2} \right] Q(\rho x, \mu) \, dx \qquad \text{(A-8-2)}$$

Similar calculations have also been carried out[1] for integrals of the form

$$\int_0^\infty x I_0(\lambda x) Q(\mu, \nu x) \, dx \qquad \text{(A-8-3)}$$

$$\int_0^\infty x^2 \exp\left(-\frac{\lambda^2 + x^2}{2} \right) I_1(\lambda x) Q(\mu, x) \, dx \qquad \text{(A-8-4)}$$

$$\int_\gamma^\infty \exp\left(-\frac{\lambda^2 + x^2}{2} \right) Q(\mu, x) \, dx \qquad \text{(A-8-5)}$$

Numbers of real integrals can also be related to results presented above by utilizing various integral representations for the Q functions or the Bessel functions.[2] Complex-plane transformations applied to the transform representations will also yield a variety of different-looking complex-plane results.[2] The following are some examples:

$$\frac{1 - \lambda^2}{2} \int_0^{2\pi} \frac{\exp(ab \cos \theta)}{1 + \lambda^2 - 2\lambda \cos \theta} \, d\theta = \exp\left(\frac{a^2 + b^2}{2} \right) Q(a, b) - \frac{1}{2} I_0(ab)$$

$$\lambda = \frac{a}{b} < 1 \quad \text{(A-8-6)}$$

$$\exp\left[\frac{1}{2} \left(a\alpha + \frac{b}{\alpha} \right) \right] Q\left(\sqrt{a\alpha}, \sqrt{\frac{b}{\alpha}} \right)$$

$$= \frac{1}{2\pi j} (|\beta|^2 - 1) \int_{\Gamma''} \frac{\exp\left\{ \dfrac{1}{2} \dfrac{a[\beta \exp(j\lambda) - p]^2 + b[\exp(j\lambda) - \beta^* p]^2}{[\exp(j\lambda) - \beta^* p][\beta \exp(j\lambda) - p]} \right\}}{[\exp(j\lambda) - \beta^* p][(\beta - \alpha) + (\alpha\beta^* - 1) \exp(-j\lambda)p]} \, dp \quad \text{(A-8-7)}$$

[1] J. J. Jones, The Probability of Error for a Four-Tone FSK Demodulator in the Presence of Crosstalk or Interference, Eng. Note 290R, Applied Research Laboratory, Sylvania Electronic Systems, February, 1962.

[2] G. L. Turin, Error Probabilities for Binary Symmetric Ideal Reception Through Nonselective Slow Fading and Noise, *Proc. IRE*, vol. 46, pp. 1603–1619, September, 1958; C. W. Helstrom, The Resolution of Signals in White, Gaussian Noise, *Proc. IRE*, vol. 43, pp. 1111–1118, September, 1955.

where a,b,α are positive real, λ is real, β is complex with $|\beta| \neq 1$, and Γ'' is the unit circle traversed counterclockwise if $|\beta| < 1$, clockwise if $|\beta| > 1$. With the same definition of parameters,

$$\exp\left[\frac{1}{2}\left(a\alpha + \frac{b}{\alpha}\right)\right] Q\left(\sqrt{a\alpha}, \sqrt{\frac{b}{\alpha}}\right)$$

$$= -\frac{1}{\pi j}\int_{-j\infty}^{+j\infty} \frac{\exp\left\{\dfrac{1}{2}\dfrac{a\exp(-j\lambda)(p-1)^2 + b\exp(j\lambda)(p+1)^2}{p^2-1}\right\}}{(p-1)\{p[1 - \alpha\exp(j\lambda)] + [1 + \alpha\exp(-j\lambda)]\}}\, dp \quad \text{(A-8-8)}$$

APPENDIX **B**

DISTRIBUTION OF HERMITIAN QUADRATIC FORM
IN COMPLEX GAUSSIAN VARIATES

1. Matrix Definitions

Let $\{z_i\}$, $i = 1, \ldots, M$ be M jointly distributed complex Gaussian variates, with mean values $\{\langle z_i \rangle\}$. Let these be arrayed in an $M \times 1$ column matrix

$$\mathbf{z} = [z_i] \tag{B-1-1}$$

Then the complex covariances among the $\{z_i\}$ are given by the elements R_{ik} of the $M \times M$ covariance matrix,

$$\mathbf{R} = \tfrac{1}{2}\langle [\mathbf{z} - \langle \mathbf{z} \rangle]^*[\mathbf{z} - \langle \mathbf{z} \rangle]^T \rangle \tag{B-1-2}$$

where $\mathbf{z}^T$ is the $1 \times M$ row matrix which is the transpose of $\mathbf{z}$. Note that while the multiplication in (B-1-2) defines an $M \times M$ matrix, multiplication in the opposite order defines a 1×1 matrix, a scalar, which is generally the squared magnitude of the complex vector involved. E.g., for a complex $M \times 1$ column vector $\mathbf{t}$,

$$|\mathbf{t}|^2 = \mathbf{t}^T\mathbf{t}^* = \mathbf{t}^{T*}\mathbf{t} = \sum_{i=1}^{M} |t_i|^2 \tag{B-1-3}$$

From (B-1-2) it is clear that

$$\mathbf{R}^T = \mathbf{R}^* \tag{B-1-4}$$

This identifies the covariance matrix as Hermitian.

For any matrix $\mathbf{F} = [F_{ik}]$, a quadratic form in complex variables $\{t_i\}$, which form the elements of a column vector $\mathbf{t}$, is defined by

$$f = \Sigma t_i^* F_{ik} t_k = \mathbf{t}^{T*}\mathbf{F}\mathbf{t} \tag{B-1-5}$$

Then $\mathbf{F}$ is said to be the matrix of the quadratic form. If $\mathbf{F}$ is Hermitian, it is readily shown that

$$f = f^* \tag{B-1-6}$$

that is, a Hermitian quadratic form is *real*. If, furthermore, $\mathbf{F}$ is such that $f > 0$ for arbitrary $\mathbf{t}$, both $\mathbf{F}$ and its quadratic form are said to be Hermitian *positive definite;* if $f \geq 0$ for arbitrary $\mathbf{t}$, they are said to be *positive semidefinite* (with similar definitions of negative definiteness). From the definition of (B-1-2), it is readily shown that any covariance matrix $\mathbf{R}$ is Hermitian, positive semidefinite. Furthermore, unless a deterministic linear relationship exists among some or all of the $\{z_i\}$, $\mathbf{R}$ will be Hermitian positive definite. The latter will be assumed to be the case below.

A standard result in matrix algebra is that an $M \times M$ Hermitian matrix has exactly

---

[1] The material here closely follows that outlined in G. L. Turin, The Characteristic Function of Hermitian Quadratic Forms in Complex Normal Variables, *Biometrika*, vol. 47, pp. 199–201, June, 1960.

M real (not necessarily distinct) eigenvalues $\{\lambda_i\}$. If the matrix is positive definite, its eigenvalues are positive real. The corresponding eigenvectors (column matrices) can be constructed to form an orthonormal set. Thus a unitary $M \times M$ matrix, $\mathbf{U}$, can be formed with the M eigenvectors of $\mathbf{R}$ as its columns, such that

$$\mathbf{U}^{T*}\mathbf{U} = \mathbf{I} \tag{B-1-7a}$$
$$\mathbf{U}^{T*}\mathbf{R}\mathbf{U} = \mathbf{\Lambda} \tag{B-1-7b}$$
$$\mathbf{R} = \mathbf{U}\mathbf{\Lambda}\mathbf{U}^{T*} \tag{B-1-7c}$$

where $\mathbf{I}$ is the identity matrix and $\mathbf{\Lambda}$ is a diagonal matrix (all elements off the main diagonal are zero) with the M eigenvalues of $\mathbf{R}$ as its elements (in the same order in which the corresponding eigenvectors appear as columns of $\mathbf{U}$),

$$(\mathbf{\Lambda})_{ik} = \lambda_i \delta_{ik} \tag{B-1-8}$$

Since $\det \mathbf{U} = 1$, it follows from (B-1-7c) that

$$\det \mathbf{R} = \prod_{i=1}^{M} \lambda_i \tag{B-1-9}$$

That is, the determinant of any Hermitian matrix is equal to the product of its eigenvalues. It is also well known that the trace (sum of the diagonal components) of a Hermitian matrix is preserved under transformations such as (B-1-7b),

$$\sum_{i=1}^{M} R_{ii} = \sum_{i=1}^{M} \lambda_i \tag{B-1-10}$$

From (B-1-9), the statement that $\mathbf{R}$ is Hermitian positive definite is equivalent to the statement that $\det \mathbf{R} > 0$, and hence $\mathbf{R}$ is nonsingular. Thus there exists a well-defined inverse of $\mathbf{R}$, written as $\mathbf{R}^{-1}$. One form for writing the inverse, related to (B-1-7c), is simply

$$\mathbf{R}^{-1} = \mathbf{U}\mathbf{\Lambda}^{-1}\mathbf{U}^{T*} \tag{B-1-11}$$

where $\mathbf{\Lambda}^{-1}$ is the diagonal matrix with positive real (nonzero) diagonal elements $\{1/\lambda_i\}$. The inverse is obviously also Hermitian, positive definite. In addition, if $\mathbf{G}(\mathbf{R}) = \Sigma a_m \mathbf{R}^m$ is any matrix polynomial in $\mathbf{R}$, the eigenvalues of $\mathbf{G}$ are given as identical polynomials in the corresponding eigenvalues of $\mathbf{R}$,

$$g_i = \Sigma a_m \lambda_i{}^m \tag{B-1-12}$$

For example, the eigenvalues of $\mathbf{I}-\mathbf{R}$ are $\{1 - \lambda_i\}$.

2. Reduction to Diagonal Hermitian Form in Independent Variates

Let the M jointly distributed complex Gaussian variates $\{z_i\}$ defined by (B-1-1) and (B-1-2) be written in terms of their real and imaginary components,

$$z_i = x_i + jy_i \tag{B-2-1}$$

With the Hermitian positive definite nature of $\mathbf{R}$ as discussed above, it is then readily shown[1] that when the quadrature components have the statistical properties of the components of stationary bandpass noise, the joint p.d.f. of the M pairs of real Gaussian variates (x_i, y_i) can be written in the form

$$p(\{x_i, y_i\}) = \frac{1}{(2\pi)^M \det \mathbf{R}} \exp\left[-\tfrac{1}{2}(\mathbf{z} - \langle \mathbf{z}\rangle)^T \mathbf{R}^{-1}(\mathbf{z} - \langle \mathbf{z}\rangle)^*\right] \tag{B-2-2}$$

[1] E.g., R. Arens, Complex Processes for Envelopes of Normal Noise, *IRE Trans. Inform. Theory*, vol IT-3, pp. 204–207, September, 1957.

Note that the complex notation in the exponential of (B-2-2) is used only as an algebraic convenience which usefully summarizes the relationships implied among the $\{x_i, y_i\}$ by the fact of their representing quadrature components of stationary complex Gaussian processes.

The problem to be considered is that of finding the p.d.f., through its characteristic function, of a general Hermitian form in the $\{z_i\}$. Let this general form (not necessarily positive definite or semidefinite) be denoted by

$$f = z^{T*}Fz \qquad (B-2-3)$$

The desired result is most easily obtained by first finding a matrix transformation which simultaneously diagonalizes F and R.

The matrix U defined in (B-1-7) immediately provides a transformation which diagonalizes R. That is, U^Tz defines a set of statistically independent Gaussian variates with diagonal covariance matrix Λ. Moreover, because of the positive real nature of the elements of Λ, there are an infinity of matrices which allow a factorization of Λ in the form

$$\Lambda = \psi^*\psi^T \qquad (B-2-4)$$

For example, one such factorization is the "square-root" matrix, in which ψ is the diagonal matrix with elements $\psi_i = \lambda_i^{1/2}$. However, if ψ is any solution to (B-2-4), then so is ψV where V is any arbitrary unitary matrix. The transformation

$$w = \psi^{-1}U^Tz \qquad (B-2-5a)$$

where ψ is any solution to (B-2-4) then further transforms the $\{z_i\}$ to a set $\{w_i\}$ which are statistically independent, and have unit variances. Thus,

$$\langle w \rangle = \psi^{-1}U^T\langle z \rangle \qquad (B-2-5b)$$

and the covariance matrix of w is simply the identity matrix I. With its real and imaginary parts defined by

$$w_i = u_i + jv_i \qquad (B-2-6)$$

the p.d.f. of these variates is simply

$$p(\{u_i, v_i\}) = \frac{1}{(2\pi)^M} \exp\left[-\tfrac{1}{2}(w - \langle w \rangle)^T(w - \langle w \rangle)^*\right]$$

$$= \frac{1}{(2\pi)^M} \exp\left[-\tfrac{1}{2}\sum_{i=1}^{M}|w_i - \langle w_i \rangle|^2\right] \qquad (B-2-7)$$

The inverse of (B-2-5a) is

$$z = U^*\psi w \qquad (B-2-8)$$

With this transformation, the quadratic form of (B-2-3) becomes

$$f = w^{T*}(\psi^{T*}U^TFU^*\psi)w = w^{T*}Tw \qquad (B-2-9a)$$
where
$$T = \psi^{T*}U^TFU^*\psi \qquad (B-2-9b)$$

is obviously also Hermitian. Thus f is now expressed as a Hermitian quadratic form in independent complex Gaussian variates. However T itself, being Hermitian, can also be diagonalized, in a form

$$T = S\Phi S^{T*} \qquad (B-2-10)$$

where S is a unitary matrix of orthonormalized eigenvectors of T, and Φ is the diagonal matrix of its eigenvalues, Φ_i (real, but not necessarily positive). Thus, one can introduce the transformation

$$\mathbf{n} = \mathbf{S}^{T*}\mathbf{w} \qquad \text{(B-2-11a)}$$
$$\mathbf{w} = \mathbf{S}\mathbf{n} \qquad \text{(B-2-11b)}$$

in terms of which the quadratic form is diagonal,

$$f = \mathbf{n}^{T*}\boldsymbol{\Phi}\mathbf{n} = \sum_{i=1}^{M} \Phi_i |\eta_i|^2 \qquad \text{(B-2-12)}$$

Moreover, the covariance matrix of the $\{\eta_i\}$ is still $\mathbf{I}$. Hence, with

$$\eta_i = \alpha_i + j\beta_i \qquad \text{(B-2-13)}$$
$$\langle \mathbf{n} \rangle = \mathbf{S}^{T*}\boldsymbol{\psi}^{-1}\mathbf{U}^T \langle \mathbf{z} \rangle \qquad \text{(B-2-14)}$$

and the relevant p.d.f. is

$$p(\{\alpha_i, \beta_i\}) = \frac{1}{(2\pi)^M} \exp\left[-\tfrac{1}{2} \sum_{i=1}^{M} |\eta_i - \langle \eta_i \rangle|^2 \right] = \prod_{i=1}^{M} p(\alpha_i, \beta_i) \qquad \text{(B-2-15)}$$

where

$$p(\alpha_i, \beta_i) = \frac{1}{2\pi} \exp\left[-\tfrac{1}{2} |\eta_i - \langle \eta_i \rangle|^2 \right] = \frac{1}{2\pi} \exp\left[-\frac{(\alpha_i - \langle \alpha_i \rangle)^2 + (\beta_i - \langle \beta_i \rangle)^2}{2} \right]$$
$$\text{(B-2-16)}$$

At the same time, the form of f in terms of these variates is simply

$$f = \sum_{i=1}^{M} \Phi_i(\alpha_i^2 + \beta_i^2) \qquad \text{(B-2-17)}$$

3. Characteristic Function and P.D.F. of Hermitian Quadratic Form

The characteristic function of f, defined as a Fourier transform on its p.d.f., is

$$G_f(\xi) = \int_{-\infty}^{\infty} \exp\ (j\xi f) p(f)\ df = \langle \exp\ (j\xi f) \rangle \qquad \text{(B-3-1)}$$

with its p.d.f. given as the inverse

$$p(f) = \frac{1}{2\pi} \int_{-\infty}^{\infty} \exp\ (-j\xi f) G_f(\xi)\ d\xi \qquad \text{(B-3-2)}$$

(If $\mathbf{F}$ were always Hermitian positive semidefinite, so that $f \geq 0$ for all $\mathbf{z}$, a Laplace-transform characteristic function would be more convenient for subsequent interpretation; the distinction is however nonessential.) With (B-2-16) and (B-2-17), one obtains immediately the evaluation

$$G_f(\xi) = \left\langle \exp\left[j\xi \sum_{i=1}^{M} \Phi_i(\alpha_i^2 + \beta_i^2) \right] \right\rangle \qquad \text{(B-3-3)}$$

$$= \prod_{i=1}^{M} \frac{1}{1 - 2j\xi\Phi_i} \exp\left[\left(\frac{j\xi\Phi_i}{1 - 2j\xi\Phi_i} \right)(\langle \alpha_i \rangle^2 + \langle \beta_i \rangle^2) \right]$$

$$= \frac{\exp\left[j\xi \sum_{i=1}^{M} (\Phi_i / 1 - 2j\xi\Phi_i)|\langle \eta_i \rangle|^2 \right]}{\prod_{i=1}^{M} (1 - 2j\xi\Phi_i)} \qquad \text{(B-3-4)}$$

This result can be reformulated in terms of the original matrices $\mathbf{R}$ and $\mathbf{F}$. To this end, it is readily shown that the eigenvalues of $\mathbf{T}$ defined by (B-2-10) are also the eigenvalues of the (generally non-Hermitian) matrix

$$\mathbf{T}' = \mathbf{U}^*\psi\mathbf{T}\psi^{-1}\mathbf{U}^T = \mathbf{U}^*\psi\psi^{T*}\mathbf{U}^T\mathbf{F} = \mathbf{R}^*\mathbf{F} \qquad \text{(B-3-5)}$$

Next, from (B-1-12) and (B-1-9), the denominator in (B-3-4) can be written as

$$\prod_{i=1}^{M}(1 - 2j\xi\Phi_i) = \det[\mathbf{I} - 2j\xi\mathbf{T}] \qquad \text{(B-3-6)}$$

But also $\det\psi^{-1} = [\det\psi]^{-1}$, and $\det\mathbf{U} = 1$. Thus, with (B-3-5), one can further write

$$\prod_{i=1}^{M}(1 - 2j\xi\Phi_i) = \det[\mathbf{U}^*\psi(\mathbf{I} - 2j\xi\mathbf{T})\psi^{-1}\mathbf{U}^T]$$

$$= \det[\mathbf{I} - 2j\xi\mathbf{T}'] = \det[\mathbf{I} - 2j\xi\mathbf{R}^*\mathbf{F}] \qquad \text{(B-3-7)}$$

For the exponential in (B-3-4), one can recognize that $1/(1 - 2j\xi\Phi_i)$ are the elements of the diagonal matrix $(\mathbf{I} - 2j\xi\mathbf{\Phi})^{-1}$. One can thus write, as alternative possibilities,

$$\exp\left[j\xi\sum_{i=1}^{M}\frac{\Phi_i}{1 - 2j\xi\Phi_i}|\langle\eta_i\rangle|^2\right] = \exp[j\xi\langle\mathbf{n}\rangle^{T*}\mathbf{\Phi}(\mathbf{I} - 2j\xi\mathbf{\Phi})^{-1}\langle\mathbf{n}\rangle] \qquad \text{(B-3-8)}$$

$$= \exp\left[-\frac{1}{2}\sum_{i=1}^{M}\left(1 - \frac{1}{1 - 2j\xi\Phi_i}\right)|\langle\eta_i\rangle|^2\right] = \exp\{-\tfrac{1}{2}\langle\mathbf{n}\rangle^{T*}[\mathbf{I} - (\mathbf{I} - 2j\xi\mathbf{\Phi})^{-1}]\langle\mathbf{n}\rangle\}$$

$$\text{(B-3-9)}$$

By inserting the definition of $\langle\mathbf{n}\rangle$ from (B-2-14), and utilizing the other matrix definitions in (B-2-10), (B-2-4), and (B-1-11), one finds the second of these to be equivalent to either of the forms[1]

$$\exp\{-\tfrac{1}{2}\langle\mathbf{n}\rangle^{T*}[\mathbf{I} - (\mathbf{I} - 2j\xi\mathbf{\Phi})^{-1}]\langle\mathbf{n}\rangle\}$$
$$= \exp\{-\tfrac{1}{2}\langle\mathbf{z}\rangle^{T*}(\mathbf{R}^*)^{-1}[\mathbf{I} - (\mathbf{I} - 2j\xi\mathbf{R}^*\mathbf{F})^{-1}]\langle\mathbf{z}\rangle\} \qquad \text{(B-3-10}a\text{)}$$
$$= \exp\{-\tfrac{1}{2}\langle\mathbf{z}\rangle^{T*}[\mathbf{I} - (\mathbf{I} - 2j\xi\mathbf{F}\mathbf{R}^*)^{-1}](\mathbf{R}^*)^{-1}\langle\mathbf{z}\rangle\} \qquad \text{(B-3-10}b\text{)}$$

Likewise, from (B-3-8) one finds the possibly more useful form

$$\exp[j\xi\langle\mathbf{n}\rangle^{T*}\mathbf{\Phi}(\mathbf{I} - 2j\xi\mathbf{\Phi})^{-1}\langle\mathbf{n}\rangle] = \exp[j\xi\langle\mathbf{z}\rangle^{T*}(\mathbf{F}^{-1} - 2j\xi\mathbf{R}^*)^{-1}\langle\mathbf{z}\rangle] \qquad \text{(B-3-11)}$$

The two results can also be related by utilizing the algebraic identity

$$\mathbf{I} = (\mathbf{I} - 2j\xi\mathbf{R}^*\mathbf{F})(\mathbf{I} - 2j\xi\mathbf{R}^*\mathbf{F})^{-1} \qquad \text{(B-3-12)}$$

With (B-3-7), and (B-3-10a) or (B-3-11), respectively, the characteristic function of (B-3-4) can be written in the respective forms

$$G_f(\xi) = \frac{\exp\{-\tfrac{1}{2}\langle\mathbf{z}\rangle^{T*}(\mathbf{R}^*)^{-1}[\mathbf{I} - (\mathbf{I} - 2j\xi\mathbf{R}^*\mathbf{F})^{-1}]\langle\mathbf{z}\rangle\}}{\det(\mathbf{I} - 2j\xi\mathbf{R}^*\mathbf{F})} \qquad \text{(B-3-13)}$$

$$= \frac{\exp[j\xi\langle\mathbf{z}\rangle^{T*}(\mathbf{F}^{-1} - 2j\xi\mathbf{R}^*)^{-1}\langle\mathbf{z}\rangle]}{\det(\mathbf{I} - 2j\xi\mathbf{R}^*\mathbf{F})} \qquad \text{(B-3-14)}$$

The Fourier-transform inversion which gives the p.d.f. from these results is given by (B-3-2).

[1] The forms in (B-3-10) coincide with those presented by Turin, *loc. cit.*

In the important case of a Hermitian form in a zero-mean complex Gaussian process,

$$\langle \mathbf{z} \rangle = 0 \tag{B-3-15}$$

the results in (B-3-13) or (B-3-14) reduce to the much simpler form

$$G_f(\xi) = \frac{1}{\det \ (\mathbf{I} - 2j\xi \mathbf{R}^* \mathbf{F})} \tag{B-3-16}$$

It was earlier noted parenthetically that when $\mathbf{F}$ is Hermitian *and* positive semi-definite, it may sometimes be more convenient to define the characteristic function as a Laplace transform on the p.d.f. Thus, rather than (B-3-1) and (B-3-2), one would have

$$G_f(s) = \int_0^\infty \exp \ (-sf)p(f) \ df = \langle \exp \ (-sf) \rangle \tag{B-3-17}$$

and the inversion

$$p(f) = \frac{1}{2\pi j} \int_{c-j\infty}^{c+j\infty} \exp \ (sf)G_f(s) \ ds \tag{B-3-18}$$

By comparing with the derivations above, it is clear that the results in this case will be the respective forms

$$G_f(s) = \frac{\exp \ \{-\frac{1}{2}\langle \mathbf{z} \rangle^{T*}(\mathbf{R}^*)^{-1}[\mathbf{I} - (\mathbf{I} + 2s\mathbf{R}^*\mathbf{F})^{-1}]\langle \mathbf{z} \rangle\}}{\det \ (\mathbf{I} + 2s\mathbf{R}^*\mathbf{F})} \tag{B-3-19}$$

$$= \frac{\exp \ [-s\langle \mathbf{z} \rangle^{T*}(\mathbf{F}^{-1} + 2s\mathbf{R}^*)^{-1}\langle \mathbf{z} \rangle]}{\det \ (\mathbf{I} + 2s\mathbf{R}^*\mathbf{F})} \tag{B-3-20}$$

and in the case $\langle \mathbf{z} \rangle = 0$,

$$G_f(s) = \frac{1}{\det \ (\mathbf{I} + 2s\mathbf{R}^*\mathbf{F})} \tag{B-3-21}$$

BIBLIOGRAPHY

L. G. Abraham, Jr., Effective Bandwidth of Tropospheric Propagation, URSI Spring meeting, Washington, D.C., 1959.

L. G. Abraham, Jr., and J. A. Bradshaw, Tropospheric Scatter Propagation Study, AFCRC-TR-59-533, General Electric Research Laboratory, October, 1959.

R. T. Adams and B. M. Mindes, Evaluation of IF and Baseband Diversity Combining Receivers, *IRE Trans. Commun. Systems*, vol. CS-6, pp. 8–13, June, 1958.

W. G. Albersheim and J. P. Schafer, Echo Distortion in the FM Transmission of Frequency-Division Multiplex, *Proc. IRE*, vol. 40, pp. 316–328, March, 1952.

J. W. Allnatt, E. D. J. Jones, and H. B. Law, Frequency Diversity in the Reception of Selectively Fading Binary Frequency-Modulated Signals, *Proc. Inst. Elec. Engrs. (London)*, vol. 104, part B, pp. 98–110, March, 1957.

Y. L. Alpert, "Radio Wave Propagation and the Ionosphere," USSR, 1960, trans. by Consultants Bureau, New York, 1963.

F. J. Altman and W. Sichak, Simplified Diversity Communication System for Beyond-the-Horizon Links, *Elec. Commun.*, vol. 33, pp. 151–160, June, 1956 (reprinted with revisions from *IRE Trans. Commun. Systems*, vol. CS-4, pp. 50–55, March, 1956).

R. E. Anderson, Sideband Correlation of Lunar and Echo Satellite Reflection Signals in the 900 mc Range, *Proc. IRE*, vol. 49, pp. 1081–1082, June, 1961.

R. Arens, Complex Processes for Envelopes of Normal Noise, *IRE Trans. Inform. Theory*, vol. IT-3, pp. 204–207, September, 1957.

L. B. Arguimbau and R. D. Stuart, "Frequency Modulation," Methuen and Co., Ltd., London, 1956.

E. Arthurs and H. Dym, On the Optimum Detection of Digital Signals in the Presence of White Gaussian Noise, *IRE Trans. Commun. Systems*, vol. CS-10, pp. 336–372, December, 1962.

E. J. Baghdady (ed.), "Lectures on Communication System Theory," McGraw-Hill Book Company, New York, 1961.

A. V. Balakrishnan and I. J. Abrams, Detection Levels and Error Rates in PCM Telemetry Systems, *IRE Intern. Conv. Record*, part 5, pp. 37–55, March 1960.

A. V. Balakrishnan and J. E. Taber, Error Rates in Coherent Communications, *IRE Trans. Commun. Systems*, vol. CS-10, pp. 86–89, March, 1962.

M. Balser and W. B. Smith, Some Statistical Properties of Pulsed Oblique HF Ionospheric Transmissions, *J. Res. Natl. Bur. Std.*, vol. 66D, pp. 721–730, November–December, 1962.

B. B. Barrow, Error Probabilities for Telegraph Signals Transmitted on a Fading FM Carrier, *Proc. IRE*, vol. 48, pp. 1613–1629, September, 1960.

B. B. Barrow, Translation of Historic Paper on Diversity Reception, *Proc. IRE*, vol. 49, pp. 367–368, January, 1961. (See A. de Haas.)

B. B. Barrow, Time-Delay Spread with Tropospheric Propagation beyond the Horizon, Applied Research Laboratory, Sylvania Electronic Systems, Res. Note 364, October, 1962.

B. B. Barrow, Error Probabilities for Data Transmission Over Fading Radio Paths, Doctoral Dissertation, Delft, 1962.

B. B. Barrow, Diversity Combination of Fading Signals with Unequal Mean Strengths, *IEEE Trans. Commun. Systems*, vol. CS-11, pp. 73–78, March, 1963.

E. Bedrosian, The Analytic Signal Representation of Modulated Waveforms, *Proc. IRE*, vol. 50, no. 10, pp. 2071–2076, October, 1962.

V. Belevitch, "Théorie des Circuits Non-Linéaires en Régime Alternatif (Redresseurs, Modulateurs, Oscillateurs)," Gauthier-Villars, Paris, 1959.

D. A. Bell, "Electrical Noise," D. Van Nostrand Company, Inc., Princeton, N.J., 1960.

R. Bellman, "Introduction to Matrix Analysis," McGraw-Hill Book Company, New York, 1960.

R. Bellman (ed.), "Mathematical Optimization Techniques," University of California Press, Berkeley, Calif., 1963.

P. A. Bello, On the Approach of a Filtered Pulse Train to a Stationary Gaussian Process, *IRE Trans. Inform. Theory*, vol. IT-7, pp. 144–149, July, 1961.

P. A. Bello, Correlation Functions in a Tapped Delay Line Model of the Orbital Dipole Channel, *IEEE Trans. Inform. Theory*, vol. IT-9, pp. 2–11, January, 1963.

P. A. Bello, J. Ekstrom, and D. Chesler, Study of Adaptable Communications Systems, RADC-TDR-62-314, Applied Research Laboratory, Sylvania Electronic Systems, June, 1962.

P. A. Bello and B. D. Nelin, Predetection Diversity Combining with Selectively Fading Channels, *IRE Trans. Commun. Systems*, vol. CS-10, pp. 32–42, March, 1962.

P. A. Bello and B. D. Nelin, The Influence of Fading Spectrum on the Binary Error Probabilities of Incoherent and Differentially Coherent Matched Filter Receivers, *IRE Trans. Commun. Systems*, vol. CS-10, pp. 160–168, June, 1962.

P. A. Bello and B. D. Nelin, The Effect of Frequency Selective Fading on the Binary Error Probabilities of Incoherent and Differentially Coherent Matched Filter Receivers, *IEEE Trans. Commun. Systems*, vol. CS-11, pp. 170–186, June, 1963; corrections in *IEEE Trans. Comm. Tech.*, vol. COM-12, pp. 230–231, December, 1964.

J. S. Bendat, "Principles and Applications of Random Noise Theory," John Wiley & Sons, Inc., New York, 1958.

W. R. Bennett, New Results in the Calculation of Modulation Products, *Bell System Tech. J.*, vol. 12, pp. 228–243, April, 1933.

W. R. Bennett, Cross-Modulation in Multichannel Amplifiers, *Bell System Tech. J.*, vol. 19, pp. 587–610, October, 1940.

W. R. Bennett, Time-Division Multiplex Systems, *Bell System Tech. J.*, vol. 20, pp. 199–221, April, 1941.

W. R. Bennett, The Biased Ideal Rectifier, *Bell System Tech. J.*, vol. 26, pp. 139–169, January, 1947.

W. R. Bennett, Distribution of the Sum of Randomly Phased Components, *Quart. Appl. Math.*, vol. 5, pp. 385–393, January, 1948.

W. R. Bennett, Spectra of Quantized Signals, *Bell System Tech. J.*, vol. 27, pp. 446–472, July, 1948.

W. R. Bennett, Methods of Solving Noise Problems, *Proc. IRE*, vol. 44, pp. 609–638, May, 1956.

W. R. Bennett, Statistics of Regenerative Digital Transmission, *Bell System Tech. J.*, vol. 37, pp. 1501–1542, November, 1958.

W. R. Bennett, "Electrical Noise," McGraw-Hill Book Company, New York, 1960.

W. R. Bennett, Amplification in Nonlinear Reactive Networks, *IRE Trans. Circuit Theory*, vol. CT-7, pp. 440–446, December, 1960.

W. R. Bennett, H. E. Curtis, and S. O. Rice, Interchannel Interference in FM and

PM Systems under Noise Loading Conditions, *Bell System Tech. J.*, vol. 34, pp. 601–636, May, 1955.

W. R. Bennett and J. R. Davey, "Data Transmission," McGraw-Hill Book Company, New York, 1965.

W. R. Bennett and S. Doba, Vario-Losser Circuits, *Elec. Eng., Trans. Sec.*, vol. 60, pp. 17–22, January, 1941.

W R. Bennett and J. Salz, Binary Data Transmission by FM Over a Real Channel, *Bell System Tech. J.*, vol. 42, pp. 2387–2426, September, 1963.

H. H. Beverage and H. O. Peterson, Diversity Receiving System of RCA Communications, Inc., for Radiotelegraphy, *Proc. IRE*, vol. 19, pp. 531–561, April, 1931.

W. J. G. Beynon (ed.), "Monograph on Ionospheric Radio," (13th General Assembly of URSI, London, September, 1960), American Elsevier Publishing Company, New York, 1962.

N. M. Blachman, The Demodulation of a Frequency-Modulated Carrier and Random Noise by an FM Receiver, *Cruft Laboratory Report* no. 31, Harvard University, Cambridge, Mass., March, 1948.

H. S. Black, "Modulation Theory," D. Van Nostrand Company, Inc., Princeton, N.J., 1953.

R. Bolgiano, Jr., N. H. Bryant, and W. E. Gordon, Diversity Reception in Scatter Communication with Emphasis on Angle Diversity, Cornell University, Dept. of E. E., *Res. Rept.* 359, January, 1958.

F. E. Bond and H. F. Meyer, The Effect of Fading on Communication Circuits Subject to Interference, *Proc. IRE*, vol. 45, pp. 636–642, May, 1957.

F. K. Bowers, What Use Is Delta Modulation to the Transmission Engineer? *Trans. AIEE*, part 1, vol. 76, pp. 142–147, May, 1957.

E. N. Bramley, Some Aspects of the Rapid Directional Fluctuations of Short Radio Waves Reflected at the Ionosphere, *Proc. Inst. Elec. Engrs. (London)*, vol. 102, part B, pp. 533–540, July, 1955.

D. G. Brennan, Linear Diversity Combining Techniques, *Proc. IRE*, vol. 47, pp. 1075–1102, June, 1959.

A. T. Brennan, B. Goldberg, and A. Eckstein, Comparison of Multichannel Radioteletype Systems over a 5000-Mile Ionospheric Path, *IRE Nat. Conv. Record*, part 8, pp. 254–260, 1958.

H. Brueckmann and R. Silberstein, HF Propagation Test of ISCAN, *IEEE Trans. Antennas and Propagation*, vol. AP-11, pp. 454–458, July, 1963.

C. R. Cahn, Performance of Digital Phase-Modulation Communication Systems, *IRE Trans. Commun. Systems*, vol. CS-7, pp. 3–6, May, 1959.

C. R. Cahn, Comparison of Coherent and Phase-Comparison Detection of a Four Phase Digital Signal, *Proc. IRE*, vol. 47, p. 1662, September, 1959.

C. R. Cahn, Combined Digital Phase and Amplitude Modulation Communication Systems, *IRE Trans. Commun. Systems*, vol. CS-8, pp. 150–155, September, 1960.

C. N. Campopiano and B. G. Glazer, A Coherent Digital Amplitude and Phase Modulation Scheme, *IRE Trans. Commun. Systems*, vol. CS-10, pp. 90–95, March, 1962.

J. R. Carson and T. C. Fry, Variable Frequency Electric Circuit Theory with Application to the Theory of Frequency Modulation, *Bell System Tech. J.*, vol. 16, pp. 513–540, October, 1937.

R. S. Caruthers, Copper Oxide Modulators in Carrier Telephone Systems, *Bell System Tech. J.*, vol. 18, pp. 315–337, April, 1939.

K. W. Cattermole, Efficiency and Reciprocity in Pulse-Amplitude Modulation, *Proc. Inst. Elec. Engrs. (London)*, vol. 105, part B, pp. 449–462, September, 1958.

J. G. Chaffee, The Application of Negative Feedback to Frequency-Modulation Systems, *Bell System Tech. J.*, vol. 18, pp. 403–437, July, 1939.

J. H. Chisholm, W. E. Morrow, Jr., B. E. Nichols, J. F. Roche, and A. E. Teachman, Properties of 400 Mcps Long-Distance Tropospheric Circuits, *Proc. IRE*, vol. 50, pp. 2464–2482, December, 1962.

J. H. Chisholm, P. A. Portmann, J. T. de Bettencourt, and J. F. Roche, Investigations of Angular Scattering and Multipath Properties of Tropospheric Propagation of Short Radio Waves beyond the Horizon, *Proc. IRE*, vol. 43, pp. 1317–1335, October, 1955.

J. H. Chisholm, L. P. Rainville, J. F. Roche, and H. G. Root, Measurement of the Bandwidth of Radio Waves Propagated by the Troposphere beyond the Horizon, *IRE Trans. Antennas and Propagation*, vol. AP-6, pp. 377–378, October, 1958.

J. P. Costas, Synchronous Communication, *Proc. IRE*, vol. 44, pp. 1713–1718, December, 1956.

H. Cramer, "Mathematical Methods of Statistics," Princeton University Press, Princeton, N.J., 1946.

H. Cravis and T. V. Crater, Engineering of Tl Carrier System Repeatered Lines, *Bell System Tech. J.*, vol. 42, pp. 431–486, March, 1963.

A. B. Crawford, D. C. Hogg, and W. H. Kummer, Studies in Tropospheric Propagation beyond the Horizon, *Bell System Tech. J.*, vol. 38, pp. 1067–1178, September, 1959.

W. B. Davenport, Jr., and W. L. Root, "Introduction to Random Signals and Noise," McGraw-Hill Book Company, New York, 1958.

K. Davies, "Ionospheric Radio Propagation," a publication of the National Bureau of Standards, 1965.

A. deHaas, *Radio-Nieuws*, vol. 10, pp. 357–364, December, 1927; vol. 11, pp. 80–88, February, 1928; translated in part by B. B. Barrow, *Proc. IRE*, vol. 49, pp. 367–368, January, 1961.

F. de Jager, Delta Modulation, A Method of PCM Transmission Using the 1-unit Code, *Philips Res. Rept.*, vol. 7, pp. 442–466, 1952.

O. E. DeLange, The Timing of High-Speed Regenerative Repeaters, *Bell System Tech. J.*, vol. 37, pp. 1455–1486, November, 1958.

J. A. Develet, A Threshold Criterion for Phase-Lock Demodulation, *Proc. IRE*, vol. 51, pp. 349–356, February, 1963.

A. R. DiDonato and M. P. Jarnagin, A Method for Computing the Circular Coverage Function, *Mathematics of Computation*, vol. 16, pp. 347–355, July, 1962.

H. F. Dodge, B. J. Kinsburg, and M. K. Kruger, The L3 Coaxial System, Quality Control Requirements, *Bell System Tech. J.*, vol. 32, pp. 943–967, July, 1953.

M. L. Doelz, E. T. Heald, and D. L. Martin, Binary Data Transmission Techniques for Linear Systems, *Proc. IRE*, vol. 45, pp. 656–661, May, 1957.

R. H. Doherty, G. Hefley, and R. F. Linfield, Timing Potentials of Loran-C, *Proc. IRE*, vol. 49, pp. 1659–1673, November, 1961.

J. Dugundji, Envelopes and Pre-Envelopes of Real Waveforms, *IRE Trans. Inform. Theory*, vol. IT-4, pp. 53–57, March, 1958.

S. Duinker, "General Properties of Frequency-Converting Networks," Thesis, Technical University of Delft, June, 1957.

B. M. Dwork, The Detection of a Pulse Superimposed on Fluctuation Noise, *Proc. IRE*, vol. 38, pp. 771–774, 1950.

C. H. Elmendorf, R. D. Ehrbar, R. H. Klie, and A. J. Grossman, The L3 Coaxial System, System Design, *Bell System Tech. J.*, vol. 32, pp. 781–832, July, 1953.

L. H. Enloe, Decreasing the Threshold in FM by Frequency Feedback, *Proc. IRE*, vol. 50, pp. 23–29, January, 1962.

C. B. Feldman and W. R. Bennett, Bandwidth and Transmission Performance, *Bell System Tech. J.*, vol. 28, pp. 490–595, July, 1949.

R. A. Felsenheld, H. Havstad, J. L. Jatlow, D. J. LeVine, and L. Pollack, Wide-Band

Ultrahigh-Frequency Over-the-Horizon Equipment, *AIEE Trans.*, vol. 77, part I (Communications and Electronics, no. 35), pp. 86–93, March, 1958.

R. G. Finney, Short-Time Statistics of Tropospheric Radio Wave Propagation, *Proc. IRE*, vol. 47, pp. 84–85, January, 1959.

E. F. Florman and R. W. Plush, Measured Statistical Characteristics and Narrow-Band Teletype Message Errors on a Single-Sideband 600-Mile-Long Ultrahigh-Frequency Tropospheric Radio Link, *J. Res. Natl. Bur. Std.*, vol. 64D, pp. 125–133, March–April, 1960.

J. T. Frankle, Frequency Modulation Noise, Report no. PIBMRI-1041-62, Electrical Engineering Dept. Polytechnic Institute of Brooklyn, August, 1962.

J. J. Freeman, "Principles of Noise," John Wiley & Sons, Inc., New York, 1958.

H. W. Fuller, Signals and Noise in a Frequency Modulation Receiver, *Cruft Laboratory Technical Report* 243, Harvard University, February, 1957.

F. R. Gantmacher, "Theory of Matrices," Chelsea Publishing Company, New York, 1959.

R. F. Garrett, T. L. Tuffnell, and R. A. Waddell, The L3 Coaxial System, Application of Quality Control Requirements in the Manufacture of Components, *Bell System Tech. J.*, vol. 32, pp. 969–1005, July, 1953.

B. Goldberg, HF Radio Data Transmission, *IRE Trans. Commun. Systems*, vol. CS-9, pp. 21–28, March, 1961.

S. Goldman, "Frequency Analysis, Modulation, and Noise," McGraw-Hill Book Company, New York, 1948.

S. W. Golomb (ed.), "Digital Communications with Space Applications," Prentice-Hall, Inc., Englewood Cliffs, N.J., 1964.

J. Granlund and W. Sichak, Diversity Combining for Signals of Different Medians, *IRE Trans. Commun. Systems*, vol. CS-9, pp. 138–145, June, 1961.

J. Greenwood and D. Durand, On the Distribution of Length and Components of the Sum of n Random Unit Factors, *Ann. Math. Stat.*, vol. 26, pp. 233–246, 1955.

U. Grenander and G. Szego, "Toeplitz Forms and Their Applications," University of California Press, Berkeley, Calif., 1958.

G. L. Grisdale, J. G. Morris, and D. S. Palmer, Fading of Long-Distance Radio Signals and a Comparison of Space- and Polarization-Diversity Reception in the 6–18 Mc/s Range, *Proc. Inst. Elec. Engrs. (London)*, vol. 104, part B, pp. 39–51, January, 1957.

J. Grosskopf and L. Fehlhaber, Rate and Duration of Single Deep Fades in Tropospheric Scatter Links, *NTZ-CJ*, no. 3, pp. 125–131, 1962.

J. Grosskopf, M. Scholz, and K. Vogt, Korrelationsmessungen im Kurzwellenbereich, *NTZ*, vol. 11, pp. 91–95, February, 1958.

H. V. Hance, "The Optimization and Analysis of Systems for the Detection of Pulsed Signals in Random Noise," Sc. D. dissertation, MIT, 1951.

J. R. Hancock and R. W. Lucky, Performance of Combined Amplitude and Phase-modulated Communication Systems, *IRE Trans. Commun. Systems*, vol. CS-8, pp. 232–237, December, 1960.

J. R. Hancock and R. W. Lucky, On the Optimum Performance of N-ary Systems Having Two Degrees of Freedom, *IRE Trans. Commun. Systems*, vol. CS-10, pp. 177–184, June, 1962.

W. W. Harman, "Principles of the Statistical Theory of Communication," McGraw-Hill Book Company, New York, 1963.

R. V. L. Hartley, Relations of Carrier and Sidebands in Radio Transmission, *Bell System Tech. J.*, vol. 2, pp. 90–112, April, 1923.

C. W. Helstrom, Resolution of Signals in White, Gaussian Noise, *Proc. IRE*, vol. 43, pp. 1111–1118, September, 1955.

C. W. Helstrom, Comparison of Digital Communication Systems, *IRE Trans. Commun. Systems*, vol. CS-8, pp. 141–150, September, 1960.

C. W. Helstrom, "Statistical Theory of Signal Detection," Pergamon Press, New York, 1960.

D. T. Hess, Theory and Design of FM Receivers, Report no. PIBMRI-1026-62, Electrical Engineering Dept., Polytechnic Institute of Brooklyn, May, 1962.

B. D. Holbrook and J. T. Dixon, Load Rating Theory for Multichannel Amplifiers, *Bell System Tech. J.*, vol. 18, pp. 624–644, October, 1939.

J. L. Hollis, An Experimental Equipment to Reduce Teleprinter Errors in the Presence of Multipath, *IRE Trans. Commun. Systems*, vol. CS-7, pp. 185–188, September, 1959.

D. F. Hoth, The Tl Carrier System, *Bell Lab. Record*, vol. 40, pp. 358–363, November, 1962.

R. P. Ingalls, L. E. Bird, and J. W. B. Day, Bandpass Measurements of a Lunar Reflection Circuit, *Proc. IRE*, vol. 49, pp. 631–632, March, 1961.

D. E. Johansen, New Techniques for Machine Computation of the Q-functions, Truncated Normal Deviates, and Matrix Eigenvalues, Applied Research Laboratory, Sylvania Electronic Systems, AFCRL-556, July, 1961.

D. E. Johansen, Final Report on Investigation of Antenna Systems for Scatter Type Reception, Applied Research Laboratory, Sylvania Electronic Systems, AFCRL-742, August, 1961.

D. E. Johansen, Binary Error Rates in Fading FDM-FM Communications, *IRE Trans. Commun. Systems*, vol. CS-9, pp. 206–214, September, 1961.

D. E. Johansen, The Tracking Antenna—A Promising Concept for Scatter Communications, *Proc. 7th Nat. Commun. Symp.*, Utica, N.Y., pp. 134–149, October, 1961.

Joint Technical Advisory Committee, Radio Transmission by Ionospheric and Tropospheric Scatter, *Proc. IRE*, vol. 48, pp. 5–44, January, 1960.

J. J. Jones, The Probability of Error for a Four-Tone FSK Demodulator in the Presence of Crosstalk or Interference, Eng. Note 290R, Applied Research Laboratory, Sylvania Electronic Systems, February, 1962.

D. B. Jordan, H. Greenberg, E. E. Eldredge, and W. Serniuk, Multiple Frequency Shift Teletype Systems, *Proc. IRE*, vol. 43, pp. 1647–1655, November, 1955.

L. R. Kahn, Compatible Single Sideband, *Proc. IRE*, vol. 49, pp. 1503–1527, October, 1961.

T. Kailath, Correlation Detection of Signals Perturbed by a Random Channel, *IRE Trans. Inform. Theory*, vol. IT-6, pp. 361–366, June, 1960.

T. Kailath, Adaptive Matched Filters, *Symposium on Mathematical Optimization Techniques*, Santa Monica, Calif., October, 1960. (See R. Bellman.)

T. Kailath, Optimum Receivers for Randomly Varying Channels, *Proc. 4th London Symp. Inform. Theory*, 1960, Butterworth Scientific Publications, London, 1961.

B. W. Kendall, Multiplex Signaling, U.S. Patent 1,459,709, June 19, 1923.

R. S. Kennedy and I. L. Lebow, Signal Design for Dispersive Channels, *IEEE Spectrum*, vol. 1, pp. 231–237, March, 1964.

R. W. Ketchledge and T. R. Finch, The L3 Coaxial System, Equalization and Regulation, *Bell System Tech. J.*, vol. 32, pp. 833–878, July, 1953.

N. H. Knudzton and P. E. Gudmandsen, Results from a Three-Hop Tropospheric Scatter Link in Norway with Parallel Operations on 900 mc and 2200 mc, *IRE Trans. Commun. Systems*, vol. CS-8, pp. 20–26, March, 1960.

V. A. Kotel'nikov, "Theory of Optimum Noise Immunity," McGraw-Hill Book Company, New York, 1960.

S. Kruse, "Theory of Rectifier Modulators," Thesis for Doctorate, K. Tekniska Högskolan, May 26, 1939. Copyright by Telefonaktiebolaget, L. M. Ericsson, Stockholm.

F. F. Kuo and S. L. Freeney, Hilbert Transforms and Modulation Theory, *Proc. Nat. Electron. Conf.*, pp. 51–58, Chicago, October, 1962.

R. E. Lacy, M. Acker, and J. L. Glaser, Performance of Space and Frequency Diversity Receiving Systems, *IRE Nat. Conv. Record*, part II, pp. 148–152, 1953.

H. J. Landau, On the Recovery of a Band-Limited Signal after Instantaneous Companding and Subsequent Band-Limiting, *Bell System Tech. J.*, vol. 39, pp. 351–364, March, 1960.

H. J. Landau and W. L. Miranker, The Recovery of Distorted Band-Limited Signals, *J. Math. Anal. Appl.*, vol. 2, pp. 97–104, February, 1961.

H. J. Landau and H. O. Pollak, Prolate Spheroidal Wave Functions, Fourier Analysis and Uncertainty—II, *Bell System Tech. J.*, vol. 40, pp. 65–84, January 1961; —III, *ibid.*, vol. 41, pp. 1295–1336, July, 1962. (See also D. Slepian.)

V. D. Landon, Theoretical Analysis of Various Systems of Multiplex Transmission, *RCA Rev.*, vol. 9, pp. 287–351, June, 1948; pp. 438–482, September, 1948.

H. B. Law, The Signal/Noise Performance Rating of Receivers for Long-Distance Synchronous Radiotelegraph Systems Using Frequency Modulation, *Proc. Inst. Elec. Engrs. (London)*, vol. 104, part B, pp. 124–129, March, 1957.

H. B. Law, The Detectability of Fading Radiotelegraph Signals in Noise, *Proc. Inst. Elec. Engrs. (London)*, vol. 104, part B, pp. 130–140, March, 1957.

H. B. Law, F. J. Lee, R. C. Looser, and F. A. W. Levett, An Improved Fading Machine, *Proc. Inst. Elec. Engrs. (London)*, vol. 104, part B, pp. 117–123, March, 1957.

J. L. Lawson and G. E. Uhlenbeck, "Threshold Signals," McGraw-Hill Book Company, New York, 1950.

J. G. Lawton, Comparison of Binary Data Transmission Systems, *Proc. 2nd. Nat. Conf. Mil. Electronics*, pp. 54–61, 1958.

J. G. Lawton, Theoretical Error Rates of "Differentially Coherent" Binary and "Kineplex" Data Transmission Systems, *Proc. IRE*, vol. 47, pp. 333–334, February, 1959.

I. L. Lebow, P. R. Drouilhet, N. L. Daggett, J. N. Harris, and F. Nagy, Jr., The West Ford Belt as a Communications Medium, *Proc. IEEE*, vol. 52, pp. 543–563, May, 1964.

A. Lender, The Duobinary Technique for High-Speed Data Transmission, *Communications and Electronics*, vol. 82, no. 66, pp. 214–218, May, 1963.

L. Lewandowski, Derivation of the Probability of Error in a PSK System Employing Phase Locked Loop, Sylvania Electronic Systems, Buffalo, N.Y., Feb. 7, 1962.

D. Linden, A Discussion of Sampling Theorems, *Proc. IRE*, vol. 47, pp. 1219–1226, July, 1959.

R. V. Locke, Jr., Experimental Comparison of Equal-Gain and Maximal-Ratio Diversity Combiners, *Proc. IRE*, vol. 48, pp. 1488–1489, August, 1960.

B. F. Logan and M. R. Schroeder, A Solution to the Problem of Compatible Single-Sideband Transmission, *IRE Trans. Inform. Theory*, vol. IT-8, pp. 252–259, September, 1962.

C. H. Looney, Jr., A Very Low Frequency (VLF) Synchronizing System, *Proc. IRE*, vol. 49, pp. 448–452, February, 1961.

W. Lyons, Design Considerations for FSK Circuits, *IRE Nat. Conv. Record*, part 8, pp. 70–73, 1954.

J. M. Manley and H. E. Rowe, Some General Properties of Nonlinear Elements, Part 1, General Energy Relations, *Proc. IRE*, vol. 44, pp. 904–913, July, 1956.

J. I. Marcum, A Statistical Theory of Target Detection by Pulsed Radar, *IRE Trans. Inform. Theory*, vol. IT-6, pp. 59–267, April, 1960; earlier *Rand Corp. Memos* RM-753, July, 1948 and RM-754, December, 1947.

J. I. Marcum, Tables of the Q-function, *Rand Corp. Memo* RM-399, January, 1950.

R. C. Mathes and S. B. Wright, The Compandor—An Aid against Static in Radio Telephony, *Bell System Tech. J.*, vol. 13, pp. 315–332, July, 1934.

L. C. Maximon, On the Representation of Indefinite Integrals Containing Bessel Functions by Simple Neumann Series, *Proc. Am. Math. Soc.*, vol. 7, pp. 1054–1062, 1956.

C. D. May, Jr., Doubling Traffic Capacity of Single-Sideband Systems, *IRE Nat. Conv. Record*, part II, pp. 145–147, 1953.

L. A. Meacham and E. Peterson, An Experimental Multichannel PCM System of Toll Quality, *Bell System Tech. J.*, vol. 27, pp. 1–43, January, 1948.

G. L. Mellen, W. E. Morrow, Jr., A. J. Pote, W. H. Radford, and J. B. Wiesner, UHF Long-Range Communications Systems, *Proc. IRE*, vol. 43, pp. 1269–1287, October, 1955.

A. A. Meyerhoff and W. M. Mazer, Optimum Binary FM Reception Using Discriminator Detection and IF Shaping, *RCA Rev.*, vol. 22, pp. 698–728, December, 1961.

S. T. Meyers, Nonlinearity in Frequency-Modulation Radio Systems Due to Multipath Propagation, *Proc. IRE*, vol. 34, pp. 256–265, May, 1946.

D. Middleton, "An Introduction to Statistical Communication Theory," McGraw-Hill Book Company, New York, 1960.

G. F. Montgomery, A Comparison of Amplitude and Angle Modulation for Narrow-Band Communication of Binary Coded Messages in Fluctuation Noise, *Proc. IRE*, vol. 42, pp. 447–454, February, 1954.

A. M. Mood and F. A. Graybill, "Introduction to the Theory of Statistics," 2d ed., McGraw-Hill Book Company, New York, 1963.

L. H. Morris, G. H. Lovell, and F. R. Dickinson, The L3 Coaxial System, Amplifiers, *Bell System Tech. J.*, vol. 32, pp. 879–914, July, 1953.

J. Neyman and E. S. Pearson, On the Problem of the Most Efficient Tests of Statistical Hypotheses, *Phil. Trans. Roy. Soc. London, Ser. A*, no. 231, pp. 289–337, 1931.

D. O. North, Analysis of the Factors Which Determine Signal/Noise Discrimination in Radar, *RCA Tech. Rep.* PTR-6-C, June, 1943; reprinted in *Proc. IRE*, vol. 51, pp. 1016–1028, July 1963.

K. A. Norton, L. E. Vogler, W. V. Mansfield, and P. J. Short, The Probability Distribution of the Amplitude of a Constant Vector Plus a Rayleigh-Distributed Vector, *Proc. IRE*, vol. 43, pp. 1354–1361, October, 1955.

A. C. Norwine, Devices for Controlling Amplitude Characteristics of Telephone Signals, *Bell System Tech. J.*, vol. 17, pp. 539–554, October, 1938.

A. H. Nuttall, Error Probabilities for Equicorrelated M-ary Signals under Phase-Coherent and Phase-Incoherent Reception, *IRE Trans. Inform. Theory*, vol. IT-8, pp. 305-314, July, 1962.

H. Nyquist, Certain Topics in Telegraph Transmission Theory, *Trans. AIEE*, vol. 47, pp. 617–644, April, 1928.

B. M. Oliver, J. R. Pierce, and C. E. Shannon, The Philosophy of PCM, *Proc. IRE*, vol. 36, pp. 1324–1332, November, 1948.

K. S. Packard, Effect of Correlation on Combiner Diversity, *Proc. IRE*, vol. 46, pp. 362–363, January, 1958.

C. H. Page, Frequency Conversion with Positive Nonlinear Resistors, *J. Res. Natl. Bur. Std. (U.S.)*, vol. 56, pp. 179–182, April, 1956.

C. H. Page, Frequency Conversion with Nonlinear Reactance, *J. Res. Natl. Bur. Std. (U.S.)*, vol. 58, pp. 227–236, May, 1957.

D. S. Palmer, A Theoretical Study of the Statistics of Working Spells and Periods of Breakdown for a Number of Radio Links in Series, *Proc. Symp. on Statistical Methods in Radiowave Propagation* (UCLA, June, 1958), Pergamon Press, New York, 1960.

R. H. Pantell, General Power Relationships for Positive and Negative Nonlinear Resistive Elements, *Proc. IRE*, vol. 46, pp. 1910–1913, December, 1958.

A. Papoulis, "The Fourier Integral and Its Applications," McGraw-Hill Book Company, New York, 1962.

A. Papoulis, "Probability, Random Variables, and Stochastic Processes," McGraw-Hill Book Company, New York, 1965.

E. Peterson and L. W. Hussey, Equivalent Modulator Circuits, *Bell System Tech. J.*, vol. 18, pp. 32–48, January, 1939.

H. O. Peterson, H. H. Beverage, and J. B. Moore, Diversity Telephone Receiving System of RCA Communications, Inc., *Proc. IRE*, vol. 19, pp. 562–584, April, 1931.

L. C. Peterson and F. B. Llewellyn, The Performance and Measurement of Mixers in Terms of Linear-Network Theory, *Proc. IRE*, vol. 33, pp. 458–476, July, 1945.

J. N. Pierce, Theoretical Diversity Improvement in Frequency-Shift Keying, *Proc. IRE*, vol. 46, pp. 903–910, May, 1958.

J. N. Pierce, Multiple Diversity with Non-Independent Fading, *Proc. IRE*, vol. 49, pp. 363–364, January, 1961.

J. N. Pierce, Theoretical Limitations on Frequency and Time Diversity for Fading Binary Transmissions, *IEEE Trans. Commun. Systems*, vol. CS-11, pp. 186–187, June, 1963; earlier, Air Force Cambridge Research Laboratory Report ERD-TR-60-169, July, 1960.

J. N. Pierce, Approximate Error Probabilities for Optimal Diversity Combining, *IEEE Trans. Commun. Systems*, vol. CS-11, pp. 352–354, September, 1963.

J. N. Pierce and S. Stein, Multiple Diversity with Non-Independent Fading, *Proc. IRE*, vol. 48, pp. 89–104, January, 1960.

F. A. Polkinghorn, A Single-Sideband MUSA Receiving System for Commercial Operation on Transatlantic Radio Telephone, *Proc. IRE*, vol. 28, pp. 157–170, April, 1940.

K. H. Powers, The Compatibility Problem in Single-Sideband Transmission, *Proc. IRE*, vol. 48, pp. 1431–1435, August, 1960.

R. Price, The Detection of Signals Perturbed by Scatter and Noise, *IRE Trans. Inform. Theory*, vol. PGIT-4, pp. 163–170, September, 1954.

R. Price, Optimum Detection of Random Signals in Noise, with Application to Scatter-Multipath Communication, *IRE Trans. Inform. Theory*, vol. IT-2, pp. 125–135, December, 1956.

R. Price and P. E. Green, Jr., A Communication Technique for Multipath Channels, *Proc. IRE*, vol. 46, pp. 555–570, March, 1958.

R. Price and P. E. Green, Jr., Signal Processing in Radar Astronomy—Communication via Fluctuating Multipath Media, M.I.T. Lincoln Lab., Tech. Rept. 234, October, 1960.

J. G. Proakis, P. R. Drouilhet, Jr., and R. Price, Performance of Coherent Detection Systems Using Decision-Directed Channel Measurement, *IEEE Trans. Commun. Systems*, vol. CS-12, pp. 54–63, March, 1964.

P. M. Rainey, United States Patent 1,608,527, November 30, 1926.

L. L. Rauch, Fluctuation Noise in Pulse-Height Multiplex Radio Links, *Proc. IRE*, vol. 35, pp. 1192–1197, November, 1947.

F. H. Reder, M. R. Winkler, and C. Bickart, Results of a Long-Range Clock Synchronization Experiment, *Proc. IRE*, vol. 49, pp. 1028–1032, June, 1961.

R. R. Reed, panel discussion on modulation techniques, *Proc. Navy R and D Clinic*, Raton, N. Mex., September 28–29, 1961.

A. H. Reeves, French Patent 853,183, October 23, 1939.

H. J. Reich, "Theory and Applications of Electron Tubes," McGraw-Hill Book Company, New York, 1944.

S. Reiger, Error Rates in Data Transmission, *Proc. IRE*, vol. 46, p. 919, May, 1958.

Report of USA National Committee to 13th General Assembly of URSI, *J. Res. Natl. Bur. Std.*, vol. 64D, pp. 612–616, November–December, 1960.

S. O. Rice, Mathematical Analysis of Random Noise, *Bell System Tech. J.*, vol. 23, pp. 282–333, July, 1944; vol. 24, pp. 96–157, January, 1945 (reprinted in N. Wax, "Selected Papers on Noise and Stochastic Processes," Dover Publications, Inc., New York, 1954).

S. O. Rice, Statistical Properties of a Sine Wave Plus Random Noise, *Bell System Tech. J.*, vol. 27, pp. 109–157, January, 1948.

S. O. Rice, "Noise in FM Receivers," chap. 25, pp. 375–424, in "Proceedings, Symposium on Time Series Analysis," M. Rosenblatt (ed.), John Wiley & Sons, Inc., New York, 1963.

J. W. Rieke and R. S. Graham, The L3 Coaxial System, Television Terminals, *Bell System Tech. J.*, vol. 32, pp. 915–942, July, 1953.

J. F. Roche and J. Chisholm, Measurements over a 188-Mile Path at 2290 Mc/s, Using 1.0 Microsecond Pulse Transmissions, URSI-IRE Fall Meeting, 1962, Ottawa, Canada.

H. E. Rowe, "Signals and Noise in Communication Systems," D. Van Nostrand and Company, Inc., Princeton, N.J., 1965.

C. L. Ruthroff, Project Echo: FM Demodulators with Negative Feedback, *Bell System Tech. J.*, vol. 40, pp. 1149–1157, July, 1961.

J. Salz and B. R. Saltzberg, Double Error Rates in Differentially Coherent Phase Systems, *IEEE Trans. Commun. Systems*, vol. CS-12, pp. 202–205, June, 1964.

J. Salz and S. Stein, Distribution of Instantaneous Frequency for Signal Plus Noise, *IEEE Trans. Inform. Theory*, vol. IT-10, pp. 272–274, October, 1964.

M. Sanchez and F. Popert, Über die Berechnung der Spektren modulierter Impulsfolgen, *Arch. Elekt. Übertragung*, vol. 9, pp. 441–452, 1955.

J. A. Saxton (ed.), "Monograph on Radiowave Propagation in the Troposphere," (*Proc. of 13th Gen. Assembly*, URSI, London, 1960), American Elsevier Publishing Company, New York, 1962.

D. L. Schilling, The Response of an APC System to FM Signals in Noise, *Proc. IEEE*, vol. 51, pp. 1306–1316, October, 1963.

D. L. Schilling and J. Billig, A Comparison of the Threshold Performance of the Frequency Demodulator Using Feedback and the Phase-Locked Loop, Report no. PIBMRI-1207-64, Electrical Engineering Department, Polytechnic Institute of Brooklyn, February, 1964.

D. L. Schilling and J. Billig, On the Threshold Extension Capability of PLL and the FDMFB, *Proc. IEEE*, vol. 52, p. 621, May, 1964.

D. L. Schilling and M. Schwartz, The Response of an Automatic Phase Control System to FM Signals and Noise, *IRE Intern. Conv. Rec.*, part 8, pp. 111–121, 1962.

A. R. Schmidt, A Frequency Stepping Scheme for Overcoming the Disastrous Effects of Multipath Distortion on High-Frequency FSK Communications Circuits, *IRE Trans. Commun. Systems*, vol. CS-8, pp. 44–47, March, 1960.

M. Schwartz, "Statistical Approach to the Automatic Search Problem," Ph.D. dissertation, Harvard University, Cambridge, Mass., 1951.

M. Schwartz, Effect of Signal Fluctuation on the Detection of Pulse Signals in Noise, *IRE Trans. Inform. Theory*, vol. IT-2, pp. 66–71, June, 1956.

M. Schwartz, A Coincidence Procedure for Signal Detection, *IRE Trans. Inform. Theory*, vol. IT-2, December, 1956.

M. Schwartz, "Information Transmission, Modulation, and Noise," McGraw-Hill Book Company, New York, 1959.

M. Slack, Probability Densities of Sinusoidal Oscillations Combined in Random Phase, *J. Inst. Elec. Engrs. (London)*, vol. 93, part III, pp. 76–86, 1946.

D. Slepian, Prolate Spheroidal Functions, Fourier Analysis and Uncertainty—IV: Extensions to Many Dimensions; Generalized Prolate Spheroidal Functions, *Bell System Tech. J.*, vol. 43, pp. 3009–3057, November, 1964.

D. Slepian and H. O. Pollak, Prolate Spheroidal Functions, Fourier Analysis and Uncertainty—I, *Bell System Tech. J.*, vol. 40, pp. 43–63, January, 1961. (See also H. J. Landau and H. O. Pollak.)

H. Staras, Diversity Reception with Correlated Signals, *J. Appl. Phys.*, vol. 27, pp. 93–94, January, 1956.

H. Staras and A. D. Wheelon, Theoretical Research on Tropospheric Scatter Propagation in the U.S., 1954–1957, *IRE Trans. Antennas and Propagation*, vol. AP-7, pp. 80–86, January, 1959.

S. Stein, Clarification of Diversity Statistics in Scatter Propagation, "Proc. Symposium on Statistical Methods in Radiowave Propagation," (UCLA, June, 1958), Pergamon Press, New York, 1960.

S. Stein, Unified Analysis of Certain Coherent and Non-Coherent Binary Communications Systems, *IEEE Trans. Inform. Theory*, vol. IT-10, pp. 43–51, January, 1964.

S. Stein, The Q-Function and Related Integrals, Res. Report 467, Applied Research Laboratory, Sylvania Electronic Systems, July, 1965.

S. Stein and D. E. Johansen, A Statistical Description of Coincidences among Random Pulse Trains, *Proc. IRE*, vol. 46, pp. 827–830, May, 1958.

S. Stein and D. E. Johansen, A Theory of Antenna Performance in Scatter-Type Reception, *IRE Trans. Antennas and Propagation*, vol. AP-9, pp. 304–311, May, 1959.

G. R. Stibitz, General Modulation with Nonlinear Resistances, Unpublished Bell Telephone Laboratories Technical Memorandum, April 6, 1932.

K. P. Stiles, F. G. Hollins, E. T. Fruhner, and W. D. Siddall, The Miami-Havana Radio System and Its Integration into the Telephone Networks, *AIEE Trans.*, vol. 77, part I (Communications and Electronics, no. 35), pp. 94–96, March, 1958.

F. L. H. M. Stumpers, Distortion of Frequency Modulated Signals in Electrical Networks, *Commun. News*, vol. 9, pp. 82–92, April, 1948.

F. L. H. M. Stumpers, Theory of Frequency-Modulation Noise, *Proc. IRE*, vol. 36, pp. 1081–1092, September, 1948.

S. M. Sussman, A Matched Filter Communication System for Multipath Channels, *IRE Trans. Inform. Theory*, vol. IT-6, pp. 367–373, June, 1960.

G. L. Turin, Communication through Noisy, Random-Multipath Channels, *IRE Nat. Conv. Record*, part 4, pp. 154–166, March, 1956.

G. L. Turin, Error Probabilities for Binary Symmetric Ideal Reception through Nonselective Slow Fading and Noise, *Proc. IRE*, vol. 46, pp. 1603–1619, September, 1958.

G. L. Turin, An Introduction to Matched Filters, *IRE Trans. Inform. Theory*, vol. IT-6, June, 1960.

G. L. Turin, The Characteristic Function of Hermitian Quadratic Forms in Complex Normal Variables, *Biometrika*, vol. 47, pp. 199–201, June, 1960.

G. L. Turin, On Optimal Diversity Reception, *IRE Trans. Inform. Theory*, vol. IT-7, pp. 154–166, July, 1961.

G. L. Turin, On Optimal Diversity Reception, II, *IRE Trans. Commun. Systems*, vol. CS-10, pp. 22–31, March, 1962.

R. H. Urbano, Analysis and Tabulation of the M Positions Experiment Integral and Related Error Function Integrals, AF Cambridge Res. Ctr., Bedford, Mass., Rept. No. AFCRC-TR-55-100, April, 1955.

H. Van de Weg, Quantizing Noise of a Single Integration Delta-Modulation System with an N-digit Code, *Philips Res. Rept.*, vol. 8, pp. 367–385, 1953.

B. van der Pol, The Fundamental Principles of Frequency Modulation, *J. Inst. Elec. Engrs.* (*London*), vol. 93, part III, pp. 153–158, May, 1946.

A. Van der Ziel, "Noise," Prentice-Hall, Inc., Englewood Cliffs, N.J., 1954.

H. C. A. van Duuren, Error Probability and Transmission Speed on Circuits Using Error Detection and Automatic Repetition of Signals, *IRE Trans. Comm. Systems*, vol. CS-9, pp. 38–50, March, 1961.

T. J. van Kessel, F. L. H. M. Stumpers, and J. M. A. Uyen, A Method for Obtaining Compatible Single-Sideband Modulation, *Proc. IRE*, vol. 50, p. 1998, September, 1962.

J. H. Van Vleck and David Middleton, A Theoretical Comparison of Visual, Aural, and Meter Reception of Pulsed Signals in the Presence of Noise, *J. Appl. Phys.*, vol. 17, pp. 940–971, November, 1946.

S. H. Van Wambeck and A. H. Ross, Performance of Diversity Receiving Systems, *Proc. IRE*, vol. 39, pp. 256–264, March, 1951.

A. Viterbi, in S. W. Golomb (ed.), "Digital Communications with Space Applications," Prentice-Hall, Inc., Englewood Cliffs, N.J., 1964, chap. 7.

H. B. Voelcker, Phase-Shift Keying in Fading Channels, *Proc. Inst. Elec. Engrs.* (*London*), vol. 107, part B, pp. 31–38, January, 1960.

J. H. Vogelman, J. L. Ryerson, and M. H. Bickelhaupt, Tropospheric Scatter System Using Angle Diversity, *Proc. IRE*, vol. 47, pp. 688–696, May, 1959.

A. Wald, "Sequential Analysis," John Wiley & Sons, Inc., New York, 1947.

G. N. Watson, "Theory of Bessel Functions," The MacMillan Company, New York, 1944.

D. K. Weaver, Jr., A Third Method of Generation and Detection of Single-Sideband Signals, *Proc. IRE*, vol. 44, pp. 1703–1705, December, 1956.

H. A. Wheeler, Design Formulas for Diode Detectors, *Proc. IRE*, vol. 26, pp. 745–759, June, 1938.

E. T. Whittaker, On the Functions Which Are Represented by the Expansions of the Interpolation Theory, *Proc. Roy. Soc. Edinburgh*, vol. 35, pp. 181–194, 1915.

J. M. Wozencraft, Sequential Reception of Time-Variant Dispersive Transmissions, in E. J. Baghdady (ed.), "Lectures on Communication System Theory," McGraw-Hill Book Company, New York, 1961, chap. 12.

L. R. Wrathall, Frequency Modulation by Non-Linear Coils, *Bell Lab. Record*, vol. 24, no. 3, pp. 102–105, March, 1946.

K. F. Wright and J. E. Cole, Measured Distribution of the Duration of Fades in Tropospheric Scatter Transmission, *IRE Trans. Antennas and Propagation*, vol. AP-8, pp. 594–598, November, 1960.

INDEX